Computer programs for the building industry

Third edition

Hutton + Rostron / E & F N Spon

Computer programs for the building industry

Third edition

Geoffrey Hutton Dip Arch, ARIBA

Michael Rostron MA, B Arch, ARIBA

E & F N Spon

© **Geoffrey Hutton and Michael Rostron**

First published 1974 Second edition 1979 Third edition 1984

ISBN 0 907101 01 1

Marketed and distributed by

E & F N Spon Limited
11 New Fetter Lane
London EC4P 4EE
and
733 Third Avenue
New York
NY 10017

The directory is available in machine-readable form, and was edited using a computer. The Indexes were generated using the Hutton + Rostron publishing computer system, which also produced the photocomposition drive tape. The information is stored on magnetic tape for ease of revision

Printed in Great Britain by The Garden City Press Limited

Computer programs for the building industry

Contents

Introduction

This is the third edition of Computer programs for the building industry. The contents have been completely revised as a result of writing to the owner of every program, and several hundred new programs have been added. The revision process is a continuous one and the editors welcome information on the programs in the directory and on sources of new programs

The number of abstracts recorded since the last edition has almost doubled and many of the new programs are suitable for use on microcomputers. Because of the increased number of programs, the layout has been changed to provide for ten entries on each page without loss of information. To achieve this the names and addresses of program owners have been consolidated in a separate section of the directory

There is now general interest in computers within the building and construction industry, and many architects, engineers and planners make use of them directly or indirectly in their everyday work. The directory demonstrates the ready availability of programs throughout the world for a wide range of applications and equipment, and should be the preferred starting point for potential and existing computer users before they buy or write their own software

The major part of the directory is made up of over 1700 program abstracts prepared in sufficient detail to enable a preliminary choice to be made. The abstracts are broadly classified but the principal method of searching for an appropriate program is by means of one of the comprehensive indexes given at the end of the book. No attempt has been made to evaluate the programs, which must be judged in relation to the user's own criteria in discussion with the owner, and in subsequent test runs. Comparative evaluation of computer programs requires considerable care and the Construction Industry Computing Association (CICA) is currently involved in research of this kind in the UK

It is becoming common for potential computer users to investigate the available software before choosing a machine on which to run it. To aid readers wishing to contact hardware manufacturers and suppliers a directory of names and addresses has been included

Also new in this edition is a section on publicly available databases. These are increasing in importance as sources of information and they are readily accessible to any microcomputer owner with access to a telephone line, for the cost of installing a modem. Computer programs for the construction industry is itself available on-line to the users of Viewdata services No charge is made to the owners of programs for an entry in this directory, so that it is as comprehensive and independent as possible. Every effort is made to ensure the accuracy of the information but the editors cannot accept responsibility for the content, performance or availablity of the programs. They would welcome notification of any inaccuracy. Among the many bodies who have assisted in gathering information on programs, the editors would particularly like to thank the CICA, the Association for Computer Aided Design (Australia) and the Danish Building Institute

The editors, who are themselves enthusiastic computer users, are always happy to help readers in their search for suitable programs and may be able to advise on appropriate sources and organisations to approach. They can be contacted at Hutton + Rostron, Netley House, Gomshall, Nr Guildford, Surrey, GU5 9QA, telephone 048 641 3221 or telex 859167

Management

CPM/PERT
Land use
Mailing lists
Other

Management

0001

CLUSTR *ABACUS studies*
This program produces a suitable structure for solving design problems. The designer describes the elements of the problem and the relationship between them. The program breaks the problem down into the sub-sets that most closely relate to these elements. It then builds the sub-sets into larger clusters and outputs a tree diagram showing the resulting problem structure

References

Availability
Purchase, hire, interactive bureau service

Language
Fortran

Computer
Univac 1108
Tektronix
graphics terminal

0002

APECS *ADP Network Services Limited*
Suitable for planning and controlling projects. It checks data, analyses time, resources and cost, updates and reports on progress. It is capable of handling networks of up to 64 000 activities, multiple projects and multiple start and finish events. Features include: elapsed time or calendar modes; multiple work patterns, with the working day or week and holidays specified by the user; output in time units or on the basis of a calendar

References

Availability
Time sharing

Language
Fortran-based

Computer
DEC

0003

ACE1 *Adroit Systems Limited*
A project planning package which makes a rapid assessment of plans in terms of time and resources (critical path analysis)

References
Personal Computing with Apple

Availability
Purchase

Language

Computer
Apple II

0004

PERT *Amplix Services Limited*
A CPA analysis program with provision for resource. Handles a minimum of 750 activities, typically 1400 per 250KB. Reports include GANTT chart and activity list; critical path and float

References

Availability
Purchase

Language
Commercial (SMB)
Cobol, Fortran

Computer
CP/M or MP/M
Microcomputer

0005

APM *Apple Computer (UK) Limited*
Project management, scheduling, tracking and analysis of the events crucial to a project (Critical Path) can be achieved

References
Personal Computing with Apple

Availability
Purchase

Language

Computer
Apple II

0006

CBACS-PERT *CBACS Limited*
Allows convenient estimating and monitoring of future and current tasks. Screen displays and printouts are presented under various selections and sequences as tabulations, bar charts or resource histograms. As work proceeds, the latest project details are input, allowing easy reviewing of previous plans. Project managers can continuously monitor status and consider alternative strategies to review areas of time criticality or resource overload. Handles up to 1200 activities. May be used by inexperienced personnel

References
Building Products, Architects' Journal, Practical Computing

Availability
Licence

Language
CPM/80

Computer
64K CP/M
microcomputer

0007

1900 PERT *Centre-File (Northern) Limited*
(Program evaluation and review technique). Critical path analysis for the examination of complex projects. Used successfully in the aerospace, shipbuilding and motorway construction industries; also suitable for activities such as moving or installing plant, controlling subcontract work or maintaining schedules. Time, resource and cost analyses may be produced for a single project or several linked activities

References

Availability
Bureau service, remote batch

Language
Plan

Computer
ICL 1900

0008

HORNET *Claremont Controls Limited*
Caters for the planning of projects, from design through to construction management, using critical path (PERT type) techniques. Hornet uses Precedence Network Analysis. Complex sequences of activities can be analysed to determine how much delay may be tolerated in each activity. The program can be updated at any time with new project information and the new schedules and bar charts will be recalculated and printed

References
Practical Computing

Availability
Purchase

Language

Computer
Commodore 8000

0009

PERT *Computel Limited*
A comprehensive set of interrelated programs for network analysis, resource allocation, multiproject scheduling and cost control

References
Program made available by ICL

Availability

Language

Computer

0010

Micronet *Construction Programming Services*
A powerful, project planning software package for building and civil engineers. Analyses the critical path through the project, the earliest and latest possible start and finish dates of each activity, the physical resources needed, such as men, machines and materials, and the effect that any changes will have on the project. Output includes: an overall project bar chart, a period bar chart, histograms of resource demand, standard and selective reports

References
Recommended by Abtex Computer Systems Limited

Availability
Purchase

Language

Computer
Apple III
CP/M and CP/M 86

NASA PERT Time II *COSMIC*
Aids the planning and control of project development variables, namely, time and performance measurements. Input information includes such factors as a subdivision of work, a contractor, an organisation, a mission, a summary, or an integration network. The program determines expected and allowed dates for each project and reports are generated from this information. As a project progresses, data and reports are updated

References

Availability
Purchase

Language
Fortran IV (96%)
Assembler (3%)

Computer
IBM 370

FCRIT *Facet Limited*
For the evaluation of the critical paths through an activity network. The program allows multiple start and finish events, and predicts the critical path to each finish event and the slack time for each activity

References

Availability
Bureau service, or under licence

Language

Computer
Prime, Norsk Data, Harris, CP/M 8-bit micros

DCF *Hevacomp Limited*
This is a management program which compares the cost in the use of alternative schemes having differing lives, capital costs and annual costs. It can handle capital allowance with capital gains tax and it allows annual cost (such as fuel) to be additionally inflated above the defined discount rate

References

Availability
Purchase

Language

Computer
Any 64K microcomputer

STATISTICS *Hevacomp Limited*
This is a management program covering: standard deviation, linear regression, correlation coefficients, lagrangian interpolation and Simpson's rule

References

Availability
Purchase

Language

Computer
Any 64K microcomputer

Project Planning and Management *Hilbern Engineering Software, USA*
Two programs based on the critical path method of project planning. The first program is for cases where resources are not limited. The second program provides a way of using the critical path method for planning projects when resources are limited

References

Availability
Purchase

Language
Basic

Computer
TRS-80, Apple II, IBM PC

IBC Master Planner *IBC Computer Systems Limited*
Handles: project planning and management; network and resource analysis; critical path analysis, resource scheduling. There is a user specified report generator; the output includes bar charts and histograms; arrow notation. Maximum of 30,000 activities with 2000 to 3000 on small machines

References

Availability
Purchase

Language
UCSD Pascal or Pascal M

Computer
64Kb computer

AMPER/PREMIS *K & H Project Systems Limited*
A complete project control system using either the arrow or precedence techniques to represent projects. Up to 64 000 activities and 99 calendars can be included in a project, with no practical limit to the number of assigned resources. Other facilities include time and resource scheduling, and multiproject scheduling. Output consists of reports in any format, bar charts, histograms and plots

References
International Directory of Software

Availability
Purchase, rental

Language
Assembler

Computer
IBM 360/370, minimum 256K

CPM Scheduling for chemical plants *A M Kinney, Inc*
Analyses a CPM network diagram to determine the total project completion in calender date, the start and finish dates for each activity or work item, and the activities critical to accomplishing the project by the completion date. The program will produce a bar graph to indicate early start date and float available for each activity

References

Availability

Language
Fortran

Computer
IBM 1130 and 370

System for Computer-Aided Network Design *Lancashire County Council*
This suite consists of five programs: control program, balanced activity length analysis, minimum crossing analysis, interactive program and plotting program. Details of activities are provided on cards. Activities are located and the network balanced. The interactive program allows input from a menu with options to move or delete an activity, to indicate a finished activity, to change duration, to add a new activity, to redraw the network and to plot. For arrow or precedence networks

References
Uses GINO-F graphics software or PTRC graphics

Availability

Language
Fortran

Computer
ICL 2976

PROJECT 5000 *Marcus Computer Systems*
A project planning package which produces a critical path analysis and plans projects with regard to resource availability. The resource levels can be manipulated to investigate the effect on the project. The package is suitable for use in the construction industry, from a given network, and includes: main program, data file control, critical path analysis and resource scheduling

References

Availability
Purchase

Language

Computer
CPM 86, MS-DOS, CPM 2.2

0021

CPM *Microcomp*
CPM uses the critical path method to plan a scheduled project. Up to 200 activities may be entered with all data being stored on disk. Output can be on screen or printer, in graphical or tabular format

References

Availability
Purchase

Language

Computer
Apple, and most microcomputers using CP/M

0022

PNA-Time, PNA-Resources (Aggregation) *NCR Limited*
This suite of programs provides an analysis of time and resources associated with a complex construction project, for which a network has been designed. PNA-Time output is in the form of source data, time master file, control master file and free format reports; PNA-Resources output is in the form of a histogram report, a tabular report and free format reports. Standard NCR validation techniques are used, including check to master file

References

Availability
Purchase, hire

Language
NCR Neat/3

Computer
Century 16k Memory (PNA-Time), 32k Memory

0023

N5500 Project Management and Control System *Nichols Associates*
Schedules multiple projects, using CPM/PERT techniques with database of resources and projects. Allocates available resources and resolves priorities; monitors physical progress, resource utilisation and expenditure; updates forecasts of completion dates, resource requirements and costs. Reports show project status and forecast performance compared with plans, estimates and budgets. Options include graphic output, report writer, interactive input and report retrieval

References

Availability
Purchase, bureau service

Language
ANSI Cobol

Computer
IBM, HP3000, DEC, Honeywell, Prime

0024

AP126: Critical path analysis *Oasys Limited*
This program includes facility for resource aggregation and cost analysis. The critical path analysis is based on calendar dates. The program computes earliest and latest times, and floats of those activities in the network. Based on earliest or latest starts, it calculates resource usage, cost rate and cumulative cost throughout the project. The HP 9845 allows automatic plotting of bar charts, resource/cost histograms and cumulative cost curves. There is a wide range of output format

References

Availability
Purchase

Language
Basic

Computer
HP 9845

0025

HOCUS IV *P-E Consulting Group*
This program builds flow diagrams which can be tested by hand simulation. Once validated, the flow can be run on a computer using the standard HOCUS program. Can be loaded on any computer with a Fortran compiler and sufficient core; applications include brewery, chemical plant, equipment utilisation, document handling, port and foundry operations, hospital and warehouse design, machine shop layout and production planning. No programming experience is necessary to carry out simulation studies

References
Details from source. Mr J Szymankiewicz

Availability
Purchase, lease or bureau: SIA, SCICON, GEISCO

Language
Fortran

Computer
Various

0026

PCM-PLANCON *Project Software Limited*
For use by engineering and construction contractors for planning the use of resources. Based on network analysis and bar charting, with extensions to cover resource handling. Output includes tabulated report and bar chart showing earliest/latest start times, float and critical path; resource output showing availability and utilisation

References
CICA Bulletin, March 1984

Availability
Licence

Language
Fortran

Computer
Minis, micros Incl PDPII Vax II, IBM PC

0027

SCAND *PTRC Education and Research Services Limited*
A system for computer aided network design which will plot a critical path network (precedence or arrow) on most makes of plotter. Facilitates interactive updating via a Tektronix display terminal showing the effects of changes made to progress or logic. May also be used to convert to and from arrow and precedence form. Input in form of I/J or node references. Output on plotter: interactive system produces update cards to amend the PERT system in use, and revised input file

References

Availability
Purchase

Language
Fortran 77, IV

Computer
Any with Fortran compiler and 32-bit, 56K

0028

CPM/1 *Quest GENESYS Limited*
For project planning and control, using the critical path method. The plan of activities is represented by an arrow diagram which can be converted into data for the program. Data is input in day or week units. The user can assign earliest starting dates, target finish dates, and produce selective results for certain operations or trades

References

Availability

Language
Gentran

Computer

0029

Critical Path Analysis *Reading Computer Services Limited*
Details of the project planning network are prepared and sent to a data file. Using this information, the program analyses the network and identifies critical paths. Resource use may be included, and up to ten resource categories may be used. A full range of reports are available on demand and the data can be easily edited and the network re-analysed

References

Availability

Language

Computer
CP/M Microcomputer

0030

DRAWNET *SIA Computer Services*
This is a system of project planning and PERT plotting programs

References

Availability
Bureau service

Language
High level

Computer
Control Data, IBM, Prime

Computer programs for the building industry

EXPERT *Systonetics, Inc*
For transforming a PERT/CPM database into easily used management graphic reports. The system offers: complete graphics, including time scaled networks, Gantt bar charts, and cost/resource graphics; plotting on most pen and electrostatic plotters; easy installation; complete project control

References

Availability
Purchase, via Euro-log Systems Limited

Language

Computer

VIS1ON *Systonetics, Inc*
A management information system for program and project management including: network scheduling of critical path and procedure models; multiple resource allocation, tracking and projection; resource constrained scheduling and levelling; cost tracking, projection and reporting; 'What if' analysis; graphical representation, eg networks, bar charts, graphs: flexible reporting formats for cost, resource and scheduling; performance measurement reporting and graphics to meet DOD, DOE and NASA requirements

References

Availability
Purchase, via Euro-log Systems Limited

Language

Computer

MICROPERT *Tandy Corporation*
A project planning and control system enabling the user to obtain current time analysed schedules together with reports and histograms of resource availabilities and requirements. Reports can be examined on the VDU or recorded on hard copy via the printer. Reports are presented in standard tabular format, user defined format, bar charts or histograms

References

Availability
Purchase

Language

Computer
Z80 compatible, 64K

SRMS *Tymshare UK*
(Scheduling and Resource Management System). A complete project management system which enables the user to control all aspects of a project from inception to completion. Comprehensive facilities for network analysis and resource scheduling. Budgeted, actual and forecast costs can be reported; sophisticated progress tracking facility. The system is totally interactive with novice, infrequent and expert modes of operation. 25 standard reports (including tabular reports), and bar charts

References

Availability
Licence

Language
PL/1 (90%)
Assembler (10%)

Computer
Any IBM system supporting VM/CMS

K & H *UCC (Great Britain) Limited*
A critical path/resource allocation system for the calculation of arrow networks. Printed and plotted output includes histograms, bar charts and cost reports

References
Developed by K & H Business Consultants Limited

Availability
Bureau service

Language
Fortran

Computer

P1 *United Information Services Limited*
A comprehensive interrelated suite of programs for project management, incorporating free format input and output, time, resource and cost analyses to user specification and special features of time, resource and cost simulation

References

Availability
Bureau service, time sharing

Language
Fortran

Computer
Honeywell Sigma 9

MILESTONE *Xitan Systems Limited*
A critical path analysis package containing screen 'window' onto planning layout. It allows up to 200 jobs within each project

References

Availability
Purchase

Language

Computer
CP/M

PROPERTY MANAGEMENT *Applied Systems Techniques (Midlands) Limited*
A system to handle the management of properties for one or more clients or landlords. Information is held for each client, property and tenancy. Output includes management warning reports, control and audit reports, client statements and enquiries

References

Availability
Licence

Language
Basic, Assembler

Computer
Any Alpha Micro Min 10 Mbyte

Property Management *CAP (Financial Services)*
Main functions of the system are to: store and maintain details of properties and tenancies; adjust rents; accept and allocate details of tenants' payments; produce rent demands and reminders; maintain details of expenditure on each property; allow enquiries on transactions during previous 12 months. Reports include quarterly rent roll, aged debtors report, quarterly rent analysis, rent review list, tenancy rent list, tenancy and property indices. Also stores information on head lease, mortgage details and insurance

References
Recommended by IBM

Availability

Language
MicroCobol under BOS

Computer
IBM Series/1

CMG Property Investment Management *CMG Computer Management Group (Scotland) Limited*
Provides a system for the management of rent collection, rent reviews, fire and investment valuations, monitoring of repairs, etc. Buildings, leases and tenants are recorded on file. Comprehensive reports and reminders are available

References
Recommended by IBM

Availability

Language

Computer
IBM System/34

0041

LAMSAC Application code 32123252190A *Hertfordshire County Council*
This program for land agents deals with pool property management. Slow peripheral units used are a tape reader and line printer. The program has been in use since 1976

References
LAMSAC

Availability

Language
Cobol

Computer
NCR Criterion
48K core
1 magnetic tape unit

0042

Property Management System *JBA (UK) Limited*
Provides a fully integrated suite of programs for the administrative and planning activities of property management. Subjects handled include: rent and service charge accounting, service charge apportionment, surcharge billing, rent review, client accounting, valuations; fully integrated with purchase and nominal ledgers; comprehensive reporting, enquiry and budgeting

References
Recommended by IBM

Availability

Language

Computer
IBM System/34

0043

KIPMAN *Kienzle Data Systems Limited*
Designed specifically for property managers, to control client reporting and rent accounting for any number of clients, properties and tenants. All the usual management functions are supported by the system, from rent demands to cash receipts and posting. Also, extensive management reporting and enquiry facilities, giving full control over the portfolio

References

Availability
Licence sale with hardware

Language
Cobol

Computer
Kienzle 9000

0044

LAMDAP *Lamex Commercial Computing Limited*
A development appraisal package to provide assistance in evaluating and preparing tenders for the acquisition of development land; monitors progress and reviews forecasted profitability on current developments. The following criteria are used: specified profit, percentage profit on building costs, and percentage profit per annum on capital employed. Information on land costs and its phased development, building costs, revenue from sales, design fees, miscellaneous expenses, and actual costs

References
Recommended by IBM

Availability

Language

Computer
IBM System/34

0045

Marketing Management *Building Centre Computers Limited*
Carries out selective customer and prospect mailing and covers: lead source analysis, market analysis, competitor and competitive produce analysis. Word processing is included

References

Availability
Purchase

Language
Basic

Computer
Mini and microcomputers single & multi user

0046

Address List and Mailing Program *Dynatech Microsoftware Limited*
The system has capacity for: 1000 names and addresses (List 1) and 750 names and addresses (List 2). There are 2 name lines (30 characters), 4 address lines (30 characters per line), and 1 reference (7 characters); the combined record must not exceed 113 characters. Various print options are available

References

Availability
Purchase

Language

Computer
48K Apple II Plus

0047

Tandymail II *Tandy Corporation*
A selective users' mailing list database sets up mailing lists with supplementary dates, values, codes, numbers, descriptions, etc for every address. Provides 4 screen formats and a printout. Summary list and full list allow multiple copies of labels. 20 extra user defined items available. Allows 1000 records on a single drive Model II; with two or more expansion drives, allows 1875 records per list

References

Availability
Purchase

Language

Computer
TRS-80
Model II

0048

Tandymail I *Tandy Corporation*
An advanced mailing database system which stores names and addresses (individual and business) and up to 20 fields of information such as dates, values, codes, numbers, and descriptions. Accounts may be listed in selected order. Up to 4 sizes of label may be used. The program can alter a batch of selected records by a single 'bulk' command. Capacity is 325 records per disk; takes up to 4 disk drives; handles 3 separate mailing lists without changing disks

References

Availability
Purchase

Language

Computer
TRS-80
Model I

0049

Tandywriter *Tandy Corporation*
A comprehensive mailing database system, which will also link to the SCRIPSIT word processing program. Features include: up to 600 records per disk; up to 100 characters per addressee; 4 different printed formats, sorted or unsorted, selective or non-selective, from simple index to full data listings. Many more features available

References

Availability
Purchase

Language

Computer
TRS-80
Models I & III

0050

COSTRAK *ADP Network Services Limited*
Used in value analysis, the program provides information on project costs in the format and level of detail required. Cost performance reports are broken down into the following structures: organisational, work breakdown, or any other required hierarchical structure. Graphics display on terminals and plotters. Linked with APECS and IPL

References

Availability
Purchase, bureau service

Language
Fortran

Computer
DEC

IPL *ADP Network Services Limited*
A database management system meeting all data entry, validation, inquiry, reporting and storage requirements. Covers the following applications: finance and accounting, marketing and sales, personnel, manufacturing. Related to APECS and COSTRAK

References

Availability
Purchase, bureau service

Language
Fortran

Computer
DEC

FCERT *Alper Systems Limited*
Part of the FACTOTUM suite for professional practices. Prints architects' certificates, notifications and directions with covering letters, including letters to employers and quantity surveyors, following the receipt of the valuation. Output includes complete certificates, directions, notifications and all covering letters, addressed, and containing information appropriate to the contract

References

Availability
Purchase

Language
Fortran

Computer
64k CP/M
Microcomputer

FVIA *Alper Systems Limited*
Part of the FACTOTUM suite. Assesses the viability of a proposed development by interactively varying the factors governing cost and finance, and examining the effect these have on the optimum profitability of the scheme for the developer. Output tables show all input and results in the same format as the screen output. The format is suitable for issuing directly to the client

References

Availability
Purchase

Language
Fortran

Computer
64k 8-bit
CP/M Microcomputer

OMS-DESIGN *Alpha Micro UK*
Allows the establishment of a database for each project, with direct linkage to Uniform Construction Index (UCI) and Material & Equipment Catalog. Features include: up to 16 buildings per project; multiple job numbers; subdivision of project into site areas, buildings, spaces and workstations; definition of design components in terms of location, environmental and occupational factors, construction, finishes, equipment, fixtures; multiple level reporting

References

Availability
Purchase

Language
Alpha Basic

Computer
Alpha Micro CPU
with 8Mbytes

OMS-JOBS *Alpha Micro UK*
Directly linked to OMS-ACCOUNTS sub-system module for automatic update of payments made and fees received on all jobs. Features include: office productivity and work in progress reports; consultant and contractor job reports; evaluation of contractor performance based on historical data

References

Availability
Purchase

Language
Alpha Basic

Computer
Alpha Micro CPU
with 8Mbytes

Data Drivers *APEC*
For use on standalone microcomputers to construct data files for input to five APEC engineering design programs. The user has two options: to transmit the files to a larger computer on which the APEC programs are installed, either in-house or on the CDC CYBERNET Network; or, if the microcomputer runs under the CP/M system, to execute the files on the same machine

References

Availability
Doris J Wallace, APEC

Language
Basic

Computer
TRS-80 Model II and III
CP/M machines

ESP-II 'Friendly prompter' *APEC*
For data preparation and program operation, developed by Ferreira & Kalasinsky Associates, Inc (FKAI) of New Bedford, Massachusetts, development contractors for APEC's ESP-II, Energy Simulation Program - Level II. It is being made available to APEC Licensees under a special agreement with FKAI

References

Availability
Doris J Wallace, APEC

Language
Basic

Computer
TRS-80 Model II

COMPASS MTS System *Bingham Blades & Partners*
A general purpose suite of programs to assist in the overall management of a labour intensive organisation. Designed specifically for the professional practices associated with the building industry

References

Availability
Purchase

Language
Fortran
(Minicomputers)

Computer
Minicomputer 64K
DTC210 Micro

CUFFS *Boeing Computer Services (Europe) Limited*
The Combs Unangst Financial Forecasting System is a financial planning, modelling, forecasting and analysis language. The program interfaces with EIS (Executive Information Services), enabling the CUFFS user to have access to EIS Graphics and report writing capabilities, and to EIS financial and statistical libraries. CUFFS may be used for capital investment analysis, corporate planning, project justification, pricing studies, etc

References

Availability
Purchase

Language

Computer

Company Secretarial and Management Services *Building Centre Computers Limited*
The modules of this system include document search and retrieval, electronic diary, portfolio valuation, accessing other computer systems, telex communications, corporate database, and word processing

References

Availability
Purchase

Language
Basic

Computer
Mini and microcomputers single & multi user

0061

Vehicle and Distribution Management *Building Centre Computers Limited*
This program covers the requirements of distribution, vehicle fleet, and maintenance management

References

Availability
Purchase

Language
Basic

Computer
Mini and microcomputers single & multi user

0062

Capital program, CAPROG *Cheshire County Council*
A small database system containing proposed building projects. The system permits changes to a project's programme year or priority. It is used by the Building Economics Group to maintain an up to date summary. The system gives immediate response to changes in value, priority, programme year, etc

References

Availability

Language
APL

Computer
IBM 3767

0063

SUBCONTRACTORS *CIMS Computer Systems Limited*
Part of the CIMS Management System designed for the construction industry. Maintains subcontractor details and accounting information. Account details are kept from the company quantity surveyors' valuations of work done, including a facility for retention of monies. Reports include, notification of future expiry dates of tax exemption certificates and a year end payment/tax declaration, by account. Through the VDU, work progression and costs are tracked and current details examined

References

Availability
Purchase

Language
RPG11

Computer
IBM System/34

0064

VEHICLE REGISTER *CIMS Computer Systems Limited*
Part of the CIMS Management System designed for the construction industry. Facilitates the management of large vehicle fleets. Maintains comprehensive employee driving licence and accident details, monthly rolling averages of miles done and mpg achieved, together with full details of employee expense reimbursements. Nominal ledger is automatically updated, and there is a cheque facility for expense payments. Reports show abnormal mpg and provide reminders of road fund tax renewal

References

Availability
Purchase

Language
RPG11

Computer
IBM System/34

0065

WORK-IN-PROGRESS *CIMS Computer Systems Limited*
Part of the CIMS Management System designed for the construction industry. Details are entered through the VDU from company quantity surveyors' valuations of work in a given period. Interim certificate details are entered and payments made or due are recorded against the set valuations with notification of retentions. Provides the surveyors with weekly information required for clients. Facilitates monitoring and control of site costs

References

Availability
Purchase

Language
RPG11

Computer
IBM System/34

0066

CAMILE *Civil and Structural Computing (Northern) Limited*
A similar language to FORTRAN with the following benefits: 1 Programming with very large arrays is possible as memory is allocated only to the specific locations used. 2 The user can often ignore data capture procedures, as any variables without an assigned value are automatically prompted for. 3 It is far more feasible to program applications with many varied conditions since instructions are monitored as they are executed, checking also for any incompatibility. Therefore undetected programming errors are less likely

References
Bradshaw, Buckton and Tonge

Availability
Bureau service, time sharing, in-house

Language

Computer

0067

NBS *Claremont Controls Limited*
The entire National Building Specification standard text is supplied on 2 magnetic disks and the text is accessed by the Wordcraft 80 package. An update service is available. A well presented copy of the draft specification may be printed at any time. The final document is produced to a high standard, with page numbers, job names, etc, automatically inserted as required

References

Availability
Purchase

Language

Computer
Commodore 8000

0068

INTERNET 80S *Computation Research and Development Limited*
An integrated network based, project management system incorporating financial modelling and systems generation. Used to plan and monitor a project from inception through design and construction to commissioning and maintenance. Output includes tables, bar charts, histograms and plotted networks

References

Availability
Lease, bureau service

Language
Fortran

Computer
ICL, CDC, IBM, with minimum 1Mb

0069

FCS-EPS *Computel Limited*
A comprehensive, interactive decision support system for financial planners in the construction industry

References

Availability
Bureau service

Language

Computer
ICL mainframe

0070

Computer Aided Design and Engineering *Computervision Limited*
Provides total project management, including: design, drawing, bills of materials, and final construction. All data can be controlled and modified interactively. Various design and drawing error checks are available. Output includes hard copy printout, or plotting (pen or electrostatic)

References

Availability
Purchase

Language
Fortran

Computer
Computervision graphics processor

Professional Services Time Recording *The Consultancy Consortium*
Designed for professional practices to maintain full client records. Allowance is made for
productive and non-productive work categories, staff details, charge rates, ledger
transactions, fee write-offs, etc

References

Availability
Purchase

Language

Computer
Sirius 1, 128K

0072

Computer assisted rating of employees *COSMIC*
Designed to compute theoretical salary based on quality and years of experience of each
member of the totem group and in industry, average salary data. Used as a management
aid, by taking an unbiased look at all members of the totem group

References
Boeing Co

Availability

Language
Fortran IV

Computer
IBM 360 series

0073

Manpower forecast program *COSMIC*
Produces five reports from input data, showing: distribution of actual manpower levels over
sections versus account, project versus sections, sections versus manpower classes, and
project offices versus sections. Where applicable, project, project office, and section
quotas are shown together with the difference between the quota and actual manpower
level

References
CAL TECH/Jet Propulsion Laboratory

Availability

Language
Cobol

Computer
IBM 7000 series

0074

Space Allocation and Timetabling System *Department of Education and Science*
A space management system to schedule people and activities to suitable times and
spaces. Application to briefing and design of new and re-use of existing buildings in
University, Higher and Further education sectors. Application to administrative, monitoring,
research, educational and appraisal needs

References
By application to DES, A & B Group

Availability
Purchase

Language
Fortran IV

Computer
IBM 360/5

0075

WIMS *DHSS*
Works Information and Management System is the generic name for a suite of over 50
programs. They are intended for use in the management and maintenance of buildings.
Implementation should commence at commissioning stage

References

Availability

Language
MBasic

Computer
Z80, 61K RAM micro
with CP/M. ABS MX
mini

0076

BUILDER *Engineering Software Services Limited*
A builder's management system enabling up to 35 separate sites to be controlled whilst
retaining overall company accounts. Full trial balance, profit and loss trading account and
balance sheet are produced

References

Availability

Language

Computer
Olivetti M20

0077

AUTOSPEC *Focus Software Consultants*
For the production of individual specification documents from libraries of standard clauses.
Used in conjunction with Wordstar. The program formats the final document layout to cater
for individual requirements. To produce a specification, once the library file(s) has been
prepared, enter a list of numbers corresponding to the required paragraphs, along with any
non-standard text using Autospec's built-in screen editor

References

Availability
Purchase

Language

Computer
CP/M or MS DOS

0078

FP2020 Financial Planner *Graffcom Systems Limited*
Provides a new approach to management planning. The system will accurately forecast the
effect of proposed actions. There are five main system options: work on a model, calculate
model, report formatter, print model, and system maintenance. Calculations use logic lines
or formulae. Special business and accounting functions are built in. Graphic output can be
provided if used with other Graffcom software products

References

Availability
Purchase

Language

Computer
8-bit microcomputer
with CP/M, 16-bit
with CP/M86

0079

Forecasting and data smoothing *Hilbern Engineering Software, USA*
The first program covers data smoothing with Fourier transforms; similar to weighted
moving averages. The double exponential smoothing method is better known than the
Fourier transform method. The final program is Quicksort

References

Availability
Purchase

Language
Basic

Computer
TRS-80, Apple II, IBM
PC

0080

PR *Hutton + Rostron*
A suite of programs used in managing large text databases for use in preparing
publications. Files are organised in chapters and paragraphs numbered sequentially for
identification and editing, and by a descriptive code such as SfB or the CIB Master List
numbering for retrieval. Commands for string insertion, replacement, deletion and
transposition operate on the codes or the text in either batch or interactive mode

References

Availability
Bureau service or purchase

Language
PAL8, NEAT

Computer
DEC PDP8
ICL 4120

0081

QBANK *Hutton + Rostron*
A program for handling structured data in the form of schedules, with or without text, for the assembly of databases. Data can be Boolean, real numbers or text. Descriptive data can be inserted by program. Data can be sorted, searched or combined by program. Output can be via a range of devices

References

Availability
Bureau or purchase

Language
PAL8

Computer
DEC PDP8

0082

SELECT *Hutton + Rostron*
A suite of programs for producing selective printouts of records from a coded text file and for assembling and formatting sub-files for use in publications, schedules, directories, indexes and labelling. Output can be arranged to operate any suitable device

References
Used to structure the contents of this book

Availability
Bureau or purchase

Language
PAL8

Computer
DEC PDP8

0083

SORT *Hutton + Rostron*
A program for rearranging records on a file by reference to any desired table of character values

References

Availability
Bureau or purchase

Language
PAL8

Computer
DEC PDP8

0084

MicroModeller *Intelligence (UK) Limited*
A complete, financial modelling and graphic display program for management use including: planning, analysis and reporting, budget preparation and monitoring, consolidations, investment analysis, etc

References
Recommended by Doulton Glass Industries

Availability
Purchase

Language

Computer
ACT

0085

Linear decision rule for production and employment scheduling *A M Kinney, Inc*
Determines the optional decision rules derived for scheduling employment and production levels. Quadratic cost functions are used. Cost coefficients involved in decision rules are calculated. Input requires 13 unit costs; output contains coefficients in the scheduling equations for employment and production levels as functions of expected orders, previous employment and inventory

References

Availability

Language
Fortran

Computer
IBM 1130 and 370

0086

Building Regs *Lancaster Computing*
The regulations are written to cover every situation and have become difficult to use. This program includes all regulations and parts of schedules 2, 7, 9, 10, 11 and 12 required on 2 disks. The first menu requires input of the Building Purpose Group (1-8); the second menu allows choice of Part (A-R), which then displays a menu of the clauses in that part. All requirements for other Purpose Groups are excluded from being displayed by the first menu choice

References

Availability
Purchase

Language

Computer
Apple II

0087

ARTEMIS *Metier Management Systems Limited*
A comprehensive project management package used from the design stage through to construction and subsequent maintenance; includes design management, resources control, target costing, cost analysis, valuation forecasting, estimating, cost control, BQ analysis, planning and scheduling, drawings and materials management. Can be used for individual projects or can coordinate and control many simultaneous projects. Extensive range of printed, plotted and screen output

References

Availability
Purchase as turnkey system, or lease

Language
Artemis high level

Computer
Artemis minicomputer

0088

MICRO PLANNER *Micro Planning Services*
Any project which requires the coordination of numbers of interdependent operations is suitable for analysis and control by MICRO PLANNER, such as: construction projects, research and development, installation and commissioning of plant or equipment, reorganisation of places of work, etc. Time analysis, bar charts, progress reporting, listings and histograms can be shown on the screen; outputs can be prepared in colour. Maximum project size, 4000 activities

References
Apple Software Directory. Recommended by Keen Computers Limited

Availability
Purchase

Language
Pascal

Computer
Apple II and III

0089

Scheme Viability Analysis *Norden Technical Computer Systems Limited*
Deals with the developer's budget and undertakes the initial viability studies traditionally carried out on the 'back of an envelope'. Cost parameters are computed to produce figures for capital profit and returns on investment. Once the cost information has been established, this will become the inital cost plan for the job

References

Availability

Language

Computer
64K microcomputer
Interset IS 2000
Digico M16E

0090

SIRK *Norwegian Building Research Institute*
A labour-saving system for the circulation of periodicals by small libraries. Used in the library of the Norwegian Building Research Institute, where 350 periodicals are circulated to 160 staff members. Six separate printouts can be produced, giving circulation lists, alphabetical lists of periodicals and information on the number and titles of periodicals circulated to staff members. 440 periodicals and 220 users can be handled

References

Availability
Purchase, bureau service

Language
Fortran IV

Computer
Univac 1100
ND-100 and
ND-500

BCHART *Oasys Limited*
A program to draw bar charts of activities against time. Drawing and character sizes, activity descriptions, bar start and end times are input interactively or via a disk file. There is a choice of time units. Bars and float bars may be expressed by absolute times or as durations. The program may be used to plot the output from another program such as a critical path analysis program

References

Availability
Bureau service

Language
Fortran

Computer
DEC10

ACTION LIST *Project Software Limited*
Designed for use by project managers in expediting and progress chasing, and for document control. Establishes schedules itemising information outstanding, drawing requirements or materials procurement programmes; these define what needs to be done, by whom and when. By regular updating the program may be used for progress chasing. Also used for maintaining correspondence and filing registers and checking the processing of payment certificates, etc. The program includes a flexible report writer

References

Availability
Licence

Language
Fortran IV, Dibol

Computer
DEC PDP11/23, 64K

MANEX - Project Manpower Expenditure *Project Software Limited*
Provides control and analysis of manhours booked to projects and overheads within a company or department. The principal input document is a weekly timesheet. Reports are generated giving the weekly and cumulative manhour totals by project, overhead, section, activity and staff agency. Project billing and department costing reports can also be produced. An integral back up program provides file security and passwords to restrict access to sensitive information

References

Availability
Licence

Language
Fortran IV, Dibol

Computer
DEC PDP11/23, 64K

INTEREST *Quest GENESYS Limited*
A construction management program for estimating for civil engineering works. There are two methods available: the unit rate method relies on recalling from the database groups of costed activities to form priced bill of quantities items. The operational method is used for long term projects; it calculates the total resource of an operation and distributes cost amongst bill items. The two methods can be used independently or combined

References

Availability

Language
Gentran

Computer

FORECAST *S D Micros Limited*
A pre and post-contract project management and quantity surveying application for forecasting likely completion date and the flow of capital expenditure on building schemes. The program also allows schemes which are running into trouble to be identified at an early stage, and predicts work duration in a delay situation. Graphical output of the cashflow both on screen and printer. Printout of all calculated cashflows

References

Availability
Purchase

Language
Basic

Computer
48K Apple,
and others

SAPPHIRE MARS *Sapphire Systems Limited*
A full management accounting system to deal with current information, planning and budgeting, and corporate modelling. The program provides almost total flexibility in report layout, and all the options are specified by the interactive option screens of the Job Editor

References
Accountancy, Micro Decision, Which Computer, Practical Computing: 1982

Availability
Purchase

Language
C Basic
C Basic 86

Computer
CP/M or CP/M86

ASSET *SIA Computer Services*
A powerful, interactive corporate modelling system used in general business planning

References

Availability
Bureau service

Language
High level

Computer
Control Data,
IBM, Prime

CONNECT II *SIA Computer Services*
A fully interactive front and back end data input, validation and control system for the PROJACS project planning system

References

Availability
Bureau service

Language
High level

Computer
Control Data,
IBM, Prime

FORECAST *SIA Computer Services*
Used for business planning, this is a financial reporting and data management system

References

Availability
Bureau service

Language
High level

Computer
Control Data,
IBM, Prime

INTERNET 80S *SIA Computer Services*
A major, integrated project planning and management information system with many capabilities

References

Availability
Bureau service

Language
High level

Computer
Control Data,
IBM, Prime

0101

PERSONNEL *SIA Computer Services*
A flexible, interactive database application for personnel management. This is used in conjunction with PPL-PAYROLL and PERSONNEL

References

Availability
Bureau service

Language
High level

Computer
Control Data, IBM, Prime

0102

PROJACS *SIA Computer Services*
This is a well known, comprehensive project planning system

References

Availability
Bureau service

Language
High level

Computer
Control Data, IBM, Prime

0103

Project Management Information *SIA Computer Services*
SIA offer engineering organisations a unique service for fully integrated, data management based project information systems. These systems use SIA proprietary products, such as SYSTEM 2000, INTERNET 80S, ASSET, etc, linked and tailored to clients' individual requirements

References

Availability
Bureau service

Language
High level

Computer
Control Data, IBM, Prime

0104

ROSTER *SIA Computer Services*
This is a flexible, interactive manpower rostering system for improved labour efficiency in service industries and organisations

References

Availability
Bureau service

Language
High level

Computer
Control Data, IBM, Prime

0105

PROMPT AID 1-ESTIMATOR *Simpact UK*
An interactive estimating tool to assist in calculating expected cost and effort of a DP development project. Particularly suited for feasibility and planning studies. Features include: initial project sizing; selection and scaling of project model; interactive adjustment of model to reflect project details and development environment; user specified adjustments; display, printing and amendment of estimate

References

Availability
Purchase

Language

Computer
CP/M

0106

BUILD/34 *SYS-Unipower Limited*
Controls projects in progress from inception through ordering to completion. Provides a multi-company solution to control contracts/projects. All information is parameterised. Offers control of commitment and expenditure. Current project progress is shown at detail level, and year-end carry over does not delete this detail. Selectable reporting is available. Data input is interactive and allows easy transfer to and from projects and or sites

References
Recommended by IBM

Availability

Language

Computer
IBM System/34

0107

Foundation 100 *System Selection (R Sherrin)*
An integrated Builders' Management System program, covering payroll, job costing, purchase ledger, profit and loss, and stock control. Full multi-tasking. Up to four screens can be used

References
Professional builder OG82

Availability
Purchase

Language
Basic

Computer
Rair black box or ICL personal computer

0108

VisiCalc *Tandy Corporation UK*
A management and engineering planning and forecasting tool. Provides numeric accuracy of up to 11 digits, scientific notation, and functions such as SIN, COS, TAN, LOG, etc. Produces bar graphs. A more comprehensive version of this program is available for the Tandy TRS-80 Model II

References

Availability
Purchase

Language
Basic

Computer
TRS-80 Models I & II

0109

Management Analysis *Tillyard AG*
Provides data for project management and control, including: time scheduling; interim payments; variations; cashflow; final accounts; analysis of completed project

References

Availability

Language

Computer

0110

Touchstone Office Administrator *Touchstone Computers Limited*
Provides complete control over office management requirements. Includes facilities to: produce specifications, maintain job costing files, record time spent on jobs, produce interim and financial records. Output includes printout of: state of jobs, cash outstanding, all ledgers, standard letters, etc

References

Availability
Purchase

Language
CP/M and MS-DOS

Computer
ACT Sirius. Rair Black Box. ICL PC

EASYPLAN *United Information Services Limited*
A flexible system designed to assist where tables of data need to be built and manipulated,
often in a planning or budgeting situation

References

Availability
Bureau service, time sharing

Language
APL

Computer
Honeywell
Sigma 9

EDMS *United Information Services Limited*
Used to organise, sort, retrieve, update and delete information stored in a central data
base. It includes a language which allows the user to specify the structure of the database

References

Availability
Bureau service, time sharing

Language
Fortran, Cobol
Assembler, APL

Computer
Honeywell
Sigma 9

GPOS *United Information Services Limited*
This program was developed from the FAPS (Financial Analysis Planning System) program
by decisions taken on-line in the United States. GPOS is a comprehensive interactive
corporate modelling system and is in use throughout the world. It has been specifically
designed for sophisticated modelling of large companies with complex organisations and
operating structures

References

Availability
Bureau service, time sharing

Language
Fortran + Assembler

Computer
Honeywell
Sigma 9

Linear programming system (LP) *United Information Services Limited*
This program, developed from the RAND Corporation code, uses the product form of the
inverse method and is particularly fast because the computation is carried out in the
computer core. In time sharing mode, the program can handle approximately 140 rows,
560 columns and up to 1700 matrix entries; the user can control and amend the data
during the run: in batch mode, larger problems may be processed

References

Availability
Bureau service, time sharing

Language
Fortran

Computer
Honeywell
Sigma 9

COMPASS *Wimpey Group Services Limited*
A complete project control and management information system using an on-site
microcomputer linked to the main computer. The modular approach gives a wide range of
interlinked facilities, adaptable for specific requirements. The program provides network
planning, database and valuations software, communications, distributed processing and
time sharing, graphics and plotting facilities, and control of systems by management

References

Availability

Language

Computer
DEC VAX
Prime

RPORTS *Yard Limited*
For large scale production of reports, technical manuals, handbooks, tender documents,
technical proposals, correspondence, etc. Files can be quickly edited and amended and
new copy produced, correctly paged and formatted. Features include: auto page
headings/numberings; auto paragraph numbering; double sided copying; line filling and
justification; illustration run-around; widow/orphan control; underlining variations; side
highlight; multiple contents; standard text insertion; font change, etc

References

Availability

Language

Computer
DEC PDP11

Bills of quantity
Plant and capital analysis
Records
Stock control
Other

0117

Bills of quantities *ABS Oldacres Computers Limited*
This suite of programs calculates dimensions taken off architects' drawings. The
dimensions are sorted into trade or other order and a draft bill of quantities is produced by
extracting phrases from various standard libraries. Amendments can be incorporated
automatically to produce a final bill and detailed abstracts are provided. Libraries include
Fletcher & Moore, MDA Monk Dunstone Mahon & Scears (SMM5, SMM6 and International
Method). Sophisticated code techniques are available

References

Availability
Bureau service

Language
PL1

Computer
IBM 360, 370
4300 series

0118

Bills of quantities, price re-analysis *ABS Oldacres Computers Limited*
These programs, which are used in conjunction with a suite for producing bills of
quantities, allow prices to be added to the items generated in the bills of quantities. The
priced items are then re-sorted to give cost data for elements, operations, locations, etc
for the proposed building

References

Availability
Bureau service

Language
PL1

Computer
IBM 360, 370
4300 series

0119

Numeric *ABS Oldacres Computers Limited*
Provides abstracts for quantity surveyors and engineers. Dimensions are coded by the user
and processed to give an abstract for each coded item. Codes refer to descriptions in
either a firm's standard bill or old bills of quantities

References

Availability
Bureau service

Language
PL1

Computer
IBM 360, 370
4300 series

0120

Specifications *ABS Oldacres Computers Limited*
This system stores standard specification clauses on the computer and allows the user to
select and extract those clauses required for a particular project. Non-standard words,
phrases or whole clauses may be inserted as necessary. The program may include the
user's own standard specifications or others which are more generally used (eg National
Building Specification)

References

Availability
Bureau service

Language
PL1

Computer
IBM 360, 370
4300 series

0121

BENDING SCHEDULES *ABS Oldacres Computers Limited*
This program produces simplified bills of quantities lists from user supplied lengths, and
price rates for concrete reinforcing bars. Data is taken from bending schedules

References

Availability
Purchase

Language
M Basic

Computer
CP/M 64K

0122

DUCTWORK-SUPADUCT *ABS Oldacres Computers Limited*
Used at the pre or post-contract stage to produce bills of quantities for rectangular
ductwork and fittings

References

Availability
Purchase

Language
M Basic

Computer
CP/M 64K

0123

Q S Package *Barcellos Limited*
Used by quantity surveyors, to produce Bills of Quantity and post-contract valuations. For
those contracts let on 40 (JCT80) or 31F (JCT63) where the NEDO formula is used for
calculation of fluctuations, the above method of valuation is carried out. The VOP is
calculated on the Provisional Indices and, when Firm Indices are available, VOP is
recalculated

References

Availability
Purchase

Language
Microcobol

Computer
Microcomputer
with MPSL, and BOS
Minimum 64K

0124

$LAMSAC Application code 32035121140A *Bradford City Council, Architect's Department*
Calculates bills of quantities for the CLASP system. Slow peripheral units used are a card
reader and tape reader. It has been in use since 1972

References
LAMSAC

Availability

Language
Cobol

Computer
ICL 1904A
12K core

0125

LAMSAC Application code 32034112040A *Buckinghamshire County Council, Architect's
Department*
Calculates bills of quantities for County architects. Slow peripheral units used are a tape
reader and line printer

References
LAMSAC

Availability

Language
Plan Cobol

Computer
ICL 2966, 8Mb
2 magnetic tapes
1 disc drive

0126

ESTIMATING (CONSTRUCTION) *C-QS Computer Services*
Can be cross referenced with Bill Production and Minute Schedule (Labour Constants).
ESTIMATING produces an estimate for construction work leading to a tender. It takes into
account labour, material and plant schedules, and a detailed user defined cost analysis. It
will provide valuations of work in progress, with analysis if required. Bills of quantities and
final accounts are also produced

References
Building Trade Journal, Building, QS
weekly

Availability
Purchase

Language
Compiled Basic

Computer
Commodore
CBM 8032, 8096

INTEREST BUILD *Camic Limited*
Designed to assist civil engineering and building estimators price bills of quantity for construction work; provides fully priced bills and comprehensive project assessment data. Comprehensive analysis of bill and contract data. Fully calculated bill items are listed with breakdown and totals

References
Construction Computing, April 1983.
Others

Availability
Purchase

Language
Fortran IV

Computer
64K RAM
20 Mbyte

Autobill *Centre-File (Northern) Limited*
Converts taking-off data into abstracts, priced or unpriced bills of quantities, cost analyses, financial accounts and other associated reports. The system may be used with a library of standard descriptions in Fletcher and Moore phraseology, to suit the user's own requirements, or the surveyor's descriptions. Alternatively, an existing standard library may be used

References

Availability
Bureau service

Language
Plan

Computer
ICL 1900

Coded quantities *Centre-File (Northern) Limited*
A library system with standard phraseology for quantity surveyors. Each code facet represents a phase of description. The insertion of variable descriptions within standard 'skeleton' items has been incorporated. The coding manual has been designed to reduce 'look-up' time to a minimum; it deals with specific natural groups of items within a trade. Automatic pricing of bills is possible

References
Specified by the Development Group of Chartered Quantity Surveyors

Availability
Bureau service

Language
COBOL

Computer
ICL 1900

CAMP02 *Civil and Structural Computing (Northern) Limited*
Produces bills of quantities relevant to civil engineering using the CESMM. The full CESMM library of descriptions is held on disk and accessed by using the standard code. Full editing facilities are provided and tender bills, priced bills, interim valuations and forecasts can be processed rapidly

References
Bradshaw, Buckton and Tonge

Availability
Bureau service, time sharing, in-house

Language

Computer

CAMP03 *Civil and Structural Computing (Northern) Limited*
Produces bills of quantities relevant to building works using a screen level library of descriptions in a similar manner to Fletcher and Moore. The library can be fully varied. Tender bills, priced bills, interim valuations and forecasts can be processed rapidly

References
Bradshaw, Buckton and Tonge

Availability
Bureau service, time sharing, in-house

Language

Computer

CAMP01 *Civil and Structural Computing (Northern) Limited*
Produces bills of quantity relevant to civil engineering using the SMM pre 1976 format. Descriptions are entered manually, allowing full editing facilities. Tender bills, priced bills, interim valuations and forecasts can be carried out rapidly

References
Bradshaw, Buckton and Tonge

Availability
Bureau service, time sharing, in-house

Language

Computer

LPM001 *Civil and Structural Computing (Northern) Limited*
Using the bill of quantities set up by CAMP01, this program allows labour, plant, materials and other reconciliations to be carried out

References
Bradshaw, Buckton and Tonge

Availability
Bureau service, time sharing, in-house

Language

Computer

LPM002 *Civil and Structural Computing (Northern) Limited*
Using the bill of quantities set up by CAMP02, this program allows labour, plant, material and other reconciliations to be carried out

References
Bradshaw, Buckton and Tonge

Availability
Bureau service, time sharing, in-house

Language

Computer

$LAMSAC Application code 32036436010A *Clwyd County Council, Architect's Department*
Calculates bills of quantities for the CLASP system, for use by architects. Slow peripheral units used are a card reader and lineprinter

References
LAMSAC

Availability

Language
Cobol

Computer
IBM 370/145
47K core
1 magnetic tape unit

Bills of Quantity Pricing System *Compuquant Limited*
An information store holding analysed price build up of bill of quantities items. Labour rates are automatically computed. The estimator inputs the build up of each individual item, broken down into material costs, tradesmens' time, labourers' time, or own subcontractors' rates for each item under its own page number or reference. On completion, the analyses, with page totals, etc are printed out in detail. The profit element can also be included

References

Availability
Purchase, lease

Language

Computer
Toshiba T200
microcomputer with
64K

0137

Take-off system *Compuquant Limited*
A series of integrated programs covering most aspects of construction and producing a fully priced, extended and totalled bill of quantities. Includes: foundations, walls, upper floors and flat roofs, pitched roofs, internal partitions, and openings including doors and windows. Also allows pricing of plastering or painting as a separate bill of quantities, suitable for subcontractors. Further programs are currently being developed

References

Availability
Purchase, lease

Language

Computer
Toshiba T200 microcomputer with 64K

0138

Mini QS *Computer Design Systems*
Enables quantity surveyors to produce bills of quantities. Libraries available are Standard Phraseology: Fletcher and Moor, or LAMSAC. Bills are produced in Trade, Elemental or other formats for Tender documents. The input of the rates of the successful tenderer will result in a priced B/Q for the contract documents and other bill sortations, including NEDO. Taking-off contains brief descriptions for the post-contract surveyor. Other features include payroll, accounts and word processing

References

Availability

Language

Computer
Minicomputer

0139

IMACE *Computer Services (South West) Limited*
Provides an interim certificate in a form that can be submitted direct to the client together with associated cost reports for internal use. It consists of item number, including bill, section and new item references; description containing up to 400 characters, unit of measurement, estimated quantity, quantity measured to date, bill rate, up to 8 cost rates and 2 sort codes that can be used to link similar items in the bill

References

Availability
Bureau service

Language

Computer

0140

CIRCE *Construction Measurement Systems Limited*
(Construction Industry Resource and Cost Estimating). For estimating by contractors and subcontractors from data in bills of quantities and the production of resource budgets. Also used for cost planning and control during the design process, as the program and data can relate building dimensions to resource needs. Output includes analysed unit rates, extensions, totals, resources, quantities and costs to match structure of bills of quantities. (Or may be user defined)

References
Technical Information Service Paper 9, Chartered Institute of Building

Availability
Purchase

Language
Fortran, Basic

Computer
Microcomputer with CP/M (full system) CBM 8000

0141

Computer Estimating System *The Consultancy Consortium*
Allows automatic compilation of labour and materials cost of a job. Up to 9000 items may be entered in the data file, and these may be split into 26 categories. Produces bill of quantities including up to 200 items per unit

References

Availability
Purchase

Language

Computer
Sirius 1, 128K

0142

Bar Reinforcement *Gerald G Darby (Computing Services)*
Converts bending schedules into a Bill format for pre or post-contract use. 2000 separate bar marks can be entered in 1 1/2 days. Weight per schedule information enables the contractor to check a post-contract account. The job can be split into any number of sections by the quantity surveyor

References

Availability
Purchase

Language
M Basic

Computer
64K

0143

BILL PREP *Gerald G Darby (Computing Services)*
This program works up a bill of quantities from the completion of taking-off

References

Availability
Under development, available in 1983

Language
M Basic

Computer
Multi-user hard disk system

0144

Taking-off *Gerald G Darby (Computing Services)*
This is a question and answer list for pre-contract purposes. It enables the quantity surveyor to maintain an effective list of questions put to the architect or engineer during Bill preparation, together with the answers. Each item can be 'lined through' by the micro as measured so that the taker-off can check that all his queries have been embodied

References

Availability
Purchase

Language
M Basic

Computer
64K

0145

LAMSAC Application code 32035122140A *East Sussex County Council*
These programs produce bills of quantities for building works and associated tasks, including priced bills, elemental analysis and NEDO calculations. The basic program has been in use since 1975 and was converted to the ICL 2900 in 1981, with enhancements

References
LAMSAC

Availability

Language
Fortran

Computer
ICL 2972 (VME)

0146

CATO (Computer Aided Taking Off) *Elstree Computing Limited*
Provides quantity surveyors with a total aid to taking-off and bill preparation, where the whole process of measurement as in manual practice is transferred to the computer. Drawings are registered on the digitiser, used for scaling of measurements. Areas of closed perimeters can be calculated and adjusted. The system includes ad hoc scaling, areas, side calculations and annotation

References
CICA Bulletin, March 1982. QS Journal, January 1982

Availability
Purchase or lease

Language
Assembler Dibol (Cobol) Fortran

Computer
DEC PDP LSI 11/23

QSUITE *Engineering Software Services Limited*
A measurement and job management package for quantity surveyors. Produces a full priced bill of quantities for work to date on a contract, including cost price fluctuation to substantiate monthly claims

References

Availability

Language

Computer
Olivetti M20

Commercial Estimating & Bill of Quantity *Estimation Limited*
The same as for 'Commercial Estimating' but with the facility to break down each section into pages and reference numbers to enable the bill to be produced in the same order as it is received

References

Availability
Purchase

Language

Computer

Commercial Estimating (EV2) *Estimation Limited*
Suitable for commercial and industrial work for all types of electrical contractors, and lists materials with cost and labour. Take-off can be sectionalised up to 99 sections. Over 2500 items are available together with facility for the user to add anything not covered by the system. All sections can be brought together for a summary of tender with job preliminaries and expenses, overheads, profit, etc. The uplifted values are then spread back across each section for producing a bill of quantities

References

Availability
Purchase

Language

Computer

Heating and Piped Services Estimating *Estimation Limited*
For large and small contractors, covering copper, steel, cast iron, plastic and valves; breakdown of categories within each material. Take-off summarised by location or material type; insulation schedules are available in addition to listing material items with costs and labour times. Subcontracts, non-productive labour, preliminaries, overheads, profit, builders' discount and bonds can be entered at summary of tender stage; up to 50 items of equipment and bill of quantities or schedule of rates produced

References

Availability
Purchase

Language

Computer

Plumbing Services Estimating *Estimation Limited*
Suitable for all types of plumbing contractors and covers a comprehensive range of copper, plastic and cast iron with the facility of breaking down the estimate into location areas for summary. A summary of tender with the facility for entering up to 50 items of equipment plus preliminaries, overhead and profit percentages and builders' discounts leads into an automatic bill of quantities in a similar manner to the Heating and Piped Services Estimating program

References

Availability
Purchase

Language

Computer

Bill of Quantities *FCG Computer Systems*
This program handles all bill of quantities functions, from bill preparation through to the preparation of certificates. It is designed for use by quantity surveyors and contractors for monthly valuations

References

Availability
Purchase

Language
Commodore Basic

Computer
Commodore 8000

LAMSAC Application code 32033432170A *Hampshire County Council*
Calculates bills of quantities for architects. Slow peripheral units used are a card reader, tape reader and line printer. This program was first used in 1971

References
LAMSAC

Availability

Language
PL/1

Computer
IBM 370/135, 145.
100K core

MANIFEST *Ronald S Harrison*
To assist the estimator in pricing bills of quantities by carrying out all extensions, totalling, rate calculations, etc. Provides useful data, with automatic revision of prices and build-ups. Output includes list of resources, priced BQ, categorised BQ, summaries and exploded BQ

References
Building Technology and Management, December 1982 and February 1984

Availability
Purchase

Language
Apple Pascal

Computer
Apple II or IIe with 64K

LAMSAC Application code 32037835530A *Hertfordshire County Council*
Provides quantity surveying services for county architects. Slow peripheral units used are a tape reader and a line printer

References
LAMSAC

Availability

Language
Cobol

Computer
NCR Criterion
48K core
1 mag tape unit

ISOPEDAC *ICI Limited*
Prepares estimates of quantities of materials needed for all phases of a process pipework project. Detailed orders, costs, labour requirements and isometric drawings can be prepared from a final run of data: facilities for control of materials are also included

References

Availability

Language
Fortran

Computer
IBM 370-145

0157

ISEC Computerised Estimating System *ISEC Computer Systems Limited*
Provides calculations, information retrieval, costs and outputs. Calculation of rates from resources and activity libraries. Resources can be allocated to Bill items using codes or individually. Broad sheet allocated into labour, plant, material, subcontract, PC and margin for each item in the Bill, and totalled by page and section. Can be used for interim valuations and final accounts

References

Availability
Purchase

Language
Mecator Business
Basic

Computer
Onyx/Mecator
2000-5000, 16-bit

0158

LAMSAC *LAMSAC*
Handles the preparation of bills of quantities and related services for quantity surveyors. Output includes abstract edit, priced and unpriced bills of quantities, financial analysis and cost analysis

References
Recommended by Derbyshire County
Council

Availability
Purchase

Language
Cobol

Computer
Burroughs, IBM,
ICL, Honeywell,
NCR

0159

QUANTITIES, THE BQ PROGRAM *Lancaster Computing*
These programs are intended to aid the surveyor in the preparation of bills of quantities. Capable of operation by one person. Create a library, select clauses, add dimensions, and a JOB file is created. Run the output program to create a TRADE bill which gives page numbering, headings, collection and item lettering. Facilities allow: a record to be kept of all dimensions input, allocation into elements, input of prices/rates, insertion of 'rogue' items, and edit of job file before final print

References

Availability
Purchase

Language

Computer
Apple II, 48K

0160

BILLMASTER *Local Business Technology Limited*
Related to BILLCOST. Designed for the simple creation of bills of quantities for quantity surveyors and builders. Data is input via the terminal. After the initial library build, dimensions are entered to select a task/definition level, then quantities are calculated automatically. Interactive validation on mis-matches, invalid data, etc. Output consists of Bills of Quantity and base library listings

References
Apple Software Directory for 1983

Availability
Purchase, bureau service via Apple
dealers

Language
UCSD Pascal 2.1

Computer
Apple II with
64K

0161

MASTERBILL *Masterbill Micro Systems Limited*
Handles the preparation of bills of quantities (including cost analysis for post contract routines) with full sortation; also deals with multi-bills, abstract, elemental, type and NEDO breakdown facilities

References
RICS Chartered Quantity Surveyor,
October 1982

Availability
Purchase

Language
Basic 4 (compiled)

Computer
Commodore 8032,
8096

0162

Housing Valuation *Mentor Systems*
Provides a full bill of quantities system; a master BQ for a standard type is maintained and used to generate modifications at a development level or plot within a development. Normal practice is to have separate bills for substructure and superstructure. Valuation input documents are produced. Entry of operations is made by the site foreman or quantity surveyor. Three methods of pricing are offered: value as BQ (norm), rate per unit of measure (foundations), and entered amount

References

Availability
Licence

Language

Computer
ICL

0163

CESMM *MicroAid Limited*
Civil Engineering Standard Method of Measurement. A bill of quantities production package. Stores complete BQ's, titles, headings, item codes, item description, quantities, units of measurement and rates. Full editing facilities. Different stages of the bill, unpriced and priced tender, valuation and final account can be set up and updated quickly. The bill can be reviewed at any stage on screen or hard copy

References

Availability
Purchase

Language

Computer
Act Sirius, Apricot,
Texas Instruments

0164

Bills of Quantities *Norden Technical Computer Systems Limited*
At the take-off stage drawings are studied and codes for analysis are given. Details are entered and the computer edits the data, sorts, checks codes and prints out the Abstract and Bill, in any specified format, as determined by the analysis code. After pricing, a cost analysis is produced

References

Availability

Language

Computer
64k microcomputer
Interset IS 2000
Digico M16E

0165

GAMMA 2000 *Redland Construction Software Limited*
Handles taking-off for measuring and pricing quantities in houses. For use by builders, developers, builders' merchants and timber frame fabricators. Produces a schedule of materials with purchase orders, or a priced schedule ready to use as a quotation. Works directly from house drawings, with the system itself taking-off the quantity and applying the pricing; uses a digitiser

References

Availability

Language

Computer

0166

$LAMSAC Application code 32035257100A *Renfrew District Council, Architect's Department*
Calculates bills of quantities for architects. Slow peripheral units used are a tape reader, lineprinter and MT encoder

References
LAMSAC

Availability

Language
Cobol

Computer
NCR Century 200
32K core
2 magnetic tape units

THE AREA PROGRAM *David Ruffle Associates*
Takes-off areas from plans and maps via a graphics tablet, with full control over units and scale factors. The program is interactive. Optional printed summary available

References
'Architects' Apples', CADCAM International Magazine, October 1982

Availability
Purchase

Language
Applesoft Basic
DOS 3.3

Computer
Apple II, 48K
Graphics tablet

0168

Builders' Estimating System *Spot Computer Systems Limited*
Allows speedy preparation of priced estimates to be produced from bill of quantities or on-site measurements. Output includes priced estimates, and priced schedules of materials with up to 99 cost centres. Other output available for stage payments or cost to complete budgeting. Database may be standard or user defined

References

Availability
Purchase

Language
Compiled Basic

Computer
64K CP/M based computer with min 320Kb

0169

Contract Quantities *Tillyard AG*
Provides accurate bills of quantities with facilities for pricing and cost analysis, including: bills of quantities in various forms; tender documents; contract documents; cost analysis of priced bills

References

Availability

Language

Computer

0170

Detailed Estimate *Tillyard AG*
Provides detailed project costs, including: detailed estimates based on functional elements; priced bills of quantities; cost analysis

References

Availability

Language

Computer

0171

CLEVA *TM Software Systems Limited*
User entry definable database in reference library form of 13 trade books with 90 sub-trade chapters of rates with make up and description of tasks. Pre-contract Bill of quantity estimating including PS and PC sums, costed preliminaries and preambles. Post-contract stage valuations supporting retention funds. Bill of omissions and additions with analysis at all stages. Can be tailored for use by general, electrical, plumbing/heating, engineering and decorating contractors, etc

References

Availability
Purchase

Language
Executable code only

Computer
Commodore 8000
Tycom 128Kb, others

0172

BAUTEXT *UHDE GmbH*
Designed to produce bills of quantities, to evaluate and compare tenders, and to print the bills of quantities contract. The system includes a library of standard descriptions which conform to DIN or other standards, and can be modified to meet different job requirements. A coding system facilitates the selection of descriptions. Bills can be translated automatically into foreign languages

References
Futterer, E, G Lang and H Wessiepe, Die Bautechnik, 51, 1974, pp 13-16

Availability
Purchase

Language
PL/1

Computer
IBM 370

0173

ESTIMATING SYSTEM *Wilcox Computers Limited*
Designed for estimators in all aspects of the building and civil engineering industries. Provides an estimate of the cost of performing any building or contracting task, large or small. The estimate is produced as a Bill of quantities, with each cost item cross-referenced to a page/item number from the original bill

References

Availability
Purchase

Language
CIS Cobol (CP/M based)

Computer
CP/M based micro. Min 64K

0174

Building valuations *ABS Oldacres Computers Limited*
Handles interim valuations and enables a surveyor to obtain a copy of any valuation within a few days of measuring. It takes measured quantities and prepares a priced valuation for building contracts. Facilities exist for collecting totals of money for various parts of the bills and for a predetermined percentage to be applied to these totals

References

Availability
Bureau service

Language
PL1

Computer
IBM 360, 370
4300 series

0175

Production and work schedules *ABS Oldacres Computers Limited*
This suite of programs deals with the production of work schedules, for repair and alteration, on building contracts

References

Availability
Bureau service

Language
PL1

Computer
IBM 360, 370
4300 series

0176

PLANT HIRE *Advanced Business Technology Limited*
Provides a system for the control of plant and labour. The program handles invoicing per contract basis, and all other documentation, such as despatch, delivery and collection notes, audit reports and ad hoc reports

References

Availability
Purchase

Language
Business Basic

Computer
Data General
CSIO upwards

0177

ASSETS *CIMS Computer Systems Limited*
Part of the CIMS Management System designed for the construction industry. Maintains detailed information on plant and other assets, including details of purchase, disposal, depreciation and technical data. Depreciation is automatically computed using accounting standard SSAP16; handles straight line, reducing balance methods, etc, and allows for the projection of depreciation charges over future periods

References

Availability
Purchase

Language
RPG11

Computer
IBM System/34

0178

PLANT *CIMS Computer Systems Limited*
Part of the CIMS Management System designed for the construction industry. Provides information on whether individual plant items are active, dormant, awaiting transport, under maintenance or due for maintenance. Control of movement is maintained by site acceptance, or modification to weekly returns. Produces weekly hire charges. Provides control of plant distribution together with information on plant profitability and utilisation

References

Availability
Purchase

Language
RPG11

Computer
IBM System/34

0179

Plant services recall system *COSMIC*
Provides an automated procedure for issuing service notices and maintains a current file of proofload test due dates, preventive maintenance due dates, and dynamic averages of hours/task work assignments. The system detects and captures all due dates, and issues recall notices and maintenance on equipment. It also maintains an average of hours per task performance, which can then be used as an estimate for schedule loading

References
North American Rockwell Corporation

Availability

Language
Cobol

Computer
IBM 360 series

0180

Equipment (instrument) status log *A M Kinney, Inc*
This program accumulates the status of all equipment (instruments) of a project. Mainly used by field personnel to coordinate their schedule, but also useful for the expediter and vendors. The report provides information sorted by the equipment (instrument) TAC number. A second report may be produced with the information sorted by follow-up dates, for use by expediters

References

Availability

Language
Fortran

Computer
IBM 1130 and 370

0181

Equipment status memorandum *A M Kinney, Inc*
Accounts for all general information of the individual pieces of equipment within a project. There is an option to request additional reports that have the equipment sorted in different sequences. Another report computes the difference between the revised ship date and required delivery dates, and prints the equipment that has a difference of 9 weeks or less; used in expediting and field management in determining lab time of transit or other delaying factors

References

Availability

Language
Fortran

Computer
IBM 1130 and 370

0182

Plant hire *Mentor Systems*
Provides for maintenance of all files required to record, for and analyse, the use and supply of equipment for hire. Also caters for the sale of associated consumables. Offers reporting facilities for availability, utilisation, cost of repair, and depreciation.
0>0182
>Mentor Systems
>!Plant hire! Mentor Systems

References

Availability
Licence

Language

Computer
ICL

0183

Economic Comparison of Systems/B *Ross F Meriwether and Associates*
Combines energy costs for a typical year, and other annual operating costs, with initial investment and the associated costs of ownership, to find the total cost of each system, year by year, for a period of up to 30 years

References
Meriwether analysis series

Availability
Bureau service, purchase

Language

Computer
Univac 1108

0184

Monthly utility costs *Ross F Meriwether and Associates*
Calculates the monthly energy costs of air distribution systems using the local utility rate schedules

References
Meriwether analysis series

Availability
Bureau service, purchase

Language

Computer
Univac 1108

0185

PLANT HIRE - CONTRACS *UCC (Great Britain) Limited*
Maintains a file of information for management and accounting of a plant depot or hire company. Reports are produced onutilisation and profitability, including costs, repairs, breakdown time and idle time. These figures are compared with budgets for similar items. Accounting information produced includes revenue accounts, asset accounts and invoicing

References

Availability
Bureau service, remote batch

Language
Cobol

Computer
Univac 1106

0186

SIMSTRAT *United Information Services Limited*
An interactive corporate modelling and project evaluation system designed for use by planners without specialised knowledge. Facilities include sensitivity analysis, aggregation, logical tests, profitability criteria. File handling facilities enable the user to lin sub-systems together and to other programs

References

Availability
Bureau service, time sharing

Language
Fortran + Assembler

Computer
Honeywell, Sigma 9

DMS *ABS Oldacres Computers Limited*
A database management system for the storage, selective retrieval and printing of a firm's jobs, clients, personnel records, stock records, etc

References

Availability
Purchase

Language
M Basic

Computer
CP/M 64K

OMICRON-POWERSYSTEMS *ABS Oldacres Computers Limited*
A suite of programs covering general business management systems, including: payroll; sales ledger; purchase ledger; general ledger and financial reporting; sales order processing and invoicing; stock control

References

Availability
Purchase

Language
M Basic

Computer
CP/M 64K

Wordstar *ACT (Microsoft) Limited*
A screen-orientated word processing system specifically designed for non-technical personnel. Print enhancements include boldface, double strike, underline, strikeout, sub and superscripts, variable character pitch, variable line height and alternative type style or ribbon colour. Flexible formatting and pagination; multiple copy and chained printing; Wordwrap and Hyphenhelp

References
Recommended by Zenithplan Limited and ABS Oldacres

Availability
Purchase

Language

Computer
ACT Sirius. Any CP/M microcomputer

OMS-PEOPLE *Alpha Micro UK*
Provides integrated information storage and retrieval system for active, past and potential clients, consultants, contractors, business associates, service companies, employees, etc. The database may be searched by last name, company name, job name, city, state, country, zipcode, people/job/work category keys, or next contact date. All information lists are sorted alphabetically and numerically. Standard mailing labels are printed automatically

References

Availability
Purchase

Language
Alpha Basic

Computer
Alpha Micro CPU with 8Mbytes

SMB Sales Order Processing *Amplix Services Limited*
Features include: multi-company operation; sales order entry routines; purchase orders for re-stock routines; FIFO stock control routines; invoicing routines; picking lists; sales analysis; reports on stock status, orders and purchases

References

Availability
Purchase

Language
Commercial (SMB) Cobol, Fortran

Computer
CP/M or MP/M Microcomputer

Applewriter III *Apple Computer (UK) Limited*
A sophisticated word processing facility. Enables the user to compose, revise and print all kinds of documents from memos and letters to manuals and books

References
Personal Computing with Apple

Availability
Purchase

Language

Computer
Apple III

SPIRES *Bensasson & Chalmers Partnership*
(Special Purpose Information Retrieval System.) For maintenance of fixed-length records, retrieval on any selected attribute by user or any other programs. Handles specific, user defined file structures based on contents of each record; appearance of each record; password system; and fields (attributed) on which records can be selected and/or sorted. Based on a binary tree search which does not require any field to identify a record uniquely. Files are stored and sorted by all attributes simultaneously

References
CICA Bulletin, June 1982

Availability
Purchase

Language
Pro-Pascal MicroSoft Pascal

Computer
Any CP/M system

Production Management *Building Centre Computers Limited*
Modular programs which interface automatically, cover parts list maintenance, drawings register, production load planning, material requirements planning, stock control, plant maintenance, purchase ordering, supplier statistics, work in progress monitoring, and works documentation (to special order)

References

Availability
Purchase

Language
Basic

Computer
Mini and microcomputers single & multi user

Professional Practice System *Building Centre Computers Limited*
Modular system covering: word processing, specifications, technical database and calculations, budgeting, financial planning, time recording, job costing, management of client contracts, fee and purchase accounting, invoicing, selective mailing, personnel management, and inter-office communication

References

Availability
Purchase

Language
Basic

Computer
Mini and microcomputers single & multi user

Sales Management *Building Centre Computers Limited*
Modular programs cover: sales force management, sales representatives' activities/diaries, quotations, delivery estimating, price list maintenance, sales order processing, invoicing, order book analysis, product and customer sales statistics, commission calculations, word processing

References

Availability
Purchase

Language
Basic

Computer
Mini and microcomputers single & multi user

0197

Architectural Costing Package *CalComp Limited*
The material take-off from APP provides the detailed project information by way of component coding. A compatible database within ACP reflects the constituents of each component and details the associated costs

References

Availability
From CalComp

Language
Fortran

Computer
Any

0198

Summation of bending schedules *Camutek*
This program sums the lengths and weights of each type of bar, for each diameter, from standard reinforcement bending schedules

References

Availability
From owner

Language
Basic

Computer
HP 9830, (2k) or (6k)
9831, 9835, 9845
Future: HP85, 86

0199

Maintenance Advanced Management System *Cheshire County Council*
Coordinates the information required to assess and prepare an annual programme of maintenance work to buildings. The system also stores details of the electrical testing programme, and is being extended to incorporate data relating to the heating plant

References

Availability

Language
APL

Computer
IBM 3767

0200

Shop drawing submittals *Civil Software Inc, USA*
Provides access to information on the progress of shop drawings, catalogue cuts, samples, etc. Reports include: drawings, summary of all drawings, lists of outstanding drawings, lists of drawings, not approved, requiring resubmission, etc

References

Availability
Purchase

Language

Computer
Apple II with CP/M,
IBM PC

0201

Data Management System *Compsoft Limited*
A system for the storage and retrieval of information. Used for personnel records, stock control, client records and mailing, etc. Features include sorting, searching, printout of lists and reports, letters, labels, VDU display, calculations, file reorganisation, links, and security

References
Over 4000 installations

Availability
Purchase

Language

Computer
Micros with CP/M,
MP/M or MSDOS.
Commodore

0202

DELTA *Compsoft Limited*
A data management system. Records consist of header information with series of sub-files attached which can record each transaction relating to an item in the main header record. Features include: data security, sorting, searching, printing lists and reports, letters, labels, calculations, data processing, and file reorganisation. 2000 characters per record, 32,000 records per file, 250,000 sub-records per main record, and 8 sub-files per file

References

Availability

Language

Computer
Microcomputers with
CP/M, MP/M,
MSDOS

0203

OFFICEMAN *Corporate Business Systems Limited*
A general office system including electronic mail, word processing, personal and corporate filing, diaries, check lists, appointments scheduling, modelling, etc. Suitable for management, professional and secretarial use, particularly in project orientated environments. Output includes text, forms, graphs, and histograms via the VDU and printer

References
Which Word Processor and Office
Systems, Sept 1982, and others

Availability
Purchase

Language
Basic

Computer
DEC PDP11
(RSTS or RSX)
DEC VAX II (VMS)

0204

ESCEP *DHSS (Department of Health and Social Security)*
Enables the user to create, store and manipulate cost information related to a hospital design. The program provides an elemental build up of departmental engineering costs for comparison with Departmental Cost Analyses. Norms are given for both costs and quantities, and costs are index linked. Appropriate for early stages of cost estimating up to about stage 1 submissions

References

Availability
Purchase

Language
M Basic, Fortran

Computer
64K microcomputer,
SEL

0205

VOP 49 *DHSS (Department of Health and Social Security)*
Used in conjunction with INDICES, for the application of the Price Adjustment Formula for Building Contracts (Series 2). The program calculates variation of price based on 49 work category indices. These are set up and stored under the INDICES part of the program. Valuations are stored and recalled for subsequent valuations, and adjustments from provisional to firm

References

Availability
Purchase

Language
M Basic

Computer
64K microcomputer

0206

CODEWRITER *Dynatech Microsoftware Limited*
A system for writing programs. Used for: data entry, storage and retrieval of records; stock control; letter/word information; fixed assets and depreciation schedules; project records and control systems; mailing and labelling systems; hotel reservation systems. Once the user has designed a program, it can be modified as required and it will not need CODEWRITER to actually run the program

References

Availability
Purchase

Language

Computer
Commodore 8000

CORP *Dynatech Microsoftware Limited*
Combined Operating Re-entrant Programming Data Base Management System. Enables inexperienced personnel to produce programs quickly, 'designed' by the user, for customised applications. Used for many types of data management, including: data storage/retrieval, stock control, word processing, fixed assets, depreciation schedules, mailing, labelling, etc

References
Developed by the Maromaty and Scotto Software Corporation

Availability
Purchase

Language
Applesoft

Computer
Apple II

0208

TECH-WRITER *Dynatech Microsoftware Limited*
Designed for quick and easy program development for the technical or scientific programmer. All generated programs are highly structured, interactive, and contain all the code for data manipulation and transfer, together with a full range of system and utility commands. Applications include: structural and finite element analysis, graphics plotting, statistical analysis etc

References
Developed by Logical Computing

Availability
Purchase

Language
Applesoft Basic

Computer
Apple II and III

0209

Bid Summary *Estimation Inc*
Allows general contractors to produce a job summary under either own or subcontractor columns into 50 user definable divisions, which may contain up to 500 items. There are provisions for separation of a job into in-house, subcontractor, or combination methods for labour and materials

References

Availability
Purchase

Language

Computer

0210

Estimating File Maintenance Version *Estimation Inc*
Includes 20 different material types of up to 500 items and 120 sizes for each type. Suitable for a mechanical contractor. Estimates are provided for residential, commercial and most industrial applications. A bid summary enables the user to develop a total bid price including quoted items, job expenses, overheads, profit, etc. The program offers the option of selecting more than 20 material categories from Estimation's library

References

Availability
Purchase

Language

Computer

0211

Wordstar/Spellstar/MailMerge *Estimation Inc*
A word processing package to handle general office functions. All documents are typed at the terminal and stored on disks for access at any time. A printout is provided for all typed material. Also incorporates Spellstar which locates spelling and typing errors automatically. A standard 20 000 word dictionary disk can be supplemented with additional lists, created by the user, of special terms or customer's names

References

Availability
Purchase

Language

Computer

0212

ESU System Facility *Estimation Limited*
Creates duplicate copies of any Estimation disk in possession, allowing the security of multiple master files. Provides a comparison of one disk to another. Checks the entry stock of disks periodically, simplifying the correction of disk errors without damaging recorded data. Allows the validation of any new disk in the drive to check possible error before usage

References

Availability
Purchase

Language

Computer

0213

File Maintenance *Estimation Limited*
Programs are available for the following: Commercial Electrical & Bill of Quantity Entry; Heating and Piped Services Estimating; Plumbing Services Estimating; H&V Insulation Estimating; Roof Plumbing. The File Maintenance program enables the user to change, add or omit items, descriptions and sizes

References

Availability
Purchase

Language

Computer

0214

Tool Inventory Control *Estimation Limited*
Allows the user to type in up to 1200 different tool descriptions, manufacturers and purchase prices. The program keeps track of each tool and location by job number. It allows the foreman to find the location of every tool, or to find out which tools are at a specific location

References

Availability
Purchase

Language

Computer

0215

SCRATCH-PAD
This program is used for information storage and retrieval, letter writing, calculations, and for its search facilities. Information is printed out or displayed on the screen. Up to 60 user defined headings are available. The calculation facility can deal with a 10 term 5th order algebraic relationship

References

Availability

Language

Computer

0216

TIME-COST *Focus Software Consultants*
A fully integrated package allowing conventional timesheet data and incurred expenses data allocated to a job to be entered to the computer and stored. Data may be used to produce control reports for projects between any two dates and performance against budgets. Data may be entered daily, weekly, fortnightly, etc, allowing flexible control of a project's cost by stages. Expense reports produced may be used as a basis for producing fee accounts, invoices, etc

References

Availability
Purchase

Language

Computer
CP/M or MS DOS

0217

Viewdata *Geest Computer Services Limited*
This facility has many applications such as: sales, marketing, engineering, retail, distribution, scheduling and order entry. All these facilities can be used on the powerful database and accessed by a VDU

References

Availability
Bureau service

Language
Cobol

Computer
ICL ME29

0218

CM 2020 *Graffcom Systems Limited*
An information management system allowing fast, easy storage, maintenance and retrieval. Applications include: personnel files, stock control/inventory, questionnaire analysis, quality control, purchasing, medical records, mailing lists, product development, industrial relations, and distribution

References

Availability
Purchase

Language
Fortran

Computer
Z80. CP/M, min 48K memory. Some 16-bit micros

0219

WP2020 *Graffcom Systems Limited*
An advanced word processing system including features such as: quick storage and retrieval, special set of keytops, easy amendment of text and page format, printed output, filing system, a 15,000 word dictionary/spelling checker, merge documents for personalising letters, etc. Ability to connect two workstations for direct mail transmission, or link a station to a remote computer via telephone dial-up

References

Availability
Purchase

Language

Computer
8080/Z80/8088 8086 based microcomputers

0220

FMS *Graham-Dorian Software Systems Limited*
A file management system to set up, store, retrieve and use data files. For the first time user, FMS provides a unique and friendly environment with a menu driven process for each function that the system performs. Five full screen editors allow simple creation of Files, Keys, Screens, Reports and Menus, in response to questions in plain English. The interactive programs are self- prompting and the accompanying primer gives full tutorial introductions to all the basic facilities

References

Availability

Language
Basic, EFM/SHELL-80

Computer
8 and 16-bit microcomputers

0221

SPECWRITER *Hevacomp Limited*
Enables specifications to be very easily produced from stored standard clauses, in conjunction with a Wordstar word processing package. Initially a specification summary is printed, containing headings of each clause. After checking, and any necessary alterations have been made, the final specification is printed with pagination, justification, adjustable page length, and all the features normally found in word processors

References

Availability
Purchase

Language

Computer
Any 64K microcomputer

0222

Drawing list and contract document list *A M Kinney, Inc*
Provides a listing of all drawings of a project sorted by the specification that the drawings were issued with. Input is divided into specification and drawing information. Drawings are sorted by the 'Specification issued with' field, grouped by the specification number and printed with the respective specification. A second report may be produced listing all drawings sorted by drawing number

References

Availability

Language
Fortran

Computer
IBM 1130 and 370

0223

Drawing number ledger *A M Kinney, Inc*
This report gives an up to date status of all drawings for a project. The coding systems may be used in any of the input/output fields, and to describe these in the report. Input/output fields are the drawing number and title, scheduled start and completion dates, actual start and completion dates, estimated per cent completion, preliminary issue date, construction issue date, bid issue date, and revision number and date. Standard sort is by drawing number sequence, with optional sorts available

References

Availability

Language
Fortran

Computer
IBM 1130 and 370

0224

ADEPT *LMR Computer Services*
A comprehensive word processing package with all the usual facilities for input, editing and formatting of text. There is an additional mailshot merge facility

References

Availability

Language

Computer
Prime
16 and 32-bit mini and microcomputers

0225

Purchase Order Control *Mentor Systems*
Allows input of material requirements together with pricing and data details. Quantity and overspend may be highlighted. Reports on outstanding orders may be made in contract or supplier sequence with detail at line level of the due date for delivery, prices, discounts, etc. Similar report for goods received. Assists with clearance of purchase invoices. Automatic posting to costing and nominal ledgers

References

Availability
Licence

Language

Computer
ICL

0226

AutoClerk *MicroProducts Software Limited*
A general purpose system which allows the non-technical user to file, maintain and retrieve his information and then to generate reports and analyses to his own specification. Designed for use by architects, builders' merchants, estate agents, property management firms, and many others

References

Availability
Purchase

Language

Computer

Autowriter *MicroProducts Software Limited*
A menu-driven word processing program to create, store and update documents, produce mailshots and standard letters. Autowriter can be integrated with a firm's business applications to form a complete office system

References

Availability
Purchase

Language

Computer
BOS/5

0228

Lexicom/2 *Microtrend UK*
A word processing system for use by typists, managers, etc. Text creation and editing facilities include horizontal and vertical scrolling, search and replace, screen calculator and screen print. File copy, rename, delete or merge facilities are included. Utility programs convert Lexicom files to CP/M source and vice versa. Also includes word count program and data selector program for searching CP/M ASCII record files for inclusion of data in file merge program

References
8000 programs sold in Europe

Availability
Purchase

Language
8080 Assembler

Computer
CP/M System with minimum 48K memory

0229

Trendisk/1c *Microtrend UK*
A data management system which allows the creation and deletion of files for processing of data in record format specified by the user. Records can be added, deleted, printed, examined, searched, or sorted into new sequences on alphabetic or numeric criteria. The system also includes a label printing program, report generator and a numeric processor. Files can be transferred to and from Lexicom/2 (Trendtext/2)

References
4000 programs sold

Availability
Purchase

Language

Computer
CP/M based microcomputer with 64Kb RAM

0230

FILETAB *The National Computing Centre Limited*
A comprehensive file maintenance and reporting system, available for many current models of mainframe computers. The facilities include input validation, file creation and maintenance, selective reporting, program testing, and information retrieval. Simple statements are used to define requirements. Decision tables are used to specify concisely the record selection and processing requirements. It is possible to interrupt the automatic sequence of operations to specify individual processing requirements

References

Availability

Language

Computer

0231

USERTAB *The National Computing Centre Limited*
A simple information retrieval system. The main features enable the user to: examine computer files; select information on the basis of specified critera; sort the information into the sequence required; print out the results in a convenient format. Other features for use by the DP department include: access to non-standard files by routines in other languages; incorporation of special routines written in FILETAB; table searching for translation of coded data; use of a separate data dictionary system

References

Availability

Language

Computer

0232

NOTIS-IR *Norsk Data Limited*
A powerful information storage and retrieval program for handling textual information. Used for a wide variety of applications, such as: library records, report and personnel archives, service records, catalogues, plant and assets register, accident and safety regulations, legal data, correspondence records, etc

References

Availability

Language

Computer
Norsk Data ND-100 Sintran III/VS operating system

0233

DRAWING REGISTER *Project Software Limited*
Maintains a record of all drawings produced for a project, and specifically designed for use on a small computer in the project manager's office. Coding format includes: project number, area code, discipline code, drawing number unique to area and discipline, drawing type number, and an optional sheet number. The system allocates revision numbers as necessary, so that only the latest drawings are issued. It also provides a list of recipients of drawings for each project

References

Availability
Licence

Language
Fortran IV, Dibol

Computer
DEC PDP11/23, 64K

0234

CUBES *Property Services Agency, Directorate of Civil Engineering Services*
Maintains records of concrete cube crushing test results and performs statistical calculations producing listing, histograms and cumulative frequency distribution diagrams

References
PSA program library

Availability

Language
Fortran

Computer
UCS DEC 10

0235

Word processing *Redland Construction Software Limited*
For general use in editing, information storage and retrieval. Handles documents of any length, line spacing, word spacing, with direct control over page length, margins, tabulation, hyphenation, indentation and pagination. Used for mail shots, quotations, delivery notes, reports, and general correspondence

References

Availability

Language

Computer

0236

SOMEL SYSTEM *Somel, Structural Steelwork Engineers, France*
For the production of steelwork fabrication shop manufacturing information (detailing, scheduling and numerical control tapes). Consists of a suite of 8 programs, some of which build up and maintain a universal library of sections, connections and drawings in parametric form, as well as information on how these are permitted to combine. Other programs use this information to create the documents needed for the fabrication of steelwork for projects

References
Constructional Steelwork SWP

Availability
Via Compower

Language
Fortan IV

Computer
IBM, DEC VAX, Univac Prime, CDC, Interdata

Computer programs for the building industry

0237

WS-11 *SysCom Computers Limited*
A word processing package for handling all types of text; it includes creating, editing, printing and maintaining indexes of documents and list processing

References

Availability

Language

Computer

0238

BILL OF MATERIAL *Tamsys Limited*
Facilities for creating, amending and maintaining a manufacturing database. Handles component structure explosion to show, for a parent part, either the first level, all levels or only the lowest level of component parts. Complemented by a component structure implosion which starts with the component part and builds up to parent parts on a single level, all levels or to the highest level only

References

Availability
Purchase

Language

Computer
CP/M, 48K

0239

Employee Records System *Tandy Corporation*
Stores comprehensive records enabling the user to perform rapid analysis of employees, including personal details, education, time keeping, holidays, etc. 1600 employee database, multiple databases (not interactive). Pre-defined screen layouts for update and enquiry allows example report and label formats together with access to all profile facilities

References

Availability
Purchase

Language

Computer
TRS-80
Model II

0240

Profile III Plus *Tandy Corporation*
Includes most of the capabilities of the TRS-80 Model II Profile and Profile Plus. Stores up to 8000 records, and can access data with up to 36 user defined search criteria. An indexing file allows high speed access. The maths package analyses records of up to 1000 characters in length. Creates up to 99 categories per record, with up to 5 screen formats per record. Stores up to 2400 records on a data disk. Prints up to 5 user defined reports per file

References

Availability
Purchase

Language
Basic

Computer
TRS-80,
Model III

0241

Profile II *Tandy Corporation*
An electronic filing system for storage and retrieval of names, addresses, accounts, bills owed and paid, personnel or customer records, etc. Contains a security function. Stores up to 99 data fields in a single record and prints up to 5 different reports for each file. Includes automatic page numbers, current date and column totals. Can be merged with SCRIPSIT. Stores up to 3000 records with a one-disk 64K Model II system, and up to 20,000 with external disk drives

References

Availability
Purchase

Language

Computer
TRS-80 Model II

0242

SCRIPSIT 2.0 *Tandy Corporation*
Forms and letters, etc, can be stored and edited. Features include: automatic block moving and duplication; page numbering, margins, line spacing and page number; search mode, for selective editing; floating format and reverse indentation for tables and special formats. Up to 20 keys for individualised use; storage of up to 11 formats. Full headers and footers, underlining, sub/superscripts, boldface, etc. Stores up to 320,000 characters on each disk. Many other features

References

Availability
Purchase

Language

Computer
TRS-80
Model II

0243

SCRIPSIT *Tandy Corporation*
Enables the user to enter, correct and edit letters, memos, reports, etc, then print the text correction-free. Letters used frequently, reports and forms are stored for repeated use, and can be quickly updated. The user can edit, insert, move or delete text; also allows a search for a specified word or phrase and can replace each occurrence with a different word or phrase. Other features include reformatting, hyphenation, automatic page numbering, etc

References

Availability
Purchase

Language

Computer
TRS-80
Models I & III

0244

Tandyscribe *Tandy Corporation*
A suite of programs comprising SCRIPSIT, TANDYMAIL I and LINK. Prints out paginated, justified letters for selected addresses already on Tandymail I. Allows many print facilities not available on SCRIPSIT, such as: large/small definitive characters may be printed, pound signs, underlining, etc. Enables the user to set up a 'parameter' file of selected phrases for personalised letter writing or specifications

References

Availability
Purchase

Language

Computer
TRS-80
Model I

0245

Bill of Materials: TABS *Transam Microsystems Limited*
Parts explosion to 10 levels. Up to 20 char ID for parts. Up to 99 parts per level, and up to 10,000 parts in an assembly. Features include: forecasting, minimum re-order levels, re-order lead time, batch entry. Integrates with Sales, Purchase, Invoice and Sales Order Modules

References

Availability
Purchase

Language
Fortran-80

Computer
CP/M

0246

QUEST *University of Edinburgh*
An information storage and retrieval system for recording and viewing information held as plain language text linked to drawings. These may be building plans or diagrams depicting organisational structure. Includes procedures for tracing (digitising) from existing drawings to a computer, and for capturing text data via user designed forms (templates) on a display screen. Users can build up and modify their own data structures for holding information

References
Graphic Interaction with Database
Systems, conference. CAD82. Brighton
1982

Availability
Purchase (Contact: Mr Aart Bijl)

Language
UNIX

Computer
Microcomputer, eg
DEC, Xylogics,
with 256Kb

Stock Controller *Anagram Systems*
Comprehensive stock control system, including the following features: recording of
purchase order information and all stock movements; up to date stock levels, outstanding
orders, free and allocated stock; weighted average method for stock valuation; cost/selling
prices can be adjusted by a percentage for all stock or just for items from a particular
supplier; assembly processing, interfaces with the Termipet hand held terminal; 14 different
printed reports

References

Availability
Purchase

Language

Computer
Commodore CBM
8032

Stock Control *Building Centre Computers Limited*
Maintains accurate records of stock movements and produces reports for stock control
management. Includes quality regrading or scrapping, allocated and free stocks, stock
issue and average usage, re-order level monitoring, signalling of out of stock items,
valuation by LIFO, FIFO, etc, individual or group written up/down valuations, stock checks,
stock variances, identification of fast moving, high value and obsolete items, items bought
and sold in different measures, etc. Interfaces with other programs

References

Availability
Purchase

Language
Basic

Computer
Mini and
microcomputers
single & multi user

STOCK *CIMS Computer Systems Limited*
Part of the CIMS Management System designed for the construction industry. Maintains
records of stock issues, delivery notes, stocktake and adjustments. Sets
maximum/minimum and re-order levels, reports on shortages and provides details of
purchase order progress. Identifies obsolete and slow moving items; maintains perpetual
inventory checks which reduce, or even eliminate, stocktaking duties

References

Availability
Purchase

Language
RPG11

Computer
IBM System/34

Stock Control *Compact Accounting Services Limited*
Provides management information on all aspects of stock and its control. Features include:
enquiry facility via the screen; evaluation of stock by average cost, standard cost or FIFO
methods; maintenance of orders placed on suppliers; highlighting of re-order levels and
minimum stock levels; allocation of stock to customers' orders. The system may be
integrated with the sales ledger and order processing systems

References
Recommended by Zenithplan Limited

Availability
Purchase

Language
Microsoft Basic

Computer
Sirius 1. Any
CP/M microcomputer
with 64K

Stock Control *Dynatech Microsoftware Limited*
Capacity for 2500 stock items and 99 suppliers. Functions include display, addition,
modification, deletion of stock items, updating stock levels, printing reports, etc.
Information stored includes: description/product code reference, supplier code and name,
quantity in stock, dates of last sale and addition, re-order level, quantity on order, date
re-ordered, cost price, and mark-up percentage

References

Availability
Purchase

Language

Computer
Apple II Plus

Stock Control System *FCG Computer Systems*
Features include: a fully integrated system, sales invoices, purchase orders, audit trail, 15
character codes, and full stock reporting. Delivered goods are entered through the Goods
Inward Program, and any discrepancies are highlighted. Sales invoices are printed and
stock levels are maintained. A Low Stock Report is printed and a Purchase Order raised to
replenish stocks

References

Availability
Purchase

Language
Commodore Basic

Computer
Commodore 8000

ADORE *LMR Computer Services*
This system uses files common to ADNDA and APICS. Document layout and content are
flexible. Facilites include: customer identification by account number or mnemonic, credit
check, stock availability, picking list, stock discrepancies/variances, printed invoice and
despatch note sets, updating of stock records and customer accounts, etc

References

Availability

Language

Computer
Prime

APICS *LMR Computer Services*
A production and inventory control system. The stock holding records are separate from
the product/part description records, thus permitting great flexibility for multiple location
users. Reports cover slow moving stock, reorder levels, recommended purchases, and lists
to assist in stock-taking operations

References

Availability

Language

Computer
Prime

STOCKMAN *SysCom Computers Limited*
An advanced, inter-branch, multi-location, real time stock control system which combines
flexibility and cost effectiveness with simplicity of use. Comprises a set of interactive
modules which provide option menus that guide the operator through the job in a series of
logical sequences. Data inputs at source are automatically transferred to other sections of
the system, and comprehensive interrogation facilities are provided

References

Availability

Language

Computer

Stock Control *Tandy Corporation*
Handles up to 1000 items per disk. Provides complete maintenance of stock records,
incorporating comprehensive information on each stock item. Features include: issuing and
receiving stock reports, monthly stock movement reports, and re-order reports. Price
list/margin reports, stock list, price changes, annual stocktaking and perpetual inventory
are also handled

References

Availability
Purchase

Language

Computer
TRS-80
Models I & III

0257

HASTY (Handling and storage in timber yards) *TRADA*
This suite of programs analyses the operation of any timber yard business, either existing or planned, and evaluates the most cost efficient handling and storage system

References

Availability

Language

Computer

0258

SIM 25 *TRADA*
A program for evaluating the effects of various re-order quantities and re-order levels of prepared timber products. The user provides historic order/sales data over a period for a selection of stock items. Lineprinter output shows input parameters (policy alternatives) and the associated consequences. A range of safety levels may be applied in relation to setting of re-order levels

References

Availability
For sale as part of consultancy

Language
Fortran

Computer

0259

TRAID (Timber records, analysis) *TRADA*
A suite of programs for order analysis and stock recording. The programs are designed specifically for softwood, hardwood or board materials, in either metric or Imperial units, and used for planning, purchasing and production

References

Availability

Language

Computer

0260

Inventory management *United Information Services Limited*
This is a three level system for recording, controlling and managing stock in different situations

References

Availability
Bureau service, time sharing

Language
Cobol

Computer
Honeywell
Sigma 9

0261

INSURANCE VALUATIONS *ABS Oldacres Computers Limited*
Calculates the total cost of insurance cover required for building when given the cost of reinstatement. Total costs include allowances for professional fees and projected inflation based on pre-sorted indices. Output includes summaries and histograms of relative costs

References

Availability
Purchase

Language
M Basic

Computer
CP/M 64K

0262

NEDO *ABS Oldacres Computers Limited*
Used at the post-contract valuation stages to produce NEDO formula price adjustment statistics using series 2 indices, including all appendices and specialist categories. Indices can be updated as necessary for firming up purposes

References

Availability
Purchase

Language
M Basic

Computer
CP/M 64K

0263

National Building Specification *Bensasson and Chalmers Partnership*
Provides a comprehensive set of specification clauses which are simple to use. The architect, engineer or surveyor need only make the changes to the standard text as necessary for each project. NBS disks are supplied from which the draft specification is initially formed. The NBS sections can be used in SfB or SMM form

References

Availability
Purchase

Language

Computer
Apple Superbrain
All computers using ASCII

0264

LAMSAC Application code 32504112040A *Buckinghamshire County Council, Architect's Department*
Provides a commitment system and calculates repairs and MTCE expenditure. Slow peripheral units used are a tape reader and line printer. The program was formulated in 1975

References
LAMSAC

Availability

Language
Cobol

Computer
ICL 2966, 8Mb
1 disc drive

0265

Sales Order Processing *Building Centre Computers Limited*
Maintains accurate records of customers' orders; produces picking lists, despatch documentation and sales invoices, alternative product suggestions, call-off orders, delivery route loading and planning, negotiated prices, seasonality of sales statistics, settlement discounts. Sales analysis by product and customer. Interfaces with stock control and sales accounting modular programs

References

Availability
Purchase

Language
Basic

Computer
Mini and microcomputers single & multi user

0266

Plant Hire Maintenance *C-Star Computer Services Limited*
This system comprises three programs: maintenance, printing and housekeeping. 1 Maintains a plant register containing details of all units owned by the user. 2 Maintains a customer register containing details of all customers currently hiring units. 3 Maintains a hire register containing details of all current hire agreements. 4 Periodically produces invoices to customers for the hire of units

References

Availability
Purchase

Language
Basic

Computer
Commodore 8000

Estimating *CACE*
A series of programs on Computer Aided Construction Estimating. Produce priced schedules of items in building work, related to the provisions of the Standard Method of Measurement of Building Works (6th Edition). Can be tested and modified to user requirement. Include rates of wages, costs of materials and plant, labour and plant constants, overheads and profits; these are separately shown as net cost and bill rates

References

Availability
Purchase

Language
Basic

Computer
Commodore 8050

OPTIM *Capricorn Computer Systems Limited*
A comprehensive system for optimisation in processing sheet materials. Primarily for use on small computers. Applications include: glass, chipboard, steel, laminates and exterior wall cladding. User defined programs include: communications, performance parameters, estimating, automated cutting, offcut allocation, reports, etc.

References

Availability
Purchase

Language
BCPL

Computer
256K RAM. CP/M86

GLAZE *Capricorn Computer Systems Limited*
For window manufacturers covering design and construction. Provides for: aluminium, pvc and timber systems; casement windows, patio and residential doors; user defined designs, dimensions and components; automatic selection of hinges, reinforcing bars, etc; control of manufacturing costs; and integration with optimisation programs and accounting systems

References

Availability
Purchase

Language
BCPL

Computer
Min 128K RAM.
CP/M86

DGLAZE *Cardale Computer Systems*
This replacement window package is user configurable. It produces cutting schedules and glass requisition lists. The program includes stock control, costing, order processing, and invoicing routines

References

Availability

Language

Computer
Olivetti M20

CASTLE ESTIMATOR *Castle Business Systems Limited*
An estimating system specially designed for the construction industry. Output includes: detailed estimate, estimate summary, bill of quantities, schedule of rates and purchasing schedule. The detailed estimate is then available for processing as necessary, using different overhead percentage, labour rates, material mark-ups, net profit percentage, etc

References

Availability
Purchase

Language

Computer
Xerox

BUMP *CBS Consultants*
A series of programs designed to provide effective control of the administration of builders' merchants. The system includes a complete Price Book for pricing and discounting sales, invoicing and accounting functions, stock control allied to purchase and sales order control

References

Availability
Purchase

Language
Dirol

Computer
DEC PDP11
VAX

Equipment Hire *Chiltern Microcomputers Limited*
Records, calculates and prints bookings, hire agreements, delivery and collection sheets, invoices and sales ledger

References
Personal Computing with Apple

Availability

Language

Computer
Apple II

Estimaid *CIC (London) Limited*
A simple but comprehensive system from which estimates may be prepared. Stock information can be updated from a manual stock take. Up to 6000 stock items can be handled, and estimates prepared listing all the items required, together with those not included in stock. Analyses this information and provides a printout. Labour element can be added, together with a work description, and allowance made for overheads, commission and profit

References
Recommended by Apple

Availability
Purchase

Language
Apple Basic
Pascal

Computer
Apple II and III

FORPA *CICA*
Designed to compute price adjustments for building contracts based on NEDO Series 2 indices. Both the Work Group and Work Category methods are available, including Fix Only items and the specialist formulae

References
CICA, LAMSAC

Availability
As a published source listing

Language
Fortran

Computer
Machine independent

BAXTER *Civil and Structural Computing (Northern) Limited*
Provides a rapid evaluation in accordance with the National Economic Development Office Price Adjustment Formula for civil engineering works. A 10 year database of indices is maintained by the user

References
Bradshaw, Buckton and Tonge

Availability
Bureau service, time sharing, in-house

Language

Computer

0277

BEAMA *Civil and Structural Computing (Northern) Limited*
Provides a rapid valuation in accordance with the BEAMA CPA Advisory Service for Electrical and Mechanical Engineering. A 10 year database is maintained by the user

References
Bradshaw, Buckton and Tonge

Availability
Bureau service, time sharing, in-house

Language

Computer

0278

CADEST *Civil and Structural Computing (Northern) Limited*
Originally developed as an estimating tool for the steel fabrication industry, but easily adapted for any industry requiring parts explosion. The simple version takes a bill of materials and explodes each item to produce detailed costs, weights and surface areas. With the enhanced version, the assemblies do not have to be standard and can contain any combination of definable rules

References
Bradshaw, Buckton and Tonge

Availability
Bureau service, time sharing, in-house

Language

Computer

0279

MATLIS *Civil and Structural Computing (Northern) Limited*
Produces a material listing of like elements of a structure, including summations of element weights. Output is formatted to produce a bill of materials on completion

References
Bradshaw, Buckton and Tonge

Availability
Bureau service, time sharing, in-house

Language

Computer

0280

NEDO *Civil and Structural Computing (Northern) Limited*
Provides a rapid valuation in accordance with the National Consultative Council Standing Committee of Indices for Building Contracts. A database of NEDO Series 2 indices is maintained by the user. The 49 basic work categories together with the 7 appendices, and the specialist engineering category, are catered for

References
Bradshaw, Buckton and Tonge

Availability
Bureau service, time sharing, in-house

Language

Computer

0281

TRIMLOSS *Civil and Structural Computing (Northern) Limited*
A 2D cutting optimiser to reduce wastage. Input can be quantities of any type of rectangular material matched against the available resources to produce cutting instructions. The user can specify multiple stock sizes, trim allowances, break-out tolerances, grain direction, cutting rules and limitations, equipment limitations, stock availability, re-useable off-cuts, racking limitations, and the type of computer output required

References
Bradshaw, Buckton and Tonge

Availability
Bureau service, time sharing, in-house

Language

Computer

0282

ARCOM *Computer Design Systems*
A management system designed for architects, to produce Building Specifications, using the National Building Specification (NBS) library. The program also handles job costing, payroll, office accounts and word processing. Reports are available on the screen or printer, giving details on activities at pre and post-contract stages, and of individual job costs

References

Availability

Language

Computer
16-bit microcomputer

0283

ESTIMATOR *Computer Management Services*
Designed by estimators specifically for construction industry companies. The program covers quantities input, pricing, tender production and company library. Features: a high degree of security via password heirarchy; existence checking and verification of input; comprehensive reporting facilities

References

Availability
Purchase

Language

Computer
Burroughs B20

0284

MICROSERV *Comsoft Associates*
Maintains details of central heating servicing. User defined system, holding between 900 and 1800 client details, and providing a list of clients whose service is due in the specified week, together with address labels for reminder cards. 240 characters of notation for each client. 30 status codes; search by status. 50 areas, allowing the system to select appropriate clients to replace cancelled services

References

Availability
Purchase

Language
Basic

Computer
Commodore 8096

0285

DRAWING REGISTER SYSTEM *Construction Programming Services*
Suitable for professional design teams (architects, engineers, etc), contractors head office and the construction site. When a batch of drawings has been entered, the system prints out distribution slips suitable for immediate posting; a summary is also printed out. At any time a register of all drawings in a file, and of all files, can be ordered. Additionally, a drawings register can be supplied containing drawings with a keyword, enabling a list of drawings relating to a part of the works to be requested

References

Availability
Purchase

Language

Computer
Apple II
CP/M and CP/M 86

0286

Vehicle and equipment operations management *COSMIC*
Developed to support the Marshall Space Flight Center by providing management reports, statistical data and preventive maintenance scheduling on wheeled vehicles and engineering equipment. Provides data as budget forecasts, manpower requirements, statistics such as mileage, cost and depreciation, and inspection work flow for maintenance shops. Generates notification of inspection requirements for vehicles, based on fuel used and/or length of time since previous maintenance

References
Computer Sciences Corporation

Availability

Language
Cobol

Computer
Univac 1100 series

NEDO *Cyderpress Limited*
A suite of programs to deal with formula price adjustment in accordance with the DoE NEDO indices

References
Personal Computing with Apple

Availability

Language

Computer
Apple II

DACODA *Gerald G Darby (Computing Servies)*
A comprehensive post-contract system for quantity surveyors, handling every aspect of valuations and cost forecasts. It will function on JCT63 or 80 Contracts, and accommodates amendments. All NEDO fluctuation calculations are automatic

References

Availability
Purchase

Language
M Basic

Computer
Any Z80 based CP/M computer

NEDO *Gerald G Darby (Computing Services)*
For use on contracts which have not been processed through the micro using the DACODA system. The quantity surveyor can still use the watching facility of the micro for NEDO calculations, and the micro can calculate the current valuation fluctuation amount. Firming up, freezing and unfreezing will then be automatic. Work categories and values are entered in detail or from a summary or collection sheet. An optional double input process enables the micro to check details

References

Availability
Purchase

Language
M Basic

Computer
64K

WINWOP *East Midland Computers*
Handles double glazing works orders. Prints high quality working drawings with measurements, cutting lists and glass size lists. Includes aluminium or hardwood double glazed systems, patio doors, aluminium doors and secondary glazing. Provides all necessary documentation from the drawing office to the fitters' instructions

References
Recommended by British Olivetti

Availability

Language

Computer
Olivetti M20

EP8000 and COMPBILL *EP Computer Systems*
Computer aids for estimators within the construction industry. The main sections are: constants, prices, build-ups, calculations and printouts, Compbill. Analysis files are user defined. The same element can be used in any number of files and these files may be grouped together

References

Availability
Purchase

Language

Computer
Commodore

Commercial and Industrial Estimating *Estimation Inc*
For commercial, institutional and light industrial work. Collects material and labour information into 15 work phases suitable for progressing by the job management program. Allows material to be segregated on take-off by system. A bid summary enables the user to produce a total bid price including quoted items, job expenses, overheads, profit, etc

References

Availability
Purchase

Language

Computer

Concrete Excavation *Estimation Inc*
The take-off segment allows the user to select a particular structure, ie footings, walls, slabs, etc, and enter appropriate dimensions. Material codes are entered and the quantities of those materials are automatically calculated and accumulated. The summary allows for material, labour and equipment units and extensions. A combined bill of materials is included

References

Availability
Purchase

Language

Computer

Drywall Estimating *Estimation Inc*
For estimating drywall partitions, suspended ceilings, channel furring systems ceilings, and acoustic ceilings. The user defines up to 25 constructions in each estimate. These definitions are referred to in the take-off, when entering the dimensions or making modifications to produce a new construction. Up to 3500 take-off items can be included in one job. Summary covers manual labour, material and an optional bill of materials, together with an overall job summary

References

Availability
Purchase

Language

Computer

HVAC Estimating *Estimation Inc*
Based on SMACNA's published standards and the material is priced and laboured on a per pound basis. Includes rectangular duct and fittings for low, medium and high pressure. Fibreboard, as well as round and spiral pipe and fittings, is included. Computes liner and accessories. Material prices, fabrication, installation and shop drawing units are all changeable by the user

References

Availability
Purchase

Language

Computer

Job Management *Estimation Inc*
For electrical, plumbing, heating, HVAC, and almost any other trade. Provides a labour report giving a job breakdown by 50 work phases. Compares estimated with actual expended hours, and develops phase and job projection allowing the manager to monitor trends. A status report compares budgeted prime cost for materials, labour and up to 25 direct job expenses to the actual cost; provides a projected prime cost at completion. This program holds information for up to 40 jobs per disk

References

Availability
Purchase

Language

Computer

Time and Material Billing *Estimation Inc*
Similar to the Commercial and Industrial Estimating program. Up to 1500 items are available. The user inputs materials used on a particular job and receives a full bill of materials with price extensions on the job, as well as the cost per hour. The report can be used as an invoice

References

Availability
Purchase

Language

Computer

0298

H&V Insulation Estimating *Estimation Limited*
Suitable for the insulation contracting industry, and covers a wide range of insulation materials and coverings. The system caters for pipework and fittings, rectangular ductwork, circular ductwork, tank and boilers with a choice of plain or pre-covered sections, mat, slab or plastic composition. A full summary and tender is available including site preliminaries, overheads and profit, projecting through to a full bill of quantities

References

Availability
Purchase

Language

Computer

0299

Roof Plumbing Estimating *Estimation Limited*
Covers a range of materials including copper, stainless steel, zinc, aluminium, lead, etc, also different gauges within the materials. Descriptions within the system cover flat roofs, slopes, verticals, dormers, gutters, copings, flashings, etc, together with various labour activities associated with these items. The program summarises materials and labour costs, produces a tender, then extends through to a bill of quantities

References

Availability
Purchase

Language

Computer

0300

Production Control *Geest Computer Services Limited*
A powerful database is provided for this system. Facilities include: manufacturing database, stock control, work in progress, requirements planning, purchase order control, cost establishment, workflow simulation and cost monitoring

References

Availability
Bureau Service

Language
Cobol

Computer
ICL: 2950, ME29, 2904 and 2946

0301

Window Cutting with Stock Control *Grist Business Services Limited*
User defined window and door frame designs are created. Cutting and fitting details are produced, together with costings

References
Personal Computing with Apple

Availability
Purchase

Language

Computer
Apple II

0302

NEDOMASTER *Kent County Council*
A suite of microcomputer programs to calculate NEDO formula fluctuations for building work. The Work Group Method is used. When the indices for each month are firmed up, the NEDO AUTOFIRM option checks through the job file and automatically produces a firm valuation for all projects which use that month's indices

References

Availability
Purchase

Language
Basic

Computer
Commodore microcomputer CBM 8032 or 8096

0303

Computerised specification writing *A M Kinney, Inc*
Produces detailed specifications for projects from punched cards or from a library of master specifications on a continuous paper offset master ready to be used on an automatic printing press. The program allows the writers or engineers to modify, delete, alter and add to the standard specifications as necessary

References

Availability

Language
Fortran

Computer
IBM 1130 and 370

0304

NEDO FORMULA *Lancaster Computing*
NEDO is the formula method of evaluating building contract fluctuations based on sets of monthly indices published by the PSA of Series 1, Series 2, fix only indices and specialist indices. The aim is to evaluate fluctuations for JCT clause 3/F; the program copes with either category or group method options, and net or gross valuation methods. Output is by printer and includes a precis valuation statement containing contract and valuation data, monthly indices and fluctuation figures

References

Availability
Purchase

Language

Computer
Apple II

0305

Baxter Price Book Generator *J Lawson and Company Limited*
Handles the creation and maintenance of data files containing descriptions of work items and associated consultants, together with resource files containing resource descriptions and current prices. Calculates item rates from the above, and prints the price book or schedule of rates. Allows immediate alteration of component prices, and labour or material constants. Each section of the price book may access up to 148 different resources which may be changed for subsequent sections

References
IOB Estimating Information Service Paper No 35 1979/80. Computer Aided Estimating

Availability
Purchase

Language
HP 9825A

Computer
HP 9825A or HP 9826A

0306

BILLCOST *Local Business Technology Limited*
For monitoring progress of construction jobs by comparing actual costs, quantities and valuation with original estimates, from a variety of viewpoints. Base job data is from BILLMASTER, or input direct via terminal. Actual cost and quantity data is input interactively. Output includes a summary analysis, a progress analysis showing the percentage of progress together with actuals, and a detailed report listing individual costs against original estimates

References
Apple Software Directory for 1983

Availability
Purchase, bureau service via Apple dealers

Language
UCSD Pascal 2.1

Computer
Apple II with 64K

MicroRAPPORT *Logica Limited*
Relational Database Management. Used to retain and retrieve data for applications such as quantity surveys, stock control, inventory, bill of materials, computer aided design, property registers, etc. The program has an interactive query and reporting language

References

Availability
Purchase

Language
Fortran

Computer
Most 8-bit micros using CP/M system; minimum 64K

RAPPORT *Logica Limited*
Relational Database Management. Used to retain and retrieve data for such applications as quantity surveys, stock control, inventory, bill of materials, computer aided design, property registers, etc. The program has an interactive query, updating, data entry and reporting language. Full back-up and recovery, data security, and multi-user facilities

References

Availability
Purchase, Bureau Service

Language
Fortran: Cobol and coral interfaces

Computer
Most mini and mainframe; 500K

Bill of Materials *LSI Computers Limited*
Provides information on which items are required at various stages of a project. It also gives the effect of the finished item of increasing the price of any one component. This package links with the stock record package

References

Availability
Purchase

Language

Computer
CP/M machines

ELECMAN *Mandata Limited*
A complete and fully comprehensive estimating package designed specifically for both large and small electrical contractors

References
Recommended by British Olivetti

Availability

Language

Computer
Olivetti M20

MARFACT *Marcus Computer Systems*
An integrated production/manufacturing suite for the planning and control of a production orientated environment. Includes: Nominal, Sales and Purchase Ledgers, Bill of Materials, Material Requirements Planning, Stock Control, Job Costing, Invoicing, Payroll, Machine Scheduling, Company Forecasting, Capacity Planning, Purchase and Sales Order Processing

References

Availability
Purchase

Language

Computer
CPM 86, MS-DOS, CPM 2.2

$LAMSAC Application code 32125121270A *Newcastle-upon-Tyne City Council, Architect's Department*
Calculates property valuations for insurance purposes. Slow peripheral units used are a card reader and lineprinter. The program has been in use since 1976

References
LAMSAC

Availability

Language
Cobol

Computer
ICL 1904S
6K core
1 magnetic tape unit

Preliminary Estimates *Norden Technical Computer Systems Limited*
Provides preliminary cost appraisals from analyses of previous projects. Various categories of building can be accommodated, together with sundry items such as external works, site preparation costs, etc. The surveyor has complete control over the data entry and production of the estimate

References

Availability

Language

Computer
64K microcomputer
Interset IS 2000
Digico M16E

BILL OF MATERIALS *Office Automation*
This system consists of 3 master files: components, sub-assembly and product file. Generates works orders and splits components into 30 sub-assemblies and products. All are carried throughout the system

References

Availability

Language

Computer
Olivetti M20

CEASAR *PMA Consultants Limited*
Computer assisted estimating system and reports. Automatic routine writing, calculating and transcribing. Two main files: The Tender file, where each tender is built up from input of bills of quantities data to a final fully priced tender. The Library file stores basic information on resources and activities. Password system is used. 50 tenders are immediately available to the estimator: off-line storage is unlimited. Printed reports are available at the user's request

References

Availability
Purchase, rental, licence

Language
Fortran IV

Computer
Minicomputer, eg Prime 250

Praxis Cost Estimating *Praxis Business Systems*
Allows the user to compile a project cost estimate from standard components which are held in a user built library. When an estimate is complete, analysis can be printed by supplier, product type, etc. A feature of the program is its speed. The standards library is held in memory, and screen response is virtually instantaneous

References

Availability
Purchase

Language
Compiled Basic + 8088 machine code

Computer
ACT Sirius 1, min 128K memory

0317

Optimiser *Quality Business Machines Limited*
Plans and estimates the cutting of sheet glass into panes of glass, with the minimum of wastage. Also produces labels for the cut glass, indication of customer's name, etc. The output from this program, in the form of a floppy disk, can be input directly into an automated cutting table

References
Development by Berlyne Bailey & Co Limited

Availability

Language

Computer

0318

Windowmaster *Quality Business Machines Limited*
This system has been designed for the fabrication of replacement windows, doors, etc to calculate and cost the materials required for a variety of unit designs and sizes. Facilities include: incorporation of user defined designs; labels for identification of cut glass and completed windows; batch usage reports to aid production; bar optimiser to reduce wastage; standard letters/estimates; handling of aluminium, UPVC and wood on the same system

References

Availability

Language

Computer

0319

Sheet Cutting Optimisation *Redland Construction Software Limited*
Produces optimum cutting schedules for sheet materials based on minimisation of the trim loss and number of cutting patterns required. Handles a combination of up to 50 stock and cut piece sizes. Output includes total number of stock sheets required of each size, area of stock used, total area of cut pieces, trim loss, total length of cutting, total perimeter length, and cutting schedule containing plots of patterns used

References

Availability

Language

Computer

0320

Reedbaron Valuation System *Reedbaron Limited*
A sophisticated system, designed for use by contract quantity surveyors. Provides: contract cost analysis of up to 15 user defined cost types; grouping of bill items under five headings; external valuation easily adjusted to produce internal valuation; automatic calculation of variation of price (NEDO and Baxter); continual monitoring of predefined elemental values; fully portable for use on site

References
Originally developed for Geoffrey Osborne Limited

Availability
Purchase

Language
Basic
C Basic

Computer
64K Z80 microcomputer

0321

ESTIMATE *S D Micros Limited*
A suite of programs for the preparation of estimates for buildings. Can be used at any stage in building design but has particular application at the feasibility and scheme design stages of a project, when the design decisions with major user effect are made. Output is in the form of comprehensive estimates on building ratios (ie wall to floor, window to wall, etc), a Shape Efficiency Index, Performance Values of Building, Mechanical Element, Statistics, etc

References

Availability
Purchase

Language
Basic

Computer
48K Apple, and others

0322

NEDOSOFT (WORK CATEGORY) *S D Micros Limited*
A post-contract quantity surveying application for use in calculating interim valuations when the NEDO price adjustment formula, work category method is used. Printouts include breakdown of all calculations together with a valuation summary

References

Availability
Purchase

Language
Basic

Computer
48K Apple, and others

0323

NEDOSOFT (WORK GROUP) *S D Micros Limited*
A post-contract quantity surveying application for use in calculating interim valuations when the NEDO price adjustment formula, work group method is used. Printout is provided for valuation calculations and summary; the program also produces all base month calculations required and prints out in standard format the group weightings

References

Availability
Purchase

Language
Basic

Computer
48K Apple, and others

0324

VALUATION *S D Micros Limited*
A quantity surveying application for use in valuing construction projects whilst in progress. The program is designed for a structural tickbook approach for one or many buildings, and incorporates NEDO fluctuation calculations

References

Availability
Purchase

Language
Basic

Computer
48K Apple, and others

0325

Skip Hire System *Spinks Computer Systems Limited*
A combined sales ledger and invoicer for the control of movement of skips on hire

References
Personal Computing with Apple

Availability

Language

Computer
Apple II

0326

Waste Disposal Skip Hire System *Spinks Computer Systems Limited*
Records skip movements and automatically calculates invoices based on a range of different rates for collection and delivery

References
Personal Computing with Apple

Availability

Language

Computer
Apple II

Building Services Estimating *TipData Limited*
Produces estimates quickly and efficiently. Complete flexibility in altering margins of overheads, profit, etc. Storage of price lists and costing data. Handles traditional method of take-off. Reports show cost summary and current profitability of contracts. Produces bills of quantities based on the estimate, and a schedule of rates for all items in the bill

References

Availability
Licence

Language

Computer
Micros. Minis.
128kb-256kb
memory

MICROSPEC *Valtec Limited*
Produces a cost estimate for housing rehabilitation work. The user enters quantities against each standardised task. Money rates are stored for each; these can be adjusted for inflation or other changes. A second printout supresses all money figures, thus providing a tender document

References

Availability
Bureau service, sale

Language
PET Basic
CP/M

Computer
Commodore PET
8032 or 8096

LAMSAC Application code 32125432390A *Wiltshire County Council, County Treasurer*
This program forms a register of property in the County for insurance purposes. Slow peripheral unit used is a lineprinter. Data entry is via key-to-disk equipment. The program was first used in 1976

References
LAMSAC

Availability

Language
PL/1

Computer
IBM 370/145
256K core
1 disc drive

Accounting

0330

FACC *Alper Systems Limited*
Part of the FACTOTUM suite. Provides a simple book-keeping and accounting aid for a small architectural or consulting engineering practice. All input data can be changed interactively. Information is output as typical ledger, VAT account, etc

References

Availability
Purchase

Language
Fortran

Computer
64k 8-bit
CP/M Microcomputer

0331

OMS-ACCOUNTS *Alpha Micro UK*
Provides initialisation and update of office accounts using a simplified two level structure. Features include: standard accounting functions; detailed and summary journal reports for cash, receivables, payables, income, expenses and capital; general ledger trial balance with period closure option; details, summary and aging reports by client or vendor; financial statements; depreciation schedules

References

Availability
Purchase

Language
Alpha Basic

Computer
Alpha Micro CPU
with 8Mbytes

0332

FRANKLIN BUILDERS' SYSTEM *Amicro Systems (London) Limited*
This system has been specially designed for builders, by builders. Includes a payroll, sales ledger, nominal ledger, general ledger, subcontractors' control file, stock maintenance file and the central job costing around which the system is designed. A user friendly, integrated system, which caters for builders' needs, eg: subcontractors' information and reports; day by day job costing reports; detailed analysis of labour, materials, administration and transport costs in addition to general job costing

References
Originally developed for Franklin
Construction Co Limited

Availability
Purchase

Language

Computer
64K RAM

0333

SMB Fixed Assets System *Amplix Services Limited*
Features include: multi-company; assets description and values file; entry of purchases, disposals, sales, transfers and adjustments; depreciation calculations are user defined; interface and postings to all SMB Ledgers; year end update routines

References

Availability
Purchase

Language
Commercial (SMB)
Cobol, Fortran

Computer
CP/M or MP/M
Microcomputer

0334

SMB Nominal Ledger *Amplix Services Limited*
Features include: multi-company; 2-digit department, 4-digit code; budget file; 3 user definable management reports; journal entry with or without job cost; trial balance report; audit list; prepayments and accruals, standing charges; postings accepted from all SMB ledgers, payrolls; month end update and consolidation; year end file cleardown

References

Availability
Purchase

Language
Commercial (SMB)
Cobol, Fortran

Computer
CP/M or MP/M
Microcomputer

0335

SMB Purchase Ledger *Amplix Services Limited*
Features include: multi-company; 6-digit alpha supplier code; supplier invoice and credit note entry with or without job cost ledger reference; prepaid invoice entry; adjustments, transfers, discounts, etc; payments routines; accounts or suppliers may be stopped for payment; print remittance advices, cheques and credit transfers; invoices, cash daybooks; ageing analysis of accounts; supplier label print

References

Availability
Purchase

Language
Commercial (SMB)
Cobol, Fortran

Computer
CP/M or MP/M
Microcomputer

0336

SMB Sales Ledger *Amplix Services Limited*
Features include: multi-company; 6-digit alpha customer code; entry of invoices and credits with or without job cost reference; optional balance forward or open line accounts; adjustments, transfers, discounts, etc; screen or printer scan; payments posted as matched or unallocated; retentions feature; statement prints; invoice and cash daybooks; ageing analysis of accounts; customer label print

References

Availability
Purchase

Language
Commercial (SMB)
Cobol, Fortran

Computer
CP/M or MP/M
Microcomputer

0337

SMB Subcontractors' Ledger *Amplix Services Limited*
Features include: multi-company; 6-digit alpha subcontractors' code; detail entry of adjustments, transfers and invoices; postings to Job Cost Ledger; taxable status entry; retentions feature; screen or printer scan of accounts

References

Availability
Purchase

Language
Commercial (SMB)
Cobol, Fortran

Computer
CP/M or MP/M
Microcomputer

0338

Integrated Sales Ledger with Stock Control *Anagram Systems*
A combination of sales ledger and stock control packages, integrated at the point of producing an invoice. Open item accounting method. Incorporates a suspense account and an 'unallocated credits' feature. Invoicing procedure allows for trade and settlement discounts. Stock items may be added, amended and deleted. Details of orders, allocations and stock movements for each item may be recorded. Suppliers' names and addresses stored; each stock item may be assigned to one or more supplier records

References

Availability
Purchase

Language

Computer
Commodore CBM
8032

0339

Integrated Sales Ledger with Stock List *Anagram Systems*
Combination of a sales ledger and a stock list, integrated at the point of producing an invoice. Option of performing basic stock control functions, or the stock section can be used as a simple price list. An open item accounting method is used. Incorporates a suspense account. The package gives current month and year to date sales and purchase figures, both units and value, for each stock item. Invoicing procedure allows for trade discounts, plus settlement discount facility

References

Availability
Purchase

Language

Computer
Commodore CBM
8032

Purchase Ledger *Anagram Systems*
Features include: open item accounting system; comprehensive details of each supplier; enquiry of supplier data; supplier accounts referred to and retrieved by name; posting of invoice figures to the supplier account and allocation of the amount(s) up to 6 nominal accounts; printing of remittance advices and debit notes, and posting amounts to supplier and nominal accounts; year to date and last year's totals for each nominal account

References

Availability
Purchase

Language

Computer
Commodore CBM 8032

Sales Ledger *Anagram Systems*
Features include: open item accounting system; comprehensive details for each customer; enquiry of customer data; customer accounts referred to and retrieved by name; printing of invoices and credit notes, and posting amounts to customer account; suspense account for unrecognised cash; accounts may be grouped into sales areas for report printing; invoices allow up to 20 lines per page, and may be multi-page; trade discounts are allowed; settlement discounts are catered for

References

Availability
Purchase

Language

Computer
Commodore CBM 8032

ACCOUNTS *Applied Systems Techniques (Midlands) Limited*
A fully comprehensive sales, purchase and nominal ledger accounting system. The accounts for a single company or group of companies may be held in the system. The current system may be used for up to 99 separate companies

References

Availability
Licence

Language
Assembler/Basic

Computer
Any Alpha Micro

CONSTRUCTION SALES LEDGER *Baring Investments Limited*
Stores up to 820 accounts. Facility for segregating retention from other balances. Debtors list aged in months with retention shown separately. Split screen input routine. Output includes: list of customers' names and addresses with site location; sales ledger on brought forward balance method with retentions separated; aged debtors list; check list of input with all references; list of sales ledger balances with customers' names

References

Availability

Language

Computer
Apple II

Financial and Accounting Management *Building Centre Computers Limited*
This system comprises modular programs which interface automatically and cover purchase accounting, cross-referencing between own and suppliers' codes, sales accounting, credit control, nominal accounting, multiple currency accounting, and stock valuation. The management accounting module includes product costing, budgeting, financial planning, cashflow, stock valuation and word processing

References

Availability
Purchase

Language
Basic

Computer
Mini and microcomputers single & multi user

CONACS *Burroughs Machines Limited*
This is a fully integrated accounting and costing system. It is extremely flexible and is tailored to the precise reporting and accounting requirements of each user. The contract cost module can monitor progress on a contract from estimates through to completion. The program is widely used in the construction industry

References

Availability
Puchase

Language
CMS Cobol

Computer
Burroughs CMS

FACS *Business Computer Systems plc*
The Federation of Master Builders Approved computer system has been designed for use in the construction industry. Handles: payroll; sales; purchase and nominal ledgers; other accounting functions; control of contract costs; administration of subcontractors; production of statutory Inland Revenue returns, profit and loss accounts and trial balances

References

Availability
Purchase

Language

Computer
Xerox Microcomputer

BR-PAC PARTNER *Business Research Systems Limited*
An integrated system for invoicing, accounting, time recording and job costing for professional offices. Output consists of a comprehensive series of 35 reports

References

Availability
Purchase

Language
Basic

Computer
Rank Zerox 820 series. Any CP/M microcomputer

BR-PAC TRADER *Business Research Systems Limited*
An integrated system for purchasing, stock control, sales order processing, product costing and accounting for building component manufacturers and builders' merchants. Comprehensive output consists of 40 reports

References

Availability
Purchase

Language
Basic

Computer
Jacquard. Rank Xerox Any CP/M micro

CABCS-PPL *CABCS Limited*
Allows subcontractors to record the claims, receipts, discounts, VAT, retention and certified amounts at each stage of each current task. Comprehensive screen/printer reports include analysis ledger, audit, progress statement and client/account, summary reports. Capacity of up to 200 current accounts, each of up to 99 stages. Unlimited completed accounts. May be used by personnel without previous computer usage experience

References
Building Products. Architects' Journal, Practical Computing

Availability
Licence

Language
CP/M 80

Computer
64K CP/M microcomputer

0350

Archaid *CIC (London) Limited*
A comprehensive accounting and job costing system spcifically written for architects. Six integrated modules provide a complete system. Analyses the cost of each job into prime costs, including time expended to date against fees received. Immediate cost reports are available for all jobs in progress, together with a list of creditors and debtors, and a breakdown of each fee, account or contract

References
Recommended by Apple

Availability
Purchase

Language
Apple Basic
Pascal

Computer
Apple II and III

0351

Contaid *CIC (London) Limited*
A fully integrated accounting and job costing program designed for the building industry. Includes: nominal ledger and trial balance, purchase and sales ledgers, contract and work in progress costing, subcontract account ledger, wages and salaries, stock control and estimating

References
Recommended by Apple

Availability
Purchase

Language
Apple Basic
Pascal

Computer
Apple II and III

0352

NOMINAL *CIMS Computer Systems Limited*
Part of the CIMS Management System designed for the construction industry. Provides records for all financial accounting data and reporting for analysis/auditing of group or individual accounts. Accounts held within the system are self balancing from trial balance through trading account and profit/loss to balance sheet. Also provides budget variance analyses, balances for interim and year end accounts, and a carry over period for year end transactions

References

Availability
Purchase

Language
RPG11

Computer
IBM System/34

0353

SALES *CIMS Computer Systems Limited*
Part of the CIMS Management System designed for the construction industry. Handles customer details and produces invoices, credit notes and invoice proof list. Reports include aged debt and VAT analyses, month end statements, sales analysis, customer turnover listings and all relevant audit reports. Full enquiry facilities are available, via the VDU, on account status

References

Availability
Purchase

Language
RPG11

Computer
IBM System/34

0354

FINANCIAL *Civilsoft (USA)*
Four independent comprehensive programs; DEP computes depreciation by month or by years, using straight line, double declining balance, sum-of-the-years-digits, and 15O per cent declining balance. DISCOUNT calculates discounted rate of return for initial investment. BOND calculates the yield of a bond. MORTGAG is a mortgage program

References
ASCE, Building Construction Digest

Availability
Purchase

Language
8080 or 8088/86

Computer
8-bit with 64K
or 16-bit with
128K memory

0355

MICROBUILDER *CMG Information Services South East Limited*
This program is part of the MICROFACT service which combines the versitility of a microcomputer with the power of a large mainframe. MICROBUILDER is designed for use by the building and construction industry and includes all aspects of accounting, payroll and word processing

References

Availability
Bureau service

Language
Cobol

Computer
Microcomputer

0356

Nominal Ledger *Compact Accounting Services Limited*
Functions as a standalone management system or may be integrated with other Compact Accounting systems thus providing automatic entry updates. Features include: double entry book keeping equation maintained; account enquiry on VDU; alternative formats available for trial balance; monthly budget analysis maintained for each account; budget variance reports available. Output on screen or as hard copy

References
Recommended by Zenithplan Limited

Availability
Purchase

Language
Microsoft Basic

Computer
Sirius 1. Any
CP/M microcomputer
with 64K

0357

Order Processing and Sales Invoicing *Compact Accounting Services Limited*
A comprehensive system which integrates stock, sales ledger and nominal ledger, with outstanding order details being maintained by customer and by stock return. Features include: control, amendment or deletion of processed orders; automatic production of invoices, credit notes, order acknowledgements and packing slips; validation of customer credit limits; back order system with provision for part deliveries; discount tables; production of profitability reports by salesman and sales territory;

References
Recommended by Zenithplan Limited

Availability
Purchase

Language
Microsoft Basic

Computer
Sirius 1. Any
CP/M microcomputer
with 64K

0358

Purchase Ledger *Compact Accounting Services Limited*
Used as a standalone package, or fully integrated with nominal ledger. Functions as an open item or brought forward system, with the company name used to personalise reports, etc. Features include: full enquiry facilities on all accounts; aged creditors listing; automatic cheque payment and bank giro options; audit trails; month end and year end routines available; VAT reports and statistics

References
Recommended by Zenithplan Limited

Availability
Purchase

Language
Microsoft Basic

Computer
Sirius 1. Any
CP/M microcomputer
with 64K

0359

Sales Ledger *Compact Accounting Services Limited*
May be used as a standalone system, or fully integrated with other Compact Accounting systems. Features include: maintenance of open item or brought forward balances; full account enquiry via VDU; batch processing options available; production of statements; aged debtors report; VAT reports and analysis; production of address labels; full audit trail

References
Recommended by Zenithplan Limited

Availability
Purchase

Language
Microsoft Basic

Computer
Sirius 1. Any
CP/M microcomputer
with 64K

Computer programs for the building industry

Accounting System *Compuquant Limited*
Designed for use by the smaller builder. Purchases, Sales and Nominal Ledger Accounts are automatically updated on posting of invoices. The system capacity is for 1000 accounts and 1500 outstanding transactions. Full reporting facility available; includes full audit trail, debtor list, sales invoices, trial balance, ledger details, cash book, profit and loss statements, VAT reports and others

References

Availability
Purchase, lease

Language

Computer
Toshiba T200 microcomputer with 64K

Invoicing *Computel Limited*
One of an integrated set of programs for invoicing in all types of organisation. Users may select their own invoice layout; the program includes facilities for the calculation of VAT, the provision of information for the sales ledger and access to the Management Information System for the analysis of invoices

References

Availability

Language

Computer

Purchase ledger *Computel Limited*
One of a set of integrated programs for accounting purposes with the following features: segregation of payment of accounts from purchase ledger; open item or balance brought forward ledger records for all suppliers with balances outstanding, and showing all transactions in current period; creditors' control list showing suppliers' balances over five months and in total; control accounts for the month; and a VAT summary

References

Availability

Language

Computer

Sales ledger *Computel Limited*
One of an integrated set of programs for accounting purposes in all types of organisation. It has the following features: open item or balance brought forward ledger records, production of statements, maintenance of up to date information on credit control, sales analysis, VAT summary and other options

References

Availability

Language

Computer

CONTRACT 6 *Computer Factors (Sales) Limited*
Enables a building contractor or civil engineering company to maximise the control of contracts and cashflow. The main components are: purchase ledger with invoice logging; contract cost ledger with dual time functions; nominal ledger with unlimited analysis; subcontractors' ledger with exemption certificate expiry checking; payroll; sales ledger; asset register with plant management function

References

Availability
Purchase

Language
Cobol

Computer
Honeywell DPS6 Minicomputer

CINTRA *Computer House*
An accounting system. Features: flexible accounting periods; use of multiple currencies; flexible reporting; alphanumeric account keys; interface database manager; audit facilities; nominal, purchase and sales ledgers

References

Availability
Purchase

Language
'C'

Computer
Various

MICROBUILD *Comsoft*
A low cost, inclusive package for the construction industry. The system is interactive and covers payroll, purchases and contract costing. Further expansion incorporates sales ledger, stock control and nominal ledger

References

Availability
Purchase of turnkey system

Language

Computer
Commodore 8000 IBM PC

FOUNDATION *Conquest Computer Sales Limited*
Developed to provide the building and construction industry with a system to suit their accounting and costing requirements. Available in modular format; modules are totally interactive. Modules are: Nominal, Purchase and Sales Ledgers, Contract Costing, Subcontractor's Ledger, Payroll and Fixed Assets Ledger

References

Availability
Purchase

Language
DIBOL
DBL

Computer
DEC Minicomputers
Plessey

BEAVER *Construction Management Computing*
This is a construction management computing system for the construction industry. The program handles estimating from drawings, bills of quantities, feasibility studies or method analysis. The program produces final accounts, valuations, material schedules, bonus targets, budgets, etc. All ledgers and financial accounts are to P/L and balance sheet stage

References
B+J, IOB Journal, Building. Recommended by TML Business Systems

Availability
Purchase

Language
Business Basic

Computer
Data General

Integrated Business System *The Consultancy Consortium*
A suite of accounting programs covering Purchase, Sales and Nominal Ledgers, and Stock Control. All modules combine conventional accounting, and office procedures. Modules may be used stand-alone or combined

References

Availability
Purchase

Language

Computer
Various

0370

CONSYST-8000 *Consyst Computer Services Limited*
A fully integrated accounting system which includes: sales, purchase, nominal, and contract cost ledgers; plant hire system; subcontract system; payroll. All systems provide for a user defined structure. Sales and Purchase Ledgers are open item with full detail recorded, whilst Nominal and Contract Cost Ledgers are brought forward balance systems with full detail for the current period

References
Building Products Monthly, March 1982

Availability
Purchase

Language

Computer
Commodore 8000

0371

Epic Contractors' Cost and Management Accounting *Epic Computer Services Limited*
A system specially designed for use by the construction industry. The System Nucleus caters for the capture of input information and for the total system of management accounting and other estimated or budgeted costs, entry of actual figures, analysis of costs and revenue. Subsidiary Modules cover: sales invoicing; sales, purchase, subcontractors' and stock ledgers; payroll

References
Recommended by IBM

Availability

Language
Basic

Computer
IBM System/23
IBM System/34

0372

General accounting system *Estate Computer Systems*
Suitable for building management, this program handles nominal accounts for each site, updated by invoices entered into the suppliers' ledger cards. It gives a total cost per site with an analysis of materials, plant hire, etc, per site. Budgets are compared to actual costs per site. Nominal accounts culminate in a company balance sheet

References

Availability
Purchase

Language
Pascal

Computer
Apple with 64K.
IBM PC

0373

Accounting Package *Estimation Inc*
A system for the contractor. Reports provide a good audit trail and important management information; these include: trial balance; income statements and balance sheets; special account report; transaction recaps - accounts payable or receivable; summary or detailed reports; ageing and update analysis; customer and vendor activity; accounts payable job cost report; utility printouts of customer information, account descriptions, general information, etc

References

Availability
Purchase

Language

Computer

0374

CIBS *fba Computer Services Limited*
The Complete Integrated Business System comprises the following modules: Nominal Ledger, Sales Ledger, Purchase/Nominal Ledger, Management Reports, Stock Control, Sales Order Processing, Purchase Order Processing, Sales Analysis, Payroll, Fixed Assets. Most modules can be run independently, but they can also be integrated with some or all other modules to suit the user's needs

References

Availability
Purchase

Language

Computer
Minicomputer or
Microcomputer

0375

Integrated Accounting System *FCG Computer Systems*
Designed for the builder and contractor. Features include: a fully integrated system, open ledgers, large capacity, automatic payments, full reporting, data security, and system maintenance. The smallest system has capacity for 2000 accounts and 2000 transactions per month, while the use of a Corvus hard disk unit increases capacity to 25 000 accounts

References

Availability
Purchase

Language
Commodore Basic

Computer
Commodore 8000

0376

Ledgers *Geest Computer Services Limited*
Integrated sales, purchase and nominal ledgers. Facilities include: preparation of statements, invoice printing, management control reports and powerful analysis facilities

References

Availability
Bureau service

Language
Cobol

Computer
ICL:2950, ME29,
2904 and 2946

0377

ISBS-F *Graffcom Systems Limited*
Designed for the small business microcomputer user. Program modules cover all standard accounting functions, including: stock control, order entry and invoicing, names and addresses, company sales, company purchases, general accounting and payroll. Each module can be used standalone or built as an integrated system

References

Availability
Purchase

Language
CBASIC

Computer
48K micro. 8 and
16-bit with CP/M or
CP/M86

0378

ISBS-W *Graffcom Systems Limited*
A professional integrated business system for microcomputers using hard disks or Winchester disks. The Business Control module acts as a task manager and supervisor for the system, which includes: stock control, order processing and invoicing, names and addresses, company purchases, purchase control, general accounting, payroll, company sales, and project control

References

Availability
Purchase

Language
CBASIC

Computer
64K micro. 8 and
16-bit with CP/M,
CP/M86

0379

Series/1 Builders' Merchants *Guardian Computer Services*
An interactive, on-line invoicing and stock control system for builders' and plumbers' merchants; also handles the complex pricing and discounting structures of the industry. Features include: invoicing with up to 64 prices per product; special contract prices and customer terms; manual override for 'one-off' prices: full stock analysis reporting; automatic purchase orders; perpetual inventory; multiple stock locations; stock enquiry facilities, etc

References
Recommended by IBM

Availability

Language

Computer
IBM Series/1 EDX

System/34 Construction Package *Guardian Computer Services*
Covers all elements of management and control of a construction company. Includes modules for: sales ledger, with the ability to handle retentions and payment on account; purchase ledger; subcontractors' ledger; payroll, to include anomalies in the industry; valuations, bills of quantities, etc; contract ledger which deals with the amalgamation and integration of all the above systems to give the ability of monitoring performance of individual projects and allow enquiries and periodic reporting

References
Recommended by IBM

Availability

Language

Computer
IBM System/34 RPGII

ACCSYS *Hutton + Rostron*
An accounts system for use with time and expenses sheets for invoicing or cost control. Data is stored on clients' instructions, budgets, amounts outstanding, charging rates, percentage additions or discounts, VAT, lump sums or periodic payments. Output is in the form of invoices, job and budget statements, work analyses and summaries for management. The program also produces input for an income and expenditure system, CASHUP

References
In use by three firms since 1968

Availability
Bureau service or purchase

Language
PAL8, ALGOL68

Computer
DEC PDP8
ICL 4120

CASHUP *Hutton + Rostron*
A system for preparing a cash book and analysis from coded income and expenditure. Input can be taken direct from vouchers or cheque stubs or be in the form of a cash book with a seven column expenditure analysis and running balance, or by use of a terminal. Over 900 sub headings can be analysed. Entries can be split between columns automatically. VAT is analysed separately

References

Availability
Bureau service or purchase

Language
PAL8

Computer
DEC PDP8

Construction Industry Package *Kalamazoo plc*
For management control, designed for the construction industry and allied trades. Includes all aspects of accounting; cost collection; full audit trail; estimating; subcontractors; and payroll analysis

References

Availability
Purchase

Language
Kabol

Computer
CP/M 2.2. K1100,
K1200

IMPACT/KICOST *Kienzle Data Systems Limited*
Complete, interactive business accounting system, incorporating: sales, purchases, nominal, stock, invoicing, purchasing, sales order processing, payroll, costing, model building and report generating. Systems are integrated or available in modular format. Parameter driven with complete range of posting, document preparation, run time enquiry and reporting facilities. Total support service provided

References

Availability
Licence

Language
Cobol

Computer
Kienzle 9000

Cash flow forecasting *Lancaster Computing*
Produces a cashflow forecast based on the DHSS 'S' curve formula. Forecasts can be projected for new and on-going contracts, and presented in graphical and tabulated format. Input consists of job data, ie name, contract amount and period, retention percentage, firm price or VOP, plus previous cumulative valuation data. A choice is made between standard (DHSS) or non-standard parameters. Output by screen (tabulated or graphical form) and printer

References

Availability
Purchase

Language

Computer
Apple II

ADNDA *LMR Computer Services*
A fully interactive accounting system which deals with sales ledger, purchase ledger, nominal ledger and management accounts, and detailed analysis

References

Availability

Language

Computer
Prime

Cost Ledger *LSI Computers Limited*
Designed for small manufacturing firms and contractors. Allows records to be kept of up to 999 jobs under 99 different headings; the heading for labour allows up to 10 different rates of pay

References

Availability
Purchase

Language

Computer
CP/M Machines

MARCOUNT ACCOUNTING SUITE *Marcus Computer Systems*
A fully integrated suite of programs including Sales, Purchase and Nominal Ledgers, Sales Invoicing, Stock Control, Job Costing, Payroll and Company Forecasting. Automatic audit trail. Handles both part and full payments. Customer coding allows up to 9 digits in alpha and/or numeric form

References

Availability
Purchase

Language

Computer
CPM 86, MS-DOS,
CPM 2.2

Accounting Plus *Mediatech*
A fully integrated, comprehensive business accounting system. Modules include: open item sales ledger and bought ledger; sales order entry; purchase order entry; nominal ledger; point of sale and payroll; stock control

References

Availability
Purchase

Language

Computer
CP/M
microcomputers

0390

Fixed Asset Register *Mentor Systems*
Maintains a register by company, group and location. Calculates depreciation which is
added to a cumulative depreciation field used to generate new written down value; also
posted to appropriate nominal ledger account. Uses straight line to a residual value, or
reducing balance. Reports are produced for asset register, valuation, additions and
disposals. Full year end clear down facilities are available

References	*Language*
Availability	*Computer*
Licence	ICL

0391

Nominal Ledger *Mentor Systems*
Facilities for trial balance, nominal statement (transaction report by account), and balance
sheet and profit and loss accounts. The latter provides for budget comparisons, reporting
at detailed account and summary level. Input facilities for journal entries, accruals and
prepayments, and standing journals

References	*Language*
Availability	*Computer*
Licence	ICL

0392

Progress Application Ledger *Mentor Systems*
Linked on the standard sales ledger, but allows for full monitoring of applications for
payment, certification by client, retention and payments. Each application is maintained as
a separate transaction, with automatic posting to sales as applicable. Daybooks, aged debt
reports, detailed reports by contract or customer, and full month end ledger details are
provided

References	*Language*
Availability	*Computer*
Licence	ICL

0393

Purchase Ledger *Mentor Systems*
Maintains an open item ledger containing documents in authorised and unauthorised
states. Offers reporting of: unauthorised invoices, items due for payment, aged creditors
report, purchase ledger report for filing, cheques, remittance advice, and cheque lists. Full
nominal ledger and bank reconciliation file updates are carried out automatically

References	*Language*
Availability	*Computer*
Licence	ICL

0394

Sales Ledger *Mentor Systems*
Provides for maintenance of an open item ledger with reporting facilities for: aged debt
report, statements at any frequency, and sales ledger report, for filing purposes. The
nominal ledger and bank reconciliations are updated automatically

References	*Language*
Availability	*Computer*
Licence	ICL

0395

Subcontractors Ledger *Mentor Systems*
Information is held by the subcontractor at contract level. Transactions are recorded in
detail with automatic prompting on retentions, expired certificates, etc. Cheques and
remittance advice notes may be automatically produced. Full year end and 715 facilities
are provided

References	*Language*
Availability	*Computer*
Licence	ICL

0396

Contractor *Micro Scope Limited*
A complete system for builders covering all accounting and business applications, including
word processing. Features a Viewdata facility enabling remote sites to communicate
directly with Head Office via Prestel terminals. The comprehensive contract ledger system
covers contract details, transactions, billing, work in progress, and sales analysis.
Contractor handles sales, purchase, nominal and contract ledgers, tax deductions and
word processing

References	*Language*
Availability	*Computer*
Purchase	MAI Basic Four
	minicomputers

0397

MPL Builders' Merchants *MPL Computers Limited*
A comprehensive invoicing and purchase ordering system specially designed for builders'
merchants. Contains a sophisticated invoicing system incorporating a variety of discount
structures. A price book is also produced which can be analysed by product, department,
etc. Specific sales analysis reports are provided, and extensive enquiry facilities support
counter salesmen and stores personnel. Modules include: sales ledger, stock recording,
invoicing, price book, sales analyses, and purchase ordering and analysis

References	*Language*
Recommended by IBM	
	Computer
Availability	IBM Series/1, EDX

0398

Interactive Financial System *NCR Limited*
A comprehensive system covering Sales Ledger, Purchase Ledger and Nominal Ledger.
Further facilities are available on a modular basis and can be added as required. Can be
linked to the Interactive Distribution Control System, covering Order Processing, Invoicing
and Stock Control. The IFS covers due dates, credit status and cashflow requirements for
rendering statements and remittance advices. Flexibility of open item and balance brought
forward, forward dates invoices, suspense balances and full VAT control are incorporated

References	*Language*
Availability	*Computer*
Purchase	

0399

Subcontractors' Accounting *NCR Limited*
Designed for the construction industry. Input of valuation data updates appropriate
subcontractor's account, contract control record, contract costing records and nominal
ledger. The same data entry produces remittance advice, cheque and cheque list. Payment
data updates the nominal ledger and creates a detailed record for the payments file.
Handles retentions, discounts, VAT, income tax, Contras and CITB. Statutory Inland
Revenue reports are produced. Full audit trail

References	*Language*
Availability	*Computer*
Purchase	

CAP *Oasys Limited*
This is a Cost Analysis and Instruction Issuing Package primarily for use by quantity surveyors working in multidisciplinary teams on management contracts. The data entry and generation are carried out on a microprocessor. The data is then transmitted to the mainframe for batch processing and bulk storage. Reports are available at varying levels of detail and cross referencing: cost plans and summaries, interim and final account statements for subcontractors, drawing registers, etc

References

Availability
Bureau service

Language
Fortran

Computer
DEC 10
Superbrain
microprocessor

0401

Contract Costing and Accounting System *PMA Consultants Limited*
Integrates the processing of financial and management accounting functions, and produces detailed contract cost and valuation comparisons. The main elements are: open item invoice register, purchase ledger, sales ledger, staff timesheet processing, fixed asset/plant hire, and contract costing. All facilities, input, enquiry and report requests, are available to the user with the correct passwords and permit codes, thus preventing any unauthorised access

References

Availability
Purchase, rental, lease

Language

Computer

0402

Project Costing and Accounting *PMA Consultants Limited*
A comprehensive, interactive system comprising six suites: project costing, timesheet processing, client billing, purchase ledger, nominal ledger and maintenance. The system allows up to 35 entries (typically a company or partnership) are input; the date of next Bill and cumulative charge are automatically calculated. Comprehensive reports are available

References

Availability
Purchase

Language
Fortran

Computer
Prime 550,
768Kb memory

0403

BIAS - Builders Integrated Accounting System *Quoin Computing Limited*
Uses a database approach, comprising three modules: accounting, subcontract management, and payroll. All completely integrated and include contract costing. Uses the open item system. Security routines are provided. Extensive selective reporting up to trial balance. Analysis under 9 user-definable cost heads. Surveyors' valuations and reserves may be recorded to show profitability levels

References
CICA bulletin, September 1983

Availability
Purchase

Language
CIS-Cobol

Computer
Cifer 2683 with
64kb memory

0404

TIMBER *Rossana Software Services Limited*
An invoicing suite that caters for all the standard requirements for timber merchants. Enables conversions to be made between Imperial and metric systems, and handles all sizing calculation requirements

References

Availability

Language

Computer
Olivetti M20

0405

BUILDAX *Scan Computers Limited*
This is a suite of over 100 programs designed specifically for the building and construction industry. It covers all aspects of accounting including payroll, subcontractors, purchase, sales, nominal and contract ledgers. It is easy to use; handles accounts for more than one company; provides multi-user facility; security of information; interactive (all files updated from a single entry); a hard disk system allows access to all information at any time

References
Contract Journal, May 1982

Availability
From Scan

Language
RM COBOLANSI 74

Computer
Onyx
Texas Instruments

0406

Complete Builder's Management System *Scope Realtime Limited*
A suite of programs which provides a complete accounting and management information system incorporating the following integrated areas: job costing; nominal, purchase and sales ledgers; payroll; stock control. The system is implemented at the start of a job. Output includes: invoices, cheques, reports, payslips, statements, etc

References

Availability
Purchased with hardware

Language
Assembler for
Sharp BA 2700

Computer
Sharp BA 2700

0407

Multi-currency accounting system *Shortlands Computing Services Limited*
A package which automatically provides details of losses and gains, currency exposure and exchange conversions. At any time, the effect of fluctuations in currency exchange rates can be seen. The program consists of: Cash Book, Sales Ledger, Purchase Ledger, General and Cost Ledger, Stock and Purchase Order Control. Full audit trails in all systems, and a choice of coding and sub-totalling levels

References

Availability
Purchase

Language
Ansi 74 Cobol

Computer
Various, including
UNIX-based 16-bit
machines

0408

PPL-GENERAL LEDGER *SIA Computer Services*
This is an extremely sophisticated and powerful general ledger system

References

Availability
Bureau service

Language
High level

Computer
Control Data,
IBM, Prime

0409

IMCA-NOMINAL LEDGER *Southern Computer Systems Limited*
Designed to produce full and accurate monthly management accounts to be used as a daily control for the firm. This is the kingpin of the IMCA suite, and many of the programs can be integrated to it. The IMCA-NOMINAL LEDGER includes a Bank Account feature which gives an up to date account of the user's cash position. A budget can be set for each nominal account; all profit and loss accounts can be sub-analysed in a maximum of 12 headings used to monitor profitability and/or costs

References

Availability

Language

Computer
48-256K under CP/M
or Apple DOS

Computer programs for the building industry

0410

IMCA-PURCHASE LEDGER *Southern Computer Systems Limited*
Brings to account suppliers' invoices, analyses purchases, extracts and reports on VAT, produces remittance advice notes, prints a creditors' aged account analysis, monitors settlement discount entitlements, and reports the cumulative expenditure with each supplier or type of supplier. Can be linked with IMCA-NOMINAL and/or COST LEDGERS

References

Availability

Language

Computer
48-256K under CP/M or Apple DOS

0411

IMCA-SALES LEDGER *Southern Computer Systems Limited*
Brings to account sales invoices, analyses sales, extracts and reports on VAT, produces statements and debtors' aged accounts listing, monitors settlement discount entitlements, and records the annual turnover with each client or type of client. It can be linked with IMCA invoicing routines, NOMINAL and/or COST LEDGERS

References

Availability

Language

Computer
48-256K under CP/M or Apple DOS

0412

FASSET *SysCom Computers Limited*
An effective and flexible fixed asset register package, created to help companies comply with the latest SSAP 16 regulations requiring the presentation in the accounts of the current year, and after, of both historic cost accounting and inflation-adjusted current cost account

References

Availability

Language

Computer

0413

BILLFLOW *Tamsys Limited*
Used by professionals who bill clients on the basis of time and materials. Provision for 12 standard charge rates; retainers and reimbursements are handled. Reports include: project review, aged debtors, sales analysis and audit. Also prints out reports of projects completed, and work in progress, by partner or fee earner, together with month end statements and VAT invoices. Interfaces with the Great Northern Ledger Package to form a complete accounting system from timesheet to balance sheet

References

Availability
Purchase

Language

Computer
CP/M, 48K

0414

General Ledger II *Tandy Corporation*
A menu driven suite of programs which allows 12 or 13 month period processing, prior year comparisons, and free format code structure. Provides maintenance of budget details, automatic reverse of accruals made in previous period, audit trails, trial balance and user defined custom reports

References

Availability
Purchase

Language

Computer
TRS-80
Model II

0415

Incomplete Record System *Tandy Corporation*
Written for accounts, and suitable for use in any small business. Features include: trial balance at any time, monthly and quarterly VAT summaries, accumulated profit and loss accounts by month or quarter, annual profit and loss accounts, balance sheets as required. Designed for limited companies, partnerships and sole traders

References

Availability
Purchase

Language

Computer
TRS-80
Models I & III

0416

Nominal Ledger *Tandy Corporation*
Handles up to 300 account headings covering 4 sections: assets, liabilities, income and expenditure. Features include: transaction register, cash disbursements, trial balance, profit and loss accounts (also by comparison), balance sheets and audit trail

References

Availability
Purchase

Language

Computer
TRS-80
Models I & III

0417

Nominal Ledger *Tandy Corporation*
Up to 1000 account headings can be established covering 4 sections: assets, liabilities, income and expenditure. Postings can be made manually or automatically from other TRS-80 Sales and Purchase Ledger or Payroll. Output includes transaction register, cash disbursement, trial balance record, income statement and comparison (profit and loss account); provides comparisions and analyses of current and previous years

References

Availability
Purchase

Language

Computer
TRS-80
Model II

0418

Purchase Ledger *Tandy Corporation*
Handles up to 250 supplier accounts and 2200 transactions per disk; up to 6 supplier disks for each accounting period. Features include: creditors control report, purchase analysis, payment selection, cheque list, journal day book, purchase day book, name and address printing and audit trail

References

Availability
Purchase

Language

Computer
TRS-80
Models I & III

0419

Purchase Ledger *Tandy Corporation*
Handles up to 500 supplier accounts and 7000 transactions per disk, with up to 6 supplier disks for each accounting period. Functions include: creditors control report with aged details of outstanding balances, total balances and postings to each account; remittance advices with automatic selection of invoices due for payment; purchase analysis, with audit trail, cheque list, journal and purchase day books, including all elements of VAT outputs. Audit trail provides detailed records of all movements within the system

References

Availability
Purchase

Language

Computer
TRS-80
Model II

Sales Ledger *Tandy Corporation*
Handles up to 750 customer accounts and 8000 transactions per disk; can use up to 6
customer disks for each accounting period. Provides maintenance of customer accounts on
an open item basis with fast, easy posting of invoices, credit notes, cash, discounts and
adjustments. Reports include: monthly statements combining remittance advice, debtors
report, monthly VAT analysis, etc. Audit trails for VAT; sales day book and journal day
book listings provide detailed printed reports of all movements, incorporating totals

References

Availability
Purchase

Language

Computer
TRS-80
Model II

Sales Ledger *Tandy Corporation*
Up to 350 customer accounts and 2500 transactions per disk. System allows use of up to 6
customers per disk for each accounting period. Features include: statements, debtor
reports, monthly VAT analysis, sales day books, cash/journal day book, name and address
printing and audit trails

References

Availability
Purchase

Language

Computer
TRS-80
Models I & III

Purchase ledger system *United Information Services Limited*
A bought ledger system for producing remittance advice and maintaining ledger accounts
in open item format. A report showing future commitments is also produced. Available as
an option are VAT audit lists and cost analysis

References

Availability
Bureau service, time sharing

Language
Cobol

Computer
Honeywell
Sigma 9

Sales ledger *United Information Services Limited*
Records all steps in a typical sales transaction, such as invoices, cash receipts and credit
notes. After checking for errors, it can provide statement, information on customer's
activity, analysis of debtors by age of debt and automatic credit control using either open
item or brought forward methods. It also gives a database from which other analyses may
be made

References

Availability
Bureau service, time sharing

Language
Cobol

Computer
Honeywell
Sigma 9

Sub-Contractors System *Wilcox Computers Limited*
Provides full monitoring and reporting of subcontractors and contracts. The system
processes certificate/surveyor's valuations, calculates tax and VAT, and produces
subcontractors' payment advices. End of year reporting for the completion of statutory
schedules is provided

References

Availability
Purchase

Language
CIS Cobol (CP/M
Based)

Computer
CP/M based micros.
Min 64K

Job costing and project management *ABS Oldacres Computers Limited*
Time and expense details are fed into the computer, which arrives at a cost for each item
and allocates it to the appropriate job number. The program can be modified to suit an
individual firm's particular requirements. Additional facilities include budget allocation,
profitability of jobs, apportioning of overheads, forecasting of fees, indication of cashflow,
general forward planning and an extension to ledger work

References

Availability
Bureau service

Language
PL1

Computer
IBM 360, 370
4300 series

SMB Job Cost Ledger *Amplix Services Limited*
Features include: multi-company; job code includes job number, stage and type, together
with cost head and type; entry of items not posted by SMB Ledgers; entry of job and detail
estimates; postings accepted from all SMB Ledgers and Payroll; reports on postings from
sources; all details held on file for duration of job; reports of WIP, job summary, closing
reports, etc; VDU and printer reports on individual jobs

References

Availability
Purchase

Language
Commercial (SMB)
Cobol, Fortran

Computer
CP/M or MP/M
Microcomputer

TEXAS *Amplix Services Limited*
Features include: monthly time and expense analysis incurred by staff against jobs; input of
billable and non-billable hours and expenses; optional monthly reports of staff, jobs, and
clients hour and expense items consolidated and sorted; maintenance of historical data for
long term job costing reports

References

Availability
Purchase

Language
Commercial (SMB)
Cobol, Fortran

Computer
CP/M or MP/M
Microcomputer

CONTRACT COST ACCOUNTS *Baring Investments Limited*
A comprehensive system handling up to 1000 accounts. Features include: costs over 5
heads, comparison with sales value or budget, prints out all entries analysed into jobs, split
screen input routine. Printout routines include: check list of all input, with account numbers
and references; complete cost accounts; entries analysed into jobs; month end schedule
for transfer to cost of sales, work in progress, or write offs; total costs against sales value
with gross profit and per cent calculated on each job

References

Availability

Language

Computer
Apple Microcomputer

LAMSAC Application code 32901141120A *Birmingham City Council, Architect's
Department*
Calculates professional fee control for architects. Slow peripheral units used are a tape
reader and lineprinter

References
LAMSAC

Availability

Language
Plan Cobol

Computer
ICL 1906A
24K core
2 disc drives

0430

CASTLECOST *Castle Business Systems Limited*
An integrated contract costing and accounting system providing details on the progress of contractors' jobs in terms of hours spent and costs accumulated. The system may be used to control many branches of the construction industry, eg building, electrical, plumbing, heating, etc. Provision is made for analysis of increased cost by contract

References

Availability
Purchase

Language

Computer
Xerox

0431

CASH FLOW *Cheshire County Council*
Calculates the standard cashflow for a building contract, and compares the actual monthly payments with this norm. The quantity surveyor enters the contract sum and completion date to produce a standard 'S' curve of cumulative monthly payments. By entering actual interim valuations, revised 'S' curves can be created predicting a new completion date and the necessary cashflow, with output in the form of graphs and tables

References

Availability

Language
APL

Computer
IBM 3767

0432

COST PLANNING *Cheshire County Council, (Construction Services)*
This system has been developed by quantity surveyors to provide a detailed cost plan of a building. Selected description codes, with quantities, are keyed in to create a printed cost plan

References

Availability

Language
APL

Computer
IBM 3767

0433

FORPAC *Cheshire County Council*
(Formula price adjustment.) Calculates the variation in price due to a contractor according to NEDO formula price adjustment rules. A monthly check is carried out against variations in the indices to calculate and report on the adjusted payment due

References

Availability

Language
APL

Computer
IBM 3767

0434

COST *CIMS Computer Systems Limited*
Part of the CIMS Management System designed for the construction industry. Handles rapid entry of costs against individual contract/cost centres by automatic transference of appropriate date from other relevant systems, thereafter providing up to date reporting on such costs. Reporting on costs is at 3 levels: 1 Overall view of costs under headings Materials, Expenses, Plant, Wages and 3 types of Subcontractors; 2 Type of cost contained in level 1; 3 Gives line details of items under groups in level 2

References

Availability
Purchase

Language
RPG11

Computer
IBM System/34

0435

Bid Sheet *Civil Software Inc, USA*
A worksheet for preparing bids. Allows for ongoing revisions and updating of information without the need for manually prepared adjustment sheets. Prepares reports as follows: computes unit cost for each item; computes total cost; adjusts totals after each revision. On separate format: user adjusts unit price (distributes overhead and profit, etc); computer prepares final report based on adjusted unit prices

References

Availability
Purchase

Language

Computer
Apple II with CP/M, IBM PC

0436

Partial Payments *Civil Software Inc, USA*
Prepares itemised statements for unit price contracts or lump sum breakdowns. Used to prepare requests for partial payments from owner and for partial payments to subcontractors. Program provides reports showing: quantity and amount of each item for billing period and quantity and amount to date; compares amount of each item to contract amount; work sheet for compiling data for next pay period

References

Availability
Purchase

Language

Computer
Apple II with CP/M, IBM PC

0437

Job Costing *Compuquant Limited*
Provides detailed job costing for an unlimited number of jobs incorporating detailed calculations for all items including daywork

References

Availability
Purchase, lease

Language

Computer
Toshiba T200 microcomputer with 64K

0438

Purchases application *Computerskills Limited*
This financial control system includes the following facilities: purchase ledger details, including VAT for current month, details of imports and items excluded from VAT, purchase ledger controls with VAT summary, list of creditors, production of cheques and list of purchase ledger balances. General financial and cost expenditure analysis is also available

References

Availability
Bureau service

Language

Computer

0439

Architect Project Cost Control *The Consultancy Consortium*
Handles resource forecasts and allocations on projects and assesses actual progress on jobs, against original forecast. Maintains staff and branch details and produces relevant reports

References

Availability
Purchase

Language

Computer
Sirius 1, 128K

Job Costing System *The Consultancy Consortium*
An integrated suite of programs that allow the input of conventional timesheet details and
materials cost data to be processed, so that charges are automatically entered to the
appropriate job files. Details entered include staff hourly charge rates, branches of the
business and work categories, against which timesheet postings are made

References

Availability
Purchase

Language

Computer
Sirius 1, 128K

Project Cost Control *The Consultancy Consortium*
Three main tasks are: time accounting; order processing and project cost control. All
materials and time expenditure are charged to the appropriate project and added to the
month's accruals. Reports include a complete project report detailing previous year's and
month's accruals and current month's time, overtime and material bookings

References

Availability
Purchase

Language

Computer
Sirius 1, 128K

CONTRACT COSTING *Crescent Business Systems*
A fully-integrated, multi-user system covering all aspects of sales, purchase and nominal
ledgers, time recording, contract monitoring and subcontracting. Further modules cover
the areas of stock recording, plant register, estimating and cashflow forecasting

References

Availability
Purchase

Language

Computer
128k memory
Onyx-Mercator
System 2000

CASHFLOW *DHSS (Department of Health and Social Security)*
A suite of programs incorporating algorithms based on a statistical study of a large
number of health buildings, enabling the user to predict various aspects of capital
expenditure. This can be used for other types of building by adjusting the forecasting
equation. It is possible to prepare total capital works expenditure forecasts over a period
of up to 10 years

References

Availability
Purchase

Language
M Basic

Computer
64K microcomputer

NCP NORM and NCP SUM *DHSS (Department of Health and Social Security)*
A suite of programs for producing a notional cost plan from the budget cost statement; the
user selects percentages for non-constructional elements and distribution of on-costs

References

Availability
Purchase

Language
Basic 80

Computer
64K microcomputer

COSTPROF *EDP Systems Limited*
A cost analysis program for professional firms. Provides management information to
monitor contract costs and fees received/expected. Costs are analysed to individual
employees within contracts, with a sub-analysis by types of activity (user defined). Totals
for branches or departments are provided if required. The system is designed for firms
such as architects, engineers, surveyors, etc, and includes a comprehensive selection of
printed reports

References

Availability
Purchase

Language
Basic (Cromemco
16K extended)

Computer
64K memory

Job Control *fba Computer Services Limited*
Consists of two modules: job estimating and job control. Assists building and construction
companies to control their costs. The degree of strictness with which job costs are
controlled is defined by the user

References

Availability
Purchase

Language

Computer
Minicomputer or
Microcomputer

CONTRACT MANAGER *Focus Software Consultants*
For the financial monitoring of contracts. Information stored is used to produce draft
documents for issue to Contractors and will automatically update the current stage of the
contract expense allowing tight budget control over project expenditure. Variation order
sums may be made against primary included sums and contingency items allowing the
program to automatically reallocate sums of money within the original tender sum

References

Availability
Purchase

Language

Computer
CP/M or MS DOS

PCC. Project Cost Control *Hevacomp Limited*
This software package is a self-contained suite of programs which will enable project fees,
timesheets and chargeable costs to be analysed, stored and continuously monitored during
a project. For each project a special Project File is set up, containing management
information, the fee estimate and the rate at which fees are likely to be expended. Each
month a profitability report is produced, identifying any projects with bad performance

References

Availability
Purchase

Language

Computer
Any 64K
microcomputer

JOB COSTING *HSV Limited*
Records of time and materials cost are input via a vdu. The system checks each
transaction to ensure it will be posted against a valid material code and
operation/employee. Complete audit trail is maintained and printed when required. Reports
include: input validation, deletion, audit list, cost report, employee file and expense code
file

References
Which Computer, January 1983

Availability
Purchase

Language

Computer

0450

Arcos *Insight Computer Systems*
This is an architect's Job Costing/Forecasting System. Job costing will take weekly timesheets and allocate time and cash charges to each project that has been worked on. The hourly charges for staff, with normal and overtime hours, are totalled, and expenditure during the various phases of the project is recorded

References
RIBA 'Architect's Guide through Computer Jungle'

Availability
Purchase

Language
Basic

Computer
Commodore

0451

Q COST-A *Lancaster Computing*
Aids the analysis, recording and retrieval of tender or other costs by reference to a maximum of 10 building groups. Data for up to 500 jobs can be stored on each disc and group headings can be user defined. Input consists of titles, locations, dates, contract particulars and contact figures using a simple, direct entry screen format; 19 items are collected for each project. Output can be by screen or printer

References

Availability
Purchase

Language

Computer
Apple II

0452

Q COST-B *Lancaster Computing*
This program comprises a database of the BCIS average building prices (ie substructures and superstructures, inclusive of preliminaries but exclusive of external works and contingencies). Buildings are filed under SfB classification and are base dated 1st quarter 1980. The program aims to permit speedy abstraction of appropriate cost data, provide regional adjustment and cost update. Screen display indicates: average building price, survey range and survey sample size

References

Availability
Purchase

Language

Computer
Apple II

0453

Time Sheet/Job Costing *Lancaster Computing*
Aids the monitoring of technical staff time expended against pre-determined targets, together with data on staff time costs for accounting purposes. The user can analyse cost across a range of jobs and stages within those jobs. The program caters for up to 45 staff and 50 jobs on any one disc, with 12 user-definable stages (based on the RIBA format). Staff names, salaries and holidays can be altered only by a password

References

Availability
Purchase

Language

Computer
Apple II

0454

Ludhouse Contract Costing *Ludhouse (Computing) Limited*
This program is integrated with sales, purchase and nominal ledgers. Its purpose is to collect cost against a contract for analysis, budget comparisons and profitability calculations. Facilities include 6 main cost headings and 36 cost sub-headings; target profit calculation; audit trail on all transactions; sorting by department and code; cost and profit/sales percentages; entry of aged information

References

Availability
Licence

Language
M Basic

Computer
64K microcomputer

0455

CONTRACTMAN *Mandata Limited*
A comprehensive contract cost ledger designed specifically for both large and small electrical contractors

References
Recommended by British Olivetti

Availability

Language

Computer
Olivetti M20

0456

MARSTRUCT *Marcus Computer Systems*
For material estimating and bill of quantities and the control and monitoring of contract cost. Allows for retentions and work certified. Complete system includes: estimating materials and labour; materials and price control; bill of quantities; contract control; purchase, sales and nominal ledgers; invoicing; payroll; subcontractors' ledger. Fully interactive

References

Availability
Purchase

Language

Computer
CPM 86, MS-DOS, CPM 2.2

0457

Contract Costing *Mentor Systems*
Can be used with the Estimating or Valuations programs. All contractual details are held on disk. Comprehensive materials purchasing functions. At any time the contract can be recosted, with costs and progress applications being instantly available. Information is displayed on screen or printout as required. Automatic posting of site charges is carried out

References

Availability
Licence

Language

Computer
ICL

0458

Contract Valuation *Mentor Systems*
Automatic calculation of increased costs may be achieved by entry of monthly valuation. Provides correct calculation of increased costs, together with printouts. Having produced a valuation, the costs to that date will be calculated with a report giving movement and profit for this valuation and to date. Produces a summary report of all contracts within a particular date range

References

Availability
Licence

Language

Computer
ICL

0459

AJACS *Mercator Computer Systems*
An architects' job analysis and costing system for recording information from timesheets, expenses and Billing returns. Fees are calculated from fee scales comprising two RIBA Scales for new works and Works to Existing Buildings. The program keeps time records of employees and accumulates costs and charges for each. Records expenses, such as: telephone calls, drawing, travelling and non-chargeable. Handles up to 350 concurrent contracts, with 26 scale fees, and records progress on each contract

References

Availability
Purchase

Language

Computer
CP/M

Building Trades Accounts and Costing *Micro Associates*
Used for the production of monthly daybooks and ledgers incorporating a facility for retention against work undertaken. Includes preparation and updating of cost estimates and work in progress, together with identification of job profitability. Output includes daybooks, job cost details, personal ledgers, control accounts, and labour analysis

References

Availability
Purchase

Language
Basic
Assembler

Computer
Commodore 32K

Cashflow Forecasting *MicroAid Limited*
Cashflow forecast is obtained with a standard S-curve formula. An estimate of cashflow for up to 20 subcontracts with known cost, start dates and durations is printed in tabular form. Front end loading can be applied to any contract. Cost control applied by entering actual cost values each period and re-calculating the cashflow for the rest of the project

References

Availability
Purchase

Language

Computer
ACT Sirius, Apricot,
Texas Instruments

Elemental Cost Analysis *MicroAid Limited*
Where an element for building is made up from standard elements, eg BCIS cost analysis elements, using cost per unit area, budget lump sum per element or percentage of overall budget, the elemental cost plan is produced and adjusted. Provides a pre-contract function and anticipated costs may be changed or re-apportioned

References

Availability
Purchase

Language

Computer
ACT Sirius, Apricot,
Texas Instrument

BUTRESS *MMG Consultants Limited*
Designed for architects and based on recommendations of the RIBA Resources Handbook. Provides integrated control of all the factors in the fee-earning and related activities of the business. Includes: Resource control system, Purchase Ledger, Client's Ledger, Bank reconciliation and Cash flow, General Ledger and Management Accounts, Analyses and Text processing

References
Program produced by Definitive
Computing Limited

Availability
Purchase. Lease

Language
UNIX

Computer
16-bit
microcomputer,
Mini, mainframe

FT Moneywise *Moneywise Software Limited*
A financial modelling package which can be used for: budgeting purposes at a design stage; cashflow forecasts; variance analysis and reporting at the building stage. Graphs can be produced

References

Availability
Purchase

Language

Computer
IBM PC, Sirius
and Victor micros,
256K

Building Cost Indices *Norden Technical Computer Systems Limited*
This program calculates building cost indices both for general use and for specific applications. Input includes details of labour and material elements, each type of which represents a percentage of the total work category. Rates for materials are obtained from several suppliers, and updated as necessary, together with labour costs

References

Availability

Language

Computer
64k Microcomputer
Interset IS2000
Digico M16E

Project monitoring and cashflows *Norden Technical Computer Systems Limited*
Assists the quantity surveyor to make cashflow predictions. Project information is input in the form of start and finish dates, value, defects liability period, etc. During the contract, actual expenditure figures are plotted against initial predictions, providing a graphic and printed representation of the site performance for each building element. Corrective measures can be taken to adjust the cashflow curve as required, and revised forecasts made during the contract. Output is in graphic and tabular form

References

Availability

Language

Computer
64k microcomputer
Interset IS 2000
Digico M16E

PCM - Project Cost Model *Project Software Limited*
Provides managers with a forecast of the cost and time required for the remaining work, based on simple records of performance to date and the current knowledge of the remaining work. Input data includes quantities, plant and labour resources, output rates, unit costs of materials, operational dependencies and contract prices. Output provides a costed work programme, a cashflow forecast and a profit and loss analysis, via a wide range of reports

References
New Civil Engineer, 13 July 1978

Availability
Licence

Language
Fortran IV, Dibol

Computer
DEC PDP11/23, 64K

PCM-STP *Project Software Limited*
Provides short term planning and cost control for contractors' operations on construction sites. Input includes plant and labour resource costs and budgets against the bill of quantities' items. The program is then used to build up a bar chart of the next 2-3 weeks' activities. This is done interactively on the VDU and a cost forecast and budget value for the emerging plan can be produced

References

Availability
Licence

Language
Fortran IV, Dibol

Computer
DEC PDP11/23, 64K

JOB COST *Radius Computer Services Limited*
For the monitoring and control of job costs. The system allows estimating to be done through a bill of quantities. There are standard interfaces with payroll, purchase invoices and stock. A separate subcontractors' ledger is available. Output includes audit and management reports

References

Availability
Licence

Language
Basic

Computer
Texas Instruments
Business System 300

0470

JCP-2 *SIA Computer Services*
A staff timesheet analysis and cost control system for professional firms

References

Availability
Bureau service

Language
High level

Computer
Control Data,
IBM, Prime

0471

IMCA-COST LEDGER *Southern Computer Systems Limited*
Written in conjunction with leading construction, contracting, engineering and processing
companies. Detailed reports and summaries of labour, material, stock and overhead
contents of jobs and contracts; each can be analysed by a maximum of 12 main and 90
sub-analysis headings. Integrated with IMCA-PURCHASE LEDGER and can be linked to
IMCA-SALES and/or NOMINAL LEDGERS. Labour is input from timesheets. Direct entries
are used for input stock, journal, adjustments, etc; detailed audit trail

References
Approved by Apple Computer Limited

Availability

Language

Computer
48-256K under CP/M
or Apple DOS

0472

Cost Ledger Suite *Spot Computer Systems Limited*
Allows running totals of cost of jobs to be maintained to provide adequate cost control.
Variance reports are available for comparing actual costs with budgeted figures, which may
be broken down into a maximum of 99 cost centres for each job

References

Availability
Purchase

Language
Compiled Basic

Computer
64K CP/M based
computer

0473

BRICS *Staveley Computing Centre*
A fully integrated cost control system for house builders. Features include: control of
subcontracts, ie costs, payments, tax information; expenses, ie ledger, payments, reports,
tax control; cash control, including cash book, cashflow, reporting, balance reports and
budgets; purchase control/ledger; nominal ledger; payroll. Developments are planned to
include estimating and full contract costing

References

Availability
Purchase

Language
Dibol

Computer
DEC-based systems
Minimum 128Kb
memory

0474

Design Evaluation *Tillyard AG*
Provides early projections of construction costs and costs in use, including: comparative
evaluation of alternative design solutions, estimates based on functional elements; costs in
use (operation and maintenance costs); cost analysis and comparison

References

Availability

Language

Computer

0475

SCORE (System for costing research expenditure) *TRADA*
This suite of programs analyses expenditure of resources against cost centres, and
produces information for project management

References

Availability

Language

Computer

0476

CONTRACT COSTING SYSTEM *Wilcox Computers Limited*
Designed for firms in the construction, civil engineering subcontractors and allied
industries. Provides accurate, detailed and up-to-date costing for each contract recorded.
It receives costs from other systems and records them, in detail and/or total, by expense
code within contract. Comparisons may be made between costs and budgets, and gross
margins are reported at contract level

References

Availability
Purchase

Language
CIS Cobol (CP/M
based)

Computer
CP/M based micro.
Min 64K

0477

Architect Project Cost Control *The Consultancy Consortium*
Handles resource forecasts and allocations on projects and assesses actual progress on
jobs, against original forecast. Maintains staff and branch details and produces relevant
reports

References

Availability
Purchase

Language

Computer
Sirius 1, 128K

0478

OMS-PAYROLL *Alpha Micro UK*
Provides initialisation and update of employees' files; payroll preparation and time cards
update with adjustments option; weekly, biweekly and monthly payroll periods; federal,
state and local withholding taxes; union dues and health insurance payments; sick leave,
vacation; monthly employer and employee taxes report. All reports are sorted
alphabetically by employee or department

References

Availability
Purchase

Language
Alpha Basic

Computer
Alpha Micro CPU
with 8Mbytes

0479

SMB Payroll *Amplix Services Limited*
Features include: multi-company; hourly, weekly and monthly systems; permanent and
temporary staff details; payroll run on temporary files to allow re-runs without affecting
year to date files; entry of job cost hours from timesheets; allowances and deductions
entry; payroll analysis by company and department; no pay report; statutory deductions
report; coin analysis; payslip print; P35 and P11D/P60 print; posting to SMB nominal and
job cost ledgers

References

Availability
Purchase

Language
Commercial (SMB)
Cobol, Fortran

Computer
CP/M or MP/M
Microcomputer

Computer programs for the building industry

Personnel Management *Building Centre Computers Limited*
Covers the requirements of personnel management including: payroll, time and sickness recording, pension fund records, wage negotiation calculations and word processing

References

Availability
Purchase

Language
Basic

Computer
Mini and microcomputers single & multi user

PAYROLL *CIMS Computer Systems Limited*
Part of the CIMS Management System designed for the construction industry. Caters for all weekly and monthly paid staff; handles payments according to trade, site conditions, bonuses, tool allowance, subsistence and travelling expenses. Comprehensive timesheet information enables individual labour costs to be reallocated to other contracts, and provides reporting on labour costs. Maintains current personnel details, calculates all pay details, timesheets, payslips, coin analysis, etc; allows payment in any form

References

Availability
Purchase

Language
RPG11

Computer
IBM System/34

Payroll *Compact Accounting Services Limited*
Features include: incorporation of program for Tax and NI tables, allowing changes to be made by the user; free format payslip design; facility for up to 20 deductions to be detailed; coin analysis; choice of cheque, cash or bank giro payment; capability for basic salary or rate plus overtime rates; monthly payroll automatically generated; reports provide details for government returns, eg P35's and P60's

References
Recommended by Zenithplan Limited

Availability
Purchase

Language
Microsoft Basic

Computer
Sirius 1. Any CP/M microcomputer with 64K

COMPANY ID *Computel Limited*
A program for use as a standard payroll system with provision for year end tax returns

References
Program made available by ICL

Availability

Language

Computer

Payroll *Computel Limited*
Designed to operate on a weekly or four weekly cycle. Payslips can show name of company, basic weekly information, and a breakdown of gross pay and deductions. Cumulative tax returns for all employees can be processed at the end of the year to give an analysis, by occupation code, to show average rates of pay, average payment and overtime

References

Availability

Language

Computer

CPAY *Computer House*
A general purpose, interactive, multi-user payroll system for up to 10,000 employees: hourly, weekly and monthly paid employees can be mixed but run separately. All reporting on record keeping is done automatically. Meets all current statutory requirements, including new Government regulations on statutory sick pay. Interfaces available to most labour and job costing systems and to most nominal ledgers

References

Availability
Purchase

Language
'C'

Computer
Various, min 11/2 Mb

Payroll package *Computerskills Limited*
This financial control system includes the following facilities: generation of payslips, cheques, credit transfers, or magnetic tape for submission to the Bankers' Automated Clearing Service, analysis of notes and coins, National Insurance quarterly schedules, tax certificates, cost analysis of gross pay and allowances, and a payroll summary, providing details for posting to the nominal ledger

References

Availability
Bureau service

Language

Computer

Payroll *Estimation Inc*
Calculates and reports all payroll functions including payables, deductions, taxes, reporting of payroll, job costing, government, union, personnel, and historical data

References

Availability
Purchase.

Language

Computer

BIZRAY *FCG Computer Systems*
Integrated to the FCG Accounts package. Designed to conduct weekly and monthly payrolls. Ouput includes PAYE and NI calculations, payslips, payroll summary, coinage summary, payslip detailed report, and cost analysis

References

Availability
Purchase

Language
Commodore Basic

Computer
Commodore 8000

Contractors' Payroll System *FCG Computer Systems*
Designed for the specific requirements of the construction industry, and to provide contract costing. Features include: national working rules, labour only subcontractors, holiday pay, travel and fares, complete job costing, data security, and system maintenance. Timesheets are entered for employees and the labour costs are posted to the contracts. The system can also track loans and repayments, provide anniversary prompts, and handle bonus methods

References

Availability
Purchase

Language
Commodore Basic

Computer
Commodore 8000

Computer programs for the building industry

0490

Manpower Systems *Geest Computer Services Limited*
This service includes: payroll, personnel, pension and statutory sick pay administration systems. The payroll system offers: job costing, proportional costing, modern design payslips, and a fast turnround of processing

References

Availability
Bureau Service

Language
Cobol

Computer
ICL: 2950, ME29, 2904 and 2946

0491

Payroll *Mentor Systems*
Provides all the normal gross to nett payroll calculation facilities with selected build-up to gross calculations. Up to ten pre- or post-tax deductions may be recorded on each individual, either as a value or a percentage, Full analyses by department and payroll are available. Payments made by cash, cheque or credit transfer

References

Availability
Licence

Language

Computer
ICL

0492

PPL-CYBORG PAYROLL *SIA Computer Services*
This is a major, comprehensive payroll and personnel management system. On-line ad hoc enquiries and data entry are provided

References

Availability
Bureau service

Language
High level

Computer
Control Data, IBM, Prime

0493

IMCA-PAYROLL *Southern Computer Systems Limited*
Designed to allow payrolls to be tailored to suit the individual requirements of a company with up to 200 employees. Handles all tax and national insurance calculations and will print payslips, summaries and departmental analyses. Up to 12 séparate taxable fields can be used, and up to 6 separate fields are also available for deductions. The system also handles holiday schemes, departmental analysis, coin analysis, P60's, etc

References

Availability

Language

Computer
48-256K under CP/M or Apple DOS

0494

Payroll *Tandy Corporation*
Handles hourly, weekly, 2, 3 and 4 weekly and monthly paid staff. 400 staff per disk and up to 10 departments. Keeps 54 items of information for each employee. Features include: calculation and printing of payslips, departmental summaries, coin analysis, cheque and bank giro lists; also handles P35 (CS), P60, and P11 forms

References

Availability
Purchase

Language

Computer
TRS-80 Model I & III

0495

Payroll *Tandy Corporation*
Handles hourly, weekly, 2, 3 and 4 weekly and monthly paid staff. Up to 700 staff in up to 100 departments per disk, with up to 84 items of information per employee. Performs the 'build up to gross', National Insurance and income tax calculations, etc. Produces payslips, salary reports and summaries. Other features include coin analysis, cheque lists, year end tax forms, etc

References

Availability
Purchase

Language

Computer
TRS-80 Model II

0496

Payroll system - COINS *UCC (Great Britain) Limited*
Calculates pay and produces individual documents and records. A weekly input of ministry number, hours worked and other items, such as subscriptions and sick time, is used to produce a payslip for each employee. Tax, National Insurance, holiday stamps and inclement weather are all provided for; a coin analysis is also produced

References

Availability
Bureau service, remote batch

Language
Cobol

Computer
Univac 1106

0497

Salary system - FLEXIPAY *UCC (Great Britain) Limited*
Produces a detailed individual payslip, complete with name and address. Details include cost allocation of salary to the appropriate department or cost centre, income tax deductions, allowances, ledgers for staff savings, loans, mortgages and end of year tax returns

References

Availability
Bureau service, remote batch

Language
Cobol

Computer
Univac 1106

0498

CASH FLOW *ABS Oldacres Computers Limited*
Used at the pre-contract stage, to produce construction cashflow statistics based on contract type, value and length. The implications of retention and inflation are also provided for. Output is in tabular and graphical form

References

Availability
Purchase

Language
M Basic

Computer
CP/M 64K

0499

SUPERCALC *ABS Oldacres Computers Limited*
A general purpose, financial modelling program suitable for budget reporting and elemental analysis

References

Availability
Purchase

Language
M Basic

Computer
CP/M 64K

FPROJ *Alper Systems Limited*
Part of the FACTOTUM suite for professional practices; used with FTIME and FSTAF.
Collects and maintains relevant details of fees, costs and work in progress including
projection of fees, and presents typical project management data in various formats. Ouput
contains accumulated tables of job summaries including fees and costs for all groups
within the practice, and for separate groups (partners). Most of the input data appears in
the tables

References

Availability
Purchase

Language
Fortran

Computer
64k 8-bit
CP/M Microcomputer

FSTAF *Alper Systems Limited*
Part of the FACTOTUM suite for professional practices; used with FPROJ and FTIME.
Maintains records of personnel, including computation of charge out and overhead rates;
provides a management tool for assessment of salary, c/o and o/t rates, etc

References

Availability
Purchase

Language
Fortran

Computer
64k 8-bit
CP/M Microcomputer

FTIME *Alper Systems Limited*
Part of the FACTOTUM suite which is designed for use by architects, engineers and
quantity surveyors; used with FSTAF and FPROJ. FTIME collects and maintains timesheet
and cost records in a professional practice, providing a basis for tailoring to individual
requirements. Input includes month, week, name, reference, job number, standard hours,
overtime, mileage, site visits, etc. Output is by person and by job, with all relevant
information

References

Availability
Purchase

Language
Fortran

Computer
64k 8-bit
CP/M Microcomputer

OMS-COST MANAGEMENT SYSTEMS *Alpha Micro UK*
A construction cost estimating, microcomputer based software package. Features three
levels of cost estimating: preliminary, approximate quantities, and detailed quantities. It is
fully integrated with the OMS - Office Management System database

References

Availability
Purchase

Language
Alpha Basic

Computer
Alpha Micro CPU
with 8Mbytes

SMB Financial Modelling *Amplix Services Limited*
Features include: multi-company; models include projected P & L account, projected
cashflow and balance sheet; maintenance of parameter files, ie sales growth, sales labour,
materials, overhead inflation cashflow drag, budgeted stock charges, capital expenditure,
capital changes and opening balance sheet; interface with SMB Nominal Ledger and Stock
File at the time of the run or from earlier copies; printed reports as specified

References

Availability
Purchase

Language
Commercial (SMB)
Cobol, Fortran

Computer
CP/M or MP/M
Microcomputer

JOBCOST *C-QS Computer Services*
For monitoring and reporting staff costs in a professional office; related to construction
projects and services provided. A program suitable for quantity surveyors, architects,
engineers, etc. Output includes full listing of entries, monthly cost totals, analysis by any
input criteria, and costs carried over from one year to the next

References
Recommended by Masterbill Micro
Systems

Availability
Purchase

Language
Basic 4 (compiled)

Computer
Commodore 8032,
8096

NEDO FORMULA *C-QS Computer Services*
Calculates increased cost of building work in accordance with DOE indices. All data,
calculations and summaries are printed out

References

Availability
Purchase

Language
Basic

Computer
Commodore
CBM 8032, 8096

COST LIMIT *Cheshire County Council*
Calculates cost limits for secondary education projects. Details such as areas, types of
accommodation, external works, abnormal costs, etc, are keyed in by the quantity
surveyor. The output is a cost limit and outline cost plan with or without a brief
specification of the various forms of SCOLA or traditional construction selected as the
basis of the costing

References

Availability

Language
APL

Computer
IBM 3767

PURCHASE *CIMS Computer Systems Limited*
Part of the CIMS Management System designed for the construction industry. Records
purchases and controls cashflow. Maintains details of suppliers, purchase orders and
invoices, mainly by transfer from COST, STOCK and NOMINAL systems. Includes list of
items needing to be paid for within a given time to qualify for discounts. Reports include
cheque proofs, aged credit analysis, payments forecast, routines for VAT analysis, and
customer account balances

References

Availability
Purchase

Language
RPG11

Computer
IBM System/34

INTEREST CE *Computer Aided Management in Construction Limited*
Designed for the construction industry. This is an interactive estimating software package
for civil engineering contractors, operating on hard disk microcomputers

References
Developed at Loughborough University
of Technology

Availability

Language

Computer
Microcomputers

0510

PLUS CASH *Computer Aided Management in Construction Limited*
A cashflow forecasting and resource aggregating software package which is linked to
INTEREST and uses the estimator's data in the calculations

References
Developed at Loughborough University
of Technology

Availability

Language

Computer

0511

Assets application *Computerskills Limited*
This financial control system includes: calculation of depreciation by the straight line or
reducing balance methods, automatic cessation of depreciation when the asset has been
written down to its residual value, grouping of low value assets as one composite asset and
various options for treatment of profits or losses on sales of assets. Non-standard routines
cover selected assets, hire purchase agreements and projected depreciation

References

Availability
Bureau service

Language

Computer

0512

Manpower Accounting *COSMIC*
Provides tabular information including: summaries for weekly and monthly activity reports;
expenditure of contractor hours and costs; summaries of charge numbers being used and
at which rate; data which can be presented to management for annual reviews, etc. The
program recognises several different breakdowns of personnel types and task categories,
and it prepares separate tables for each of them. There are 12 different tables output

References
CAL TECH/Jet Propulsion Laboratory

Availability

Language
Fortran IV

Computer
IBM 360 series

0513

PACE II Pricing and cost estimating handbook *COSMIC*
Performs all mathematical and clerical functions automatically once basic inputs are
derived. The system can also be used in trade-off studies, change estimates and budgetary
studies. Features include: work breakdown structure, labour rate structure, format for data
input and output, and methods for applying overhead, general and administrative cost, fees
and escalation. Output consists of a cost estimate report showing cost breakdown per
fiscal year of the estimate project

References
NASA Marshall Space Flight Center

Availability

Language
Cobol

Computer
Univac 1100 series

0514

Weekly manpower analysis *COSMIC*
A labour cost summary of tasks with applicable personnel per division and section, with
hours and overtime worked per week. Provides weekly reporting of labour hours by
individuals. At least 25 jobs and 11 work areas can be included. Labour costs can be
added if required. Output includes: a listing of each job worked on; the personnel involved;
their division, straight time hours and overtime hours

References
CAL TECH/Jet Propulsion Laboratory

Availability

Language
Fortran IV

Computer
IBM 1620

0515

Fee Calculations *Gerald G Darby (Computing Services)*
Calculates the quantity surveyor's fees on a contract using the RICS Scale of Charges

References

Availability
Purchase

Language
M Basic

Computer
64K

0516

ESTIMATING SYSTEM *Digital Building Systems Limited*
Provides an easy, efficient and economical method of producing accurate estimates.
Estimating practices are followed closely, but the system can be up to five times faster
than other methods. Output includes listings for: data and price, and for rates of labour,
plant and material; printed estimates. Free query service is provided, together with free
software support for up to 5 years

References

Availability
Purchase

Language
CBASIC

Computer
Digico Prince,
CP/M2.2,
64K bytes

0517

FINAL *D M England and Partners*
A multi-dimensional financial analysis and modelling system which is sophisticated, yet user
friendly. Free format reports enable the user to specify heading, underlines, footnotes,
descriptive names, spacing, etc. Used in corporate planning for functions such as
forecasting, budgeting, cashflow, etc

References
Recommended by Euro-log Systems
Limited

Availability
Purchase

Language

Computer
Most micros with
CP/M; mini and
mainframes

0518

Fixed Assets *fba Computer Services Limited*
Caters for both historic and current cost accounting and allows the user to depreciate
using either a straight line or reducing balance basis. Current cost updates can be carried
out manually or by reference to index numbers. Period depreciation report details the
depreciation charges against all assets and totals by nominal code, asset location and
asset group and will then update to nominal ledger, if required

References

Availability
Purchase

Language

Computer
Minicomputer or
Microcomputer

0519

EstiMATE *Focus Software Consultants*
Stores cost-related data for items of plant, materials, etc at any level of breakdown
required. Caters for material costs and labour rates. Cost data file is used when producing
a cost estimate for a project. Reports produced by EstiMATE include the contents of cost
data files, project/job data files and the complete contents of an estimate including a
summary and total cost

References

Availability
Purchase

Language

Computer
CP/M or MS DOS

DIGICALC *Hourds Computing Limited*
A financial modelling program, used for any type of numeric calculation. Displays a tabular worksheet on the VDU and can call on numerous mathematical functions. Enables the user to prepare everything from budgets to multi-year forecasts with accuracy and speed. Used for: financial forecasting, corporate budgeting, econometric modelling, investment analysis, resource allocation, cost distribution, scheduling, costing and analysis, chemical formulation conversion, energy utility applications, and tax forecasting

References
Developed by Why Systems Inc

Availability
Licence

Language

Computer
DEC

0521

HIPHICS *Hunting Computer Services Limited*
A plant hire system for minicomputers. Includes a plant register, plant invoicing, accounts and payroll. All aspects are integrated to the plant cost ledger. A full audit trail is provided. All data is user defined, and the program is designed for use by unskilled personnel

References

Availability
Purchase with or without hardware

Language
Cobol

Computer
Data General CS/5
64K memory

0522

Cash flow forecast *A M Kinney, Inc*
Estimates the net cash available to equity in each year for the lifetime of a project; the program will also compute the discounted rate of return. Designed to accept 4 methods of depreciation: double decline, straight line, sum of years digits, and decline balance. Output contains a tabulation of information for 20 years

References

Availability

Language
Fortran

Computer
IBM 1130 and 370

0523

Discounted rate of return on investment *A M Kinney, Inc*
Computes the discounted rate of return, which is based on average continuous rate of compound interest earned by a project on the money invested in that project over the life assignable to it. The program will also calculate the zero interest break-even point and a cumulative cashflow during the end of each period. Can be run independently or linked with 'Cash flow forecast' program

References

Availability

Language
Fortran

Computer
IBM 1130 and 370

0524

CONPAK *Lamex Commercial Computing Limited*
For project costing and financial management within the construction, building and civil engineering industries. Modules include subcontractors', purchase, sales and cash ledgers; payroll, project costing, work in progress, and nominal ledgers with budgeting. The system incorporates Lamex's working knowledge of subcontractor legislation and the National Working Rule agreement

References
Recommended by IBM

Availability

Language

Computer
IBM System/34

0525

LAMSUB *Lamex Commercial Computing Limited*
An interactive system designed to simplify the control and operation of subcontractor payments. Calculation and recording of CITB levy, insurance, tax, discount, contra's, VAT and retentions on both work and materials. Cash book reconciliation and allied reports are printed on request; tax return information is stored for annual and quarterly reporting according to legislation. Up to 40 trade codes per certificate. Retention reports and VAT analysis. Open item file system. Certificates, cheques etc. produced

References
Recommended by IBM

Availability

Language

Computer
IBM System/34

0526

INTEREST BUILD *Loughborough University of Technology*
A computer aided estimating system for builders in the UK. Allows the user to price items as unit rates, operational rates, combinations of both, or 'spot' items. At the completion of the direct cost estimate the available reports are: bill listings, direct cost summaries, and resource reconciliations. The system allows for: surcharges, overheads, profits and rate loadings

References
Recommended by Computer Aided Management in Construction

Availability

Language

Computer
Microcomputers eg Cromemco Z2H; Prime

0527

Bank Reconciliation *Mentor Systems*
This program extracts data from sales and purchase ledgers. Facilities are provided to enable miscellaneous bank details to be input. This enables a file of cheques issued and received to be maintained. Details of bank statements are then input and matched against this file enabling both a reconciled and unreconciled cheques report to be produced

References

Availability
Licence

Language

Computer
ICL

0528

Estimating *Mentor Systems*
Provides a simple method of collecting and building up prices to give a final tender figure. The system allows 'All in' or 'LMP' rates. Full integration with valuation and contract costing programs will allow accurate profit reporting during a contract. A security safeguard has been incorporated

References

Availability
Licence

Language

Computer
ICL

0529

Labour Costing/Analysis *Mentor Systems*
A fully integrated payroll is provided. Entry can be for single or multi site operations. Postings to contracts may be made at levels of trade, contract, operation and employee. Further analysis of hours and value may be used as appropriate

References

Availability
Licence

Language

Computer
ICL

0530

TIRE *MicroAid Limited*
For professional office time recording. Time can be charged at two rates and expenses can be in one or more of three types: cash, credit card, travel (miles or £p). Includes housekeeping tasks, information entry and analysis routines. Each option, except for the TIME Input routine, is password protected

References

Availability
Purchase

Language

Computer
ACT Sirius, Apricot, Texas Instruments

0531

LAMSAC Application code 32504122270A *Northamptonshire County Council, Architect's Department*
Provides a commitments account for architects. Slow peripheral units used are a tape reader and lineprinter. The program was first used in 1969

References
LAMSAC

Availability

Language
Plan

Computer
ICL 1904S
7K core
5 magnetic tape units

0532

JOB COSTING *Office Automation*
This system caters for both product and process costing, and comprises 3 files: the component file, process file and product file. The latter contains description, unit cost, average weight, selling price, and up to 20 processes which can affect the end product. Originally designed for food processing but can be adapted to suit other applications

References

Availability

Language

Computer
Olivetti M20

0533

FINESSE *P-E Consulting Group*
A financial modelling system, originally developed by PE for use by consultants on client assignments. Now available externally. The program is used for project evaluation, corporate planning, budgeting, inter-company comparisons, leasing studies, investment appraisals and evaluating production and marketing strategies

References
.Les Hunt (1980) Computer models as aids to financial planning. Process Engineering, November

Availability
Purchase, lease

Language
Fortran

Computer
Any mainframe or Minicomputer with Fortran compiler

0534

microFINESSE *The P-E Consulting Group*
A complete and comprehensive desktop financial planning system for micros; based on FINESSE. Features include: large model matrix; simple English-like logic; flexible report layouts; graph and histogram output (and optional colour graphics); What if....? questions; step by step sensitivity analysis; target search; DCF investment appraisal; tax and depreciation functions; consolidation of models. The system can be used by accountants, business and financial analysts with no previous programming experience

References
Available from Source (Mr JZ Szymankiewicz)

Availability
Purchase

Language
Pascal

Computer
Apple II and III, IBM PC, others

0535

JOIN COST *Radius Computer Services Limited*
Generates customer quotations for window and door frames, door casings and staircases. The system is designed to be used by the estimator to produce printed quotations. Output includes audit trails, quotations and individual unit breakdown

References

Availability
Licence

Language
Basic

Computer
Texas Instruments
Business System 300

0536

AIDA *S D Micros Limited*
A post-contract aid to handling contract instructions, producing cost reports and the final account

References

Availability
Purchase

Language
Pascal p-system

Computer
Any for UCSD p, with 64K

0537

CASHFLOW *S D Micros Limited*
Forecasting cashflow on capital works projects using the mathematical formula developed by the DHSS. Output is a predicted cashflow for the contract based on the contract period and sum, taking into account selected retention percentages

References

Availability
Purchase

Language
Basic

Computer
48K Apple, and others

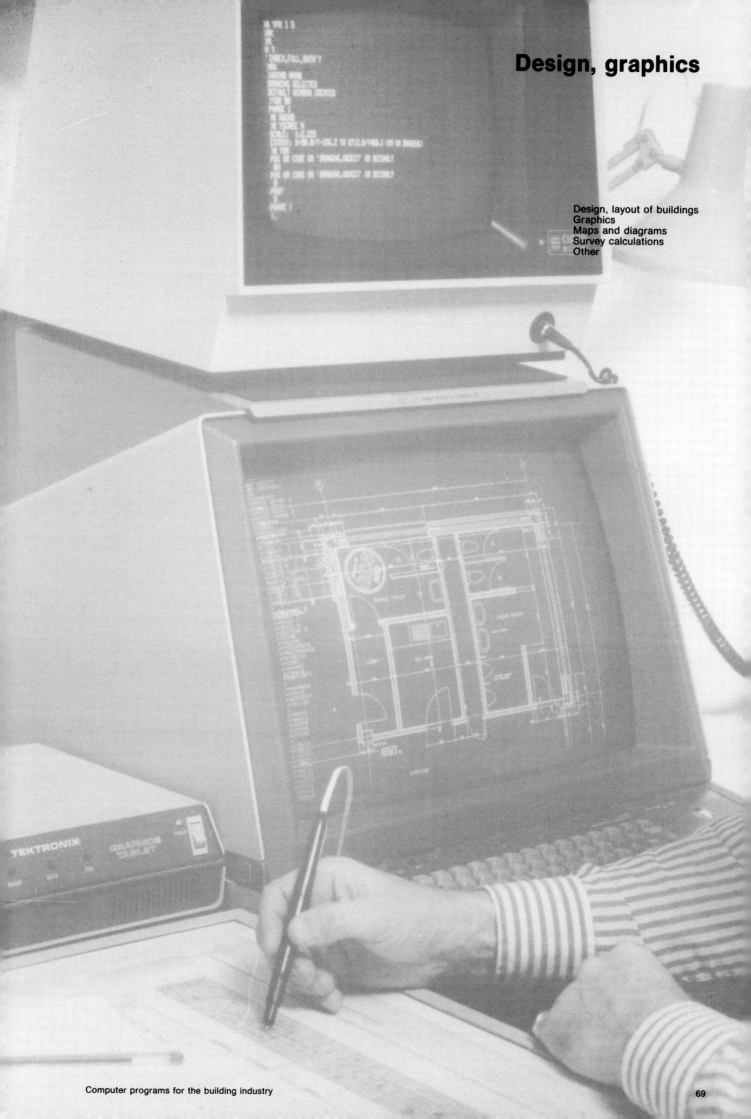

Design, graphics

Design, layout of buildings
Graphics
Maps and diagrams
Survey calculations
Other

0538

ASSIGN/TRANSP *ABACUS studies*
ASSIGN can be used to solve assignment problems. Given n functions, n spaces and the matrix for costs of allocating each one, it assigns the functions to the spaces with the minimum cost. It can be used for allocating room positions in an envelope, or functions to room, depending on serving load. TRANSP is used to solve the related transport problem

References

Availability
Purchase, lease, interactive bureau service

Language
Fortran

Computer
Univac 1108
Tektronix graphics terminal

0539

ECOLE 1 *ABACUS studies*
Used to design secondary school accommodation. Generates a schedule of accommodation which can form part of a brief or investigate alternative strategies of operation. Input comprises: school data, including curricula for each year and subject; allocation data, including areas for pupils and teacher and non-teaching areas; teaching data, including school organisation and shared accommodation; and cost data

References
ABACUS Occasional Paper No 40

Availability
Purchase, hire, interactive bureau service

Language
Fortran IV

Computer
Univac 1108
Tektronix graphics terminal

0540

ECOLE 3 *ABACUS studies*
This package models and appraises buildings at the scheme/detail design stage. The designer builds up a scheme description in terms of the geometry, site data, block and room layout, structural form and cladding arrangement. This data can be input on-line or by paper tape together with the cost and planning input data. Functional appraisals relating to planning efficiency, environmental performance and cost are also performed

References
SITE, ESP, ECOLE 1, ABACUS Occasional Papers Nos 40, 48, 61, 63

Availability
Purchase, hire, interactive bureau service

Language
Fortran IV

Computer
Univac 1108
Tektronix graphics terminal

0541

GRAMP *ABACUS studies*
This package produces a 2D sketch of a proposed scheme at an early stage of planning and/or design. It consists of a set of routines with which the designer can operate on the layout to produce sketches quickly

References

Availability
Purchase, lease, interactive bureau service

Language
Fortran

Computer
Univac 1108
Tektronix graphics terminal

0542

HELP (Housing Evaluation Layout Package) *ABACUS studies*
A design aid to modelling a housing layout. Input comprises files for: site, house, development, layout and network. Graphic output gives site, layout model showing roads and footpaths, and stepped elevations for a given terrace. Tabular output appraises costs, area provision, densities and access. Daylight, sunlight and privacy can be assessed for the complete layout or any individual house

References
SITE
ABACUS Occasional Paper No 64 (HELP)

Availability
Purchase, lease, bureau service

Language
Fortran IV

Computer
Univac 1108
Tektronix graphics terminal

0543

HLE *ABACUS studies*
Displays perspective views of rectilinearly built forms, and eliminates lines hidden from view. Two versions are available: one draws the view on a graph plotter, the other on a direct-view storage tube display terminal. The input must describe the form in terms of coordinates, surfaces, viewing point and angle of vision

References

Availability
Purchase, lease, interactive bureau service

Language
Fortran

Computer
Univac 1108
Tektronix graphics terminal

0544

PACE 1 *ABACUS studies*
This on-line program is used for evaluating a particular building design at the outline proposal stage. The designer submits full details of his proposed scheme and the computer produces a series of cost and performance data. The scheme may then be modified and reappraised as many times as required

References

Availability
Purchase, lease, interactive bureau service

Language
Fortran

Computer
Univac 1108
Tektronix graphics terminal

0545

PARTIAL *ABACUS studies*
Enables a non-professional to generate sketch designs and compare them with existing designs. Graphic output gives: a 'drawing' of the design; bar charts showing the percentage of deviation of the performance of the design from that of similar designs; and information showing, for each room type, the area selected by the operator, the area required to meet minimum requirements and optimum area

References
ECOLE 3
ABACUS Occasional Paper No 63

Availability
Purchase, lease, bureau service

Language
Fortan

Computer
Univac 1108
Tektronix graphics terminal

0546

PHASE *ABACUS studies*
Models the built form of a hospital at the design stage and extracts information enabling a large set of measures to be appraised. Graphic output shows site boundary with ground floor, any one floor, axonometric view, or section through site and/or model. Appraisal output is a synoptic table of measures concerning department and boilerhouse location, heatgain/loss diagnostics, and capital and energy costs

References
ACTNET, SERNET, HLE

Availability
Purchase, hire, interactive bureau service

Language
Fortran IV

Computer
Univac 1108
Tektronix graphics terminal

0547

SPACES 2 *ABACUS studies*
This program is an aid to producing a diagrammatic layout of a proposed building at the outline proposal stage. From a schedule of accommodation and the relationships between spaces, the program produces bubble diagrams. With standard routines the designer can manipulate the bubbles to satisfy given constraints. Each time a layout is produced, an appraisal of the planning efficiency and the constraints affecting the building are given

References
SPACES 1, SPACES 3. ABACUS Occasional Paper No 21 (SPACES)

Availability
Purchase, hire, interactive bureau service

Language
Fortran IV

Computer
Univac 1106
Tektronix graphics terminal

Computer programs for the building industry

SPACES 3 *ABACUS studies*
Gives an appraisal of the performance of buildings such as schools. Input consists of geometry of the building, site description, interdepartmental associations, construction, cost, and environmental and climatic data. Output gives floor and wall areas, wall to floor ratios, compactness and planning efficiency indices, figures for heatloss or gain, lighting requirements, boiler plant size, costs, and drawings

References
SPACES 1, 2 and 3, ABACUS Occasional Papers No 21

Availability
Purchase, hire, interactive bureau service

Language
Fortran IV

Computer
Univac 1108
Tektronix graphics terminal

0549

SPACES 1 *ABACUS studies*
Explores the spatial implications of alternative curricula, teaching methods and educational policies. Data is collected for each subject in the curriculum. Each form records the number and size of groups and time spent in various settings. Minimum space standards appropriate to each setting within each subject are also input. Output gives detailed schedules of accommodation, seat and room utilisation indices and summaries

References
SPACES 2 and 3, ECOLE 1, ABACUS Occasional Paper No 21 (SPACES)

Availability
Purchase, hire, interactive bureau service

Language
Fortran

Computer
Univac 1106
Tektronix graphics terminal

0550

BDS (Building Design Systems) *ARC Limited*
Integrates all stages of a project design. Stores a building as a 3D computer model, used to generate any plan, elevation, section or perspective, and printed documents. Sub-systems handle briefing information for evaluation, including cost and environmental analysis. Also provides detail design and documentation for drawings or scheduled information including Bills of Quantity

References

Availability
Sale, rental

Language
Fortran

Computer
Prime 250 MkII

0551

LAMSAC Application code 32205121140A *Bradford City Council, Architect's Department*
This architectural design program enables a graphical manipulation of housing sites to be made. Slow peripheral units used are a tape reader, lineprinter, nova term, graphic term and teletype. The program was first used in 1975

References
LAMSAC

Availability

Language
Fortran DG Nova Code

Computer
ICL 1904A
32K core

0552

CP110 *Building Computer Services Limited*
This is a design and analysis system comprising a database and a series of application programs, controlled by a plain English language. The structure is defined by the engineer and stored in the database so that selective details and analyses can subsequently be extracted

References

Availability
Bureau service, hire, sale

Language
Fortran

Computer
DEC

0553

UNI *Computer-Aided Design Group, USA*
A powerful, general purpose facility space programming tool. Used at a general level for building sizing and area projections, and for determining criteria for interior planning at a detailed level. Particularly useful for facility programming with repetitive elements, eg offices, medical facilities, laboratories, etc. Output consists of 19 different reports

References

Availability
Purchase, bureau service

Language
ANSI, Fortran IV

Computer
DEC PDP-11, VAX, IBM. Most mini or mainframes

0554

Shopfront and Window Estimating *The Consultancy Consortium*
An integrated suite of programs for preparing shopfront and window estimates from standard raw material and labour-rate data. Comprises: Purchase Ledger, Stock Control, Shopfront and Window Estimating procedure. Produces elevation and plan drawings of the shopfront or window

References

Availability
Purchase

Language

Computer
Sirius 1, 128K

0555

Scribe *Datron Micro Centres*
Used for architectural planning. Permits the drawing of 3D models for producing perspectives, plans and a variety of projections. Incorporates 3D hidden line removal, text annotation and continuous rotational viewing of the model. Cost and thermal evaluation of the building is included, accounting for effects of structure type, climate, time of day and year, solar inclination and heating over up to a 10 node thermal network

References
Owned by Sheffield University, Mr C Green

Availability
Purchase

Language
Applesoft Basic (compiled)

Computer
Apple II or III, minimum 48K

0556

CASE *DHSS (Department of Health and Social Security)*
This is a computer aided, substructure evaluation program for use during the early planning stages of health buildings, when limited information is available. It is used for comparative costing, but incorporates an updating facility for the assessment of real cost

References

Availability
Purchase

Language
PET, M Basic

Computer
64K microcomputer

0557

CEDAR *DHSS (Department of Health and Social Security)*
The Building Modelling Program is an interactive, integrated computer system developed to assist in the design of buildings at the sketch plan stage by facilitating the analysis and comparison of alternative designs. Includes daylighting, heatloss and solar gain. The program gives hidden line perspectives

References

Availability
Purchase

Language
Fortran IV

Computer
SEL

0558

SITE MODELLING *DHSS (Department of Health and Social Security)*
Combination of two programs which test the positioning of a building on one or more possible sites, in terms of 'cut and fill' and general placements. Digitised input of contours and building shapes can be viewed in perspective and section. The file is designed to accept and handle outline building descriptions, site service runs and trenching. Graphic input and output require a digitising board and plotter

References

Availability
Purchase

Language
Fortran 77

Computer
SEL, Prime

0559

SOLPRO *Ecotech*
Part of the SCRIBE system. Provides projection of the design as 'seen' by the sun at particular latitudes, dates and times, or continuously over the whole day to study overshadowing and solar orientation

References
RIBA Journal, June 1982 Architects' Journal, June 23 and 30 1982

Availability
Purchase

Language
Compiled binary code

Computer
Apple II +

0560

CIBS *Hevacomp Limited*
Checks the design of a building for compliance within Part 2 of the CIBS Energy Code. A building is defined in terms of its walls, windows, floors, roof and roof light areas, U values and admittances. The following aspects are computed: heating energy consumption, heat gains, hot water service energy and lighting energy. Facilities are available to enable heat recovery type schemes to be examined. The program prints the site energy used and primary energy, together with the CIBS target figures

References

Availability
Purchase

Language

Computer
Any 64K microcomputer

0561

INFIL *Hevacomp Limited*
Computes the natural infiltration rates for a building, using wind pressure, building height, window construction, crack lengths and building internal layout. Infiltration rates for individual rooms are calculated, as well as the total building infiltration

References

Availability
Purchase

Language

Computer
Any 64K microcomputer

0562

PARTFF *Hevacomp Limited*
Checks a building for compliance with Part FF of the Building Regulations: it enables wall and roof constructions to be checked, together with glazing by windows and roof lights. Trade-off is allowed between walls and the roof. The program indicates acceptable solutions for non-compliant designs; it also enables sills, lintels and jambs to be considered

References

Availability
Purchase

Language

Computer
Any 64K microcomputer

0563

SPEED *Hevacomp*
This suite of programs examines the effect of building construction, room size, and orientation on the thermal and visual conditions. The program dealing with daylight evaluation is based on an approximation of the CIE Standard Overcast Sky. A simplified form of the BRE split flux method is used for the calculation of the reflected component, and the luminance of outside surfaces is assumed to be 20 per cent of that of the sky

References
DOC Evaluation Report No 3

Availability
See DOC Report No 3

Language
Fortran IV
Microsoft Basic
CP/M microcomputer

Computer

0564

3D View *Ibbotsons Design Software*
Perspective generator. Enables wireframe models to be constructed from interactive coordinate input routine, and viewed in perspective from any angle or distance. Useful as basis of finished design perspectives, or at any stage of the design process by any discipline

References

Availability
Purchase

Language
BBC Basic

Computer
BBC microcomputer, 32K RAM

0565

Digital Drawings *Ibbotsons Design Software*
Interactive, computer aided drawing production system for small-format drawings. For use by the building industry for all stages of the design process

References
RIBA journal, Building, CADCAM International, others: 1983

Availability
Purchase

Language
BBC Basic/Assembler

Computer
BBC microcomputer, 32K RAM

0566

MICRODESIGNER *KGB Micros Limited*
This program is used to produce architectural drawings. It is ideal for design work, especially where there is repeated use of standard symbols

References

Availability
Purchase

Language

Computer
8 or 16-bit microcomputer eg Superbrain, Sirius

0567

GABLE *Quest GENESYS Limited*
A CAD system for architects providing 2D and 3D drawings from the building model stage. The architect can transfer any plan, elevation or section, to provide a final working drawing. GABLE uses an overlay procedure to produce a highly complex final drawing which can include up to 20 drawings, overlayed in a single drawing. Final drawings contain plans, sections, elevations, site layouts and details on a single drawing. Scales may be changed as necessary

References

Availability

Language
Gentran

Computer

PLANTMAN *Quest GENESYS Limited*
A fully interactive CAD system for plant layout, design and detailing, based on 3D modelling techniques. Features include: interactive control; information storage and retrieval; 3D modelling with draughting facilities to produce fully dimensional drawings, views from any eyepoint, isometric drawings, schedules, bill of materials, etc. PLANTMAN contains a number of modules: archive, process, planning, 3D, production, pipe support, civil and structural, and operation and maintenance

References

Availability

Language
Gentran

Computer

HETOP-16 *Shade (Computer Services) Limited*
For the design of timber framed buildings. Determines details of loadings, truss positions, joist positions and wall placement from information supplied on an architect's plan drawing. The system designs wall panels to suit the specified loading conditions. Output includes full timber and sheathing material cutting lists, a summary of materials used, a log of the structural calculations and production tickets. Plan and frame drawings are plotted and output suitable for NC frame maker is generated

References

Availability
Purchase

Language
Extended Fortran IV

Computer
16-bit minicomputer
with 128K

ARCH:MODEL *University of Michigan*
A general purpose geometric modelling relational database system into which 3D geometry has been fully integrated. It supports building models and analyses sub-systems at all phases of design. Output includes: alphanumeric table-like reports of relations; drawings of spatial attributes in relations, optional in perspective, with hidden surface removal

References

Availability
On request from Harold J Borkin at
the University

Language
Fortran 66

Computer
Amdahl 470V/8

HLEIN *ABACUS Services*
Simplifies the definition of an object in a form intelligible to a program for perspective drawing. It provides a conversational means of data input and allows definition of a body and repetition of it as many times as required, shifting and scaling it in all directions and rotating it about a vertical axis. Up to eleven different bodies can be so defined

References
DOC

Availability

Language
Univac Fortran V

Computer
Univac 1106

EASYDRAF 2 *Admel Limited*
A computer aided draughting system designed for architectural work, developed to include mechanical, electrical, schematic draughting, and general drawing. It handles 2D draughting and parts listing, and can be used to assist design, draughting and for producing schedules. The program includes: zoom, interrogation, editing, translation, and scaling; automatic dimensioning; ability to interrogate and change drawings; symbol and parts list facilities

References

Availability
Purchase, complete turnkey system

Language
HP extended
Basic and Assembler

Computer
HP9845

STRESSPLOT *Amplix Services Limited*
Features include: Tektronix 4010 or compatible VDU graphics package; display of geometry defined in a STRESS data file; display may be scaled, rotated or windowed; display written to a named file for optional hardcopy plotter or printer

References

Availability
Purchase

Language
Commercial (SMB)
Cobol, Fortran

Computer
CP/M or MP/M
Microcomputer

APPLE PLOT *Apple Computer (UK) Limited*
Enables results to be plotted quickly and accurately. Multiple sets of data can be compared on the same report and displayed on the screen

References
Personal Computing with Apple

Availability
Purchase

Language

Computer
Apple II

Business Graphics III *Apple Computer (UK) Limited*
Allows the user to convert any numerical data into easily read, comprehensive charts and graphs. The program is highly interactive, and is based on a simple command language

References
Personal Computing with Apple

Availability
Purchase

Language

Computer
Apple III

Business Graphics II *Apple Computer (UK) Limited*
Allows the user to transform numerical data into a wide variety of easily understood charts and graphs

References
Personal Computing with Apple

Availability
Purchase

Language

Computer
Apple II

Series 4000 *Applicon Limited*
A multi-station design and draughting system for: VLSI, hybrid, PCB, diagramming, piping, layout, mechanical engineering and manufacturing, together with analysis and design verification software, NC output, output to phototypesetters for manuals

References

Availability
Purchase

Language

Computer
DEC VAX

0578

2-DG *ARC Limited*
This package is a 2D device independent graphics system providing 2D facilities only, serving a range of Tektronix devices and plotters. It includes several useful macro facilities; 2-DG is written in Fortran with a few calls to Macro Assembler routines for character output

References

Availability
Purchase

Language
Fortran

Computer
Prime, etc

0579

GDS (General Drafting System) *ARC Limited*
A computer based draughting package to help draughtsmen and designers produce drawings quickly and accurately. Used to draw: details, plans, sections, elevations, perspectives, isometrics, general arrangements, flow charts, schematics and artwork for slides, manuals and other printed matter. It will also generate schedules

References

Availability
Purchase, rental

Language
Fortran

Computer
Prime 250 MkII

0580

AUTOLIGHT *Autographics*
Calculates daylight factors and displays them on a wire line perspective view. Interactive operation with a flat bed plotter to generate data. Output consists of multicolour perspective views with light levels indicated by a warped grid. Related to AUTOPLAN, AUTOVIEW and AUTOSUN

References
'Low cost microprocessor based draughting system'. Coates, Frazer, Frazer, CAD 1982

Availability
Purchase

Language
6502 Code and Compiled Basic

Computer
Commodore 8032 32K

0581

AUTOPLAN *Autographics*
This is a 2D draughting package, suitable for details, plans or sections. Interactive operation, with a flat bed plotter to generate draughting data. Output consists of a Multipen/Linetype plot on A3, or larger if required. Related to AUTOVIEW, AUTOSUN and AUTOLIGHT

References
'Low cost microprocessor based draughting system'. Coates, Frazer, Frazer, CAD 1982

Availability
Purchase

Language
6502 Code and Compiled Basic

Computer
Commodore 8032 32K

0582

AUTOSUN *Autographics*
Draws sunlight patches on perspective projections. Used for design analysis and evaluation. Interactive operation with a flat bed plotter to generate data. Output consists of a multicolour plot with sunpatches drawn on walls and floor. Related to AUTOPLAN, AUTOVIEW and AUTOLIGHT

References
'Low cost microprocessor based draughting system'. Coates, Frazer, Frazer, CAD 1982

Availability
Purchase

Language
6502 Code and Compiled Basic

Computer
Commodore 8032 32K

0583

AUTOVIEW *Autographics*
A perspective package for use both at the sketch design stage, and for presentation. Interactive operation with flat bed plotter to generate data. Output consists of a Multipen/Linetype plot on A3, or larger if required. Related to AUTOPLAN, AUTOSUN and AUTOLIGHT

References
'Low cost microprocessor based draughting system'. Coates, Frazer, Frazer, CAD 1982

Availability
Purchase

Language
6502 Code and Compiled Basic

Computer
Commodore 8032 32K

0584

ACROPOLIS *BDP Computing Services Limited*
This is a 3D, graphic modelling and draughting system which consists of components which are called into a project model. This may be viewed from any position, and drawings may be dimensioned and annotated before being output into a pen plotter. Used by architects, engineers and quantity surveyors from sketch design through to production drawing

References

Availability
Purchase, rent, bureau service

Language
Fortran

Computer
HP3000 with 1/2 mb memory. 50Mb disk

0585

IGS60 *British Olivetti Limited*
A 2D, interactive, computer aided design and draughting system with user defined symbols. Graphic description consists of reference to basic elements such as lines, circles, characters. Dimensions of graphic items may include expressions and variables. The system is suitable for architecture, building services design, factory planning, kitchen design, electrical design, flow charting and mechanical engineering

References

Availability
Purchase

Language
Basic

Computer
P6066

0586

GTD *British Olivetti Limited*
A general purpose, 2D draughting system. Up to 6 different line styles may be defined, and the line style of any element, or the plotter pen which will draw elements, may be changed at any time. User may query features of any element or relationship between elements. Numeric data from query routines or keyboard, may be assigned to user variables. Numeric input may include complex mathematical expressions. Parameters include text size, angle and justification, leader line lengths, fillet radii values, and pen selections

References

Availability
Purchase

Language
Basic

Computer
Olivetti M30, M40

0587

Architectural Design Package *CalComp Limited*
ADP provides the architect with a sophisticated set of general purpose design/draughting tools. Extensive geometric construction aids enable rapid and accurate drawing creation, together with comprehensive editing facilities. ADP offers text handling, automatic dimensioning, handling of non-graphics attributes and drawing interrogation for length, area, distances and angles

References

Availability
From CalComp

Language
Fortran

Computer
Any

Architectural Production Package *CalComp Limited*
Based on the CI/Sfb system. Starting with building grid creation, the package handles drawings from the initial design stage through to detailed drawing, without the need for redraws. APP provides complex graphics creation and editing based on component coding. There is an automatic system of levels to facilitate trade orientated drawings and a system for material take-off

References

Availability
From CalComp

Language
Fortran

Computer
Any

Architectural Visualisation Package *CalComp Limited*
APV enables the architect to present the client with conceptual plans and design alternatives in a fast and simple manner, based on standard plans and elevations. The view point, focal point and horizon lines are selected interactively. In addition to perspectives, cabinet and isometric projections are available

References

Availability
From CalComp

Language
Fortran

Computer
Any

IGS *CalComp Limited*
This interactive graphics system offers architectural and engineering firms an efficient tool for design and draughting. Handles: small scale and detailed floor plans; equipment locations and office layout; foundation, framing and roofing plans; schematics, one lines and diagrams; reflected ceiling plans; interference checks; standard details and drawings. Libraries of standard symbols used in the building trade; graphic elements; copy and repeat; geometrical constructions; material shading; curves; bills of materials

References

Availability
From CalComp

Language
Fortran

Computer
Any

CASC-AID TO DRAFTING *Civil and Structural Computing (Northern) Limited*
A suite of programs handling batch and interactive production of engineering and architectural drawings. Developed in close collaboration with engineers and draughtsmen, to meet their requirements. Graphic features include: various line and arc types; blend radii; polygon statement - numerous features such as hatching and hidden line removal; dimensions and labelling

References
Bradshaw, Buckton and Tonge

Availability
Bureau service, time sharing, in-house

Language

Computer

PLTON 6 *Computational Mechanics Consultants Limited*
For plotting graphs on line printers and non-graphic terminals. Allows up to 4 different graphs to be plotted on a single lineprinter page, complete with user specified headers and labelled axis; either axis may have a linear or a logarithmic scale. Ideal for quick graphical output and for plotting experimental data

References

Availability
Licence

Language
Fortran

Computer
Microcomputer with minimum 16-bits

Draft Plot *Computer Design*
Part of the COSPACK package. Provides isometric drawings of 2D and 3D structural assemblies. Options include various perspective projections

References
Sirius Computing. January 1983

Availability
Purchase, lease

Language
Basic

Computer
ACT Sirius 1 256K. Plotter

ICEM *Control Data Limited*
For integrated computer aided engineering and manufacturing. This is a 3D design, draughting and geometric modelling system which uses a robust data management system

References

Availability
Bureau service

Language

Computer
Cyber 170

Design engineering bar chart system *COSMIC*
Developed to provide a graphics display capability. Produces bar charts which produce graphic displays of fixed or variable formats, character displays of fixed formats, and bar displays. Used as a visual aid for schedule development and monitoring. Bar charts can be scaled in years, quarters, or months with variable calender scale from one to twelve months or one to six months

References
NASA Kennedy Space Center

Availability

Language
Cobol

Computer
GE 635 series

MEDUSA *Cranfield Product Engineering Centre*
A leading turnkey draughting system used in the UK, USA and Europe. Features include: full range of electrical and mechanical draughting facilities; extraction of data from drawings for parts lists, etc; generation of accurate perspective views for technical illustration, etc

References

Availability
Lease, hire

Language

Computer
Prime with 1Mb memory, 64Mb disk CalComp plotter

BUILD-AID *Data Resource*
This is a draughting system for drawing production information. It is used in conjunction with a graphic tablet, a printer and a plotter. Used for simple line drawings up to assembly details, location plans, elevations and section, and complex architectural renderings. Includes an elements and symbols library. Portions of drawings may be manipulated as in scale models. Output includes compilation of schedules, area and volume computations, and 3D graphics

References

Availability
Purchase

Language
Basic

Computer
Tektronix 4054

0598

PEAC *Decision Graphics UK Limited*

A CADD system for use in architectural interior planning, engineering and construction fields. The unified database gives complete compatibility between 2D and 3D data and between metric and Imperial units. Hard copy options are a quick snapshot print (280mm square) of the current display, or a precision ink plot by the host system. 3D data can be viewed in plan, elevations, isometric and true perspective. Features include schematic design, detail draughting, drawing overlays and standard symbols

References

Availability
Purchase

Language

Computer
DEC PDP11/24
256K byte, DEC
11/44, DEC VAX

0599

GINTRAN *Design Computing Limited*

A graphics system for architects, engineers and builders. Consists of a series of interactive, on-line modules used to produce a 3D model of a design proposal. This model can be displayed, manipulated, edited and projected in various ways. Drawing projections (plans, elevations, sections, perspectives and trimetics) are produced. Includes material take-off, scheduling and costing

References
Various in CAD

Availability
Purchase

Language
Fortran IV, V, 77

Computer
Various, Min 64K
bits.
Min disc 2 1/2 Mb

0600

SHAPER *DHSS (Department of Health and Social Security)*

Enables complex engineering assemblies to be created from elementary shapes. The program enables a user to create unique components or assemblies for use with a SCAMP program. The complete range of engineering services can then be modelled, and drawings produced for any particular project

References

Availability
Purchase

Language
Fortran

Computer
SEL, Prime

0601

HIPERS *Ecotech*

Part of the SCRIBE system. This program covers vertical perspective of plans with partial hidden line removed

References
RIBA Journal, June 1982 Architects'
Journal, June 23 and 30 1982

Availability
Purchase

Language
Compiled binary
code

Computer
Apple II +

0602

HITEX *Ecotech*

Part of the SCRIBE system. Produces: high resolution annotation of graphics page, typing in text starting at the cursor position, simple drawing and erasing lines, storage of page to diskette

References
RIBA Journal, June 1982 Architects'
Journal, June 23 and 30 1982

Availability
Purchase

Language
Compiled binary
code

Computer
Apple II +

0603

PLOTLINK *Ecotech*

Part of the SCRIBE system. Used to produce output of projections to a high resolution plotter. The module is dependent on the plotter used

References
RIBA Journal, June 1982 Architects'
Journal, June 23 and 30 1982

Availability
Purchase

Language
Compiled binary
code

Computer
Apple II +

0604

ROTAB *Ecotech*

Part of the SCRIBE system. For fast generation and continuous rotation of line perspectives and projections

References
RIBA Journal, June 1982 Architects'
Journal, June 23 and 30 1982

Availability
Purchase

Language
Compiled binary
code

Computer
Apple II +

0605

SKETCHTAB *Ecotech*

Part of the SCRIBE system. Functions include: drawing input, transformations, 3D projections, coding, erase, alterations load, and save data model to diskette (versions for input from Apple Graphic Tablet, joystick/paddles, keyboard)

References
RIBA Journal, June 1982 Architects'
Journal, June 23 and 30 1982

Availability
Purchase

Language
Compiled binary
code

Computer
Apple II +

0606

SOLDAT/D and SOLDAT/S *Ecotech*

Part of the SCRIBE system. Used for the generation of direct, diffuse and reflected radiation on surfaces of any slope or orientation for average or clear days. Results are tabulated and presented graphically with a facility for comparisons

References
RIBA Journal, June 1982 Architects'
Journal, June 23 and 30 1982

Availability
Purchase

Language
Compiled binary
code

Computer
Apple II +

0607

TRANSTAB *Ecotech*

Part of tne SCRIBE system. Used for transformations of data model in: inversion, reflection, recoding, rescaling and base level changes

References
RIBA Journal, June 1982 Architects'
Journal, June 23 and 30 1982

Availability
Purchase

Language
Compiled binary
code

Computer
Apple II +

CAD 100 *Engineering Computer Services Limited*
A 2D draughting system which can be directly linked to an NC tape preparation system

References

Availability
Purchase

Language

Computer
HP9845 20Mb
A1 plotter, tablet

GRAFT *Facet Limited*
This program is used to plot graphs of user-defined data to any format and scale.
Individual lines and axes may be labelled if required

References

Availability
Bureau service, or under licence

Language

Computer
Prime, Norsk Data,
Harris,
CP/M 8-bit micros

SUNPATH *Facet Limited*
This program is used to generate a sunpath diagram on the plotter for any given building latitude

References

Availability
Bureau service, or under licence

Language

Computer
Prime, Norsk Data,
Harris,
CP/M 8-bit micros

CAM-X *Ferranti Cetec Graphics Limited*
An integrated Computer Aided Engineering system offering solid 3D geometric modelling at the design stage, and engineering records management; these functions, linked with those of CAD and CAM, form the CAE system. Basically designed for the mechanical engineering industry, but also used in the construction industry for such functions as the manufacture of heating and ventilating equipment, ducting, lift and escalator products. Also used to establish how equipment should be installed in buildings. Output on printer and plotter

References

Availability
Purchase

Language

Computer
DEC-VAX

AUTOPROD *Autoprod Computer Graphics (Marketed by GMW Computers Limited)*
A modelling program handling: Imperial, metric, etc; scaling, shifting, rotating, reflecting, shearing; line types as solid, broken, construction or special; hidden lines and automatic generation of interpenetration lines on complex surfaces. Offers 20 projections, stereoscopic presentation, five picture generation options, including animation sequence generation, cartesian or polar coordinates and section of object by up to 3 mutually independent planes. Interface available to RUCAPS

References

Availability
Purchase. Bureau service - Scicon
Computer Services

Language
Fortran

Computer
Most mainframes
and minicomputers

RUCAPS *GMW Computers Limited*
Assists architects and engineers to evolve a full size 3D model of a building from sketch design to production stage. Each element or detail need be entered only once, and any number of different plans, sections, elevations, perspectives (hidden lines suppressed, dotted or in full), schedules or detail drawing can be produced to any scale with total coordination and consistency. Output includes drawings, plans, elevations, sections, 3D projections, and schedules of quantities

References
Available from GMW

Availability
Purchase, turnkey system

Language
Fortran

Computer
DEC-PDP11/24 with
256Kb. Prime.
Rucaps workstation.

DATAPLOT *Grafox Limited*
A business graphics system for analysing time series and other data in colour. User defined graphical files can be set up, and lines, bars, dots, histograms and pie charts can be displayed. All screen images can be sent to the plotter for hard copy. Used by accountants, managers and project evaluators. Data is entered using the VDU or via the SUPERCALC spread sheet package. Data may be received from remote source and updated into the DATAPLOT database

References

Availability
Purchase

Language
Fortran 66

Computer
Micro with CP/M or
MP/M system

GRAPHNET *Graphic Horizons, Inc*
A fully interactive graphics system for draughting, simulation, layout and data management. Features include: creation of drawings from tablet; scaling and windowing; storage and retrieval of graphics; draftpad; layered drawing techniques; 3D simulation; space programming and outfitting; layout optimisation to provide an evaluation framework

References

Availability
Purchase with hardware

Language

Computer
Graphic Horizons

Ergos 240 *Harper and Tunstall Limited*
A 2D distributed system producing scaled and/or symbolic drawings for architects, engineers and other disciplines

References
Developed by Omnitech Graphics
Systems Inc, Canada

Availability
Purchase

Language

Computer
CA Naked Mini
Benson 1302 pen
plotter

STARPLOT *Hydro Systems (USA)*
A set of three plotting programs. Survey plotting: utilising previously generated coordinates to plot points. Stadia plotting: generates & plots points, point numbers, elevations and descriptions, from data entered from the field book. Vertical alignment and profile plotting: allows the user to begin at any station to generate tangent grade and vertical curve data as a continuous operation to any other station

References

Availability
Purchase

Language

Computer
Apple, IBM, TRS-80
with CP/M

0618

Innovator *Intergraph (Great Britain) Limited*
A 2D/3D interactive graphics design system with powerful database management for utility mapping, electrical and mechanical design and draughting, with interfaces to NC, FEM and third party software

References

Availability
Purchase

Language

Computer
DEC PDP11/23 with 1Mb memory, 84Mb disk. Plotter

0619

VAX Interactive Graphics Design System *Intergraph (Great Britain) Limited*
A multi-user, multi-discipline computer graphics system (wire frame, complex surface generation and solids) for land use and resources management, cartography, architectural design, mechanical design and manufacturing, plant design, and petroleum industry processing. Capability to run third party software for structural analysis and NC

References

Availability
Purchase

Language

Computer
DEC VAX11/750 with 1Mb memory, 84Mb disk

0620

CADBIRD *International Research and Development Company Limited*
A 2D draughting system capable of producing drawings to BS 308. Includes symbol definition, 6 line types, fillets, mirroring, zoom, auto-dimensioning, and parts list

References

Availability
Purchase

Language

Computer
Tektronix 4054
A3 plotter

0621

Graphmagic *International Software Marketing*
For graphics representation of numeric data. Reads VisiCalc and Mathemagic files; may be used as a standalone product. Features: stores up to 40 variables in one set; user defined parameters for output; hard copy support for graphs and variable sets; editing function; graph titles, x and y axis labels, statistics, grid displays easily added to graphs; colour or monochrome; hard disk facilities; overlay graphs for representation of linear regression, break even analysis, data comparison, etc

References

Availability
Purchase

Language

Computer
Apple II, IBM PC
Future: CP/M 2.2,
NEC PC

0622

CUECHART *ISSCO UK Limited*
Used in connection with TELL-A-GRAF, and consists of a library of graphs. The standard library supplied can be customised, added to or modified. CUECHART graphs are pre-designed using TELL-A-GRAF software. CUECHART stencils form the basis of the library; the stencils are high quality TELL-A-GRAPH charts with questions embedded into them which, when answered, will complete the chart. Once the stencils are designed, users can produce high quality graphics

References

Availability
Purchase

Language

Computer

0623

DISSPLA *ISSCO UK Limited*
A data presentation graphics program producing high quality bar, line and pie charts, tables and text, maps, 3D charts, contour plots, etc. Features include: graph set-up routines structured for calendar axes, as well as linear, logarithmic, semi-log, polar, etc; bars, pie charts and curves scaled to fit axes boundaries; 13 alphabets in 8 styles; blanked-out areas; automatic grid drawing; formula writing feature; legend and text block control; flexible shading features; 3D curve production; special effects/symbols

References

Availability

Language

Computer

0624

TELLAGRAF *ISSCO UK Limited*
A computer graphics system which produces quality graphs for immediate publication or presentation. Output is on a variety of media, including paper, overhead transparencies, 35mm slides or VDU. Generates various graph types, eg line, bar, pie, as well as text pages. The system has built-in designs for producing standard graphs, and numerous enhancement options for generating intricately tailored charts

References

Availability
Purchase

Language

Computer
Various computers and plotting devices

0625

CAD/GRAPHICS *Itech Information Technology Services*
A keyboard, menu or tablet driven graphics package for CAD applications, comprising a wide range of scaling, graphics and library facilities. The system can be configured to operate via RS232 or 1EEE input/output ports

References

Availability

Language

Computer
Olivetti M20

0626

1130 Flow charting *A M Kinney, Inc*
The program accepts IBM 1130 Fortran source statements as input to draw a flow chart of the program on the 1132 or 1403 printer. In addition to drawing a unique block for each type of executable statement, the program will list all non-executable statements. The program has provision for page headings and will print page, card, and statement numbers. IBM 026 and 029 key-punched source cards are accepted

References

Availability

Language
Fortran

Computer
IBM 1130 and 370

0627

DIAD *Lucas Logic Limited*
A computer aided draughting system. Features include: construction of drawings with up to 30 layers on each drawing sheet; drawing elements (profiles, symbols, etc); matching and dimensioning are semi-automatic. The program handles: design of components; 2D drawings; calculation of sectional properties; detail drawings with metric or Imperial dimensions; modification and storage of drawings, with security from unauthorised personnel

References
Computer Management, December 1981

Availability
Purchase, lease

Language

Computer

LUNDYDRAW *Lundy-Farrington Limited*
A front end, computer aided draughting system. Input is by tablet or terminal. Output is by electrostatic printer-plotter or pen plotter

References

Availability
Purchase

Language

Computer

Unigraphics (ADS-100) *McAuto (UK) Limited*
A 3D CAD/CAM system which is capable of supporting multiple terminals

References

Availability
Purchase, bureau service

Language

Computer
Data General S140.
Plotter

AIDS *McGrane Computer Systems Limited*
'Advanced Interactive Draughting System'. This is a general purpose computer aided draughting system, which enables the user to input, edit and plot drawings with greater ease and accuracy than with manual methods. Suitable for use during all stages of building design. Input is via a digitising tablet or terminal. Drawings are output on a plotter. Reports listing current jobs and drawings may be produced on request

References

Availability
Purchase

Language
Data General
Extended Basic

Computer
Data General Micro
Nova with 64K

MLD *Mountford and Laxon Company Limited*
A 2 1/2D draughting and design system for architects and mechanical engineers. Includes parametrised draughting, and user defined constructions

References

Availability
Purchase

Language

Computer
Minicomputer
Plotter

Electronic measurement *Norden Technical Computer Systems Limited*
Used by quantity surveyors and architects for the preparation of Bills and Estimates, the system links the digitiser board to the microcomputer. Drawings are placed on the digitiser and the light pen used to indicate areas, lengths, etc. Data is transmitted from the board to the computer which calculates areas and prints the results. Every type of measurement can be undertaken, from simple rectangles to the most complex site area. Output is provided graphically or printed

References
Recommended by Cyril Sweett &
Partners
Building 8.10.82

Availability
Purchase

Language
Microsoft Basic

Computer
North Star Advantage
Microcomputer

DRAFTY *Norrie Hill Limited*
A low cost, 2D interactive drawing package, suitable for architects and engineers. Drawing features include: 6 line types; arcs; text; hatching, which may be applied to any closed polygon, to a complexity of 200 sides; 200 built-in library symbols for architectural, mechanical, electrical and schematic components; up to 200 other user defined segments; automatic dimensioning facility; editing features including locate, block definition and repeats

References

Availability
Purchase

Language

Computer
Hewlett-Packard 86A
with 192Kb
Plotter

SORCE *Norrie Hill Limited*
A 2D, interactive draughting system, producing drawings of any size up to 20 metres by 20 metres, accurate to within 0.33mm. Can hatch any irregular shape, and coordinate input via a digitising tablet. Also has an automatic dimensioning facility. Up to 90 plotting symbols in addition to user defined symbols. The program is suitable for electrical diagrams, architectural, mapping and road layout drawings, engineering manufacturing drawings, process flow and logic diagrams, plot plans, flow charts and graphical presentations

References

Availability
Purchase

Language

Computer
HP 9845

AUTOPROD *North-East London Polytechnic*
Provides an instrument for the 3D presentation of objects, showing perspective or axonometric views on to any defined plane. Obscured lines are shown dotted or are omitted. Sections can also be drawn. The results are drawn on a storage tube or plotter

References
DOC Evaluation Report No 1

Availability

Language
Fortran

Computer
Univac 1108 and
others

CADRAW *Oasys Limited*
An advanced computer graphics system for the production of high quality working drawings. Drawing components can be initiated at the concept stage of the design. Output is in data form or as direct representation. Plots can be of any size, up to the limits of the plotter

References

Availability
Purchase

Language
Pascal

Computer
ICL Perg
(Microcomputer)

BOXER *Pafec Limited*
Extends the capabilities of DOGS by producing a complete 3D computer aided engineering and design system. The full solid modeller enables the user to construct accurate 3D structures that are informationally complete. Provides the user with a complete system for visualisation, manufacture, design, mass calculation and robotics. The system aims to solve any problem concerned with volume, mass and 3D shape. Together with DOGS, it produces arbitrary views for labelling and dimensioning

References

Availability
Purchase

Language
Fortran IV

Computer

0638

DOGS *Pafec Limited*
A computer aided draughting package. Design features cover 10 pages of the menu, each page dealing with related functions. Following comprehensive draughting capabilities, there is a complete computer aided engineering and design system featuring: properties, non-graphical database and automatic parts listing; 3D abilities; wire framing system for piping and cabling, numerical control system; user defined symbols and commands

References

Availability
Purchase

Language
Fortran IV

Computer
Apollo Domain, 32-bit. Benson 1302 drum plotter

0639

ELEPHANTS *Pafec Limited*
A multi-level substructure package; fully integrated with PAFEC 75. Once a substructure has been described in data it may be reflected, rotated, translated and repeated to form other substructures. Provides an efficient solution when only partial symmetry exists in a structure. The system is particularly useful when a large analysis shows that a minor design change is needed; the user then changes only that substructure, and re-runs just part of the job

References

Availability
Purchase

Language
Fortran IV

Computer

0640

FERRET *Pafec Limited*
Performs a large variety of operations on structural mass and stiffness matrices. Mainly for dynamic analysis but can perform many functions useful in static work. Interfaces with PAFEC 75 finite element system. A primary function is that of substructuring. The use of FERRET for producing matrices and finding frequencies of the assembly removes the need for further costly finite element solutions

References

Availability
Purchase

Language
Fortran IV

Computer

0641

FINITE ELEMENT THERMAL ANALYSIS *Pafec Limited*
A finite element program for calculation of thermal behaviour of complex structures. Useful to designers of engines, pressure vessels, nuclear plants, boiler plants, and heat exchangers. Features include: steady state and transient temperature distributions; thermal stresses; specification of temperatures or heat fluxes at points; material property dependence upon temperature; output in form of contours and graphs; mesh generation aids; boundary layer elements for structure/fluid interaction

References

Availability
Purchase

Language
Fortran IV

Computer

0642

LUBRICATION ANALYSIS *Pafec Limited*
Used in conjunction with PAFEC 75 to enhance the lubrication analysis; extensive capabilities for structural analysis. Features: steady state pressure distribution; specification of pressure at points or along boundaries; specification of viscocities and temperature values; graphical output of pressure contours and displaced shape of bearing; calculation of load carrying capacity; mesh generation aid (PAFBLOCKS)

References

Availability
Purchase

Language
Fortran IV

Computer

0643

PAFEC *Pafec Limited*
A general purpose, 3D finite element system for solving problems in linear and non-linear statics, dynamics and heat transfer. Interactive graphics, using the PIGS system, provides the ideal method of preparing data. Enables the user to generate finite element meshes from scratch on a graphics terminal. Printed output includes sample tables, summaries and histograms. The system handles passive graphics, interactive post-processing, thermal problems,non-linear capabilities and dynamic analysis

References

Availability
Purchase

Language
Fortran IV

Computer
Prime, IBM, DEC Honeywell, ICL, Burroughs, CDC, etc.

0644

PIGS *Pafec Limited*
An interactive graphics pre- and post-processor designed specifically for use with the PAFEC infinite element system. Enables the user to construct, modify and analyse finite element models as they appear on the screen. Features include: digitised input, interactive modelling, mesh modification options, analysis of results from static, dynamic and thermal analyses. Various other features are available

References

Availability
Purchase

Language
Fortran IV

Computer

0645

CADAM distributed system *Perkin-Elmer Data Systems Limited*
A 2 1/2D multi-terminal workstation providing CAD/CAM, NC, 3D surface, 3D mesh, FEM and bills of materials

References
Developed by CADAM Inc, USA (Lockeed Corp)

Availability
Purchase

Language

Computer
Perkin-Elmer 32-bit Supermini, 80Mb disk Plotter

0646

PFS Graph *Personal Computers Limited*
Allows any numeric and/or VisiCalc data to be displayed as bar charts, line graphs or pie charts. The program is quick and simple to use

References
Personal Computing with Apple

Availability

Language

Computer
Apple III

0647

GRID *Ponder Associates BV*
A 2D, interactive draughting package for architects, engineers and cartographers. Functions include; erase, copy, zoom, pan, store, load, fill, new symbol, parameter, clear and help. Basic draughting routines are: polylines, circles, arcs, rectangles and symbols

References
Developed by Graphics Research

Availability
Purchase

Language
Basic, Fortran, Pascal

Computer
CP/M, CP/M86, MSDOS, RSX11

Quadrant *Quest CAE*
A 2D mechanical draughting system which draws up to BS 308 standard; it has an extensive text annotation suite for automatic dimensioning and symbol annotation, and has constructive geometry functions

References

Availability
Purchase

Language

Computer
Microcomputer with 18Mb Winchester disk. Plotter

GINO *Quest GENESYS Limited*
A library of drawing and administrative routines capable of handling graphic output on most computers for a large range of graphic devices. Tasks range from simple 2D drawing to complex 3D interactive systems. GINO-F is a library of sub-routines which perform the functions of character generation, curve and line drawing, drawing control and device control

References

Availability

Language
Gentran

Computer

SSCOGO-PLOT *Quest GENESYS Limited*
Both calculation and plotting facilities are included within this program. The calculation options are not as extensive as those within SSCOGO, but plotting facilities include scaling, orientation and shading of enclosed areas. Defined lines may also be chain-dotted and dimensioned

References

Availability

Language
Gentran

Computer

SSCOGO *Quest GENESYS Limited*
This coordinate geometry program uses problem orientated commands. Use of the program is interactive and the user selects options from the COGO vocabulary to locate a series of points on a traverse, sub-division, or on some alignment. The point data generated can be used for immediate calculation, or stored for later use. There are facilities to build up alignments from bearings, arcs and spirals, calculate intersection points and enclosed areas

References

Availability

Language
Gentran

Computer

DUCT *Robinson Ford Associates*
Provides design aids for 3D complex surface design; creates objects as a series of surface building blocks of ducts that are blended together. The user inputs data defining the individual ducts, together with blending ducts that dictate the shape of the blends. Information is provided for: surface area and volume of a component or part of one; split line definition for pattern making; finite element mesh generation

References
Developed by industry, Government and the Depart of Mech Eng at Cambridge University

Availability
Purchase

Language
Fortran

Computer
Data General

BIT STIK *Robocom Limited*
An interactive graphics system for designers, draughtsmen, architects and engineers. Provides accurate drawing from the origination of graphic material and text through to multi-colour plotted hard copy. Input of drawn information is through the 3 axis controller. After editing and proofing, the finished artwork is plotted out on paper. Incorporates a powerful zoom facility enabling the user to enter fine detail and text specifications at a high level of resolution

References
Recommended by Apple

Availability
Purchase

Language

Computer
Apple II Europlus with 48K

THE PERSPECTIVE PROGRAM *David Ruffle Associates*
Allows the designer to rapidly build a 3D wire-frame model of a building and view it from any angle with full control of all viewing parameters. Any view can be printed to any size by a dot-matrix printer

References
'Architects' Apples', CADCAM International; Magazine, October 1982

Availability
Purchase

Language
UCSD Pascal

Computer
Apple II, 64K
Graphics tablet

GIPSYS *Scott Wilson Kirkpatrick and Partners*
A computer aided draughting system for rapid production of high quality drawings. The suite of programs comprises general draughting routines with special packages for reinforcement detailing, structural steelwork plans and airport planning. GIPSYS has also been integrated with design programs for road design and transportation planning. Output includes plotted drawings and material schedules. The system has particular relevance to the construction industry

References

Availability
Purchase, lease

Language
Fortran

Computer
Digital VAX/VMS
Digitizing tablet
Plotter

ROMULUS 2 *Shape Data Limited*
A solid geometric modeller system for the creative designer, and for dealing with 3D problems in design or analysis. Provides an interactive graphical interface and produces a solid model of the building, etc. Libraries of standard parts can be accessed. Hidden line and colour shaded drawings can be produced automatically from any angle. Ductwork, pipework, steel frames and all building materials can be represented

References

Availability
Purchase

Language
Fortran 66

Computer
DEC VAX, Prime, Apollo, Norsk, IBM

SUPERPLOT *I P Sharp Associates Limited*
A plotting package producing graphs to user specifications. Output includes bar chart, split graph, multi-colour lines and shading. Features: state of the art presentation of numeric data; device independent (flatbed plotters, graphics screens, hardcopy terminals); colour plots; plots on transparencies for overhead presentations; linked with MAGIC, providing access to public and private databases; plot storage facility for later playback or remote plotting

References

Availability
Time sharing

Language

Computer

Computer programs for the building industry

0658

High level and general graphics systems *SIA Computer Services*
A series of eight programs which include facilities such as: general high level graphics
sub-routine libraries; 2D computer assisted draughting package; various programs for
users of Tektronix, APL and Hewlett Packard plotters; line and box drawing aid package

References

Availability
Bureau service

Language
High level

Computer
Control Data,
IBM, Prime

0659

KEY-GRAPHICS *SIA Computer Services*
This is a 2D, computer assisted, general purpose draughting package

References

Availability
Bureau service

Language
High level

Computer
Control Data,
IBM, Prime

0660

Low level graphics device libraries *SIA Computer Services*
A series of eight programs dealing with: basic plotting sub-routines for CalComp, Benson,
CIL, for Tektronix and Hewlett Packard plotters, and for Diablo and Anderson Jacobson
daisywheel terminals

References

Availability
Bureau service

Language
High level

Computer
Control Data,
IBM, Prime

0661

SUMMADRAFT *Summagraphics Limited*
An advanced, low cost, computer aided design/draughting (CAD) system, having graphic
and alphanumeric CRT's and digitisers. Features include: geometric constructions,
definition and calculation; file management; display commands; graphics operations, such
as cross-hatching, dimensioning and symboling; grouping; editing; construction aids. The
system can be expanded up to a dual user version

References

Availability
Purchase, turnkey system

Language

Computer
64K bytes RAM, or
128K bytes RAM
for dual user version

0662

DESIGN SYSTEM ALPHA *System Simulation Limited*
A graphics editing system for architects, engineers and designers, comprising a
coordinated set of drawing and drawing management functions. Uses a combination of
basic elements such as lines, arcs, text, markers and library symbols. These components
can be saved, redrawn, rotated or modified as required, and the whole can be edited.
Drawings can be named for storage and retrieval, access to them can be limited by using a
password system

References

Availability
Licence

Language
C, under UNIX (TM)
operating system

Computer
DEC LSI 11/23

0663

G-LASS *System Simulation Limited*
Assists with the creation, storage, modification and draughting of architectural drawings

References

Availability
Purchase

Language
Basic (Tektronix)

Computer
Tektronix 4054 and
Filemanager,
PDP 11/23

0664

Interactive graphics library *Tektronix UK Limited*
Used in the operation of Tektronix graphics equipment. It enables a programmer to
produce elementary computer graphics immediately, and also to develop sophisticated
interactive systems. It is also a suitable basis for applications programs and includes
advanced features for graphics text, panel fill, line smoothing and 3D support

References

Availability
Contact owner. Also available in USA,
Holland, Japan, Australia, Canada

Language
Fortran IV

Computer
Available for most
32-bit or virtual
memory computers

0665

DRAFTING - 4054 D08 2-D *Tektronix UK Limited*
This program is for any 2D draughting application. Data is entered interactively when the
drawing is constructed. Output is in the form of a drawing

References

Availability
Purchase or rental

Language
Basic

Computer
4054 desktop
with 64K

0666

GINO-F *United Information Services Limited*
A library of routines for plotting. Suitable for commercial, architectural and engineering
applications, and capable of driving most types of graphic device, including Tektronix
screens, flatbed and drum plotters, and various time sharing plotters

References

Availability
Bureau service, time sharing

Language
Fortran

Computer
Honeywell, Sigma 9

0667

STAG drawing system *University of Edinburgh*
For use by architects and others, for constructing 2D line drawings; it offers a good
upgrade path for expanding computing operations in an office. STAG includes line styles,
curves, symbol repetition, handling, rotation, stretching and scaling, drawing windowing
and nesting, optional grids and anchor points, and text fonts. Users control all drawing
operations via a VDU, with minimum typing

References
Dumb Drawing Systems and
Knowledge Engineering, conference,
CAD82, Brighton 1982. Others

Availability
Purchase (Contact: Mr Aart Bijl)

Language
UNIX

Computer
Microcomputer, eg
DEC, Xylogics, with
256Kb

Computer programs for the building industry

ARCH:SKETCH *University of Michigan*
Used to sketch architectural plans in preparation for computerised analysis programs, and draughting quality plots. Incorporates fixed data including: wall material names, door, window, furniture and equipment names and associated graphic symbols. Output consists of draughting quality plots and summary tables

References

Availability
On request from Harold J Borkin at the University

Language
Fortran 66

Computer
Various machines approx 1 megabyte

3DHIST *ARC Limited*
Produces 3D histograms and surfaces which are defined as 2D matrices. Data will be accepted as a matrix or as values at random points. Continuous or angular surface representations may be produced

References

Availability
Purchase

Language
Fortran

Computer
Prime
VAX

CIIS (Contouring, Interpolation and Integration of Surfaces) *ARC Limited*
CIIS is a fully transportable program for taking 2D and 3D data, and constructing and manipulating surfaces from it. In the case of 2D point data, the surface is derived from attribute values relating to each point. CIIS offers user controlled contouring, depth of detail, perspective views with selection of viewing point and scale, and volume calculations. Output is either to a graphics terminal or a digital plotter

References

Availability
Purchase

Language
Fortran

Computer
Prime
VAX

NETMAP *ARC Limited*
For manipulation, analysis and mapping of network based data. A basic data file is created, which may be manipulated, checked or restructured. Shortest routes or critical paths through the network can be isolated. Maps of selected parts of the network can be output

References

Availability
Purchase

Language
Fortran

Computer
Prime
VAX

OVERLAY *ARC Limited*
This system allows the user to overlay a square grid on a map of polygonal areas. This is created using POLYMAP. The scale of the grid is defined by the user

References

Availability
Purchase

Language
Fortran

Computer
Prime
VAX

POINTMAP *ARC Limited*
POINTMAP is a library of routines orientated towards spatial search of point located information, particularly appropriate in local authority and planning tasks. They provide for setting up to the point located information and for spatial search on a circular linear path or polygonal basis, identifying these points within the search pattern. Supplied with ARC's 2-DG software or with manufacturer's device dependent drivers

References

Availability
Purchase

Language
Fortran

Computer
Prime
VAX

POLYMAP *ARC Limited*
POLYMAP is a library of subroutines for the transformation of parcel information plotting boundaries, plotting data in polygons in alphanumeric or symbolic form and shaded or dotted line maps. POLYMAP is also associated with GINO as GINOZONE but can be run independently via ARC's graphics package 2-DG, or simply using manufacturer supplied software for storage tubes or plotters

References

Availability
Purchase

Language
Fortran

Computer
Prime
VAX

DRAGON *Compeda Limited*
A computer aided draughting system. Drawings are in ink on tracing paper or polyester film and include 2D engineering drawings in any size or format in the following applications: pipework and instrumentation diagrams, electrical schematics, logic and circuit diagrams, specification sheets, form layouts, Critical Path Networks, and precedence diagrams

References

Availability
Licence

Language
Fortran

Computer
Minicomputer

HIDEM *Ecotech*
Part of the SCRIBE system. Caters for the removal of lines hidden by 'walls' in perspectives, plus 3D projections and display, in colour, or planes (if a colour monitor is used)

References
RIBA Journal, June 1982 Architects' Journal, June 23 and 30 1982

Availability
Purchase

Language
Compiled binary code

Computer
Apple II +

IGDS8 *Intergraph (Great Britain) Limited*
A 2D, 2 1/2D and 3D multistation design system for mapping, mechanical, electrical piping, plant, etc. Features include: a 1280 x 1024 dual raster display, linked database management, file processor between CPU and disk, 16 workstations; can drive a workstation 1 mile away using coax cable

References

Availability
Purchase

Language

Computer
DEC PDP11/23 with 1Mb memory, 84Mb disk. Plotter

0678

MAPCK *Microcomp*
Allows an engineer or surveyor to check tract and parcel maps for correctness before recording. Can be run interactively or in batch mode. The user traverses around the boundary using known or stored bearings. Curves are traversed by either bearings or the central angle. Closure information includes area and error in latitude and departure. The program uses double precision arithmetic for all calculations

References

Availability
Purchase

Language

Computer
Apple, and most microcomputers using CP/M

0679

GINOGRAF *Quest GENESYS Limited*
Statistics can be more acceptable and readily understood when displayed in the form of graphs, histograms or bar charts. When used in conjunction with GINO-F, interactive windowing and scaling facilities are all available

References

Availability

Language
Gentran

Computer

0680

GINOSURF *Quest GENESYS Limited*
A facility for displaying 3D surfaces as contour maps or as isometric projections. From user defined random spaced surface points levels, or regular grid points, the surface can be displayed in contour form

References

Availability

Language
Gentran

Computer

0681

GINOZONE *Quest GENESYS Limited*
Mapping information related to areas can be a long and tedious task. This program takes digitised zone boundary data and produces zone maps

References

Availability

Language
Gentran

Computer

0682

CONTRIV *SIA Computer Services*
This is a fast contouring system used in survey, mapping and surface modelling

References

Availability
Bureau service

Language
High level

Computer
Control Data, IBM, Prime

0683

GPCP *SIA Computer Services*
This is a general purpose contouring program, used in survey, mapping and surface modelling

References

Availability
Bureau service

Language
High level

Computer
Control Data, IBM, Prime

0684

GRID *SIA Computer Services*
A system for analysis and mapping of grid references and digitised data, of use in survey analysis

References

Availability
Bureau service

Language
High level

Computer
Control Data, IBM, Prime

0685

SACM *SIA Computer Services*
This is a powerful surface approximation and contour mapping system

References

Availability
Bureau service

Language
High level

Computer
Control Data, IBM, Prime

0686

SITE *ABACUS studies*
Gives a graphic representation of a given site which can be used to calculate the net site area. For use with ECOLE 3 and HELP. Input comprises a site file containing coordinates of spot heights, soil tests, services and other features, and a network file containing coordinates of roads and footpaths. Graphic output includes site boundary, soil condition indices, contours and road networks

References
ECOLE 3, HELP
ABACUS Occasional Paper No 61 (SITE)

Availability
Purachase, hire, bureau service

Language
Fortran IV

Computer
Univac 1108
Tektronix graphics terminal

0687

Site investigations: TRIBOR *Cheshire County Council*
This program holds an index to all site investigation data prepared by the County since 1969. Data is stored, such as the number and date of the order for the work to be carried out, the OS reference, project number, and a summary of the report contents

References

Availability

Language
APL

Computer
IBM 3270

CHART *Computel Limited*
A set of programs for calculating and plotting positions of survey paths

References
GEOCOMP

Availability

Language

Computer

Seismic Actions on Buildings *Computer Design*
Part of the COSPACK package. For the evaluation of earthquake actions and safety factors according to the POR Method

References
Sirius Computing, January 1983

Availability
Purchase, lease

Language
Basic

Computer
ACT Sirius 1 256K.
Plotter

EDMPLAN *Construction Measurement Systems Limited*
Part of MICROSURVEY for use by architects, builders, building surveyors, engineers, etc. Determines the plan coordinates of detail points observed from survey stations using electro-magnetic distance measurement methods (EDM tacheometry). For detail reduction only and not for EDM traverse, but may be used to fix position of one station from another, giving plan coordinates of the observed station point. Up to 50 detail points may be entered from one survey station. Faster than EDMTACHE

References

Availability

Language
Compiled

Computer
CBM 4032 and CBM 8032 microcomputers

EDMTACHE *Construction Measurement Systems Limited*
Part of MICROSURVEY for use by architects, builders, building surveyors, engineers, etc. Determines the coordinates and reduced levels of detail points observed from survey stations using electro-magnetic distance measurement methods (EDM tacheometry). For detail reduction only, and not for EDM traverse; may be used to fix the position of one station from another, giving both the plan coordinates and the height of the observed station point. Up to 50 detail points entered from one station

References

Availability

Language
Compiled

Computer
CBM 4032 and CBM 8032 microcomputers

LEVELS *Construction Measurement Systems Limited*
Part of MICROSURVEY for interactive use by architects, builders, building surveyors, engineers, etc. Calculates reduced levels, used for level grids, contouring, the establishment of TBM's, level transfer across a site, etc. Interactive and accepts keyboard entry of ordinary level staff readings (backsights, intermediates, foresights) and BM heights. In a single run, up to 100 foresights may be handled, with an overall maximum of 101 staff positions, including the first backsight reading

References

Availability

Language
Compiled

Computer
CBM 4032 and CBM 8032 microcomputers

SET OUT *Construction Measurement Systems Limited*
Part of MICROSURVEY for use by architects, builders, building surveyors, engineers, etc. Determines the bearings and distances to plan points from a survey station; sets out plan positions where drawings have been produced on a coordinate grid. Interactive, accepting keyboard entry of the survey station and reference object coordinates, and the RO direction; coordinates of all the plan points. Bearings and distances for setting out are then computed automatically

References

Availability

Language
Compiled

Computer
CBM 4032 and CBM 8032 microcomputers

TRANSFORM *Construction Measurement Systems Limited*
Part of MICROSURVEY for use by architects, builders, building surveyors, engineers, etc. Computes the transformation of a set of point coordinates from one plane rectangular system to another. Transforms site points from one grid system to another. Interactive, accepting keyboard entry of the coordinates of two points known in both systems, and deducing the scale factor, swing and shift values. Values for points are then computed automatically

References

Availability

Language
Compiled

Computer
CBM 4032 and CBM 8032 microcomputers

TRAVERSE *Construction Measurement Systems Limited*
Part of MICROSURVEY for use by architects, builders, building surveyors, engineers, etc. Comprises 4 integrated programs for computation of traverse surveys. Given the appropriate linear, angular and coordinate data, these programs may be used for closed loop traverses, traverses closed between two coordinated points, and simple open traverses. Up to 25 lines may be included in a single traverse. The 4 programs are: Initial Bearing, Bearings, Traverse and Lines

References

Availability

Language
Compiled

Computer
CBM 4032 and CBM 8032 microcomputers

TRIGONOMETRY *Construction Measurement Systems Limited*
Part of the MICROSURVEY range of software intended for interactive use by architects, builders, building surveyors, engineers, etc. TRIGONOMETRY is a menu-driven program, providing a large number of calculation routines which are frequently used in surveying and setting out. Options available are: coordinate problems, solution of triangles, angle, distance and area conversions, calculation of areas and volumes, and preliminary reminders. Any option choice of these items will lead to a further menu of routines

References

Availability

Language
Compiled

Computer
CBM 4032 and CBM 8032 microcomputers

ECLIPSE CIVIL ENGINEERING DESIGN *Eclipse Associates Limited*
A suite of programs to create a triangular DTM from survey information. Allows interactive highway and drainage design together with volumetric calculation. All use interactive graphics and produce setting out data for site use. Input is by data logger, keyboard and digitiser. Output is by printer, plotter and graphics

References

Availability
Purchase, bureau service (SCIA SV, ST DATA APS)

Language
Wang Extended Basic
HP Basic

Computer
Wang 2200

0698

PCOGO *Facet Limited*

Calculates civil engineering geometry problems. It can be applied to the computation problems involved in highway design, land surveying, bridge geometry, and construction layout. Engineers are able to state the input in familiar terminology such as azimuth, deflection and traverse adjustment. Every command defined by the user is followed by the specified data for that command. Output is interspersed with input; a record of the whole run may optionally be printed and the 'figures' used may be plotted

References

Availability
Bureau service, or under licence

Language

Computer
Prime, Norsk Data, Harris,
CP/M 8-bit micros

0699

SURVPAK *D J Herriott Limited*

A suite of programs providing an integrated land survey package which can be used for initial survey of a site, and subsequent setting out of designers' plans

References

Availability
Purchase or hire

Language
Basic

Computer
Hewlett Packard
HP85/86/87
HP9826/36.

0700

Boundary Survey *Hydro Systems (USA)*

Balances a closed loop traverse or an open traverse to the known starting and ending coordinates. Input provides for bearings, north azimuths, included and deflected angles. Distances may be adjusted by slope angles and temperature. Legs may be entered optionally as side shots or held constant. Curve selections include radius or tangent legs. Available options include: automatic, manual or no angle balance; compass rule, Crandall's rule or no adjustment; list field data, angular and linear error trials

References

Availability
Purchase

Language

Computer
Apple, IBM, TRS-80
with CP/M

0701

Extensive Coordinate Geometry *Hydro Systems (USA)*

Accesses randomly stored coordinates; computes and stores additional coordinates with: bearing, north azimuth, included or deflected angles, distances adjusted for slope angles, temperature, and/or converted from meters to feet. Includes extensive grouping of curves; offset intersection to locate distances and intersection coordinates of points 90° from a line defined by 2 coordinate points. Many other features

References

Availability
Purchase

Language

Computer
Apple, IBM, TRS-80
with CP/M

0702

MOSS *Moss Systems Limited*

A modelling system which handles the collection and reduction of land survey data (aerial or ground), and storage, in 3D digital models. Used for the design of roads, railways, airports, pavements, dam geometry, mine planning, management, area and volume calculations, production of setting out data, and production of plan, section, perspective and contour drawings to contract standard

References
List available from Moss Consortium

Availability
Licence, rental, bureau service

Language
Fortran IV

Computer
All main frame and
32-bit minicomputers:

0703

CP101: Traverse reduction *Oasys Limited*

Deals with the reduction of plane traverse data to determine rectangular coordinates of stations and bearings of lines for closed, controlled, open and deviation traverses. After survey data is entered, there is automatic selection of the readings required for the reduction calculations. Angle errors are distributed equally between all angles in the traverse, and closure errors remaining after angle error distribution are distributed by the Bowditch rule. A plot of the traverse is produced on screen and printer

References

Availability
Purchase

Language
Basic

Computer
HP 9845 HP 85/87

0704

CP102: Reduction of levels *Oasys Limited*

Staff readings are entered as recorded in the field. The program automatically adjusts all levels to ensure closure on the correct final level. Program output consists of a tabular summary of input data, the Height of Collimation for all instrument positions, and the reduced level of all staff positions

References

Availability
Purchase

Language
Basic

Computer
HP 9845 HP 85/87

0705

CP103: Reduction of precise levels *Oasys Limited*

Staff and micrometer readings are recorded from both left and right hand sides of the staff, and levels are calculated for both readings. Program output consists of a tabular summary of the input data, the Height of Collimation at all instrument positions, and the reduced level at all staff positions

References

Availability
Purchase

Language
Basic

Computer
HP 9845 HP 85/87

0706

CP104: Tacheometric Survey *Oasys Limited*

For each instrument station position, the reduced level height of telescope and x, y coordinates are entered. For each staff position, three stadia hair readings are entered, together with vertical and horizontal angles. Calculates distance to staff, and the reduced level and coordinates at the staff. For each instrument position, output consists of a listing of the instrument station data, followed by a table showing input data and calculated values of distance, reduced level and x, y coordinates for each staff position

References

Availability
Purchase

Language
Basic

Computer
HP 9845 HP 85/87

0707

LOCPT *Quest GENESYS Limited*

Points surveyed from known stations can be located. A reference line is defined, together with the angle and distance to the detail point. Designed for use with a drum plotter. If the plot is too large for the plotter, the program automatically divides the data and produces separate sheets for plotting, each overlapping the previous one to ensure matching

References

Availability

Language
Gentran

Computer

PLTPT *Quest GENESYS Limited*
A plotting program for TRAV and LOCPT. From a user defined scale, this program plots and connects the various base station and detail points. The levels and point numbers can be shown and there are options to superimpose grids and also rotate the drawing

References

Availability

Language
Gentran

Computer

TRAV *Quest GENESYS Limited*
A land surveying program for traverse adjustment using the least squares method. Traverses can be closed, open with known points at both ends or open with only the start point known. The user specifies coordinate data, accuracy required, the whole circle bearing for the first leg, and for each other leg, the length and clockwise angle from the previous leg. Output includes final adjusted coordinates and the lengths and azimuths of all the legs. Results also confirm closure accuracy

References

Availability

Language
Gentran

Computer

Surveying, Setting Out *Reading Computer Services Limited*
A series of utilities to undertake traverse calculations (which may be closed, or start and end at known points), or process as tachometric survey from field notes

References

Availability

Language

Computer
CP/M Microcomputer

RGSP (Rothamsted general survey program) *Rothamsted Experimental Station*
For the construction, manipulation and printing of multi-way tables from survey data. Hierarchical data structures can be handled. Data can be accepted at one time or in successive batches; late returns and amendments are accommodated. Data may be input from cards, paper tape or existing computer files. All common types of card coding, including multiple punching, are acceptable

References

Availability
Lease

Language
Fortran

Computer
ICL System 470, 370
CDC 6600, 7600

FLUSH *SIA Computer Services*
This program is used for soil-structure dynamic (seismic) analysis

References

Availability
Bureau service

Language
High level

Computer
Control Data,
IBM, Prime

GENEDIT *SIA Computer Services*
A generalised vetting program for survey data

References

Availability
Bureau service

Language
High level

Computer
Control Data,
IBM, Prime

GENTAB *SIA Computer Services*
A generalised survey tabulation program suite

References

Availability
Bureau service

Language
High level

Computer
Control Data,
IBM, Prime

SGI-HASP DIGITAL IIS *Survey and General Instrument Co Limited*
For land surveying and planning. A coordinate geometry and draughting module, based on proximity searching. Surveyed field data may be modelled to enable the automatic interpolation of contours and volumes. Compatible with British Ordnance Survey digital database, enabling the system to store, display and plot full information contained in the OS files. Standard system has 3 programs: basic operating program, survey traverse analysis and adjustment, coordinate map preparation

References

Availability
Purchase, turnkey system

Language

Computer
HP9816, 16-bit
GTCO digitiser tablet
HP7470 plotter

POINTPLOT *Survey Three Limited*
A land survey point plotting system which generates film or paper plots of traverse stations and detail points, annotated (if required) with numbers and/or heights. The topography and detail are added by the surveyor prior to the drawing stage. Traverse station coordinates are entered, followed by field readings of radial detail points obtained by EDM methods (in HD or SD formats). Computes rectangular coordinates, generates coordinate ranges, identifies boundary points and prints out field data and results

References
Apple II Applications List

Availability
Purchase

Language
Applesoft Basic

Computer
Acclaim 64K
Apple II 64K

GROUSE *University of Edinburgh*
A ground modelling system which generates ground surfaces from random spot height survey data, and displays contoured representations of surfaces. Features: user can modify surfaces; program calculates cut and fill requirements; ability to superimpose objects, eg buildings, or vegetation on a ground form, and obtain area values, density of objects within an area, linear distances and slope conditions. The emphasis is on congenial user interaction

References
Research meets practice: Edinburgh Architectural Research, vol 9, 1982

Availability
Purchase (Contact: Mr Aart Bijl)

Language
UNIX

Computer
Microcomputer, eg
DEC, Xylogics, with
256Kb

0718

WILD GEOMAP *Wild Heerbrugg Limited*
An interactive graphics system for surveying applications. Options include contour interpolation, volumes, cross-sections and profiles, and network adjustment. Input is flexible and can be adapted to user's requirements. An automatic plotting table is required for graphic data output. The system handles field survey to finished drawing, and is suitable for a wide range of possible applications in surveying

References

Availability
Purchase

Language
Basic

Computer
Tektronix 4054
Digital plotting table

0719

SDRC GEOMOD *CAE International*
An interactive, 3D solid modelling program to develop geometric description of components to display and explore design alternatives. The data can be easily transferred to CAD systems, finite element analysis, NC and system design programs. Input is via VDU or digitiser. Output provides information on all object properties, eg geometry, surface area, mass, inertias, etc

References
Owned by SDRC, USA

Availability
Purchase, bureau service

Language
Fortran

Computer
DEC VAX

0720

SDRC IMP *CAE International*
An interactive, 3D mechanism analysis program for the kinematic, static and dynamic analysis of mechanisms. Output includes printout and graphics: kinematic positions, equilibrium and dynamic positions, velocities, accelerations and forces

References
Owned by SDRC, USA

Availability
Bureau service

Language
Fortran

Computer
DEC VAX, CDC,
IBM 4300, 3030, 370

0721

SDRC MODAL-PLUS V.7 *CAE International*
Used to collect, analyse and display data from artificial excitation tests. A complete modal database of the structure is developed and verified. Input direct from analogue digital converter or from correct format data files. Graphical and tabular outputs, and animated displays

References
Owned by SDRC, USA

Availability
Purchase

Language
Fortran

Computer
DEC PDP11/34,
DEC VAX

0722

SDRC SABBA *CAE International*
Handles the evaluation of dynamic behaviour for different load conditions and modifications. Primarily uses test data as the structural model. Direct interface with MODAL-PLUS. Output includes tabular and graphics displays, and data for animation in MPLUS. The user requires a good knowledge of structural dynamics

References
Owned by SDRC, USA

Availability
Purchase

Language
Fortran

Computer
DEC PDP/11, DEC
VAX

0723

SDRC SUPERB *CAE International*
A general purpose, finite element program for static and dynamic structural analysis and heat transfer analysis. Contains a large library of isoparametric and conventional finite elements. Extensive output in form of printout and graphic display of stresses, displacements, etc. Links to SUPERTAB for results display

References
Owned by SDRC, USA. Related to
SUPERTAB and SYSTAN

Availability
Purchase, bureau service

Language
Fortran

Computer
DEC VAX, CDC,
IBM 4300, 3030, 370

0724

SDRC SUPERTAB *CAE International*
An interactive, finite element pre- and post-processing program with powerful mesh generation capabilities, interfacing to all major finite element programs. Post-processing includes colour stress contours, criterion plots, X, Y graphs, and displacement plots. Output in the form of graphical display or model and results

References
Owned by SDRC, USA

Availability
Purchase, bureau service

Language
Fortran

Computer
DEC VAX, PDP11/34,
IBM 4300, 3030, 370.
CDC, Prime

0725

SDRC SYSTAN *CAE International*
For the system analysis investigation of dynamics of built-up systems components being represented from several sources. Highly interactive/graphical model creation. Used at concept stage through to prototype and production, troubleshooting natural frequency and forced response solutions. Input via VDU/digitiser tablet. Output is tabular/graphical with animation in colour

References
Owned by SDRC, USA

Availability
Purchase, bureau service

Language
Fortran

Computer
DEC VAX11/7
IBM

0726

SDRC System Design *CAE International*
An interactive, 3D tool for true solid modelling of components. These can be brought together to create mechanical systems with checking of interface. Output includes all mass properties and interface check

References
Owned by SDRC, USA

Availability
Purchase, bureau service

Language
Fortran

Computer
DEC VAX

0727

CALMA DDM *Calma (UK) Limited*
Used by the manufacturing industry: enables the design engineer to analyse design alternatives and produce the optimum part; assists planning and scheduling departments including the production of bills of material; accurate 3D models and detailed design information handle tooling design; used for both prototypes and production; assists with quality control

References

Availability

Language

Computer

FEM (Finite Element Modelling) *Calma (UK) Limited*
A pre-processing step for FEA (Finite Element Analysis) and a post-processing display of
the results. The program handles: automatic, semi-automatic or user controlled mesh
generation and numbering or naming of nodes; allows verification, editing and changing of
the mesh as required, and assigns attribute data to points on the mesh (forces,
temperatures); generation of FEA input files by the FEM module for mainframe analysis;
post-processing and display of FEA results; editing, changing and re-analysis of the model

References

Availability

Language

Computer

Properties of Plane Section II *Camutek*
Calculates the section properties of any plane area. The area is defined by specifying the
coordinates of points around the perimeter. A sketch is then presented for any necessary
correction to be made. The coordinates of the centroid of the area are calculated, together
with the area, the second moment of area about both axes and the radii of gyration. The
angle between the new and old axes is output with a table of revised coordinates and
section properties

References

Availability
From Camutek

Language
Basic

Computer
HP 9835, 98
Future: HP 8

Properties of Plane Section I *Camutek*
Calculates the section properties about one axis only of an area composed entirely of
rectangles. Each component rectangle is specified by the distance from an arbitrary datum,
its depth and its breadth. The properties calculated are the area, position of neutral axis,
second moment of area, radius of gyration, elastic moduli and plastic modulus

References

Availability
From Camutek

Language
Basic

Computer
HP 9835, 9845
Future: HP 85 & 86

CEADS-CADD *Civil and Structural Computing (Northern) Limited*
Computer aided design and draughting in the following applications: mechanical,
architectural, structural and electrical draughting and design; assembly layouts; geometric
constructions; pattern grading; construction details; printed circuit boards; integrated
circuit layouts; detailed schematics; piping diagrams; utility networks; wiring layouts;
facilities and graphic design

References
Bradshaw, Buckton and Tonge

Availability
Bureau service, time sharing, in-house

Language

Computer

Plant Design Management System *Compeda Limited*
Provides 3D design and analysis of process plant from conception through to construction,
with built-in checks for integrity and interferences. Reports, MTO and graphical output can
be produced at any stage of the design cycle. Input is interactive via the terminal keyboard
or tablet. Output includes: dimensioned drawings, isometrics and perspective views;
reports and analyses; interfaces to pipe stressing and material control

References

Availability
Licence

Language
Fortran IV

Computer
Minicomputer
with 3/4 Mbyte

2D BEPP *Computational Mechanics Consultants Limited*
Computes the 2D steady state potential in zoned anisotropic media. Used for soil seepage
and temperature distribution problems, etc. Accurate and convenient because it uses the
boundary element method. The program can approximate any geometrical shape. It can
solve soil seepage problems with permeable soil layers for isotropic, anisotropic, stratified,
homogenous and inhomogenous media. For heat conduction, bodies composed of layered
or zoned materials of differing conductivity may be analysed

References

Availability
Licence

Language
Fortran IV

Computer
Microcomputer with
minimum 25K

Axisymmetric Shell Analysis *Computational Mechanics Consultants Limited*
For the linear elastic static analysis of axisymmetric shells subject to non-axisymmetric
loading. The program can analyse distributed loads, curved thin shell elements, elements of
variable thicknesses and material properties, with any number of branches. Applications
include engineering problems, such as tanks, pressure vessels, cooling towers, rotating
machinery, etc

References

Availability
Licence

Language
Fortran

Computer
Microcomputer with
minimum of 24K

BEAPP *Computational Mechanics Consultants Limited*
For the solution of steady state potential problems in axisymmetric orthotropic media.
Typical applications are well seepage and temperature distribution. Uses the boundary
element method, thus reducing the system of equations and the amount of data
preparation required; also achieves a higher level of numerical accuracy than from finite
element analysis

References

Availability
Licence

Language
Fortran IV

Computer
Microcomputer with
minimum 24K

BEASY *Computational Mechanics Consultants Limited*
A general purpose program that solves a wide variety of engineering analysis problems
using the Boundary Element Method. Capabilities include static stress analysis, electrical
conduction, potential flow, and other types of field problems. The Boundary Element
method is similar to the Finite Element method, except that only the surface of the problem
requires subdivision into elements; by thus reducing the dimensionality by one, problems
can be solved with less effort, and sometimes with greater accuracy

References

Availability
Licence

Language
Fortran

Computer
Microcomputer

Boundary Element Computer Tape *Computational Mechanics Consultants Limited*
The tape contains a series of programs for the solution of potential and elasticity problems
using the Boundary Element Method; also included is a file containing 25 routines for
matrix operations. Suitable for solving problems with infinite domains, such as in soil
mechanics, hydraulics, stress analysis, etc. The tape aims to introduce the fundamentals of
boundary elements in a simple manner to enable the user to go on to solve more complex
problems

References
The Boundary Element Method for
Engineers, by C A Brebbia

Availability
Licence

Language
Fortran IV

Computer
Microcomputer with
minimum of 32K

Computer programs for the building industry

0738

DISPER *Computational Mechanics Consultants Limited*
Used to solve time dependent or steady state dispersion of one constituent for either concentration or temperature problems. Potential and streamline problems can be solved and the corresponding velocity fields calculated. Based on the finite element method with an isoparametric shaped element with 6 nodes; this element can be distorted to represent curved or irregular boundaries. The program has been widely used for design of engineering works in various countries, and is thoroughly tested

References

Availability
Licence

Language
Fortran IV

Computer
Microcomputer with minimum 64K

0739

STACKING PLAN AND BLOCK PLAN *Computer-Aided Design Group, USA*
Provides space planners with a powerful but simple tool for producing locational stacking plans and schematic block floor plan layouts for buildings in such a way that highly interrelated activities are placed onto the same, or adjacent, zones, and onto floors that are located close together. Output is in the form of a graphic layout of stacking and block plans

References
Computer-Aided Design Magazine, September 1981

Availability
Purchase, bureau service

Language
ANSI Fortran IV

Computer
DEC PDP11, VAX, IBM. Most mini or mainframes

0740

Isometric Piping Drawing System *COSMIC*
Provides a fully dimensional isometric drawing. The system comprises: an isometric piping drawing; an isometric symbol drawing; material report; an instrument point report; drawing dimensions of the piping system, with extension lines. When a drawing is completed, information is printed consisting of input data, calculated values and error messages. The drawing is produced on magnetic tape to be plotted by a CalComp plotter

References
Ontario Hydro Limited

Availability

Language
Fortran IV (96%)
Assembler (4%)

Computer
Univac 1100 series

0741

Kitchen Design *Designer's Aid*
This program allows the user to design a kitchen in 3D. On completion of design the program prints out plans, elevations and isometric drawings. Also provides detailed costings, descriptions, size etc. of the kitchen. A database of the manufacturer's catalogue is supplied with the software (currently available for 34 manufacturers). Input required includes overall room dimensions, size of obstructions, etc, manufacturer's unit codes, and position of units

References
Kitchen News, Builders' Merchants Ass

Availability
Purchase

Language
Basic o ASB

Computer
Apple II 48K

0742

SCAMP *DHSS (Department of Health and Social Security)*
Enables the user to enter a detailed 3D component model into the computer and checks for clashes between services. Limited to about 1000 components (pipes and fittings). Enables drawings to be prepared from any viewing angle, eg plan, elevation and isometric. Some annotation is provided but manual annotation necessary to provide working drawings. Facilitates preparation of base drawings until they can be produced directly from an architectural package

References

Availability
Purchase

Language
Fortran

Computer
SEL, Prime

0743

SCIA: Finite Element Analysis of potential fields *Eclipse Associates Limited*
The basic version (FLOW) determines the potential lines for a flow problem, using the Poisson equation. Applications include soil water flow, magnetic fields, heat transport and electrostatic fields. Expansion modules of this program include graphical input and output

References

Availability
Purchase, bureau service (SCIA SV, ST DATA APS)

Language
Wang Extended Basic, HP Basic

Computer
Wang mini and microcomputers

0744

SCIA: Finite element program for axi-symmetric and plane stress and strain analysis
Eclipse Associates Limited
Basic version covers static elastic analysis of arbitrary elasticity problems. For strength analysis of walls, excavations, tunnelling, axi-symmetric shell structures, reactors and pressure vessels or machines. The extended version includes a semi graphical output on plotter, and a graphical input and output program

References

Availability
Purchase, bureau service (SCIA SV, ST DATA APS)

Language
Wang Extended Basic, HP Basic

Computer
Wang mini and microcomputers

0745

DA-1. Dynamic analysis *Ecom Associates, Inc*
Determines natural frequences of vibration, characteristic mode shapes, and modal participation factors for a multi-degree elastic system with lumped masses. The dynamic response to any portion of the system to a given acceleration spectrum may then be determined using the modal method of analysis

References

Availability
Purchase

Language
M Basic

Computer
HP

0746

BUILDING VIBRATIONS 1 *ESDU International Limited*
Estimates natural frequencies, mode shapes, normal mode generalised masses and stiffnesses for both lateral and torsional undamped modes of vibration of shear buildings. (It is assumed that columns are inextensible and floors rigid, so preventing joint rotations.) Input consists of the number of storeys, number of natural modes, and stiffnesses of storeys and their lumped masses. Alternatively, a graphical procedure is provided to facilitate rapid solutions for certain categories of structure

References

Availability
Licence

Language
Fortran IV
Basic

Computer
Minicomputer
Mainframe

0747

BUILDING VIBRATIONS 2 *ESDU International Limited*
Provides estimates of modes of undamped natural vibrations of core buildings. Related to BUILDING VIBRATIONS 1

References

Availability
Purchase

Language
Fortran

Computer
Most mini or mainframe computers

POLYFIT/MURG *Facet Limited*
The curve fitting package consists of two programs, POLYFIT and MURG, which enable a line or surface to be fitted to a set of data with one or more independent variables. In every case, the user has a choice (within specified limits) of the form of the equation that will be used to fit the data. Optionally, a hard copy of the regression analysis can be obtained in the form of a graph, and a detailed printout of the results is generated to a user-specified file

References

Availability
Bureau service, or under licence

Language

Computer
Prime, Norsk Data, Harris,
CP/M 8-bit micros

ISOSTEEL *Imperial Chemical Industries, PLC*
Used for the analysis of structural steelwork, design systems, producing calculations, drawings, quantities. Input is from interactive graphical source. Output includes design calculations, steelwork layout drawings, quantities, and interfaces to modelling systems

References

Availability
Purchase

Language
Fortran

Computer
Vax 11780
Prime 400/750

CP30 *National Research Council of Canada*
A program to analyse results and prepare graphs for fire resistance test reports

References
G Williams-Leir

Availability

Language

Computer

CP31 *National Research Council of Canada*
Calculates the natural modes of vibration for multistorey buildings with or without foundation flexibility

References
J H Rainer

Availability

Language

Computer

AP117: Finite element-plane stresses/strain *Oasys Limited*
Designed to minimise preparation and output data. Program features include: coordinates of nodes defining structure can be input manually or from scaled drawings, using the HP9872 flatbed plotter; after input, a finite element mesh is generated using 4 noded quadrilateral elements; nodal renumbering; 3 independent load cases; nodal, point, edge and in-plane distributed loading; structure and/or loading modification and re-run facility

References

Availability
Purchase

Language
Basic

Computer
HP 9845

AP118: Finite element plate bending *Oasys Limited*
The interactive linear elastic analysis of laterally loaded isotropic thin plates using finite elements. Standard grillage beam element can be incorporated; a finite element mesh is generated using 4 noded quadrilateral elements; nodal renumbering; free, rigid or flexible supports; 3 independent load cases; nodal, point, edge and area distributed loading. Method of solution is by matrix stiffness method; solutions of equations are by Gaussian elimination

References

Availability
Purchase

Language
Basic

Computer
HP 9845

Shopfront Designer & Estimator *Quality Business Machines Limited*
Designs customised shopfronts, producing a scale drawing, and listing materials used, together with cutting instructions. Additionally, all costs are calculated and incorporated in a letter of quotation, which is produced automatically. A typical estimate, including a scale drawing of the shopfront, can be completed in about 15 minutes

References

Availability

Language

Computer

CAPS *Redpath Engineering Limited*
A computer detailing system which provides drawings and associated workshop lists for beam/column orientated steel structures. Buildings of irregular layout are easily handled and all member connections are automatically selected from a wide range of options. Input includes details of: contract, connections, fittings, additional sections, grid, floor data and erection sequence

References

Availability
Lease

Language
S-Algol

Computer
DEC/VAX
Minicomputers

ROSE *Robinson Ford Associates*
A low cost, interactive post-processing system that interfaces to the end of finite element analysis programs. It organises, manipulates and outputs results for specific areas. Features: search to find values outside given range; calculations involving one or more values: tabulates results in specified regions; sorts results into specified order: plots results; checks computed values against codes of practice. Optional equipment can include graphics display terminals and communication to host computers

References

Availability
Purchase

Language
Fortran

Computer
Data General, from
16-bit MP/200 micro
NOVA

FASTPLOT *Scicon Limited*
A graphics system for the operation of incremental plotters at high speed via a low speed Post Office line

References
Developed by the Production
Engineering Research Association

Availability
Bureau service. Available in USA

Language
Fortran

Computer
Univac 1100/62

0758

NASTRAN *Scicon Limited*
The MacNeal-Schwendler version of this comprehensive, general purpose, finite element analysis system

References
MacNeal-Schwendler Corporation

Availability
Bureau Service

Language

Computer
UNIVAC 1100/62

0759

SESAM 80 *Scicon Limited*
A suite of programs based on the superelement technique with automatic mesh and element generation, post-processing and plotting

References
Written by A S Computas

Availability
Bureau service

Language

Computer
UNIVAC 1100/62

0760

HETOP *Shade (Computer Services) Limited*
A computer design aid for timber structures. Input is an ASCII coded description of the wall panels required, detailing positions of windows, doors, etc. This information is decoded and the panels designed. Full timber and sheathing material cutting lists are produced, as well as a summary of materials, production tickets and frame sketches. All system outputs are to a graphics printer

References

Availability
Purchase

Language
Fortran IV,
Fortran 66 and 77

Computer
CP/M

0761

Bolts *Technical Services*
Used to design a bolt group of a specified pattern. The geometric layout of the group is specified, and the forces in the bolts are calculated for specified loading. The applied loading may be in direct forces in any of the 3 principal directions, and/or moments about the 3 principal axes. Bolt types may be black bolts, grade 4.6 and 8.8, high strength friction bolts. Results are printed out as a calculation sheet giving the properties of the bolt group and the stresses in the chosen bolt size

References

Availability
Purchase

Language
Basic

Computer
Olivetti P6060,
and P6066, 16K

0762

Welds *Technical Services*
Used to design a specific weld pattern. The geometric layout of the pattern is specified, and the forces in the welds calculated for specified loading. Applied loading may be direct forces in any of the 3 principal directions and/or moments about principal axes. Weld metal is assumed to be mild steel. Results are printed out in the form of a calculation sheet giving the properties of the weld patterns, the stresses at critical sections, and the size of welds required

References

Availability
Purchase

Language
Basic

Computer
Olivetti P6060,
and P6066, 16K

0763

ANSYS *UCC (Great Britain) Limited*
For structural and heat transfer analysis. This is a large scale, general purpose, finite element program using the matrix displacement method of analysis for the solution of several classes of engineering problems. Types of analysis are: static, dynamic and heat transfer, and substructures

References
Swanson Analysis Systems Inc

Availability
Bureau service from UCC

Language

Computer

0764

SET *Technische Universitat Mu nchen*
The FE-program suite SET provides calculations in design work, and consists of autonomous parts for statistics, design, groundwater flow and heat transfer. It solves linear and non-linear problems, such as large displacements, plasticity or free surfaces in seepage problems. Output includes printout or plot of displacements, stresses, potentials and temperatures

References
K Axhausen et al 'Die Programmkette SET, I, II, III. CAD-Berichte kfk 173-175 Kern forschungszentrum Karlsruhe

Availability
Purchase

Language
Fortran IV

Computer
32-bit CPU

Civil engineering

Bridges
Continuous beams
Foundations, retaining walls
Earthworks
Highways
Waterways
Other

0765

Circular reinforced concrete columns design *A M Kinney, Inc*
Computes maximum bending moments with corresponding axial loads for a circular reinforced concrete column with given steel areas; done on the basis of cracked or uncracked section, depending on eccentricity. Output includes moments, axial loads, area of steel for increment of percentage of steel increase, and each increment of eccentricity increase

References

Availability

Language
Fortran

Computer
IBM 1130 and 370

0766

Rectangular reinforced concrete column design *A M Kinney, Inc*
Computes the maximum steel stress, the maximum compressive steel stress and all four-corner concrete stresses in a rectangular or squared reinforced concrete column with an eccentric axial load. An option is provided to determine the stress on the basis of the cracked or the uncracked section. Design specification used is the AASHTO standard for Highway Bridges, 8th edition

References

Availability

Language
Fortran

Computer
IBM 1130 and 370

0767

Bridge/1 *Quest GENESYS Limited*
This sub-system enables an engineer to analyse bridges which, when the effect of the distribution of transverse loads is ignored, can be considered as continuous beams. A bridge may be of constant or varying cross-section, with an inclined or horizontal surface. Any degree of stiffness can be applied to elastic supports, to meet site and construction requirements

References
GENESYS program library

Availability
Bureau service, hire

Language
Gentran

Computer
DEC 10, Honeywell, IBM, ICL, PE, Philips, Prime, others

0768

Slab-bridge/1 *Quest GENESYS Limited*
This sub-system enables an engineer to analyse the finite elements of concrete bridge slab (or slab and beam) structures. It is suitable for most bridges of regular or semi regular shape, including those with arbitrary support conditions such as elastic bearings

References
GENESYS program library

Availability
Bureau service, hire

Language
Gentran

Computer
DEC 20, Honeywell, IBM, ICL, Philips, Prime Univac,

0769

INFLUENCE-LINES/1 *Quest GENESYS Limited*
With the introduction of the B116 Bridge Design Code of Practice, the use of influence lines in the design process becomes more important. This program produces influence line analysis including the effect of moving train loads on bridge structures. Structures permitted are those of line beams of variable section properties. The program calculates influence line data for reactions, axial and shear force and bending moment

References

Availability

Language
Gentran

Computer

0770

SBRIDGE *Quest GENESYS Limited*
Finite element solution techniques are used for this suite of three programs: SBRIDGE-PREPARE/1 is used for data preparation; the loading facilities are more extensive than for SLAB-BRIDGE/1, and include those forms of loading specified by the current Technical Memoranda issued by the UK DOT and the new bridge design Code of Practice BS5400. Analysis is performed by SBRIDGE-ANALYSE/1 and the results can be filed, or output by SBRIDGE-OUTPUT/1

References

Availability

Language
Gentran

Computer

0771

CASKET *SIA Computer Services*
This is a program for general bridge analysis

References

Availability
Bureau service

Language
High level

Computer
Control Data, IBM, Prime

0772

FISBOP/FISPEF *SIA Computer Services*
This program deals with finite strip analysis for bridge structures

References

Availability
Bureau service

Language
High level

Computer
Control Data, IBM, Prime

0773

GRIDS *SIA Computer Services*
A program for the analysis of bridge deck by grillage

References

Availability
Bureau service

Language
High level

Computer
Control Data, IBM, Prime

0774

MINIPOINT *SIA Computer Services*
A civil engineering program for long span bridge frame analysis

References

Availability
Bureau service

Language
High level

Computer
Control Data, IBM, Prime

MUPDI *SIA Computer Services*
A box structure bridge analysis program

References

Availability
Bureau service

Language
High level

Computer
Control Data,
IBM, Prime

RCULIB *SIA Computer Services*
This is a library of user contributed bridge programs

References

Availability
Bureau service

Language
High level

Computer
Control Data,
IBM, Prime

STRAND *SIA Computer Services*
An RC concrete bridge deck finite element analysis suite

References

Availability
Bureau service

Language
High level

Computer
Control Data,
IBM, Prime

Suspension bridge dynamic relaxation program *UMIST*
Calculates natural modes and frequencies of vibration of three-span suspension bridges.
Torsional, coupled and both vertical and lateral flexural vibrations can be calculated

References

Availability
Sale or hire negotiable

Language
Fortran IV

Computer
CDC 7600

Suspension bridge flutter program *UMIST*
This program calculates the critical wind speed which induces flutter in suspension bridges

References

Availability
Sale or hire negotiable

Language
Fortran

Computer
CDC 7600

Suspension bridge program *UMIST*
Carries out non-linear elastic analysis of suspension bridges and other cable structures (for
example, cable roofs and guyed masts). Analysis is 3D. The program takes account of
slack hangers and open joints

References

Availability
Sale or hire negotiable

Language
Algol 60
Fortran IV

Computer
CDC 7600

ZEN-Bridge suite *Zentech Limited*
These programs solve the erection conditions for the following bridge types: continuous
beams; slabs, using finite element, grillage and space frame techniques; box girders and
suspension and curved bridges. Pre-processors generate structure geometry, support
conditions and loading. Post-processors can be used for creating and merging files,
combining loading conditions and producing maximum forces

References
ZENTECH program library

Availability
Purchase, hire, bureau service

Language
Fortran V

Computer
Univac, CDC, DEC
System 10, IBM, ICL

CONKER *Amplix Services Limited*
Features include: design of reinforced structures to CP110; analysis of loaded continuous
beams; optimised selection of steel required over all spans, shear link requirement, bond
check and curtailment; up to 10 spans capacity; data entry and editing module for all
parameters; 2-way spanning slab with full detailing with BS4466 bending, fixing and weight
schedules; flat slab design includes analysis, design and detailing with BS4466 bending,
fixing and weight schedules

References

Availability
Purchase

Language
Commercial (SMB)
Cobol, Fortran

Computer
CP/M or MP/M
Microcomputer

MOMENT 1 *Associated British Consultants (Computers) Limited*
Used for moment analysis of continuous beams or slabs on pin supports. The program
handles up to 10 spans with various types of loading. There are versions for CP114 and
CP110. The program contains a screen editing system. Output includes shear and moment
envelopes, and a summary of critical values

References

Availability
Purchase

Language
Basic

Computer
64K TRS80 Model 2

Multi span beam analysis *Camutek*
Analyses continuous beams by automatically applying the correct combination of load
factors for any specified load case without the need for re-entering the loads. The load
factors may be standard (to CP110:1972) or specified

References

Availability
From owner

Language
Basic

Computer
HP 9830, (2k) or (6k)
9831, 9835, 9845
Future: HP85, 86

CBEAM *Civil and Structural Computing (Northern) Limited*
Analyses continuous beam subjected to various loading conditions. Output is produced graphically, and optionally includes bending moments, shear force diagrams, influence line diagrams or max/min envelopes. Various support conditions may be included, and the graphical output may be sent to plotting devices for retention or submission. Output from the program may be retained for use in subsequent member design programs

References
Bradshaw, Buckton and Tonge

Availability
Bureau service, time sharing, in-house

Language

Computer

0786

Continuous Beam *Computer Design*
Part of the COSPACK package. Determination of bending moments and shear forces for a multispan continuous beam with constant and non-uniform cross-section

References
Sirius Computing, January 1983

Availability
Purchase, lease

Language
Basic

Computer
ACT Sirius 1 256K.
Plotter

0787

Influence Lines for Multispan Beams *Computer Design*
Part of the COSPACK package. Handles the determination of influence lines of bending moments or shear forces for a continuous beam

References
Sirius Computing, January 1983

Availability
Purchase, lease

Language
Basic

Computer
ACT Sirius 1 256K.
Plotter

0788

SCIA: Continuous beam analysis *Eclipse Associates Limited*
Includes: continuous beam, arbitrary loadings and supports, semi graphical output of bending moment distribution, automatic load combinations and influence lines; calculation and plotting of beam reinforcement; beams on elastic foundations where fixed or extra spring supports are possible; sheet wall calculation; prestressed concrete where, for a composed profile, the optimal prestressing reinforcement is calculated

References

Availability
Purchase, bureau service (SCIA SV, ST DATA APS)

Language
Wang Extended Basic, HP Basic

Computer
Wang mini and microcomputers

0789

CD-1. Reinforced concrete beam design *Ecom Associates, Inc*
Designs beams by either the ultimate strength or working stress method of AC1 318-77. Flexural reinforcement requirements are given for rectangular, T or ledger beam sections. Cut off locations are given for various bar sizes chosen by the designer. End sections and midspan section may be of different size

References

Availability
Purchase

Language
M Basic

Computer
HP, DEC, Wang, Apple, Tandy TRS-80, IBM PC

0790

TRAIN *Tony Gee and Partners*
A continuous beam analysis program for structural engineers. Having defined a pattern of loads, the user can increment their position as many times as required to provide an envelope of bending moments, shear forces, deflections and slopes. Output can be specified for all points at all load positions; maximum and minimum values; graphical envelopes

References

Availability
Purchase

Language
HP Enhanced Basic

Computer
Hewlett-Packard HP9845 B/C

0791

C-PLOT *Tony Gee and Partners*
An easily used program for structural engineers, which provides graphic displays of bending moments, shear forces, deflections and slopes of a multispan continuous beam of constant section. Numerical output is also given at positions specified by the user

References

Availability
Sale

Language
HP Enhanced Basic

Computer
Hewlett-Packard HP9845 B/C

0792

CONT *Grist Business Services Limited*
Used for the design of continuous beams of steel, concrete, timber, etc. Handles up to 20 spans of arbitrary width; overhangs may be included. Output includes displacements, bending moments and shears at 6 points along each span, and also the support reactions

References

Availability
Purchase

Language
Fortran

Computer
Apple II 48K

0793

Multi-span continous beam analysis *Hydro Systems (USA)*
Analyses a multi-span continous beam with pinned column connections. Cantilevers are allowed. The user can investigate beam for any combination of uniform and point loads for each span. Also investigates simple spans for internal moments. Capacity with 48K is over 500 spans

References

Availability
Purchase

Language

Computer
16K RAM minimum

0794

Analysis and design of flat plates and continuous concrete frames *A M Kinney, Inc*
The program divides the structure into a series of bents, each consisting of a row of columns supporting slab strips. The bent may be one to 12 spans, with or without cantilevers at each end. Varying slab widths are considered. The program may be used for analysis and design of continuous frames consisting of colums and beams. The input slab thickness is checked against the code provisions for minimum thickness, and the allowable shearing stress is computed for beams and for slab action

References

Availability

Language
Fortran

Computer
IBM 1130 and 370

CBEAM *Microcomp Limited*
A program for continuous beam analysis. The load input is given as 5 simple load types which can be combined to represent any typical loading. Once the initial analysis is complete, the loads may be continually recombined to give bending moments, shear forces and reactions in both graphical and tabular format for different load factors

References

Availability
Licence

Language
Basic

Computer
Apple II 48K

AP102: Continuous beam analysis *Oasys Limited*
This may be used as a self contained program to produce summarised or detailed output for hand design of beams, or in conjunction with DP102 to produce a complete automatic reinforcement design. Analysis is in accordance with CP110

References

Availability
Purchase

Language
Basic

Computer
HP 9845 HP 85/87

AP107: Continuous beam influence lines *Oasys Limited*
Produces influence lines for bending moment or shear force for continuous beams of up to 8 spans. Features include: pinned, fixed or cantilever ends; columns; constant or variable E1 within spans; point, uniformly distributed, trapezoidal or triangular loading; point or range for influence lines; enveloping of load train results for range of influence lines; tabular and graphical output

References

Availability
Purchase

Language
Basic

Computer
HP 9845 HP 85/87

DP102: Continuous beam design *Oasys Limited*
A complementary program to AP102, which produces a reinforcement design in accordance with CP110. Output is longitudinal reinforcement through the spans with curtailment dimensions, link groups with curtailment dimensions and a span/depth ratio check. All interactions between various sections within a span and across supports are taken into account

References

Availability
Purchase

Language
Basic

Computer
HP 9845 HP 85/87

DP108: Deflection of beam *Oasys Limited*
Determines the deflections of a single span beam or cantilever in accordance with Appendix A of CP110. The member type can be specified as reinforced concrete or homogenous. Alternatively, curvatures at points along the span may be entered directly to utilise only the curve fitting section of the program

References

Availability
Purchase

Language
Basic

Computer
HP 9845 HP 85/87

CP110-BEAMS/1 *Quest GENESYS Limited*
This sub-system enables an engineer to analyse and design continuous, reinforced concrete beams in accordance with CP110:Part 1:1972. The method used is one of sub-frame analysis, and includes column lifts. Line loading patterns are automatically applied. Moment redistribution is effected by user control

References
GENESYS program library

Availability
Bureau service, hire

Language
Gentran

Computer
DEC 10, Honeywell IBM, ICL, PE, Prime, others

CP110-BEAMS 1 *Quest GENESYS Limited*
For design and detail of reinforced concrete continuous beams in accordance with the UK Code of Practice, CP110. Many options of loading are provided, with the self weight and superimposed load patterns being generated automatically. The designer can control support moment redistribution and other design options including bar sizes and numbers. Detailing covers bar fixing and bending schedules

References

Availability

Language
Gentran

Computer

Analysis of Continuous Beams with Varying Section Properties *Reading Computer Services Limited*
Any straight, continuous beam with varying cross-sectional shape can be analysed under complex applied bending moments and shear forces. Output can be searched for maximum under load case combinations. Can be used in conjunction with the prestressed beam program

References

Availability

Language

Computer
CP/M Microcomputer

Design of Continuous Prestressed Beams *Reading Computer Services Limited*
Continuous beams with varying section properties and specified prestressing tendons can be designed very rapidly using this system. The user can define the tendon shape and built in stresses prior to prestress. Friction loss along tendons can be included as well as staged construction. The maximum number of spans is limited to 7, with up to 20 tendons in any construction stage

References

Availability

Language

Computer
CP/M Microcomputer

CONBEAM 4 and 5 *Scott Wilson Kirkpatrick and Partners*
CONBEAM 4 carries out the analysis and CONBEAM 5 handles the structural design of continuous beams in accordance with CP110. CONBEAM 4 calculates bending moments and shear force envelopes for limit state conditions; these may be plotted. CONBEAM 5 calculates reinforcement required in one or more layers. Stopping off points for all bars are calculated, and the size and spacing of links are produced. Plots bar stopping off positions superimposed on the moment envelope diagrams

References
DOC Evaluation Report No 2

Availability
Purchase or lease

Language
Fortran

Computer
DEC VAX/VMS Plotter

Computer programs for the building industry

0805

FOCALS *The Association for Computer Aided Design Limited*
For the design of raft foundations, footings and slabs on ground. Analyses a plate of arbitrary rigidity and variable thickness on a cross-anisotropic elastic layered medium. Rectangular plate elements are used. Can deal with any number of horizontal material layers of infinite extent in the horizontal direction. Problem symmetry can be taken into account using beam and plate elements. Automatic mesh generation can be used

References

Availability
Bureau: contact ACADS

Language
ANSI Fortran IV

Computer
Cyber

0806

BB *British Olivetti Limited*
For the analysis of reinforced concrete members and foundations. Calculates the highest stresses induced in the concrete and the steel reinforcement of a beam, column or bridge pier subject to biaxial bending and thrust

References
Copyright: Alcock Shearing and Partners

Availability
Purchase

Language
Basic

Computer
Olivetti minicomputer

0807

PP *British Olivetti Limited*
For the analysis of structural piling systems. This program calculates displacements and forces induced at the heads in a rigid pile cap or foundation pad subject to any pattern of static loading. Piles may be vertical or battered

References
Copyright: Alcock Shearing and Partners

Availability
Purchase

Language
Basic

Computer
Olivetti minicomputer

0808

DSIGN *Building Computer Services Limited*
Comprises a series of linked sub-systems to process beams, columns and foundations, producing reports on final design to CP114, steel fixing details, bar schedules and steel, concrete and shuttering quantities. Data may be prepared using related programs. Outputs for beams and columns comprise a table of design requirements, while pad foundation fixing details are in tabular form and bar schedules are as for beams and columns

References

Availability
Bureau service, hire, sale

Language
Fortran

Computer
DEC

0809

Concrete pad foundation design *Camutek*
Designs reinforced concrete pad foundations to resist specified vertical loads and bending moments and maintain the bearing pressure within specified limits

References

Availability
From owner

Language
Basic

Computer
HP 9830,(2k) or (6k) 9831, 9835, 9845
Future: HP85, 86

0810

Design of bored, in-situ piles *Camutek*
The pile diameter is input with the shaft adhesion factor, end bearing factor and required factor of safety. Soil is specified by defining successive strata. Individual piles are designed by specifying the load capacity required. When the design of a series of piles has been completed, a table summarising the results is printed out, listing the reference number of each pile in numerical order, the working load and the total strength

References

Availability
From Camutek

Language
Basic

Computer
HP 9835, 9845
Future: HP 85 & 86

0811

FICHK *Civil and Structural Computing (Northern) Limited*
Performs portal frame boundary condition fire collapse analysis based on Constrado References. Foundation moments and forces are determined for the collapse conditions. Wind loading considerations may be included if required

References
Bradshaw, Buckton and Tonge

Availability
Bureau service, time sharing, in-house

Language

Computer

0812

FOUNDS *Civil and Structural Computing (Northern) Limited*
Carries out the design of mass or reinforced concrete pad foundations subject to external forces. Factor of safety checks and the design of steel reinforcement are included

References
Bradshaw, Buckton and Tonge

Availability
Bureau service, time sharing, in-house

Language

Computer

0813

FOUNDS *Civil and Structural Computing (Northern) Limited*
Performs a serviceability analysis on a pad foundation, either mass or reinforced concrete foundations. Up to 15 load components may be applied, as DEAD, IMPOSED or WIND. Each component can consist of a stanchion axial tension or compression, a major axis moment and a horizontal force. Stanchions can be offset on the foundation. For each load combination (up to 6), the bearing pressure diagram and factors of safety against overturning and sliding are calculated and compared to limiting values

References
Bradshaw, Buckton and Tonge

Availability
Bureau service, time sharing, in-house

Language

Computer

0814

PILEG *Civil and Structural Computing (Northern) Limited*
Analyses a group of piles connected to a rigid pile cap. Lateral earth pressure is not taken into account. Mainly used for pile groups which are end bearing and relatively free-standing over a large proportion of their length, such as piles driven into soft soil or mud or in jetties and dolphins

References
Bradshaw, Buckton and Tonge

Availability
Bureau service, time sharing, in-house

Language

Computer

Computer programs for the building industry

PTAIN *Civil and Structural Computing (Northern) Limited*
Automatically designs the minimum section size for a reinforced brickwork pocket retaining wall subject to specified constraints

References
Bradshaw, Buckton and Tonge

Availability
Bureau service, time sharing, in-house

Language

Computer

RTAIN *Civil and Structural Computing (Northern) Limited*
Allows the user to design a reinforced concrete cantilever retaining wall. The program is interactive and is in accordance with CP2 Earth retaining structures, and CP110 The structural use of concrete

References
Bradshaw, Buckton and Tonge

Availability
Bureau service, time sharing, in-house

Language

Computer

SPILE *Civil and Structural Computing (Northern) Limited*
Analyses a sheet pile wall for bending moments, shears and deflections. Multiple soil layers and different water levels on the two faces of the wall can be entered as data. The program allows water pressure at the toe either side of the wall to be either equal or a full hydrostatic head. Stiffness of the wall and elasticity of the soil are taken into account; imposed forces and moments can be applied to the structure

References
Bradshaw, Buckton and Tonge

Availability
Bureau service, time sharing, in-house

Language

Computer

FOOTER DESIGN *Civil-Ware (USA)*
Determines the adequacy of a non-reinforced continuous spread concrete footing. The design is based on the soil conditions and the specific loading on the footer

References

Availability
Purchase

Language
Applesoft

Computer
Apple II+ (48K)

PAD DESIGN *Civil-Ware (USA)*
Determines the physical size, thickness, steel rebar size and steel area required for a square concrete pad supporting a concentrated column load. Design considerations are from the 1977 ACI codes

References

Availability
Purchase

Language
Applesoft

Computer
Apple II+ (48K)

GROUP *Computel Limited*
A set of programs, based on the integration of Mindlin's Solution, for considering the lateral, vertical and applied moments on a pile group

References
GEOCOMP

Availability

Language

Computer

RETAINING WALL *Computrav (UK) Limited*
This program designs a vertical cantilever wall and footing in reinforced concrete

References
Approved by ACT Sirius

Availability
Purchase

Language
Basic

Computer
Minimum 32Kb on 8 and 16-bit micros under CP/M

CD-4. Footing design *Ecom Associates, Inc*
Designs or checks an isolated column footing for dimensions, steel requirements, and quantities. Factors are included for wind or earthquake load conditions. Also included is a check and design for horizontal keys to resist sliding

References

Availability
Purchase

Language
M Basic

Computer
HP, Apple, Tandy TRS-80, IBM PC

SHEET PILE *Engineering Software Services Limited*
Performs the analysis and design of multi-frame sheet piled walls or cofferdams. The suite allows up to 12 different group strata and up to 8 different frames to be considered

References

Availability

Language

Computer
Olivetti M20

VERT-PILE *Tony Gee and Partners*
A program for structural engineers. It provides analysis of pile loads under a rigid pilecap having a wide variety of loadings, using simple elastic theory. Input may be interactive or from data lines within the program. Allows for variables for pile positions and loadings. Output includes pile moduli, load case resultants and pile loads

References

Availability
Purchase

Language
HP Enhanced Basic

Computer
Hewlett-Packard HP9845 B/C

0825

RETWALL 1 *Geocomp UK Limited*
Calculates active and passive pressures, depth of penetration, bending moments and shear stress for retaining walls of sheet pile type in multilayered soils. Cantilevered or anchored walls can be analysed. For anchored walls the required tie force is calculated. The effects of water on the active and/or passive side of the wall, and of seepage cracks owing to tension, may also be considered

References

Availability
Sale or hire negotiable

Language
Fortran IV

Computer
ICL 1900, CDC 6600
PDP 11/34

0826

RETWALL 2 *Geocomp UK Limited*
This is a stress analysis program to aid in the design of multi-stage, anchored retaining walls. The program calculates horizontal movements, wall rotations, shear forces and bending moments. Variables which can be controlled on input include geometry of the wall, soil properties, anchor forces and earth pressures

References
Soil Mechanics Limited

Availability
Purchase or hire

Language
Fortran

Computer
28K Memory.
PDP 11/34

0827

SHEETPILE-2 *Grist Business Services Limited*
Developed for civil engineering applications, for design of single tied, multi tied or cantilevered sheet pile retaining walls in multilayered soils; uses either the free or fixed earth support method in analysis. The program accepts: up to 20 soil types and up to 15 ties; water on both the active and passive side of the wall; a uniform active surcharge. Output consists of: active and passive soil pressures; length and penetration of pile; maximum bending moments; tie forces per metre run

References

Availability
Purchase

Language
Fortran

Computer
Apple II 48K

0828

Cantilever Wall Analysis *Hydro Systems (USA)*
Analyses stability of a cantilever retaining wall. Allows inclusion of base key, water table at any depth behind wall, any backfill angle, and any soil depth at the toe. Outputs include overturning and resisting moments with safety factor, sliding and resisting forces with safety factor, toe and heel pressures, and location of vertical resultant acting on base. Also outputs maximum internal moment and shears in stem, toe, heel and key

References

Availability
Purchase

Language

Computer
48K RAM
minimum

0829

Dike settlement *A M Kinney, Inc*
Originally to determine settlement beneath large earth fill structures; now developed to determine vertical, radial, tangential, and shear stresses at any point beneath a loaded area. Calculates problems of stress distribution and walls, vertical excavations, and underground structures. Will also calculate settlements based on the vertical stress changes calculated along with time rates of settlements

References

Availability

Language
Fortran

Computer
IBM 1130 and 370

0830

Settlement analysis *A M Kinney, Inc*
Calculates settlement for footings using triangular approximations, Boussinesq or Westerguard methods of stress calculation. Output can be tailored for specific information to determine effects of increased loading on existing or new footings, loads upon existing adjacent footing, surcharge loading, and rate of settlement

References

Availability

Language
Fortran

Computer
IBM 1130 and 370

0831

Specialised programs *A M Kinney, Inc*
The Soils and Material Engineering Dept has developed programs to solve special soils engineering problems. An example was the determination of consolidation factors for volume estimates for partially submerged sediments. This involved 7 million cubic yards of sediment over a 15-year life expectancy at varying fill rates, highly compressible bottom characteristics, and other variables. Another involved the use of sheet pile retaining walls with multiple tie back requirements and associated stress calculations

References

Availability

Language
Fortran

Computer
IBM 1130 and 370

0832

Terzaghi bearing capacity determination *A M Kinney, Inc*
Analyses for bearing capacity of rectangular, continuous or circular footings. Input allows use of construction sequence effects such as excavations around existing footings, or surcharging prior to construction

References

Availability

Language
Fortran

Computer
IBM 1130 and 370

0833

Time rate of settlement *A M Kinney, Inc*
Calculates the settlement at 20, 40, 60, 80 and 90 per cent consolidation in terms of time and degree of settlement

References

Availability

Language
Fortran

Computer
IBM 1130 and 370

0834

SLOPE *Microcomp*
Computes the slope stability of an earth embankment against sliding. Input includes minimum and maximum radii for radius arc failure, unit weights of soil above and below a water table, friction angles and cohesion values. Output consists of location of centre of arc and the safety factor for each location; the minimum value found in the factor of safety. An optional detailed output contains information for each soil layer, including the friction angle, tangential forces and friction resistance

References

Availability
Purchase

Language

Computer
Apple, and most microcomputers using CP/M

Brick Pier Design *Microsoft Structural Control Systems Limited*
Permits rectangular brick/block piers or sections of wall to be rapidly designed to BS CP111

References
Personal Computing with Apple

Availability

Language
Applesoft Basic

Computer
Apple II

Rectangular Pad Footing Design *Microsoft Structural Control Systems Limited*
Any number of loads or moments can be applied to the footing. Moments about both axes. Resultant anywhere under the base

References
Personal Computing with Apple

Availability

Language
Applesoft Basic

Computer
Apple II

VDISP *Oasys Limited*
A fully interactive program which calculates elastic settlements and stresses at various levels below rectangular and circular foundations subjected to vertical pressure loadings. Features include: a number of horizontal soil layers may be specified; linear variation of soil modules may be specified for each soil layer; displacements and stresses may be calculated at several levels; solution is based on an integration of the Boussinesq equation

References

Availability
Bureau service

Language
Fortran

Computer
DEC10

CP111: Retaining walls *Oasys Limited*
Analyses gravity and cantilever walls retaining frictional or cohesive soils including silts and partially saturated clays in any combination. Given the wall geometry and the soil properties, the program calculates the pressures against the wall and under the base, the moments and shear forces in the wall, and the factors of safety against overturning and sliding. Features include: angled walls, base keys, retained soil surface slope, water table, ten different soil strata, ground anchors and loading

References

Availability
Purchase

Language
Basic

Computer
HP 9845, HP 85/87

DP101: Foundation sizing and design *Oasys Limited*
For sizing and reinforcement design of rectangular column bases in accordance with CP110. The program allows the user to vary the geometrical parameters of the base to produce a satisfactory bearing pressure. Negative pressure (tension) is not allowed under the base, and an iterative procedure is used to calculate the pressures where this occurs. Top and bottom steel is calculated; shear and local bond is checked and adjusted as necessary

References

Availability
Purchase

Language
Basic

Computer
HP 9845 HP 85/87

NON-CIRCULAR SLIP/1 *Quest GENESYS Limited*
This sub-system enables an engineer to examine the stability of a slope, using the Morgenstern and Price method. The number of soils and geometry of slope to be considered are not limited by the sub-system. The size of problem to be handled is limited only by the size and type of computer used

References
GENESYS program library

Availability
Bureau service, hire

Language
Gentran

Computer
DEC 20, Honeywell IBM, ICL, PE Prime, others

PILE-2D/1 *Quest GENESYS Limited*
This sub-system enables an engineer to analyse the behaviour of groups of piles in long rows. Forces are considered in two dimensions. Bending, shear and axial forces are determined in vertical or raked piles

References
GENESYS program library

Availability
Bureau service, hire

Language
Gentran

Computer
DEC 10, Honeywell IBM, ICL, PE Prime, others

PILE-3D/1 *Quest GENESYS Limited*
This sub-system enables the engineer to analyse the behaviour of groups of piles in long rows. Forces are considered in three dimensions. Bending, shear and axial forces are determined in vertical or raked piles

References
GENESYS program library

Availability
Bureau service, hire

Language
Gentran

Computer
DEC 20, Honeywell IBM, ICL, PE Prime, others

SHEETPILE/1 *Quest GENESYS Limited*
This sub-system enables an engineer to design single and multiple anchor retaining walls of the sheet pile type for various depths. There are no limits to the numbers of layers or types of soil to be considered

References
GENESYS program library

Availability
Bureau service, hire

Language
Gentran

Computer
DEC 10, Honeywell IBM, ICL, PE, Prime, others

RETA/1 *Quest GENESYS Limited*
Stability analysis of cantilever retaining walls or abutments, in accordance with CP2, can be performed by this program. Effects of active and passive pressures, water levels, uplift and tension cracks can be considered. A line printer sketch of the retaining wall can be produced. Results include safety factors against overturning, slip and sliding, and bearing pressures; also calculated are moment and shear forces on the wall

References

Availability

Language
Gentran

Computer

0845

SKETCH/1 *Quest GENESYS Limited*
Used when dealing with retaining wall systems. The results produced by SHEETPILE/2 can also be presented in graphical form using this program. Bending moments, shear forces and deflections can be plotted in simplified form on the line printer

References

Availability

Language
Gentran

Computer

0846

Calculation of Loads in Pile Group (2D and 3D) *Reading Computer Services Limited*
Loads are described using standard components such as rectangular, triangular dead load masses, earth pressures, fluid pressures, etc. The group is defined by rows and columns, and eccentricities can be related to any key dimension. Alternatively, piles can be reduced to a grid system. Pile loadings are calculated together with moments and shears in individual piles. The effect of the pile cap is included

References

Availability

Language

Computer
CP/M Microcomputer

0847

Design of Sheet Pile Walls *Reading Computer Services Limited*
This program enables the casual user to quickly produce a sheet pile wall design which, when corrected by factors such as those based on Rowe's method, follows closely that obtained using well established hand methods. Applicable to both cantilever or single anchored walls, the program automatically generates earth pressures from soil parameters with consideration given to limits imposed by the Code of Practice

References

Availability

Language

Computer
CP/M Microcomputer

0848

Reinforced Concrete Base Design to CP110 *Reading Computer Services Limited*
Using applied loadings, the program calculates bearing pressures, full section and punching shear. Bending and shear steel are output and the ultimate resistance moment is also calculated

References

Availability

Language

Computer
CP/M Microcomputer

0849

PFAHL 2 *RIB*
Determination of the stress resultants of 2D and 3D pile foundations with rigid pile cap slabs. Provides a stability check of the total system

References

Availability
Purchase

Language
Fortran IV

Computer
CPU 64K

0850

PGELV *SIA Computer Services*
A vertical pile group analysis program

References

Availability
Bureau service

Language
High level

Computer
Control Data,
IBM, Prime

0851

RAFTSIM *SIA Computer Services*
A program for the analysis of raft foundation

References

Availability
Bureau service

Language
High level

Computer
Control Data,
IBM, Prime

0852

CONCRETE *Systemshare*
Analyses stress in reinforced concrete sections and foundations in the design of construction and civil engineering projects. Handles: sections and foundations with up to 100 section coordinates. 100 reinforcing bars and up to 10 individual loads; circular sections; hollow sections; load conditions can be eccentric axial, eccentric axial plus fixed moments, axial load at the centroid plus fixed moments, or just fixed moments. Second moments of area can be obtained. Cross-sections can be plotted on the screen

References

Availability
Purchase

Language
Applesoft Basic

Computer
Apple II, 48K

0853

FOUNDATIONS: BASE 1 *Technical Services*
Calculates maximum and minimum ground bearing pressures under a rectangular base. If the eccentricity of loading is such that 'tension' develops under part of the base, the maximum ground pressure is calculated together with the length of the base which is in positive ground contact. The program accepts vertical loads, bending moments and horizontal loads at a stated distance above the lower edge of the base

References

Availability
Purchase

Language
Basic

Computer
Olivetti P6060,
and P6066, 16K

0854

REINFORCED CONCRETE CANTILEVER RETAINING WALL *Technical Services*
For designing a cantilever reinforced concrete retaining wall of inverted T cross-section. The geometry of the wall may be specified, and various applied forces can be used. Factors of safety against overturning and sliding are calculated, and the maximum and minimum ground pressures due to the applied loads. The length of base or heel, may then be modified. Internal bending moments and shear forces are printed out, together with a full calculation sheet

References

Availability
Purchase

Language
Basic

Computer
Olivetti P6060,
and P6066, 16K

PGROUP *UCC (Great Britain) Limited*
Analyses groups of piles. The geometry of the piles and the loads to which they are subjected are at the discretion of the user. Output gives settlement, moments, shear and axial loads, and a full listing of input data

References
Developed by the computer branch of the DoE (Highway Engineering)

Availability
Bureau service

Language
Fortran

Computer

SPILE *UCC (Great Britain) Limited*
Analyses any arrangement of a group of piles supporting one pile cap. Output gives moments, axial shears and forces, and a full listing of input data

References
Developed by the Midland Road Construction Unit

Availability
Bureau service

Language
Fortran

Computer

SLIP *Civil and Structural Computing (Northern) Limited*
Examines slope stability using a circular slip failure criterion. Up to 50 soil layers comprising up to 30 different soil types can be specified. A piezometric surface can be included and point loads may be applied. Slip circles can be defined using a grid of circle centres, and either a point through which they pass or a line to which they are tangential

References
Bradshaw, Buckton and Tonge

Availability
Bureau service, time sharing, in-house

Language

Computer

EARTHWORK *Civil-Ware (USA)*
Computes earthwork cut and fill volumes based on the Average End Area method. Up to 35 separate cross-sections with 25 existing and 25 proposed data points per cross-section are accommodated. All cross-sections are maintained in memory and can be reviewed at any time

References

Availability
Purchase

Language
Applesoft

Computer
Apple II+ (48K)

EARTH *Computational Mechanics Consultants Limited*
Used for road or general earthwork computations. Output includes: stations of first and last cross-sections of the analysis; the amount the final cross-sections were raised or lowered by the user on computer; horizontal shift and left/right superelevation; current bulking and compaction factors; total unadjusted cut and fill; total haulage adjusted with bulking factor; combined total without compaction factor applied

References

Availability
Licence

Language
Fortran IV

Computer
Microcomputer with minimum 16K

GEO 15 *Computel Limited*
A program concerned with the stability of 3D wedges

References
GEOCOMP

Availability

Language

Computer

Slope Stability *Computer Design*
Part of the COSPACK package. For the determination of safety factors for the stability of slopes or embankments, using Bishop's method where failure surfaces are taken as circles. The slope is subdivided into 150 slices allowing for any description of the profile, any subdivision into layers and any definition of prescribed tangency lines for the circles

References
Sirius Computing, January 1983

Availability
Purchase, lease

Language
Basic

Computer
ACT Sirius 1 256K. Plotter

SLIP CIRCLE *Computrav (UK) Limited*
Calculates the safety factors of slip circles in an embankment. The soil blocks are described by discrete lines. Ground water pressures can be included automatically

References
Approved by ACT Sirius

Availability
Purchase

Language
Basic

Computer
Minimum 32Kb on 8 and 16-bit micros under CP/M

SLIPSYST *Geocomp UK Limited*
Calculates the factor of safety against sliding for either a circular or a non-circular slip surface. The effect of excess water pressure in pores, Ru values, tension cracks, point or uniformly distributed loads and also earthquake effects may be considered on a section with up to twenty soil types and up to ten phreatic surfaces

References

Availability
Sale or hire negotiable

Language
Fortran IV

Computer
ICL 1900, IBM 360 CDC 6600, PDP 11/34, Prime

WEDGE *Geocomp UK Limited*
Calculates the factor of safety against sliding of a wedge of material. Forces required to maintain a specified factor of safety are determined. The program will analyse several planes, at which failure is possible, in one run. Varying properties of soils and effects of cracks owing to tension may also be considered

References

Availability
Sale or hire negotiable

Language
Fortran IV

Computer
ICL 1900, CDC 6600 PDP 11/34

0865

SLIPCIRCLE-1 *Grist Business Services Limited*
For civil engineering applications. Used to calculate the optimum slope in excavation, or to check existing slope stability. Deals with multilayered soils, with the presence of water and superimposed loads. Minimum factor of safety computed from specified grid of slip circles. The program accepts up to 20 soil types. Output consists of the factor of safety for each specified circle, and the minimum factor of safety for a grid of trial circles

References

Availability
Purchase

Language
Fortran

Computer
Apple II 48K

0866

Consolidation test program *A M Kinney, Inc*
Calculates continuous void ratio changes with percentage of consolidation in loading increments from 1/16 to 20 ton/ft^2 and reports the theoretical coefficient of permeability and the coefficient of consolidation

References

Availability

Language
Fortran

Computer
IBM 1130 and 370

0867

Constant and falling head, or capillary permeability *A M Kinney, Inc*
The program calculates the coeffeicient or permeability in cm per sec, ft per sec and ft per min

References

Availability

Language
Fortran

Computer
IBM 1130 and 370

0868

Generalised sliding wedge method for slope stability and earth pressure analysis *A M Kinney, Inc*
The program calculates factors of safety for complex soil conditions, and where obvious failure surfaces are irregular and non circular

References

Availability

Language
Fortran

Computer
IBM 1130 and 370

0869

Index test program *A M Kinney, Inc*
The program calculates liquid limit, plastic limit, plasticity index, flow index, toughness index, and liquidity index

References

Availability

Language
Fortran

Computer
IBM 1130 and 370

0870

Sieve and/or hydrometer analysis *A M Kinney, Inc*
The program calculates percentage of sand, silt, clay and colloids in a sample, in a size range from 7.62mm to 0.00120mm

References

Availability

Language
Fortran

Computer
IBM 1130 and 370

0871

Slope stability analysis *A M Kinney, Inc*
Using the modified Swedish slip circle method, the program computes the factor of safety against sliding for a particular failure arc for an earth embankment for conditions involving drawdown, steady seepage, or partial pool. The cohesion and friction angle values for a segment of arc are determined by comparing the scope of line and the slope of tangent to the failure arc at the intersection on the right end of the specific segment

References

Availability

Language
Fortran

Computer
IBM 1130 and 370

0872

Slope stability search *A M Kinney, Inc*
Computes factors of safety by two methods; the ordinary method of slices, and the Bishop equation. The centres of rotation and lengths of the failure arcs are systematically changed until the minimum factor of safety is determined

References

Availability

Language
Fortran

Computer
IBM 1130 and 370

0873

Specific gravity *A M Kinney, Inc*
The program calculates the specific gravity from a minimum of three test runs

References

Availability

Language
Fortran

Computer
IBM 1130 and 370

0874

Swedish slip circle slope stability analysis *A M Kinney, Inc*
'The Method of Slices' program. This follows the same procedure as set out in the Corps of Engineers Civil Works Engineering Manual, EM 1110-2-1902, Appendix VI. Determines a factor of safety by dividing the resisting forces by the driving forces

References

Availability

Language
Fortran

Computer
IBM 1130 and 370

Computer programs for the building industry

Triaxial test program *A M Kinney, Inc*
Calculates unconsolidated undrained, consolidated undrained, and consolidated drained
test types, reporting all initial, final and intermediate specimen characteristics. Includes
continuous reporting at approximately 0.5 per cent strain intervals of deviation stress, pore
pressure, actual and effective chamber pressures, total and effective principal stress, and
per cent volume change

References

Availability

Language
Fortran

Computer
IBM 1130 and 370

Unconfined compression program *A M Kinney, Inc*
The program calculates stress at approximately 0.5 per cent intervals to 20 per cent strain,
and reports maximum stress at a respective strain in tsf

References

Availability

Language
Fortran

Computer
IBM 1130 and 370

Unit density *A M Kinney, Inc*
This program will calculate the dry and wet unit weights of any samples

References

Availability

Language
Fortran

Computer
IBM 1130 and 370

Water contents *A M Kinney, Inc*
This program will calculate moisture contents for any samples

References

Availability

Language
Fortran

Computer
IBM 1130 and 370

SLOPE *Oasys Limited*
A fully interactive program for the 2D solution of slope stability problems. Features include:
methods for modelling pore pressure distribution; analysis of submerged or partially
submerged slopes; soil strengths represented by specifying cohesion and/or angles of
shearing resistance, or linear variations and strength with depth and/or overburden
pressure; analysis methods are Swedish circle (Fellenius), Bishop's or Janbu's; circular or
non-circular slip surfaces

References

Availability
Bureau service

Language
Fortran

Computer
DEC10

CP109: Slope stability *Oasys Limited*
Uses Swedish Circle (or Fellenius' method), Bishop's or Janbu's method. Describes up to 9
soil strata with different strength poperties. Pore pressures described by direct input of
local piezometric heads, or calculated from a known water table, with a maximum soil
suction. Pore pressure ratio may be given. External forces may be applied to the ground
surface. Circular or non-circular slip surfaces may be analysed. Examination of circles of
varying radii at each centre; finding the worst safety factor

References

Availability
Purchase

Language
Basic

Computer
HP 9845

Slip-circle/1 *Quest GENESYS Limited*
This sub-system enables a designer to examine the stability of slopes by the method of slip
circle failure. The number of soils which may be considered is not limited by the
sub-system, and any geometry can be analysed. The size of the problem to be handled is
limited only by the size and type of computer used

References
GENESYS program library

Availability
Bureau service, hire

Language
Gentran

Computer
DEC 10, Honeywell
IBM, ICL, PE Prime,
others

EARTHWORKS/1 *Quest GENESYS Limited*
Calculates earthwork quantities using digitised information from section drawings, or data
extracted from tables of cross-section data. Output includes a plot of sections, gross areas
and volumes, top soil stripping and reducing finished road surfaces to formation level.
Suitable for any earthwork calculations where irregular terrain or excavation can be divided
into elemental slices. Applications have included flood water measurement and mining
excavations

References

Availability

Language
Gentran

Computer

Calculation of Earthwork Quantities *Reading Computer Services Limited*
A series of eastings, northings and levels plus a list of triangle connections provides the
ground model. The density of survey can be varied by the user. The earthworks are defined
in a similar way and the user can then command the program to calculate the cut/fill
volumes. Staged working can be included

References

Availability

Language

Computer
CP/M Microcomputer

Stability of Slopes *Reading Computer Services Limited*
This program undertakes the stability analysis of earth slopes as, for example, in cuttings,
embankments and dams. The assumed failure surface can be circular or non-circular, using
either Bishop's method or Morgenstern and Price methods. Almost any geological profile
can be specified, together with complex ground water conditions

References

Availability

Language

Computer
CP/M Microcomputer

0885

CIRCA *SIA Computer Services*
This program deals with slip circle analysis

References

Availability
Bureau service

Language
High level

Computer
Control Data,
IBM, Prime

0886

GEOCOMP *SIA Computer Services*
This is a powerful soil mechanics program suite

References

Availability
Bureau service

Language
High level

Computer
Control Data,
IBM, Prime

0887

SETTLE *SIA Computer Services*
A program used in soil mechanics, to carry out settlement analysis of embankments

References

Availability
Bureau service

Language
High level

Computer
Control Data,
IBM, Prime

0888

BISHOP *Structures and Computers Limited*
For stability analysis of embankments where it is justifiable to assume that slip surfaces will be close to circular arcs in cross-section. Used in the analysis stage of the building design process. Can be used in conjunction with MORGEN (for general slip surfaces) and ACTRES (for plotting input data and results)

References

Availability
Purchase

Language
Fortran IV

Computer
64K

0889

MORGEN *Structures and Computers Limited*
Used for the stability analysis of embankments where the slip surfaces have an arbitrary cross-sectional shape. The program is based on the method of Morgenstern and Price. Used in the analysis stage of the building design process. Can be used in conjunction with BISHOP and ACTRES

References

Availability
Purchase

Language
Fortran IV

Computer
64K

0890

STAB *United Information Services Limited*
This program calculates slope stability, or the factor of safety against circular slip

References

Availability
Bureau service, time sharing

Language
Fortran

Computer
Honeywell
Sigma 9

0891

MWAY *ARC Limited*
Calculates noise values generated by a road, to the DoE's CRTN Methodology. Traffic flow, ground levels and the vertical alignment of the road and associated structures, such as buildings, cuttings, embankments and edge barriers, are taken into consideration. Noise levels are calculated in relation to the surrounding topography. Noise levels and all input data can be output to a graphics screen or a digital plotter

References

Availability
Purchase

Language
Fortran

Computer
Prime
VAX

0832

MTC *Centre de Recherches Routieres*
Computes stress at any point inside an elastic, layered structure resting on an elastic half space, with non-slip or fully slippery interfaces, under a uniform (normal or shear) circular load applied at the surface. Deflections on load axis are also produced

References
ROMAIN, JE, Stresses, strains and deflections in elastic layered systems

Availability
Purchase, bureau service

Language
Fortran

Computer
GE235
CDC 7000
TI 990/IL

0893

ORN *Centre de Recherches Routieres*
Computes the predictable deformation ('rut depth') of a road, pavement or assimilated system, from the thicknesses and deformation properties of the materials, the traffic and the stress distribution inside the structure. Can be coupled with program MTC for stress computation

References
ROMAIN, JE, Rut Depth Prediction in Asphalt Pavements

Availability
Purchase, bureau service

Language
Basic

Computer
GE235
CDC Cyber

0894

BIPS *Computel Limited*
BIPS (British Integrated Program System) carries out all calculations involved in road design. The program prints out the results in tabulated form. It can also transform numerical output into contract drawings by means of a graph plotter

References
Program made available by the Department of the Environment

Availability

Language

Computer

FREEWAY *Computel Limited*
An alternative program to HOPS or BIPS which can carry out all calculations involved in road design, including the finding of the optimum vertical alignment when considering the line of the road. The program is suitable for more complex interchanges than are HOPS or BIPS

References
Program made available by the Department of the Environment

Availability

Language

Computer

HOPS *Computel Limited*
HOPS (Highway Optimisation Program Systems) is used to refine the calculation of the line of the road and to minimise costs. It is applied to find the optimum vertical alignment

References
Program made available by the Department of the Environment

Availability

Language

Computer

VALOR *Computel Limited*
VALOR (Vertical Alignment Optimisation of Roads) is used for road design in urban areas where most of the work is confined to realignment or widening of existing roads

References
Program made available by the Department of the Environment

Availability

Language

Computer

BIPS3 *Facet Limited*
This is a suite of over 30 programs for the design of highways. The programs are divided into 10 groups, each dealing with one of the following design problems: horizontal alignment; vertical alignment; superelevation; ground models; ground cross-sections; road cross-sections; full cross-sections; earthworks quantities; preliminary design; automatic plotting and perspectives

References

Availability
Bureau service, or under licence

Language

Computer
Prime, Norsk Data, Harris, CP/M 8-bit micros

Street Intersection Design *Hydro Systems (USA)*
Intersections may be of two or three straight streets, two curved streets, or straight and curved streets. Minimal input is required to produce complete intersection data

References

Availability
Purchase

Language

Computer
Apple, IBM, TRS-80 with CP/M

SSLEW *Oasys Limited*
Given a vertical alignment, road section and ground data, this program produces cross-sectional plotting data, earthworks and pavement quantities, tabulation of finished road profile levels and grades, and slope lengths for single or dual carriageways. Output gives all quantities related to the road cross-section

References

Availability
Bureau service

Language
Fortran

Computer
DEC 10

ROAD *Oasys Limited*
Enables a complex road section to be created, stored and edited as a templet from which construction quantities and/or earthwork volumes can be calculated given a vertical alignment and ground data. All results are output on a tabulated A4 page suitable for filing

References

Availability
Bureau service

Language
Fortran

Computer
DEC 10

HIGHWAYS/1 *Quest GENESYS Limited*
This sub-system enables an engineer to design highways from preliminary stages through to final quantities and setting out information. The method used is one of longitudinal and horizontal alignments, with lateral templates. Ground information is in the form of variable digital models or cross-sections

References
GENESYS program library

Availability
Bureau service, hire

Language
Gentran

Computer
.Honeywell, IBM, ICL, PE, Prime, others

Design of Highways *Reading Computer Services Limited*
A suite of five programs to undertake horizontal alignment, vertical alignment, superelevation, cross-sections and earthworks. The complete suite is integrated and superelevation may be designed to British or American Standards

References

Availability

Language

Computer
CP/M Microcomputer

BIPS (British Integrated Program System) *Scicon Limited*
Geometric design of highway alignments. A stage by stage approach is used, similar to that in a drawing office. Cross and longitudinal sections, plans and earthworks can be output graphically. The system comprises several groups of programs, each of which performs a specific function. At each stage, data is input and intermediate results may be inspected

References

Availability
Bureau service

Language

Computer
Univac 1100/62

0905

HOPS *Scicon Limited*

A system comprising five programs designed to assist the engineer in generating alignments of highways from ground data, and in planning earthworks and structures at the lowest cost. Any one of the five programs may be used individually. They cover ground data processing, generation of initial vertical alignments, phasing of horizontal and vertical curves, reduction of costs of earthworks and structures, and analysis of earth moving

References
Developed by the Transport and Road Research Laboratory

Availability
Bureau service

Language

Computer
Univac 1100/62

0906

COSMOS *SIA Computer Services*

This program is used as a road construction cost estimating model

References

Availability
Bureau service

Language
High level

Computer
Control Data, IBM, Prime

0907

DAPHNE *SIA Computer Services*

A program for the analysis and design of highway drainage networks

References

Availability
Bureau service

Language
High level

Computer
Control Data, IBM, Prime

0908

GRIP *SIA Computer Services*

This is a computer aided design system used in highway engineering. It provides interactive road plan geometry design

References

Availability
Bureau service

Language
High level

Computer
Control Data, IBM, Prime

0909

HIGRAPH *SIA Computer Services*

This is an advanced contract drawing and graphics system used for highway design

References

Availability
Bureau service

Language
High level

Computer
Control Data, IBM, Prime

0910

PRISE *SIA Computer Services*

Used in project control for highway engineering. The program provides automatic production of bills of quantities to CSMM and MMRB

References

Availability
Bureau service

Language
High level

Computer
Control Data, IBM, Prime

0911

BIPS-3 *United Information Services Limited*

This is an implementation of the DoE highway design system, which is capable of operation in batch or time sharing modes. The suite of programs covers all aspects of highway design, including initial alignment, cross-sections and earthworks quantities

References

Availability
Bureau service, time sharing

Language
Fortran

Computer
Honeywell Sigma 9

0912

SURFACE AND FOUL WATER DRAINAGE DESIGN *ABC Data Limited*

Handles the hydraulic design of small and medium drainage systems and checking of pipe strengths. Invert level, depth of inspection chamber, accumulated contributing area, rate of flow and minimum pipe diameter are calculated for each pipe run. Existing systems can be checked for new loads. Maximum pipe diameter for surface drainage calculations is 600mm

References

Availability
Purchase

Language
Compiled Basic

Computer
Commodore 8032/8096. 32K/96K

0913

RORB *The Association for Computer Aided Design Limited*

Calculation of flood hydrographs from storm data; also design of retarding basins. Deals with normal catchment storage, retarding basins, reservoirs, lakes, and flood plain storage. Areal and temporal variations of rainfall intensity and of loss parameters are provided for. Catchment storage may be linear or non-linear. For output, the user selects from peak discharges, hydrographs, rainfall and rainfall-excess hyetographs, data listings and data checking messages

References

Availability
Purchase

Language
Fortran

Computer
Burroughs DEC, Olivetti, Univac, others

0914

HYDRA *Amplix Services Limited*

Deals with the design of foul and surface water drainage systems based on RRL design procedures. The design scope is dependent on the amount of disk storage, but is typically 1000 lines of data. Features include: up to 30 pipes per joint-set; 5 pipe section types including channels; pipes designed from 150mm diameter; non standard rainfall profiles; user entered hydrograph

References

Availability
Purchase

Language
Commercial (SMB) Cobol, Fortran

Computer
CP/M or MP/M Microcomputer

DRAIN 1 *Associated British Consultants (Computers) Limited*
Used for the design of a surface water drainage network based on the Colnbrook White
Equation and Bilham Formula. There is an extension to cover domestic foul sewers. Output
includes critical flows and pipe sizes

References

Availability
Purchase

Language
Basic

Computer
64K TRS80 Model 2

OPEN CHANNEL *Civil-Ware (USA)*
Computes the flow capacity for a given depth of flow in a trapezoidal, triangular or
rectangular channel, using Manning's equation. Critical depth is also calculated for the
channel section. User can display a graphic cross-section plot in HI-RES graphics

References

Availability
Purchase

Language
Applesoft

Computer
Apple II+ (48K)

OCH *Civilsoft (USA)*
Used in open channel hydraulics. Solves for any one missing hydraulic parameter from the
possible choices of discharge, bed slope, depth, base width or Manning's n. Assuming
uniform steady flow, answers include the missing parameter and 13 others, including
critical depth. Froude, critical slope, velocity head and pressure plus momentum. Can be
used for any trapezoidal, rectangular or triangular channel

References
ASCE, Building Construction Digest

Availability
Purchase

Language
8080 or 8088/86

Computer
8-bit with 64K or
16-bit with 128K
memory

Design Hydrographs *Hilbern Engineering Software, USA*
Four variations of a program for the computation of a hydrograph from a complex drainage
basin. Hydrographs of runoff from the various sub basins comprising the total basin are
computed by the application of rainfall-excess to the unit hydrograph of each basin. These
hydrographs are then combined and flood routed through channel and/or reservoir storage
to give the total basin hydrograph

References

Availability
Purchase

Language
Microsoft Basic

Computer
Osborne, IBM PC,
HP, TRS-80,

Pumping Station Analysis *Hilbern Engineering Software, USA*
Analyses storm water pumping stations and keeps a running account of pumping station
operation with time. Inputs are: storage in the basin at successively higher elevations, the
pump on and off elevations and the pump capacities in gpm. Inflow hydrographs to the
pumping installation may be input manually or from disk file

References

Availability
Purchase

Language
Basic

Computer
Osborne, TRS-80,
IBM PC, Apple

Sanitary Sewer System *Hilbern Engineering Software, USA*
Three sections: 1 for the analysis of sanitary sewer system; 2 for the design of sanitary
sewer system; 3 for the analysis of force mains or water transmission mains

References

Availability
Purchase

Language
Basic

Computer
Osborne, HP85,
TRS-80, IBM PC

Stormwater Management *Hilbern Engineering Software, USA*
Series of 32 programs for the preliminary analysis and final design of storm water
management systems for urban areas. Includes 8 programs in hydrology and 20 programs
in hydraulics

References

Availability
Purchase

Language
Basic

Computer
Osborne, HP85,
TRS-80, IBM PC

Urban Hydrograph *Hilbern Engineering Software, USA*
Santa Barbara urban hydrograph method utilising runoff curve numbers. Rainfall excess
increments are computed by a modification of the standard Soil Conservation Service
rainfall runoff equation. The summed rainfall excess increments are routed through an
imaginary linear reservoir with a time delay equal to the time of concentration of the basin.
The computed runoff hydrograph is then plotted

References

Availability
Purchase

Language
Basic

Computer
Osborne, TRS-80,
IBM PC, Apple
DOS/CP/M

DRAINCALC *Hydro Systems (USA)*
A hydrology system that will accept, analyse and model a wide variety of watersheds. The
model is used to analyse and design different controls and structures used in drainage
systems. The program performs calculations showing controlled run-off with minimal effect
on the abutting drainage areas, then graphs the results for reports and presentations. Up
to 30 different watersheds may be incorporated into one problem. Designs drainage
systems, calculates pipe sizes for a given flow, and stores drainage data

References

Availability
Purchase

Language

Computer
Apple, IBM, TRS-80
with CP/M

HYDRO *Hydro Systems (USA)*
A menu driven group of programs for hydraulics analysis and design, including: Circular
pipes (pressure lines-Hazen-Williams, and sewer lines- Manning), Trapezoidal Triangular,
Rectangular and Parabolic channels, Pipe network analysis, Orifice analysis, and
Broad-crested weir analysis. Output for channel sub-routines include total energy, Froude
number, critical depth, critical velocity and critical discharge

References

Availability
Purchase

Language

Computer
Apple II, TRS-80
IBM PC 32K RAM
minimum

0925

HYDRO *Hydro Systems (USA)*
A menu driven group of programs for hydraulics analysis and design, including: Circular pipes (pressure lines-Hazen-Williams, and sewer lines- Manning), Trapezordal Triangular, Rectangular and Parabolic channesl, Pipe network analysis, Orifice analysis, and Broad-crested weir analysis. Output for channel sub-routines include total energy, Froude number, critical depth, critical velocity and critical discharge

References

Availability
Purchase

Language

Computer
Apple II, TRS-80
IBM PC
52K RAM minimum

0926

BESTWELS *In-situ, Inc. USA*
Optimises the location of wells within a project site for maximum water production. Includes influence from existing wells in adjacent properties. Graphic output

References

Availability
Time sharing

Language
Fortran, Basic, Cobol, Datatrieve

Computer
DEC VAX 11/780
plotter

0927

DELAY 2 *In-situ, Inc. USA*
Calculates the well function (unconfined aquifer) for a partially or fully penetrating well

References

Availability
Time sharing

Language
Fortran, Basic, Cobol, Datatrieve

Computer
DEC VAX 11/780
plotter

0928

DRAINFLD *In-situ, Inc. USA*
Model for unsaturated flow in a porous medium underlying a drainfield treatment facility. Can observe transient or steady state water saturation on an arbitrary grid underlying the drainfield. Applicable to waste disposal sites

References

Availability
Time sharing

Language
Fortran, Basic, Cobol, Datatrieve

Computer
DEC VAX 11/780
plotter

0929

DWATER *In-situ, Inc. USA*
Calculates the effects of dewatering for a system of pits or wells. Generates drawdown data resulting from dewatering. Designs a wellfield to meet water supply needs. Calculates water supply available from existing wells. Applicable to mine dewatering

References

Availability
Time sharing

Language
Fortran, Basic, Cobol, Datatrieve

Computer
DEC VAX 11/780
plotter

0930

GWATVEL *In-situ, Inc. USA*
Computes groundwater velocity based on piezometric surface measurements and hydrologic parameters. Graphic output

References

Availability
Time sharing

Language
Fortran, Basic, Cobol, Datatrieve

Computer
DEC VAX 11/780
plotter

0931

TRACER2D *In-situ, Inc. USA*
A global finite element model for determining the leachate and groundwater flow during in-situ operations, wellfield design and optimisation, aquifer restoration, contaminant transport and dispersion, and waste disposal. Can model leaky and confined aquifers, steady or time-dependent conditions, and fully penetrating wells. Graphic output

References

Availability
Time sharing

Language
Fortran, Basic, Cobol, Datatrieve

Computer
DEC VAX 11/780
plotter

0932

TRACER3D *In-situ, Inc. USA*
Similar to TRACER2D, but extended to include partially penetrating wells with arbitrary perforation depths and intervals. Graphic output

References

Availability
Time sharing

Language
Fortran, Basic, Cobol, Datatrieve

Computer
DEC VAX 11/780
plotter

0933

Hypothetical hydrograph computation and flood routing *A M Kinney, Inc*
Computes a hydrograph from a given unit hydrograph and given rainfall excess values, and routes the hydrograph through a control structure. Input required is: storm frequency data; hydrograph data; interval for the unit graph drainage area; unit graph for 1 and 6 hours, routing base data; inflow hydrograph and discharge data. Output includes: rainfall excess values, surface run-off, base flow, incremental and accumulated discharge, drainage area and total discharge hydrograph

References

Availability

Language
Fortran

Computer
IBM 1130 and 370

0934

Water surface profile *A M Kinney, Inc*
Computes the flow at critical depth and the head losses in a circular sewer using Mannings formula. Input data includes: initial flow, pipe size, slope, section length, and pipe inverted elevation. Output contains: hydraulic gradient, initial and final hydraulic grade in feet, head loss in feet, velocity of flow in feet per second, and final depth in feet

References

Availability

Language
Fortran

Computer
IBM 1130 and 370

Drains *Lancaster Computing*
Aids the design of foul, surface water, or combined drainage systems of up to 50 pipes and up to 999mm diameter. The protected program disk runs in drive 1, and a data disk in drive 2 stores information produced by the operation of the program, as well as data input. Input information includes pipe reference number, upstream and downstream node numbers, pipe lengths, area drained, permeability, gradient, and invert at the top of each branch of the system

References	*Language*
Availability Purchase	*Computer* Apple II

BKWR *Microcomp*
A backwater curve analysis program. The solution may be for either subcritical or supercritical flow in any prismatic channel for an S1, S2, M1 or M2 curve. Input includes a beginning station, invert elevation and initial depth. Output includes the station, water surface elevation and depth of flow

References	*Language*
Availability Purchase	*Computer* Apple, and most microcomputers using CP/M

FLDRT *Microcomp*
An unsteady flow hydraulics program for routing floods through any prismatic channel. Input consists of any hydrograph representing the incoming flood. The program routes the flood through the channel. Output consists of flow rate, depth and velocity at user selected time intervals. FLDRT uses an explicit numerical scheme for solving the partial differential equations of flow. FLDPLOT will plot the hydrographics using a high speed Zeta pen plotter

References	*Language*
Availability Purchase	*Computer* Apple, and most microcomputers using CP/M

STORM *Microcomp*
A storm drain analysis program which calculates the hydraulic grade line elevations of a proposed or existing storm drain system, given the physical characteristics and discharge. Circular or rectangular cross-sections can be analysed for pressure flow or partial flow. System losses calculated include friction, minor and junction losses. Calculates location where flow changes from full to partial and where any hydraulic jump occurs. An unlimited number of pipes and laterals can be handled

References	*Language*
Availability Purchase	*Computer* Apple, and most microcomputers using CP/M

CP108: Surface water drainage *Oasys Limited*
Sewer sizes and invert levels are calculated to achieve a minimum excavation design within constraints set by the user. The re-run facility is an important feature enabling the user to impose additional constraints on the size of sewer lengths or non-standard minimum soil cover requirements for particular lengths. The layout of a sewer system may be described by coordinates of manholes or sewer lengths. The Colebrook-White or the Crimp and Bridges pipe flow formulae may be used

References	*Language* Basic
Availability Purchase	*Computer* HP 9845 HP 85/87

BACKWATER/1 *Quest GENESYS Limited*
This sub-sytem enables an engineer to calculate by the standard step method, surface profiles of water, for gradually varied flows in open, non prismatic waterways

References GENESYS program library	*Language* Gentran
Availability Bureau service, hire	*Computer* DEC 10, Honeywell, IBM, ICL, PE Prime, others

STORM-SEWER/1 *Quest GENESYS Limited*
The TRRL hydrograph method is used to analyse the flow in drainage networks. Standard storm profiles obtained from the UK Meteorological Office are stored in the program. Pipe network for analysis and design must be of a tree structure. Pipes can be of a variety of cross-section profiles, and the designer may specify the length, gradient and roughness coefficient. Results include full data check, rainfall rates of storm profile, output hydrographs and pipe design

References	*Language* Gentran
Availability	*Computer*

CULV *Scicon Limited*
This system provides designs for reinforced culverts. It is based on the elastic method of design and provides the cheapest arrangement of roof, wall and floor thicknesses and their associated reinforcement

References	*Language*
Availability Bureau Service	*Computer* Univac 1100/62

SSDP (Storm sewer design) *Scicon Limited*
Used for the design of storm sewers. It is based on the TRRL hydrograph method and operates in metric and/or Imperial units. It is capable of analysing networks of up to 20 branches, each of which may consist of up to 99 lengths. One to 20 year rain profiles, and circular, rectangular, trapezoidal and egg-shaped sections can be allowed for. The system produces a comprehensive output of network results and hydrographs

References	*Language*
Availability Bureau service	*Computer* Univac 1100/62

CULV *SIA Computer Services*
This program carries out automatic RC culvert design and detailing

References	*Language* High level
Availability Bureau service	*Computer* Control Data, IBM, Prime

Computer programs for the building industry

0945

HYDRAN *SIA Computer Services*
This program is used for the design and checking of surface water sewer systems

References

Availability
Bureau service

Language
High level

Computer
Control Data,
IBM, Prime

0946

NETMODS *SIA Computer Services*
A water network analysis and design program

References

Availability
Bureau service

Language
High level

Computer
Control Data,
IBM, Prime

0947

SEWER *SIA Computer Services*
This program is used for the checking and profile plotting of sewer networks

References

Availability
Bureau service

Language
High level

Computer
Control Data,
IBM, Prime

0948

SURGE *SIA Computer Services*
This program is used for water distribution networks. It calculates surge pressures in fluid networks exhibiting Newtonian behaviour

References

Availability
Bureau service

Language
High level

Computer
Control Data,
IBM, Prime

0949

WATNET *SIA Computer Services*
A program used for water supply network analysis and design

References

Availability
Bureau service

Language
High level

Computer
Control Data,
IBM, Prime

0950

WRCBASE *SIA Computer Services*
This program is the Water Research Authority's database of standard pumps, valves and equipment

References

Availability
Bureau service

Language
High level

Computer
Control Data,
IBM, Prime

0951

SEWNET *Structures and Computers Limited*
Calculates the flow in each branch of a sewerage network, and evaluates the pipeline and excavation quantities of the network. Used in the analysis stage of the building design process

References

Availability
Purchase

Language
Fortran IV

Computer
64K

0952

CULV *UCC (Great Britain) Limited*
Analyses and designs cross-sections of culverts by the elastic stiffness method. The design process gives the best arrangement of reinforcement for the minimum cost. Output gives moments, shears, thrusts, the diameters and arrangement of bars, plus a full listing of input data

References
Developed by the computer branch of the DoE (Highway Engineering)

Availability
Bureau service

Language
Fortran

Computer

0953

HYANDRY *United Information Services Limited*
Designs large tree structure drainage schemes, taking account of the storage capacity of the pipes. It uses the Hydrograph method of the Road Research Laboratory, and is based on the Colebrook-White equation

References

Availability
Bureau service, time sharing

Language
Fortran

Computer
Honeywell
Sigma 9

0954

DECIDE *Civil and Structural Computing (Northern) Limited*
An integrated suite of interactive programs for the design of structural reinforced concrete to CP110:1972. All aspects of design are covered from analysis through to bar curtailments. The suite provides the engineer with maximum flexibility in use whilst removing the tedium of calculation

References
Bradshaw, Buckton and Tonge

Availability
Bureau service, time sharing, in-house

Language

Computer

Computer programs for the building industry

HARBOR *Computational Mechanics Consultants Limited*
For the deterministic and probabilistic analysis of harbour resonance. Radiation conditions can be applied to represent accurately harbour entrances, and the angle of the incoming wave can be specified. The program can also be used to analyse diffraction problems. Results are presented in graphical form

References

Availability
Licence

Language
Fortran

Computer
Microcomputer

GEO 12 *Computel Limited*
A suite of programs for the analysis of dewatering systems

References
GEOCOMP

Availability

Language

Computer

GEO 16 *Computel Limited*
A program concerned with pressures in seepage pores of fully saturated media

References
GEOCOMP

Availability

Language

Computer

High pressure gas storage system *COSMIC*
A simulation model for predicting the pressure and temperature histories occurring in recharge or blowdown processes for high pressure gas storage systems. Allows for real gas effects as well as conductive, convective and radiative heat transfer to the storage container walls for any environmental boundary conditions. Can be applied to sizing and performance prediction of industrial high pressure gas storage systems subject to time varying thermal environmental conditions

References
Rockwell International Corporation

Availability

Language
Cobol (85%)
Fortran IV (15%)

Computer
IBM 370

PLATE *Grist Business Services Limited*
A combination of three powerful programs for the anlaysis of: 3D rigidly jointed frames; membrane plates (ie in-plane or 'stressed skin' loading); plate bending, using the Q19 quadrilateral element. Includes up to 100+ nodes, up to 30 beam types and 30 plate types. Used for: grillages and other 3D frames; plates/slabs, including irregular shapes; floors, bridge decks, retaining walls, foundation rafts, pilecaps, airfield runways, etc; plate/shell structures with edge beams

References

Availability
Purchase

Language
Fortran

Computer
Apple II 48K

MIXC *Microcomp Limited*
Provides rapid preliminary concrete mix data. The user inputs the required 28 days strength and details of the aggregate available and required slump. Output consists of mix proportions by volume and by weight, water/cement ratio, and materials required per cubic yard of concrete. Intended only for mixes containing ordinary Portland cement

References

Availability
Licence

Language
Basic

Computer
Apple II 48K

MIXD *Microcomp Limited*
A concrete mix design program for ordinary Portland cement, enabling checks to be made for strength, workability, correct proportioning, etc. The program can operate in metric or imperial units. Default values can be used when information is lacking. Input consists of mix proportions, aggregate gradings type and specific gravity, and plant standard deviation. Ouput includes theoretical mean and minimum compressive strength, slump and compacting factor, mix proportions, minimum strength, and batch quantities

References

Availability
Licence

Language
Basic

Computer
Apple II 48K

PNC1 *The Northern Ireland Polytechnic*
This program, for undergraduate teaching, uses a metric version of The Road Research Laboratory's report Road Note 4, to design the cheapest concrete mix, subject to the input of certain criteria including standard supervision, types of cement and aggregates, vibration of sections and reinforcement

References

Availability
At terminal for on-line use

Language
Fortran IV

Computer
ICL 19

GENESYS *Quest GENESYS Limited*
This is a library of related programs intended to solve various problems of engineering design. The designer need have no knowledge of computers. Programs in the library cover design and analysis of roads, bridges and buildings. They are described individually elsewhere

References

Availability
Bureau service, hire

Language
Gentran

Computer
Burroughs, DEC 20
Honeywell, IBM, ICL
PE, Philips, others

RC building/1 *Quest GENESYS Limited*
This sub-system enables an engineer to analyse, design and detail reinforced concrete buildings constructed from beams, solid slabs and vertical columns. The overall shape of the building need not be rectangular, and storey heights, bay centres and foundation levels need not be constant. The number of beams, slabs, columns and loading conditions which may be considered is not limited by the sub-system

References
GENESYS program library

Availability
Bureau service, hire

Language
Gentran

Computer
DEC 10, Honeywell
IBM, ICL, PE Prime,
others

0965

CP110 *Quest GENESYS Limited*
A suite of fully integrated programs developed to handle the computer aided design and detail of reinforced concrete structures. Focal point is the program RC-STRUCTURE; this establishes a database where positions of grid lines, components, loads, stresses and material properties are defined. From this base, the various design and detail programs can function. The programs can be used for small 2-storey blocks or large multistorey developments

References

Availability

Language
Gentran

Computer

0966

DECIDE *Reading Computer Services Limited*
A program on reinforced Concrete Design to CP110. Facilities include continuous beams, section design, column section design, flat slab, circular column, subframe analysis, serviceability, shear, slab, wind analysis, reinforced columns, simply supported beam, slender column, draw bending moment, and section properties

References
Recommended by SIA Computer Services

Availability

Language

Computer
CP/M Microcomputer

0967

BARSHEAD *SIA Computer Services*
Designed for the civil engineer. This program is used for reinforced concrete steel reinforcement detailing and scheduling

References

Availability
Bureau service

Language
High level

Computer
Control Data, IBM, Prime

0968

BS449 *SIA Computer Services*
This program is used in steel design for civil engineering. It is a design code post-process to the LEAP 4 system

References

Availability
Bureau service

Language
High level

Computer
Control Data, IBM, Prime

0969

CUTSHED *SIA Computer Services*
Used in civil engineering for steel stock cutting optimisation

References

Availability
Bureau service

Language
High level

Computer
Control Data, IBM, Prime

0970

DEAP *SIA Computer Services*
For the civil engineer. This program is for leap dynamics post-processing

References

Availability
Bureau service

Language
High level

Computer
Control Data, IBM, Prime

0971

CP110 - ULTIMATE LOAD DESIGN OF RC SECTION *Technical Services*
Checks the strength of a concrete section subjected to a stated bending moment and shear force, and calculates the area of tensile and compression reinforcement required. Rectangular, T and L sections may be analysed. Also calculates the shear strength of the section and the area of any necessary shear reinforcement, together with the area of nominal links for a given shear force

References

Availability
Purchase

Language
Basic

Computer
Olivetti P6060, and P6066, 16K

0972

Flange design *United Information Services Limited*
Originally developed to design or analyse flanges to ASME VIII or BS 1500-1515 by Whessoe Limited. The time sharing version designs a single plate, flat, lap or tapered hub flange, and the batch program can process up to four designs, and includes floating head flanges with backing rings

References

Availability
Bureau service, time sharing

Language
Fortran

Computer
Honeywell Sigma 9

0973

Zentech program library *Zentech Limited*
Includes programs for analysing and designing offshore structures, commercial and industrial buildings, bridges, stadia, exhibition centres, transmission towers, and mechanical and nuclear engineering projects. Information is given in tabular or graphic form in a format to the client's specification. Results include deflections, member forces and reactions

References

Availability
Purchase, hire, bureau service

Language
Fortran V

Computer
Univac, CDC, DEC System 10 IBM, ICL

Structural frames

Two-dimensional frames
Three-dimensional frames
Offshore structures
Other

0974

FRAMEN *The Association for Computer Aided Design Limited*
This program makes a static elastic analysis of frames consisting of straight, prismatic members. Six types of frame can be analysed: continuous beam, plane truss, plane frame, grid, space truss, and space frame. Facilities are provided for generation of repetitious data to simplify preparation of input. Loads can be applied directly to joints, or as concentrated, uniform or triangular loads to members, along the axis of member or structure

References
ACADS (Melbourne)

Availability
Contact ACADS

Language
Fortran IV

Computer
Univac 1108,
CDC 6600, others

0975

STRESS *Amplix Services Limited*
Features include: elastic analysis of loaded skeletal structures as designed by MIT in the USA; structure types include plane frame, truss and grid space frame and truss; 300 joints, 100 members and 10 loading conditions; load combinations; temperature gradients, strain in members, lack of fit, support settlement; member and joint releases can be specified; output comprises any combination of displacements at joints, forces at ends of members and support reactions; free format data input

References

Availability
Purchase

Language
Commercial (SMB)
Cobol, Fortran

Computer
CP/M or MP/M
Microcomputer

0976

TRUSS 1 *Associated British Consultants (Computers) Limited*
Analyses pin jointed 2D frames with up to 65 members and up to 5 load cases. Checks include a screen plot of the frame

References

Availability
Purchase

Language
Basic

Computer
64K TRS80 Model 2

0977

STRESS *British Olivetti Limited*
For the linear analysis of skeletal structures. Includes: plane truss, plane frame, plane grid, space truss, and space frame. This program has been extended to deal with strains and temperature effects, while allowing for structures to be supported elastically as well as rigidly

References
Copyright: Alcock Shearing and Partners

Availability
Purchase

Language
Basic

Computer
Olivetti desktop
minicomputer

0978

Structural Analysis *British Olivetti Limited*
For architectural practices, structural steelwork manufacturers, consulting engineers, and others in the construction industry. Data and results are recorded on disk. Printer provides plot of structure. Includes: plane frame, space frame, grid, plane truss, space truss. Maximum dimensions: 250 joints and 300 members for plane structures and space truss; 80 joints and 100 members for space frame. Output includes displacements of each joint, moments and shear forces at the end of each member, and reactions at each support

References

Availability
Purchase

Language
Basic, Assembler

Computer
P6066 minicomputer
48Kb memory

0979

FRAME *Building Computer Services Limited*
Analyses 2D orthogonal frames and continuous beams comprising slender prismatic members. Non-prismatic members may be represented by dividing the member into prismatic sub-members and providing 'dummy' joints between each sub-member. Input data should include relationships of members to joints, physical dimensions, moduli of elasticity and loadings

References

Availability
Bureau service, hire, sale

Language
Fortran

Computer
DEC

0980

CDMFLOBM *Cadsteel Limited*
Sizes each member of a framework. Member loads are passed out through the frame automatically. Each member is regarded as being simply supported. Accuracy of deflection results is achieved by numerical integration. Analysis and member sizing is in accordance with BS 449. Section sizes may be chosen from the following steel tables: universal beams, universal columns, channels, and joists. Comprehensive output in tabulated form

References
Construction Steelwork SWP

Availability
Purchase

Language
Fortran IV

Computer
IBM mainframe
CP/M

0981

Pin jointed plane frame analysis *Camutek*
This program analyses statically determinate frames

References

Availability
From owner

Language
Basic

Computer
HP 9830 (2k) or (6k),
9831, 9835, 9845
Future: HP85, 86

0982

Plane frame elastic analysis *Camutek*
Analyses plane frames which are statically indeterminate. It gives the axial and shear forces and the bending moments at each end of every member. It also gives the deflection at every point on the structure

References

Availability
From owner

Language
Basic

Computer
HP 9830 (2k) or (6k),
9831, 9835, 9845
Future HP85, 86

0983

Timber Strut Design *Camutek*
This program forms the design of a timber strut in compression or in tension subject to bi-axial bending. The maximum allowable slenderness ratio is output with the minimum breadth and depth of the section. Timber species and grade may be specified. The final output gives actual and permissible stresses for each load case, together with the sum of stress ratios. The depth to breadth ratio is also given, with a warning if it approaches the CP112 limits

References

Availability
From Camutek

Language
Basic

Computer
HP9835, 9845 Future:
HP 85 & 86

FRAME *Cheshire County Council*
(Structural Frame Analysis.) This is a program covering the analysis of plane structures using matrix technics. Under development

References

Availability

Language
APL

Computer
IBM 3767

D4 package (DTAIL, DSIGN, DFLEC and DPICT) *Civil and Structural Computing (Northern) Limited*
A suite of programs which carries out the plastic design and elastic analysis of multibay portal frames, used especially in industrial and agricultural buildings

References
Bradshaw, Buckton and Tonge

Availability
Bureau service, time sharing, in-house

Language

Computer

DFLEC *Civil and Structural Computing (Northern) Limited*
This program (part of the D4 package) is used to carry out an elastic deflection analysis under working load conditions of a portal frame. The program is run interactively; if the deflections of the frame are critical, the engineer can alter eaves and apex haunches and section sizes to obtain a more acceptable design. In this way, each design can be assessed and the economics of alternative designs compared

References
Bradshaw, Buckton and Tonge

Availability
Bureau service, time sharing, in-house

Language

Computer

DPICT *Civil and Structural Computing (Northern) Limited*
This program, which is part of the D4 package, plots the deflected forms of a portal frame and the plastic bending moment diagrams. The designs can then be visually assessed

References
Bradshaw, Buckton and Tonge

Availability
Bureau service, time sharing, in-house

Language

Computer

DSIGN *Civil and Structural Computing (Northern) Limited*
Carries out the plastic design of the portal frame defined in DTAIL. The program can be run interactively, allowing the engineer to make pertinent decisions, and providing accurate design and estimating information quickly. Foundation reactions, bending moments and restraint information are output, together with section sizes and weights

References
Bradshaw, Buckton and Tonge

Availability
Bureau service, time sharing, in-house

Language

Computer

DTAIL *Civil and Structural Computing (Northern) Limited*
This program forms part of the D4 package. It calculates input frame data geometry, haunching requirements, feet fixity and loading. The data can be easily corrected or altered and can be stored on disc for future use

References
Bradshaw, Buckton and Tonge

Availability
Bureau service, time sharing, in-house

Language

Computer

EVCON *Civil and Structural Computing (Northern) Limited*
Makes an analysis of a bolted column/beam moment connection. Column/rafter sections, haunch depth/length and bolt details are input by the engineer. Six loadings can be applied and each load can consist of a moment and a vertical shear

References
Bradshaw, Buckton and Tonge

Availability
Bureau service, time sharing, in-house

Language

Computer
Hewlett Packard
9800
and others

FRAME *Civil and Structural Computing (Northern) Limited*
Performs the elastic analysis of plane frames by the stiffness method, with additional features. The version of stiffness analysis used assumes small deflection theory. Frames are made up of straight uniform members connected at nodal points. Various types of connection can be made between members; loads can be applied horizontally, vertically, rotationally and normal to members

References
Bradshaw, Buckton and Tonge

Availability
Bureau service, time sharing, in-house

Language
Basic, Fortran

Computer
Hewlett Packard,
DEC, Data General,
Prime, others

GRID *Civil and Structural Computing (Northern) Limited*
Analyses a plane grid of simply supported beam elements subject to static vertical loading. The loading can be a combination of point loads, moments and uniformly distributed loads applied directly to members. Axial loading on individual members can also be input. The program calculates the loading on every member due to the loads input and loads transferred from other members. Beam end reactions are output

References
Bradshaw, Buckton and Tonge

Availability
Bureau service, time sharing, in-house

Language

Computer
Hewlett Packard
9800
and others

FAB 59 *Computational Mechanics Consultants Limited*
This system (frame and beam) is a ROM module containing structural engineering software for use in the Texas Instruments 59 programmable calculator. A PC-100A/B/C printer is mandatory. Consists of two programs: multistorey plane frame structures; continuous beams on spring supports

References

Availability
Licence

Language

Computer
Texas Instruments
59 calculator

0994

FESPAC *Computational Mechanics Consultants Limited*
An interactive, easy to use, structural and stress analysis system providing the user with sophisticated analysis capabilities. Uses: for the structural analysis of plane and space trusses and frames, and grillages; elasticity, plates, axisymmetric solids, and thermal conduction. Frame analysis is one of FESPAC's most useful programs

References

Availability
Licence

Language
Fortran

Computer
Microcomputer

0995

Finite Element Computer Tape *Computational Mechanics Consultants Limited*
Supplied on 9-track magnetic tape or paper tape. Contains programs for the structural analysis of 2D trusses and frames, and finite element programs for the solution of 2D elasticity and 2D thermal or fluid mechanics problems. The tape contains programs for: static analysis of plane trusses and of plane frame systems; dynamic analysis of plane frame systems; solution of the generalised Laplace's equation; solution of bidimensional elasticity problems; matrix manipulation

References
Computational Methods for the Solution of Engineering Problems by C A Brebbia and A Ferrante

Availability
Licence

Language
Fortran IV

Computer
Microcomputer with minimum 32K

0996

MEGRAT *Computational Mechanics Consultants Limited*
May be run in batch or interactive mode to assist the user of finite elements by generating all the node and element data for a 2D mesh. Any plane shape can be analysed into either triangular or quadrilateral elements, with the option to create mid-side nodes. The program outputs the connectivity and coordinates of the finite element mesh, numbered for minimum bandwidth and ordered for efficient use by a frontal solver. The mesh may be drawn on a plotter, line printer, graphics terminal or teletype

References

Availability
Licence

Language
Fortran IV

Computer
Microcomputer with minimum 24K

0997

Plane Truss Analysis *Computer Design*
Part of the COSPACK package. Provides 2D analysis of statically determinate or indeterminate pin-jointed frameworks, using the displacement method

References
Sirius Computing, January 1983

Availability
Basic

Language

Computer
ACT Sirius 1 256K.
Plotter

0998

Program Frame Analysis *Computer design*
Part of the COSPACK package. Provides analysis of plane rigid-jointed frameworks, using the displacement method to compute the nodal displacement and member forces

References
Sirius Computing, January 1983

Availability
Purchase, lease

Language
Basic

Computer
ACT Sirius 1 256K.
Plotter

0999

Reinforced Concrete Members *Computer Design*
(Reinforced concrete members under combined compression and bending.) Part of the COSPACK package. For the evaluation of the longitudinal stress distribution over a section of a reinforced member having any polygonal shape, but with an axis of symmetry

References
Sirius Computing, January 1983

Availability
Purchase, lease

Language
Basic

Computer
ACT Sirius 1 256K.
Plotter

1000

Space Frame Analysis *Computer Design*
Part of the COSPACK package. Handles the 3D static analysis of rigid-jointed frameworks

References
Sirius Computing, January 1983

Availability
Purchase, lease

Language
Basic

Computer
ACT Sirius 1 256K.
Plotter

1001

Steel Frames for Industrial Buildings *Computer Design*
Part of the COSPACK package. Handles the determination of the foundation loads for a multi-bay steel frame. The stanchions can have a variable section, they are fully constrained at the base and pin-jointed with a truss roofing

References
Sirius Computing, January 1983

Availability
Purchase, lease

Language
Basic

Computer
ACT Sirius 1 256K.
Plotter

1002

FRAME *Computrav (UK) Limited*
Elastic analyses of 2D structures loaded in their own plane; range from pinned trusses to cable-stayed bridges. Loads specified as applied to members and can be in any direction or position. Temperature effects are also dealt with. Data can simulate and test the effects of changes in structural geometry and/or loadings. Output includes: a check on structural geometry, graphical representation of the structure, static checks and values of reactions. Results at node points and mid points of all elements

References
Approved by ACT Sirius

Availability
Purchase

Language
Basic

Computer
Minimum 32Kb on 8 and 16-bit micros under CP/M

1003

GRID *Computrav (UK) Limited*
Performs elastic analyses of 2D structures for which loads are at right angles to the plane of the structure. Members need not be orthogonal. In other respects, GRID has similar facilities to FRAME

References
Approved by ACT Sirius

Availability
Purchase

Language
Basic

Computer
Minimum 32Kb on 8 and 16-bit micros under CP/M

Computer programs for the building industry

SUBFRAME *Computrav (UK) Limited*
Provides analyses of one sub-frame of a framed structure, ie one continuous beam with or without columns above and below. The beam elements may be any mixture of prismatic relative, prismatic dimensioned, stepped, haunched or T section. Loads may be points, uniformly distributed or linearly variable. The program automatically factors and positions loads for the most critical results. Results are combined and redistributed in accordance with CP110 or CP114, and an envelope of maximum moments produced

References
Approved by ACT Sirius

Availability
Purchase

Language
Basic

Computer
Minimum 32Kb on 8 and 16-bit micros under CP/M

SCIA: GRID-Structures *Eclipse Associates Limited*
The basic version covers static elastic analysis of arbitrary grid structures, ie various loadings and types, such as uniform loading, concentrated load, torsional moments, trapezoidal loading, temperature, imposed displacements; possible eccentric and elastic connections, and spring supports. The extended version includes a graphical input and output program for graphic screen and/or plotter

References

Availability
Purchase, bureau service (SCIA SV, ST DATA APS)

Language
Wang Extended Basic, HP Basic

Computer
Wang mini and microcomputers

SCIA: PLATE Structures - Finite Element Method *Eclipse Associates Limited*
The basic version carries out static elastic analysis for arbitrary plates, eventually reinforced with ribs or beams. The program includes GRID. Included is a subdivision in triangular finite elements, and arbitrary loading (uniform, partial, point loads, temperature, imposed displacements). Extended versions include: a pre-processor for automatic generation of finite element mesh for arbitrary plates; semi graphical output by plotter; graphical input and output program

References

Availability
Purchase, bureau service (SCIA SV, ST DATA APS)

Language
Wang Extended Basic, HP Basic

Computer
Wang mini and microcomputers

FA-1. Continuous frame analysis *Ecom Associates, Inc*
Solves for critical shears and moments in multiple-span continuous beams of a single level with or without columns above and below the level. Equivalent column stiffness is used to account for torsional flexibility of span-to-column connections. Spans and columns may have variable section. Cantilevered members and loads may be input at either or both ends. Loads may be concentrated and uniform, and can include live and dead portions

References

Availability
Purchase

Language
M Basic

Computer
HP, Wang

FA-2. Multistorey frame analysis *Ecom Associates, Inc*
Determines moments in members for a planar multistorey frame. Calculates beam shears, loads in columns and lateral displacements. All members must be vertical or horizontal and may be nonprismatic. Moments and vertical loads may be added to any joint in addition to those imposed by the beam loads. Lateral loads may be applied to any level. Load combinations can be created from basic load cases

References

Availability
Purchase

Language
M Basic

Computer
HP, Wang

FA-3. General frame analysis *Ecom Associates, Inc*
Determines critical moments, shears, axial loads and the displacements at all joints for a plane frame of any configuration. Initial axial displacements are allowed in order to evaluate effects of settlements, member shrinkage or member temperature change. Members may have variable section. Members may have uniform (full or partial length) or concentrated loads

References

Availability
Purchase

Language
M Basic

Computer
HP, Wang

FA-4. Beam span analysis *Ecom Associates, Inc*
Calculates shears, moments, and deflections for a beam span including a) simply supported beam with or without cantilevers or b) spans of continuous frame using data from the Continuous Frame program. End moments may be input. Variable sections considered. For reinforced concrete, calculations can be based on effective moment of inertia

References

Availability
Purchase

Language
M Basic

Computer
HP, Wang

STRAAD *Ecom Associates, Inc*
For structural analysis and design. Graphics options available for input checking and for examining deformed geometry. Analyses and designs space frames and trusses, plane frames and trusses, and grid networks

References

Availability
Purchase

Language
M Basic

Computer
HP9845

FRAME *Facet Limited*
Analyses plane frames on elastic supports by the stiffness method. Within FRAME, structures are defined by nodes and members with facilities for the automatic generation of regular patterns of data. Output data includes: results of accuracy check, nodal displacements; axial forces, shear force, and bending moment at member ends; support reactions. Diagrams and influence lines may be plotted

References

Availability
Bureau service, or under licence

Language

Computer
Prime, Norsk Data, Harris, CP/M 8-bit micros

GRID *Facet Limited*
A program designed to analyse plane grillages on elastic supports by the stiffness method. A grillage is defined by nodes and members with facilities for the automatic generation of regular patterns of data. A listing of input data is given and an option exists to plot the structure as a data check

References

Availability
Bureau service, or under licence

Language

Computer
Prime, Norsk Data, Harris, CP/M 8-bit micros

1014

PLANE *Facet Limited*
This is a plane stress finite element program to analyse in-plane loadings on a slice of material of any Poisson's Ratio. Possible applications include the analysis of: local stress concentrations, typically under point loads; deep beam bending; shear walls

References

Availability
Bureau service, or under licence

Language

Computer
Prime, Norsk Data, Harris,
CP/M 8-bit micros

1015

SPACE *Facet Limited*
Analyses rigid space frames on elastic supports, by the stiffness method. Output information includes: nodal displacements: axial forces, shear forces, and bending moments at member ends; support reactions. An isometric or perspective structure plot may be produced by the use of an allied program SPDRAW. This plot can include numbered nodes and members if required

References

Availability
Bureau service, or under licence

Language

Computer
Prime, Norsk Data, Harris,
CP/M 8-bit micros

1016

MINILEAP *Flint & Neill Partnership*
Analyses skeletal frames including beams, trusses, grids, plane and space frames. For use in the structural design stage. Output in the form of A4 paged, giving information on deflections, member forces, reactions, equilibrium checks. Interactive structure plots are standard. Deflection plots and member force plots are optional. Cross-referenced with mainframe program LEAP

References

Availability
Purchase, hire, bureau service (SIA)

Language
Basic

Computer
HP.9845B Some
other 64K micros

1017

Pf82 *Gang-Nail Software*
This is a plane frame analysis program. It caters for maximums of 100 joints, 200 members and 50 member types. The loading types are: joint, point, UDL, triangular, trapezoidal, prescribed displacement, prescribed rotation and prescribed angled displacement. The member connections are: rigid, hinged or flexible. The support types are: pinned, rigid, spring, flexible, sliding and angled sliding. Results cover joint displacements, rotations, member displacements, member forces, moments and reactions

References

Availability
Purchase

Language
Microsoft Basic V5.2

Computer
58K CP/M
Microcomputer

1018

ELANA *General & Engineering Computer Services Limited*
Provides a general linear elastic analysis of structural frames and grillages. Geometrical and loading data is entered direct (interactive). Output includes joint displacements, member end forces, support reactions, and member forces along the length of loaded members

References

Availability
Purchase

Language
Basic
Fortran

Computer
Micro with CP/M
and M Basic

1019

ELANA *General and Engineering Computer Services Limited*
This program provides general linear elastic analysis of structural frameworks. Input is in the form of geometrical loading information either on preprinted forms (batch) or direct via VDU (interactive). Output includes paginated A4 reports on joint displacements, member end forces, support reactions and member forces at intervals along their length

References

Availability
Purchase

Language
Fortran IV
Basic

Computer
Prime 50 Series

1020

FRAM-PAC *Tony Gee and Partners*
A plane frame structural analysis program with CP110 beam and column sub-frame facility. Caters for non-prismatic members and gives comprehensive output with graphical display of deformation, bending moment and shear force diagrams. CP110 output provides bending moment and shear force envelopes with optional redistribution. Processing of multiple run data allowing accumulation of results from changing structures. 6 output options with numerical or graphical output of deflections and member forces

References

Availability
Purchase

Language
HP Enhanced Basic

Computer
Hewlett-Packard
HP9845B/C

1021

P-LOAD *Tony Gee and Partners*
A pre-processor for FRAM-PAC, which allows the effects of prestressing cables to be entered as a series of equivalent loads. A version also exists for use with MINILEAP. Parabolic or straight cable elements may be specified and losses due to lock off, wobble and curvature are calculated. The output is saved as a FRAM-PAC input file which can be modified or run directly

References

Availability
Purchase

Language
HP Enhanced Basic

Computer
Hewlett-Packard
HP9845 B/C

1022

DYF (Dynamics) *Grist Business Services Limited*
Provides a practical dynamic analysis of any structure which can be idealised as a plane frame, in particular building frames. Up to 60 nodes and 100 elements. Calculation of natural frequencies and node shapes, calculation of dynamic responses due to earthquakes, sinusoidal harmonic loads due to machinery, etc, and step loads due to blasts, impact loads, etc

References

Availability
Purchase

Language
Fortran

Computer
Apple II 48K

1023

Frame analysis for critical loading *Hydro Systems (USA)*
Analyses multistorey, multi-bay continuous frames with rectangular bays. Inputs include structure geometry and dead and live loadings. Outputs are the critical design loadings for beams and columns. Capacity with 48K is about 15 members

References

Availability
Purchase

Language

Computer
32K RAM minimum

Frame Analysis *Hydro Systems (USA)*
Analyses multistorey, multi-bay continuous frame with rectangular bays. End cantilevers may be present. Allows inclusion of any combinations of point loads and uniform loads for each span. Wind loads are allowed at each level. Inputs include structure geometry and loadings. Outputs are beam and column end moments and shears, column axial loads and rotation and translation at joints. Capacity with 48K is about 100 members

References

Availability
Purchase

Language

Computer
16K RAM minimum

Lateral load analysis of multistorey frames with shear walls *A M Kinney, Inc*
Analyses regular rectangular frames which vary in size from one bay by one storey to either 9 bays by 109 storeys, or 14 bays by 74 storeys. The method of analysis is that of slope deflection, modified to include the effect of the vertical displacement of the end of the girders due to the flexural rotation of the shear walls. All members must have the same modulus of elasticity. The inclined members cannot be handled through the program

References

Availability

Language
Fortran

Computer
IBM 1130 and 370

ADEPT *Manchester University, Simon Engineering Laboratories*
Designs multistorey, rigid sway frames subjected to dead, imposed and wind loads applied in-plane. Uses a rigid plastic analysis of multistorey steel frames, combined with an optimisation technique based on linear programming. Elastic check on stresses and deflections of the resulting frame. Tables of economic steel sections capable of plastic action are used as the basis of design. The yield stress for each section is automatically selected. Efficient for tall frames with 2 or 3 bays

References
Constructional Steelwork SWP

Availability
Purchase

Language
Algol

Computer
CDC7600

FRAM *Microcomp Limited*
Analyses displacements, resultant forces and reactions at the nodes of 2D frame structures. The program is simple to use and may be continually re-analysed allowing for: different positions of joints, new member types, loads, and any type of member loading up to a partially distributed trapezoidal load, self weight, any degree of fixity at supports and prescribed settlement

References

Availability
Licence

Language
Basic

Computer
Apple II 48K

GRIL *Microcomp Limited*
Calculates static deformation, member forces, moments, and reactions within a plane grillage structure subjected to normal loadings of several types. Concentrated loads are permitted both at joints and on members. Self weight can be included. Distributed loads are handled by an approximate method, which divides the loads into several concentrated loads along the member. Joints can be rigid, pinned or spring supported. Displacements can be prescribed

References

Availability
Licence

Language
Basic

Computer
Apple II 48K

POTB *Microcomp Limited*
Analyses potential problems using the boundary element technique. Calculates values of potential at interior and boundary points of singly connected 2D problems of arbitrary shape. Boundary potentials and fluxes can be prescribed and multiple cases can be analysed. The program allows an unlimited number of internal solution points, and permits interactive searching for potential extremes and evaluations of internal gradients. A boundary element with a constant interpolation function is used

References

Availability
Licence

Language
Basic

Computer
Apple II 48K

STRESS *Microcomp Limited*
Performs linear analysis of elastic, statically loaded, framed structures. The engineer specifies the geometry of the structure, its member characteristics and the loads to which it is subjected, then STRESS computes joint displacements, member end forces and moments, and the joint reactions at support joints. The program is flexible so that all structures can be handled, whether they have pinned or rigid joints, and whether they are subjected to concentrated or distributed loads, support movements, or member distortions

References

Availability
Licence

Language
Basic

Computer
Apple II 48K

TRUS *Microcomp Limited*
Calculates static deformation, member forces and reactions within a plane pin-jointed frame structure subjected to in-plane loadings of several types. Concentrated loads are permitted at joints. Self weight can be included. Joints can be pinned, sliding or spring supported. Displacements can be prescribed. Data can be re-analysed, varying parameters such as nodal positions, element properties, loads and boundary conditions, without having to re-enter the basic data

References

Availability
Licence

Language
Basic

Computer
Apple II 48K

STRF *Microcomp*
Calculates the static deformation and stress field within a 2D (plane stress or strain) body using the finite element method. The program uses a triangular finite element with 6 degrees of freedom. Concentrated load at node points, displacement conditions and gravity loading are permitted. Constraint types include spring, pinned or sliding supports at any angle

References

Availability
Purchase

Language

Computer
Apple, and most microcomputers using CP/M

JUNCTION/2 *Microsoft Structural Control Systems Limited*
Analyses bolted or welded steel connections to produce a satisfactory design. Usage includes: bolt/weld layout, connection size and design parameters. Output provides information on load capacity, shear/moment capacity, permissible stresses, weld size, weld stress, and load intensities

References

Availability
Purchase

Language
Applesoft Basic

Computer
48K Apple II

1034

FRANCIS *Oasys Limited*
A system of interactive programs for the analysis of interactive frameworks and trusses. Features include: hinges at member ends, rigid or elastic supports, member loading in member or global axes system, data editing and saving, paged output for job calculation file

References

Availability
Bureau service

Language
Fortran

Computer
DEC 10

1035

AP109: Plane frames *Oasys Limited*
This program includes: the facility for frame members to have any combination of pinned or fixed flexural connections to their end joints; rigid/flexible supports; external joint loading; external member loading on local and global directions; loading modification and re-run facility; data saving/retrieving facility. Output includes: joint displacements; internal member loads and stresses; a permanent record of data supplied, in tabulated and paged form

References

Availability
Purchase

Language
Basic

Computer
HP 9845 HP 85/87

1036

AP110: Grid frames *Oasys Limited*
The program features include: facility for members to have any combination of pinned or fixed flexural connection to their end joints; rigid/flexible supports; external joint loading; external member loading normal to the plane of the frame; loading modification and re-run; data saving/retrieving facility. Output includes: joint deflections; end rotations; internal member loads and stresses; a permanent record of all data, in a tabulated and paged form

References

Availability
Purchase

Language
Basic

Computer
HP 9845 HP 85/87

1037

AP122: Buckling analysis of struts *Oasys Limited*
Determines the elastic buckling loads and safe working loads of complex slender steel compression members. Allows for variations of cross-section and axial load with position, and for provision of rigid or flexible supports at any location. Safe load calculations use program assumed initial out-of-straight values sympathetic to the BS449 treatment of simple members, or they use engineer specified out-of-straightness and/or eccentricity of loading

References

Availability
Purchase

Language
Basic

Computer
HP 9845 HP 85/87

1038

Plane-frame analysis *John FS Pryke and Partners*
Analyses plane frames (including ring frames and continuous beams) of up to 12 joints and 15 members. It gives the displacements of joints, reactions of supports and forces on members

References

Availability
From owner

Language
Basic

Computer
Hewlett-Packard 9830

1039

SUBFRAME/1 *Quest GENESYS Limited*
This sub-system enables a designer to analyse simple frames consisting of a beam string with column lifts above and below, in accordance with CP110:Part 1:1972 or CP114:1969

References
GENESYS program library

Availability
Bureau service, hire

Language
Gentran

Computer
.Honeywell, IBM, ICL, PE, Prime, others

1040

SPADAS/1 *Quest GENESYS Limited*
To analyse the frequencies and modes of free vibration of elastic structures. Compatible with SUSAN/1. Available elements are: bar elements for plane frame, grillage and space frames; plate bending elements. Results include nodal displacements for each natural frequency of the structure

References

Availability

Language
Gentran

Computer

1041

SUSAN/1 *Quest GENESYS Limited*
A finite element program for the static analysis of elastic structure. Available elements include: bar elements for plane frame, grillage and space frames; membrane elements for in-plane and plate bending; combined elements for analysis of shells using assembly of flat elements. Loading may be point, line or area loads, with self weight automatically calculated. Supports may be rigid or spring. Output includes displacements, shears, moments and reactions; 2D and 3D plots of the structure

References

Availability

Language
Gentran

Computer

1042

TYGA *Quest GENESYS Limited*
For steel space frame structures of the double layer grid, ball jointed type. Handles non-linear load/deformation behaviour, and can examine the magnitude of stresses and deflections when structures are loaded beyond the elastic limits. The program can analyse the effect of stiff roof or composite floor construction, and of support settlement. Results include displacements, loading per member, and the effect of structure recovery after overload

References

Availability

Language
Gentran

Computer

1043

Elastic Analysis of Frames *Reading Computer Services Limited*
2D framed structures can be quickly analysed. Beams can be rigidly or pinned connected, and load case combinations with maximum envelopes can be obtained. Numerous methods of load specification exist

References

Availability

Language

Computer
CP/M Microcomputer

Elastic Grillage Analysis *Reading Computer Services Limited*
Analyses a grillage of any shape subject to nodal loading. Supports may be specified at any nodes and may be rigid or springs

References

Availability

Language

Computer
CP/M Microcomputer

GTSTRUDL *SIA Computer Services*
An advanced, powerful STRUDL structural analysis system

References

Availability
Bureau service

Language
High level

Computer
Control Data,
IBM, Prime

HINGE *SIA Computer Services*
A program for the plastic/elastic analysis of steel/concrete frames

References

Availability
Bureau service

Language
High level

Computer
Control Data,
IBM, Prime

LEAP 4+ *SIA Computer Services*
Used in structural analysis. A powerful frame analysis and civil engineering design system

References

Availability
Bureau service

Language
High level

Computer
Control Data,
IBM, Prime

LEAP5 *SIA Computer Services*
Used in structural analysis. This is a new, interactive/batch, database, command driven, frame analysis program

References

Availability
Bureau service

Language
High level

Computer
Control Data,
IBM, Prime

PLANE *SIA Computer Services*
A simple, 2D beam plane frame civil analysis program

References

Availability
Bureau service

Language
High level

Computer
Control Data,
IBM, Prime

Gridworks *Structural Members Users Group, USA*
The program treats uniform grillages subjected to uniform, hydrostatic and concentrated forces. Stability and free vibration analyses can also be handled

References
Book published by McGraw Hill, 1978

Availability
Purchase

Language
Fortran IV

Computer
CDC, IBM, Univac,
VAX, Prime

CADFRAM *Structural Software Services*
For the analysis of plane framework of arbitrary geometry including: portals (multi or single bay), rigid frames, braced frames, continuous beams, sub-frames, lattice girders, trusses, etc. CADFRAM will execute the simultaneous solution of up to 9 load cases, and an unlimited number of combinations can then be performed with user selectable partial safety factors. Handles structures of up to 100 members and 72 nodes. All commonly encountered load types may be included

References
Structural Engineer, July 1982

Availability
Purchase

Language
Basic/Machine code

Computer
Apple II with
48K

FRAM2DPC *Structural Software Systems*
For static analysis of a 2D frame by the Stiffness Method. The frame may be subjected to any combination of: linearly distributed member loads; concentrated joint loads; concentrated member loads; and support joint displacements. Members may be rigidly attached or pinned to joints at their ends. Output includes: joint displacements; support joint reactions; member and axial forces, shear forces and bending moments

References

Availability
Lease

Language
IBM BASIC
interpreter

Computer
IBM PC

ESAS-2 *Structures and Computers Limited*
For the linear static analysis of 2D framed and plated structures. Used in the analysis stage of the building design process

References

Availability
Purchase

Language
Fortran IV

Computer
64K

1054

PLONEF *Structures and Computers Limited*
A program for the analysis of plates and grillages resting on an elastic foundation idealised as an elastic half space. Used in the analysis stage of the building design process

References

Availability
Purchase

Language
Fortran IV

Computer
64K

1055

EPA-80 *John Surtees*
For the elastic analysis of general plane frameworks using Choleski decomposition of banded stiffness matrix and back substitution of separate load cases. Forces and displacements may be obtained at any load factor. SI units are used. A typical 2 bay N-truss portal with single load is solved in 12 seconds. Processes frames of up to 100 members or joints. Output consists of member forces and joint displacements at unit load factor or at any specified load factor

References
Construction Steelwork SWP

Availability
Purchase

Language
Z80

Computer
CP/M with
minimum 40K bytes

1056

PPA-80 *John Surtees*
For the elastic-plastic analysis of plane frameworks. Involves repeated analysis of frame under increasing proportionate loading with plastic hinge insertion until valid collapse mechanism forms or specified load factor is reached. SI units are used. A typical 2 bay portal frame with single load case is solved in 20 seconds. Output consists of member forces and joint displacements at unit load factor; similar information at collapse load; summary of plastic hinge locations and load factors at which hinges formed

References
Constructional Steelwork SWP

Availability
Purchase

Language
Z80

Computer
CP/M with
minimum 40K bytes

1057

STRUCTURAL ANALYSIS *Systemshare*
Handles continuous beam, plane truss, plane frame and plane grid. Typical maximum sizes are: 48 joints, 80 members and bandwidth of 18; alternatively there can be 50 joints, 91 members and bandwidth of 15. Loads may consist of joint loading, and point and distributed member loads. Members may have a linearly varying value of inertia. Supports may be fixed or sprung to allow for problems like beams on elastic foundations, frames on semi-rigid supports, or bridge grillages with idealised columns

References

Availability
Purchase

Language
Applesoft Basic

Computer
Apple II, 48K

1058

PLANE *United Information Services Limited*
This program is for the analysis of plane structural frames for varying loading conditions, sizes, constants, etc

References

Availability
Bureau service, time sharing

Language
Fortran

Computer
Honeywell
Sigma 9

1059

Elasto-plastic analysis of steel frames *Warwick University*
For the analysis of ultimate load of plane steel frames under proportional loading, including effects of overall frame instability and development of plastic hinges. Uses iterative solution of stiffness equations. Collapse is indicated by the determinant of the stiffness matrix becoming non-positive. Where a plastic hinge forms, the following information is output: load factor, location of new hinge, joint deflections, member end moments and axial forces

References
Constructional Steelwork SWP

Availability
Bureau service, purchase

Language
Algol

Computer
Burroughs 6700

1060

Plastic analysis and design of steel frames *Warwick University*
For the rigid-plastic analysis or minimum weight design for a plane frame under specified loading. Uses a 'steepest descent' procedure to produce a set of plastic moments of resistance which provide the specified load factor against collapse, whilst minimising weight. Output for each loading case includes load factor at collapse (analysis mode only), and factored bending moment distribution throughout the frame at collapse. The positions of plastic hinges are indicated

References
Constructional Steelwork SWP

Availability
Bureau service

Language
Algol

Computer
Burroughs 6700

1061

ZEN-Plastic analysis *Zentech Limited*
Performs a linear plane frame analysis with provisions for calculating plastic collapse. Lists data on the geometry and calculations involved in setting up the initial stiffness matrix for each load. Using an elastic analysis, the given load is applied and the deformations and moments calculated. Values representing the remaining load are applied to the model of the modified structure and the position of new hinges is calculated

References
ZENTECH program library

Availability
Purchase, hire, bureau service

Language
Fortran V

Computer
Univac, CDC, DEC
System 10, IBM, ICL

1062

SCADA *American Computers and Engineers*
For static and dynamic analysis of all standard finite elements, 2D and 3D trusses, frames, shear walls, plates, shells, elastic solids and axisymmetric structures (out of core solution allowing for unlimited size capability). Dynamic analysis will consider: modal analysis, time history, response spectrum, base motion; designs steel and concrete beams and columns. For use by civil or structural engineers; interactive input via vdu. Output includes information on strains and stresses

References

Availability
Purchase

Language
Fortran IV and 77

Computer
Microcomputer

1063

B & W FINEL *B & W Engineering*
For analysis of stress owing to stationary and transient heat conduction in 2D and 3D structures. Isotherms and heat current functions can be output. It is possible to examine structures composed of different materials with various conditions of surface temperature

References
Danish Building Research Institute
Abstract 48 14 010

Availability
Bureau service

Language
Fortran 77

Computer
IBM 3033

BSC4 Space Grid for Pin-jointed Structures *British Steel Corporation*
Analyses 3D, pin-jointed structures, with hollow sections using the BSC's Nodus jointing system. Determines axial forces in members of pin-jointed structure; computes moments due to joint eccentricity and adds moments due to loads applied directly to chord members; distributes moments to chord members according to their stiffness. Members checked for combined bending and axial stresses. Output includes table for each member; summary giving maximum deflections, reactions and unity factors

References
Constructional Steelwork SWP

Availability

Language
Fortran

Computer
IBM 370

DIMENSION III *Calma (UK) Limited*
A computer aided design system enabling architects, engineers and constructors to graphically create 3D models as they design. Quickly converts any steel design into a complete finite element model, enabling the user to measure the deflection of any point of the design, and to analyse structural stress. Also provides current bills of materials containing information on quantities, stock code numbers, weights, etc

References
Building Products Monthly, January 1982

Availability

Language

Computer

SPACE *Civil and Structural Computing (Northern) Limited*
Analyses 3D statically indeterminate frames subject to varying load conditions including factored combination. Internal frictionless pins may be included together with varying restraint conditions. Output includes nodal forces and displacements for individual load cases or factored combinations

References
Bradshaw, Buckton and Tonge

Availability
Bureau service, time sharing, in-house

Language

Computer

GPTS *Computational Mechanics Consultants Limited*
Performs linear, elastic analyses of 3D structural systems. These systems may be composed of combinations of a number of structural element types. The present version contains: 3D beam elements; plate and shell elements; loading. Designed to run on very small systems having a considerable amount of low speed (disk) storage

References

Availability
Licence

Language
Fortran

Computer
Microcomputer with minimum of 64K

Space Truss Analysis *Computer Design*
Part of the COSPACK package. Provides 3D analysis of statically determinate or indeterminate pin-jointed frameworks, using the displacement method

References
Sirius Computing, January 1983

Availability
Basic

Language

Computer
ACT Sirius 1 256K. Plotter

FRAME2/TRUSS3 *Grist Business Services Limited*
Consists of 2D rigidly jointed frame and a 2D or 3D pin jointed truss. Most 3D building frames can be analysed using FRAME2. Most symmetrical or asymmetrical portal frames can be analysed

References

Availability
Purchase

Language
Fortran

Computer
Apple II 48K

MICROFRAME *Mellor Computer Consultancy*
A stress analysis program designed for use by civil engineers, and featuring: 3D frameworks, pin-jointed and stiff-jointed structural members, distributed, point and gravity loads, 3D views of structure, full reports of analyses, and self-running demonstration packages. Caters for 3D arbitrary frameworks made up of stiff-jointed beams and/or pin-jointed tie rods or struts. These are not limited to vertical or horizontal planes. Produces report on analysis of the structure

References

Availability
Purchase

Language

Computer
ACT Sirius 1 with 128K RAM. Plotter

MicroSTRESS *Microcomp*
Linear static analysis of 2D and 3D framed structures. User specifies the geometrical and material properties of a structure, as well as the loads acting on it. Produces member end forces and moments, support reactions and joint displacements. Structures include: plane truss, plane frame, plane grillage, space truss and space frame. Maximum number of joints is 127; maximum number of members is 250. Includes curved or non-prismatic members, joint and member releases, member distortions and loads

References

Availability
Purchase

Language

Computer
Apple, most micros using CP/M, min 32K memory

Cage 1 *Microsoft Structural Control Systems Limited*
Analyses pin-jointed 3D structures; frame displayed on screen. Up to 100 joints and 228 members. Outputs all forces and displacements

References
Personal Computing with Apple

Availability

Language
Applesoft Basic

Computer
Apple II

SKELETON IV *Microsoft Structural Control Systems Limited*
Analyses any plane frame up to 90 joints and 153 members (fixed joints), or 152 joints and 301 members (pinned joints). The program can analyse complex frameworks to describe complicated member-end connections; also used for simple structures. Output includes information on member forces and deformations, joint displacements and support reactions

References

Availability
Purchase

Language
Applesoft Basic

Computer
48K Apple II

1074

DAFT *Oasys Limited*
Provides a dynamic analysis of 2D and 3D land based or offshore structures. Earthquakes or wave forces may be considered, if required. Details such as the number of nodes, coordinates, number and type of members, load conditions, foundations and type of output are entered, and the program is run. Results may be numerical or graphic (plotter). The program assumes rigid soil structure interfaces

References

Availability
Bureau service

Language
Fortran

Computer
DEC 10

1075

AP114: Space frames *Oasys Limited*
Handles the interactive analysis of 3D, rigid-jointed frameworks. Features include: facility for frame members to have any combination of pinned or fixed flexural connections to their end joints: rigid/flexible supports; external joint loading; external member loading in local and global directions; loading modification and re-run facility; data saving/retrieval. Output includes: joint displacements; internal member loads and stresses; a permanent record of data in tabulated and paged form

References

Availability
Purchase

Language
Basic

Computer
HP 9845

1076

Frame analysis/2 *Quest GENESYS Limited*
This sub-system enables an engineer to analyse a frame which may be a space frame, a plane frame loaded in its own plane or a grid loaded normal to its own plane. The number of members, joints and loading conditions which may be considered is not limited by the sub-system. The size of problem to be handled is limited only by the size and type of computer used

References
GENESYS program library

Availability
Bureau service, hire

Language
Gentran

Computer
DEC 20, Honeywell
IBM, ICL, PE
Philips, others

1077

TRAIN *Robinson Ford Associates*
A low cost, interactive, finite element system for stress analysis. Interfaces to the results processing system, ROSE. Feature include: electrostatic stress analysis; 2D and 3D general structures; displacement and stress-based elements for a wide range of problems; applied nodal forces and moments; distributed loads, pressures and temperature loads applied to elements; structural constraints at nodes with zero or non-zero values

References

Availability
Purchase

Language
Fortran

Computer
Data General, 16-bit
and 32-bit
minicomputer

1078

STRESS *Scicon Limited*
A program used for the design of framed structures, either space frames or plane frames. It is especially useful for small to medium sized structures. Joint displacements, member end forces and moments, member distortions and the reactions at support joints are calculated for a given geometry of structure. The program is capable of handling a wide range of structures, including off-shore platforms

References

Availability
Bureau service

Language

Computer
Univac 1100/62

1079

EFAP *Structures and Computers Limited*
A program for the linear static analysis of 3D framed structures. Used in the analysis stage of the building design process

References

Availability
Purchase

Language
Fortran IV

Computer
64K

1080

GENFAP *Structures and Computers Limited*
A general non-linear frame analysis program for the linear, non-linear and buckling analysis of 3D framed structures. It is particularly suitable for the analysis of scaffolding structures. Used in the analysis stage of the building development process. Output is by line printer (alpha numeric); graphical output is available through an additional Strucom package

References

Availability
Purchase

Language
Fortran IV

Computer
128K

1081

RAMSES (R01054) *Teknikdata AB*
A finite element program for linear static and dynamic analysis of general frame and shell structures. Dynamic analysis includes modal analysis, time history due to transient and harmonic loads, and response spectrum analysis. Concentrated and distributed loads, temperature loads, forced deformations and loads of inertia are applicable

References

Availability
Contact owner

Language
Fortan IV

Computer
Honeywell H6080

1082

EUFEMI *Teknikdata*
A finite element program for linear static analysis of truss, frame, membrane, plate, shell or 3D solid element structures. Pre-programs included for temperature distribution (TEUFEM) and reinforced concrete structures (PLATON). Extensive load combination including automatic calculation of dimensioning load case output on printer and plotter

References

Availability
Purchase, bureau service

Language
Fortran 77

Computer
32-bit computer

1083

Finite element system *UMIST*
Analyses 2D and 3D space frames by the linear finite element method. Deflections and stresses in members are calculated and the equilibrium of forces is checked

References

Availability

Language
Fortran V

Computer
CDC 7600

Computer programs for the building industry

Non-linear plane frame *UMIST*
Analyses skeletal plane frames taking into account factors such as stability, change of geometry, bowing of members, plastic hinges and improperly fitting components

References

Availability
Sale or hire negotiable

Language
Atlas Autocode

Computer
Any with 64K
with AA compiler

Non-linear space frame program *UMIST*
Performs analysis of plastic space frames, allowing for changes of the geometry of the frame

References

Availability

Language
Algol 60

Computer
CDC 7600

Reinforced concrete frames *UMIST*
Carries out analysis of concrete plane frames under various levels of stress to the point of collapse. It is intended to be used as an overall check on design. Concrete not under tension, variable reinforcement along beams, slender columns, building sway, shear walls and plastic hinges are taken into consideration

References

Availability

Language
Atlas Autocode

Computer
ICL 1906A

SPACE *United Information Services Limited*
Analyses 3D structural frames under a variety of loading conditions

References

Availability
Bureau service, time sharing

Language
Fortran

Computer
Honeywell
Sigma 9

ZEN-Design *Zentech Limited*
Produces lists of those selected members capable of supporting the corresponding governing combinations of loading conditions and satisfying the pertinent requirements of codes of practice and engineering criteria. It also gives the maximum stresses, the ratios of actual and admissible stresses, and the total structural weight of members

References
ZENTECH program library

Availability
Purchase, hire, bureau service

Language
Fortran V

Computer
Univac, CDC, DEC
System 10, IBM, ICL

ZEN-Finite element analysis *Zentech Limited*
This program determines, for each loading condition or combination, translations and rotations of joints; internal efforts of beams, quadrilateral and triangular panels, and solid elements; tri-axial corner forces and stresses at all nodes of 20 node and 32 node solid elements; reactions. The maximum number of joints, elements and loading conditions is limited only by the computer configuration used

References
ZENTECH program library

Availability
Purchase, hire, bureau service

Language
Fortran V

Computer
Univac, CDC, DEC
System 10, IBM, ICL

ZEN-Frame analysis *Zentech Limited*
Determines, for each loading condition or combination, translations and rotations of joints; axial and shear forces on each member; bending and torsional moments; reactions. The maximum number of joints, members and loading conditions is limited only by the computer configuration used. Members of different materials and with semi-rigid connections are acceptable and, for straight members, variable section

References
ZENTECH program library

Availability
Purchase, hire, bureau service

Language
Fortran V

Computer
Univac, CDC, DEC
System 10, IBM, ICL

3D LAUNCH *Computational Mechanics Consultants Limited*
Capable of simulating response of steel structures during launch operations associated with installation. Computes the motion and position of the structure relative to the water surface and launching barge. The program is fully 3D and computes the trajectory of the system. Consideration is given to gravity, winch forces, friction forces, hydrodynamic drag and added mass, in addition to buoyancy forces

References

Availability
Licence

Language
Fortran

Computer
Microcomputer

OFFPAF *Wimpey Offshore Limited*
This is a development of PAFEC 75 for the analysis of offshore steel jacket structures. OFFPAF analyses steel jacket structures subjected to wave, wind, current, buoyancy and marine growth hydrodynamic forces, the forces being calculated automatically. The program is also capable of undertaking code checks (member stability and punching shear), and fatigue analysis. The program is not a series of pre- and post- processors; it has been programmed to be an integral part of the PAFEC 75 program

References
PAFEC Users' Meeting 9/9/82
Report No OES 166/82

Availability
Purchase, hire

Language
Fortran

Computer

ZEN-Offshore structures *Zentech Limited*
This system of programs solves problems associated with steel and concrete offshore structures. Wave loading programs include WAVEGEN, suitable for steel jackets, and NPLWAVE, suitable for concrete platforms. Pre-processors generate geometry, properties of members and loading. Post-processors can be used for combining loading conditions producing actual combined loads, load factors and allowable loads

References
ZENTECH program library

Availability
Purchase, hire, bureau service

Language
Fortran V

Computer
Univac CDC DEC
System 10, IBM, ICL

1094

CDMGANT *Cadsteel Limited*
Sizes each member of a conveyor gantry and calculates a total weight of steelwork for estimate. Output is in two forms: 1 Minimum output - a summary list of member types, lengths and section sizes chosen, together with total weight of steel used. 2 Maximum output - tabular form including wind force analysis in top and bottom frames for each gantry bay, load analysis of side frames, space frame analysis and gantry deflection, and member types, lengths and section sizes with weights

References
Constructional Steelwork SWP

Availability
Purchase

Language
Fortran IV

Computer
IBM mainframe
CP/M
microcomputers

1095

Reinforced Concrete *Cambridge Interactive Systems (Products) Limited*
A new module in the CIS MEDUSA system to handle the production of reinforced concrete details and bar bending schedules to BS 4466. Defines bar shapes from parameterised input; the number of bars in a group are determined automatically by specifying a bar spacing, and graphically displayed start/finish points. Calculates cutting and bending tolerances and verification of bar parameters. Provides weight analysis for straight and bent bars

References
Developed jointly with the Severn-Trent Water Authority

Availability
Contact CIS (Nigel Payne or Peter Bush)

Language

Computer

1096

Integral structural design system *Camutek*
Calculates the loading on every element of a building from the overall geometry of the building and the superimposed loading. It uses sub-routines to design automatically each element in the chosen material

References

Availability
From owner

Language
Basic

Computer
HP 9830 (2k) or (6k),
9831, 9835, 9845
Future: HP85, 86

1097

FEINP and ELEMP *Civil and Structural Computing (Northern) Limited*
The package is a general purpose, finite element analysis suite capable of analysing numerous types of structure. Various loading and boundary conditions may be applied, and output includes the normal features

References
Bradshaw, Buckton and Tonge

Availability
Bureau service, time sharing, in-house

Language

Computer

1098

IVAL *Civil and Structural Computing (Northern) Limited*
Calculates section properties for built up sections. Second moment of area radius of gyration and cross-sectional area are produced from rectangular, circular or triangular elements combined to form complete body

References
Bradshaw, Buckton and Tonge

Availability
Bureau service, time sharing, in-house

Language

Computer

1099

PROPS *Civil and Structural Computing (Northern) Limited*
This program calculates the cross-sectional torsional properties for various types of section built up from smaller elements

References
Bradshaw, Buckton and Tonge

Availability
Bureau service, time sharing, in-house

Language

Computer

1100

EASANAL *Computel Limited*
For solving structural engineering problems. The program is based on structural and finite element analysis

References

Availability

Language

Computer

1101

COMPOSITE *Computrav (UK) Limited*
Performs stress checks on a composite section formed from a precast, prestressed unit and an in-situ topping. The check includes shrinkage and creep effects, and differences in elasticity between unit and topping

References
Approved by ACT Sirius

Availability
Purchase

Language
Basic

Computer
Minimum 32Kb on 8
and 16-bit micros
under CP/M

1102

PSC SECTION DESIGN *Computrav (UK) Limited*
Performs all the normal elastic design calculations involved for a prestressed concrete section, from moment calculation through optimum section choice to allowable zone for cable or compressive resultant. The program is fully interactive; results from previous calculations are continually presented as potential input data for subsequent calculations

References
Approved by ACT Sirius

Availability
Purchase

Language
Basic

Computer
Minimum 32Kb on 8
and 16-bit micros
under CP/M

1103

PSC ULTIMATED MOMENT *Computrav (UK) Limited*
Calculates the ultimate moment capacity of a generalised prestressed concrete section. The method used involves integration of the stress block over the compressed area. Results are presented with and without the material partial safety factors of CP110 and are compared with the empirical method of CP110

References
Approved by ACT Sirius

Availability
Purchase

Language
Basic

Computer
Minimum 32Kb on 8
and 16-bit micros
under CP/M

MOMENT and SHEAR *Computrav (UK) Limited*
Designs rectangular or T sections in reinforced concrete to resist specified bending moments and shears in accordance with CP110

References
Approved by ACT Sirius

Availability
Purchase

Language
Basic

Computer
Minimum 32Kb on 8 and 16-bit micros under CP/M

1105

ACCESS 3 *COSMIC*
A new method of minimum weight design for structural systems. For practical structural design applications, programming is complicated due to the large number of design variables and the large set of inequality constraints. ACCESS 3 provides an explicit, mathematical analysis through the use of design variable linking, constraint deletion techniques, and explicit approximations for retained constraints. The program modifies the sizing of the finite elements, eg cross-sectional areas or thicknesses

References

Availability
Purchase

Language
Fortran IV

Computer
CDC Cyber 70

1106

GS-1. General section properties *Ecom Associates, Inc*
Determines properties of irregularly shaped sections, area elements, line elements and concrete elements. Gross, uncracked transformed and cracked section properties for normal or lightweight concrete are calculated for reinforced concrete sections. Effective moments of inertia can also be obtained for an applied moment

References

Availability
Purchase

Language
M Basic

Computer
HP

1107

LUSAS *Finite Element Analysis Limited*
A general purpose, structural analysis program for frames, grillages, trusses, plane stress/strain, plates, shells and solids. The program has been designed to solve a comprehensive range of problems including static, dynamic, non-linear and thermal problems. Provides graphical and printed output

References
Numerous technical publications; details available on request

Availability
Purchase, bureau service

Language
Fortran 77

Computer
1 Mbyte main memory
50 Mbyte disk

1108

SAFE *Freeman Fox and Partners*
This program deals with finite element analysis of engineering structures for plane truss, plane frame, space truss, space frame, grillage, plate bending, plate membrane, shell, box girders, and solid structures. Approved by the Department of Transport. Output includes printed tables of displacements, stresses, forces and reactions, together with a plot of the structure or displaced structure

References

Availability
Bureau Service from CRD Limited; sale or lease

Language
Fortran IV

Computer
Minimum 32-bit, 48K computer

1109

PLNFRMB *Freeman Fox and Partners*
Deals with the linear plastic analysis of plane frame structures; a non-linear version is also available. Features include influence lines, enveloping, tapered beams, elasto plastic supports, and HA and HB loadings. Approved by the Department of Transport. Output includes printed tables of displacements, forces and reactions

References

Availability
Bureau service from CRD Limited; sale or lease

Language
Fortran IV

Computer
Minimum 32-bit, 36K computer

1110

1130 Structural engineering system stress solver *A M Kinney, Inc*
Performs the linear analysis of elastic, statically loaded structures composed of prismatic slender members, ie those which are represented by their centroidal axis and analysed as line elements. The solution provides member forces, such as axial and shear force, and moment at the member ends, reactions, joint displacements, and support displacements

References

Availability

Language
Fortran

Computer
IBM 1130 and 370

1111

STRB *Microcomp Limited*
Calculates static deformation and stress field within a 2D isotropic body using the boundary element method. The program uses a series of elements with constant interpolation to discretise the surface of the body, and it can analyse bounded and unbounded domains. Particularly suited to infinite domain problems which finite element programs are incapable of dealing with. Prescribed forces or displacement conditions can be specified on each boundary element

References

Availability
Licence

Language
Basic

Computer
Apple II 48K

1112

Bar Reinforcement Schedule Calculation *Norden Technical Computer Systems Limited*
Calculates and prints out the reinforcement quantities required from bar schedules produced by the engineers

References

Availability

Language

Computer
64K Microcomputer
Interset IS 2000
Digico M16E

1113

AP104: Section properties *Oasys Limited*
A program to determine the centroid, area and second moments of area of sections about axes parallel to reference axes, principal axes and any other axes specified by the user. Sections may be built up of individual components specified by the user, or standard shapes with differing modular ratios

References

Availability
Purchase

Language
Basic

Computer
HP 9845 HP 85/87

Computer programs for the building industry

1114

AP106: Bending schedule weighting *Oasys Limited*
Calculates the weight of reinforcement specified in bending schedules. The weight for each type and size of reinforcement bar specified is given for individual schedules, and also in a summary covering all reinforcement weighted

References

Availability
Purchase

Language
Basic

Computer
HP 9845 HP 85/87

1115

NODIM and NODEV *Redpath Engineering Limited*
Produces detailed dimensional information required to detail and fabricate welded tubular structures. Estimating information is also produced in the form of quantities, including volume of weld. Primarily intended for tubular jacket structures used in the offshore industry, but can handle any welded tubular structure. Dimensioning and weld details conform respectively to API and AWS specifications. Metric units are used. The program segregates different grades of material for the purpose of listing quantities

References

Availability
Purchase

Language
Fortran IV

Computer
PDP 11/70 Prime 550

1116

Simple Coordinate Geometry *Redpath Engineering Limited*
From given information defining positions of intersection points (nodes) in 3D space, and straight lines between these points (members), the program produces: true lengths of all members, true angles of intersection between every pair of intersecting members, and global orientation of every member defined by a plan angle (alpha), and an angle of inclination (beta). Applications include any structural shape involving intersecting straight lines

References

Availability

Language

Computer

1117

QUER2 *RIB*
Computes section properties of thin walled cross-sections as well as normal and shear stresses due to internal forces and moments of magnitude 1

References

Availability
Purchase

Language
Fortran IV

Computer
CPU 64K

1118

REBARS *S D Micros Limited*
Designed to speed the process of calculating the weight of steel reinforcing bars from bar schedules; provides reliable checking facilities to significantly reduce errors. Data is entered as recommended for bar schedules by BSI, with the ability to default repetitive data, thus reducing typing of entries

References

Availability
Purchase

Language
Pascal p-system

Computer
Any for UCSD p, with 64K

1119

STRUDL *Scicon Limited*
For use in analysis and design of structures such as drilling rigs, storage tanks and derricks. Forces and stresses within members may be analysed and a combination of results, such as maximum stresses and force and stress envelopes, produced. Different loading conditions may be considered and analysed. The finite element method of analysis is used

References

Availability
Bureau service

Language

Computer
Univac 1100/62

1120

Circular plate *Structural Members Users Group, USA*
Calculates the deflection, slope, radial moment, shear, transverse moment and twisting moment for static and steady state conditions. Determines the critical load and mode shape for stability, and natural frequencies and mode shapes for transverse vibrations. The plate can be formed of uniform rings with any loading, in-span supports, foundations and boundary conditions. The user can include unsymmetric loading for applied forces and moments

References
Book published by McGraw Hill, 1978

Availability
Purchase

Language
Fortran IV

Computer
CDC, IBM, Univac, VAX, Prime

1121

Disks *Structural Members Users Group, USA*
The radial displacement, radial force and tangential force are found for static and steady state conditions. The disk can be rotating. The natural frequencies and mode shapes are calculated for radial vibrations. The theory is based on a plane stress assumption with either isotropic or orthotropic material. The loading and responses are axially symmetric

References
Book published by McGraw Hill, 1978

Availability
Purchase

Language
Fortran IV

Computer
CDC, IBM, Univac, VAX, Prime

1122

Extension systems *Structural Members Users Group, USA*
For static and steady state axial loads, the program finds the axial displacement and force. The torsion system can be a bar formed of uniform segments with any loading, gears, branches, foundations, and boundary conditions

References
Book published by McGraw Hill, 1978

Availability
Purchase

Language
Fortran IV

Computer
CDC, IBM, Univac, VAX, Prime

1123

Rectangular plate *Structural Members Users Group, USA*
Two opposing edges of the plate must be simply supported. Other boundary conditions, loading, etc, are arbitrary. Static, steady state, stability and free vibration problems are solved. The plate may be isotropic or orthotropic

References
Book published by McGraw Hill, 1978

Availability
Purchase

Language
Fortran IV

Computer
CDC, IBM, Univac, VAX, Prime

Sectional properties *Structural Members Users Group, USA*
Cross-sectional properties of a bar of any cross-sectional shape are calculated. Properties include area, centroid, moments of inertia about any axes, radii of gyration, shear centre, shear deformation coefficients, torsional constant, and warping constant. Modulus weighted properties are calculated for composite sections

References
Book published by McGraw Hill, 1978

Availability
Purchase

Language
Fortran IV

Computer
CDC, IBM, Univac, VAX, Prime

Stress analysis *Structural Members Users Group, USA*
The normal and shear stresses are found on the cross section of a bar of any cross-sectional shape. The material can be composite. The stresses include bending stresses, shear stress due to torsion and warping, shear stresses due to transverse loads and normal stresses due to warping

References
Book published by McGraw Hill, 1978

Availability
Purchase

Language
Fortran IV

Computer
CDC, IBM, Univac, VAX, Prime

Strings *Structural Members Users Group, USA*
Both small, longitudinal and linear, transverse motion of strings under arbitrary loading can be handled. Static response and natural frequencies are found

References
Book published by McGraw Hill, 1978

Availability
Purchase

Language
Fortran IV

Computer
CDC, IBM, Univac, VAX, Prime

CSTPC *Structural Software Systems*
Finite element plane stress or plain strain analysis using constant strain triangle elements. The Stiffness Method of analysis is used. The finite element mesh may be subjected to any desired combination of nodal loads and support node displacements

References

Availability
Lease

Language
IBM BASIC interpreter

Computer
IBM PC

Structural Analysis *Transam Microsystems Limited*
Modules include: analysis of bolted joints, welded joints, fracture mechanics, strain gauge; mathematical sub-routines; beams, trusses, rigid frames, plane grills, complex frames, idealised N-Span bridge systems, suspension cables

References

Availability
Purchase

Language
Fortran-80

Computer
CP/M

COGO *United Information Services Limited*
This program is a coordinate geometry system, originally part of the ICES suite, and has been adapted for time sharing use

References

Availability
Bureau service, time sharing

Language
Fortran

Computer
Honeywell Sigma 9

ZEN - Non-linear analysis *Zentech Limited*
This iterative program uses the Newton-Ralphson method to evaluate geometrical (large deflection) and non-linear stability effects. It uses S and C stability functions and modifies inertial properties depending on the axial forces in the members. At the start of each iteration, the deformed shape obtained at the end of the previous one is taken as the input and all transformation matrices are modified accordingly

References
ZENTECH program library

Availability
Purchase, hire, bureau service

Language
Fortran V

Computer
Univac, CDC, DEC System 10, IBM, ICL

ZEN-Dynamic analysis *Zentech Limited*
Analyses the natural frequencies, modes and responses of structures under dynamic loads, such as earthquakes, over a period of time. Structures can include beams, triangular and quadrilateral plates, and solids in any combination. Joints may have up to six degrees of freedom. Masses may be lumped at joints with up to three dynamic translational degrees of freedom

References
ZENTECH program library

Availability
Purchase, hire, bureau service

Language
Fortran V

Computer
Univac, CDC, DEC System 10, IBM, ICL

Computer programs for the building industry

Structural elements

Floors
Roofs, trusses
Girders, beams
Slabs
Structural walls
Columns
Other

1132

SCIA: CAD of prefab floors *Eclipse Associates Limited*
The optimal placement of prefabricated floor elements is drawn for a given arbitrary floor plan. This covers possible cuts, holes, etc, and the calculation of the reinforcement and drawing. Also provides production plans for individual elements

References

Availability
Purchase, bureau service (SCIA SV, ST DATA APS)

Language
Wang Extended Basic, HP Basic

Computer
Wang mini and microcomputers

1133

Structural steel beam framing design *A M Kinney, Inc*
This program will design an entire floor framing system of simple supported beams subjected to any combination of concentrated and uniform loads, symmetrically or unsymmetrically placed. Output includes: the beam number, left and right reactions, moments, point of zero shear from left end, section modulus required and furnished, beam shape selected, actual and allowable stresses, maximum and allowable imbraced lengths, standard connection capacity, and total weight of all designed beams

References

Availability

Language
Fortran

Computer
IBM 1130 and 370

1134

COMP-CONSTRUCT/1 *Quest GENESYS Limited*
This sub-system enables an engineer to design, analyse, detail and cost a simply supported composite deck, including shear connectors, constructed in accordance with CP117:Part 1:1965 and Part 2:1967. The program incorporates a data table of universal beams. Slab design is in accordance with CP110:Part 1:1969

References
GENESYS program library

Availability
Bureau service, hire

Language
Gentran

Computer
DEC 20, Honeywell, IBM, ICL, PE, Philips, others

1135

Precast Concrete Flooring Systems *Quest GENESYS Limited*
A development of the CP110 Suite used to form the basis of a precast concrete floor design, detail and scheduling system; accommodates steel or concrete framed structures and can determine the number of individual precast units required for a given floor area. Drawings are produced for floor components with skewed ends, cutouts or special reinforcement requirements. All quantities are scheduled. General arrangement drawings show floor layout and unit numbering

References

Availability

Language
Gentran

Computer

1136

D4 *Amplix Services Limited*
Features include: design of minimum weight steel portal frames under the action of vertical and horizontal loads using plastic collapse design method; multi-bay, regular or staggered pitch; calculation of stanchion and rafter restraint requirements; selection of steel section from steel tables held on file, or section check; elastic frame deflection check

References

Availability
Purchase

Language
Commercial (SMB) Cobol, Fortran

Computer
CP/M or MP/M Microcomputer

1137

IEDS *Baric Computing Services Limited*
Integrated Engineering Design Service for Structural Steelwork. Handles plastic design and elastic analysis of single and multi-span portal frames; uses the 'minimum weight - ultimate strength' method. Input: geometry of frame, including purlins and rails, and details of dead or superimposed loads for members not designed by the programs. Selects rails and purlins, designs canopies, crane rails and support brackets, then outputs the plastic moduli required, with sizes and costs of sections

References
Constructional Steelwork SWP

Availability
Bureau service, purchase

Language
Fortran IV

Computer
ICL 1904A

1138

CDMPORT *Cadsteel Limited*
Used for plastic analysis of portal frames. The current version has been modified to take advantage of the facilities of microcomputers. The program analyses single bay portals and can take into account: snow, wind, rafter and crane loads. It does not check for web buckling. Runs interactively within the limitations of the system software under which it is installed

References
CICA Bulletin, September 1982

Availability
Purchase

Language
Fortran, Basic

Computer
IBM, CP/M

1139

Single bay portal frame design *Camutek*
Designs portal frames. Given the geometry, basic loading and wind pressure, the program automatically calculates the pressure coefficients. It also gives the load factors and deflections under various load combinations, the weight and the sizes of the columns, rafters, haunches and ridge gussets

References

Availability
From owner

Language
Basic

Computer
HP 9830 (2k) or (6k), 9831, 9835, 9845 Future: HP85, 86

1140

BRACE *Civil and Structural Computing (Northern) Limited*
Analyses and designs the longitudinal bracing elements of portal frames. Numerous types of bracing configurations may be designed and compared, including compound panels and rectangular portals

References
Bradshaw, Buckton and Tonge

Availability
Bureau service, time sharing, in-house

Language

Computer

1141

GABLE *Civil and Structural Computing (Northern) Limited*
This program analyses and designs gable frames, including horizontal and vertical bracing, and design of gable posts in accordance with BCSA recommendations and current Codes of Practice

References
Bradshaw, Buckton and Tonge. Recommended by Radan Computational Limited

Availability
Bureau service, time sharing, in-house

Language

Computer

HSTAB *Civil and Structural Computing (Northern) Limited*
Performs stability checks on the tapered haunch sections of portal frames in accordance with currently available recommendations from accepted papers. Haunches may be built up from plates or I-section cuttings, and restraint considerations may be included

References
Bradshaw, Buckton and Tonge

Availability
Bureau service, time sharing, in-house

Language

Computer

MCON *Civil and Structural Computing (Northern) Limited*
Carries out ultimate plastic analysis/design of moment connections based on the latest Constrado Publications. Applies to eaves or apex connections and includes design of bolt diameter, plate thickness and stiffeners. Connections are checked for buckling and stability criteria which allow the designer to produce optimised designs extremely quickly

References
Bradshaw, Buckton and Tonge

Availability
Bureau service, time sharing, in-house

Language

Computer

PURLIN and SPAR *Civil and Structural Computing (Northern) Limited*
Used to design purlins and side rails selected from the major Manufacturers' Section Lists or the user's own range. Manufacturers' requirements for sag rods and wind uplift considerations are included

References
Bradshaw, Buckton and Tonge

Availability
Bureau service, time sharing, in-house

Language

Computer

WIND *Civil and Structural Computing (Northern) Limited*
This program performs wind analysis for rectangular clad buildings in accordance with CP3 ChV Pt2 1972 for various types of portal frame, including frictional drag forces if required. Wind data is automatically generated for subsequent use in the portal element design programs

References
Bradshaw, Buckton and Tonge

Availability
Bureau service, time sharing, in-house

Language

Computer

Structural Design System *Datron Micro Centres*
For the design and analysis of plastic portal frames including sub-frames, beams, masonry panels, slabs and plane frames, all to CP110:1972 standards. Results are output on screen and printer

References
Owned by Sheffield University

Availability
Purchase

Language
Basic (Applesoft)

Computer
Apple II

TA-1. Plane truss anlaysis *Ecom Associates, Inc*
Analyses statically determinate and indeterminate plane trusses. The structure is assumed to consist of prismatic members which carry only axial forces connected at pinned joints. Output includes joint displacements, member forces and stresses, and reactions

References

Availability
Purchase

Language
M Basic

Computer
HP

PP12 *Engineering Software Services Limited*
A portal frame design and analysis suite by the plastic analysis method. Used for single bay structures and includes crane loads

References
Recommended by British Olivetti

Availability

Language

Computer
Olivetti M20

Truss Analysis *Hydro Systems (USA)*
Solves for member forces in a determinate plane truss. Inputs are structure geometry and loading. Outputs are member forces and reactions. Various loading combinations and member configurations may be examined. Capacity with 48K is about 75 members

References

Availability
Purchase

Language

Computer
16K RAM minimum

PDPF *Microcomp Limited*
For the design of single span, pinned base portal frames under dead plus imposed load, using plastic theory. Can justify a frame with known section and haunch sizes, or to establish suitable sizes. A data file is used containing properties of British Standard universal beams, universal columns and joists. The program deals with: frame dimensions, approximate elastic design, plastic design and stanchion design

References

Availability
Licence

Language
Basic

Computer
Apple II 48K

AP108: Plane trusses *Oasys Limited*
A program for the interactive analysis of plane trusses. Features include: rigid/flexible supports; external joint loading; loading modification and re-run facility; data saving/retrieving facility. Output consists of joint displacements, internal member loads and stresses, together with a permanent record of the data supplied. All are in tabulated, paged form

References

Availability
Purchase

Language
Basic

Computer
HP 9845 HP 85/87

Computer programs for the building industry

1152

AP111: Space trusses *Oasys Limited*
The program features include: rigid/flexible supports; external joint loading; loading modification and re-run facility; data saving/retrieving. Output consists of joint deflections, internal member loads and stresses, records of all data in tabulated and paged form

References

Availability
Purchase

Language
Basic

Computer
HP 9845 HP 85/87

1153

AP115: Portal frame data generation *Oasys Limited*
This program operates interactively with AP109. Features include: the specification of variable span lengths; rafter, stanchion and haunch dimensions and section sizes; an option on stanchion continuity, and the UDL on each span acting over the rafters. Output consists of tabulation of data and a plot of the structure. There is an option to save the data and retrieve it at a later date from AP109

References

Availability
Purchase

Language
Basic

Computer
HP 9845

1154

PORTAL-FRAME/1 *Quest GENESYS Limited*
For the design of single and multi-span, steel portal frames. Calculations include stability checks for each frame member, and elastic deflection. The program can accept monopitch, monitor roof, north light profile or frames with asymmetric spans. Loading can include superimposed, wind and crane loading including surge. Results include section sizing, axial, shear and bending moments for the frame, elastic deflection checks and stresses

References

Availability

Language
Gentran

Computer

1155

Plastic Analysis of Single Bay Portal Frames *Reading Computer Services Limited*
Calculates the load factor for any single bay portal frame consisting of three or four straight members, plus an eaves tie if required. Frame data and loading is generated from the minimum of user input, and haunch data can also be specified

References

Availability

Language

Computer
CP/M Microcomputer

1156

ALPHA 2000 *Redland Construction Software Limited*
A suite of programs for timber frame manufacturers. Deals with preliminary quotation through the production of drawings, cutting, manufacturing and assembly data to detailed cost analysis. Client drawings do not need to be to scale, nor fully dimensioned providing these factors are defined. Programs include: Timber Frame House Panel and Special Panel, Timber Frame Panel Calculations, House Floor and House Roof

References

Availability

Language

Computer

1157

CONCEPT 2000 *Redland Construction Software Limited*
A complete suite of programs for the trussed rafter manufacturer, dealing with roof quotation through fabrication to stock control, production analysis and local market forecasting. Programs are fully interactive and include: House Roof, Roof Truss Design and Estimation, Roof Truss Production Control, Roof Truss Stock Control and Roof Truss Market Forecasting

References

Availability

Language

Computer
CP/M
microcomputers

1158

Roof Tile Estimating *Redland Construction Software Limited*
Produces quotations of materials and parts required for roof tiling; fully priced, extended and totalled with user defined allowances for cutting and breakages. A library of common roof shapes is provided; the user may add to the library using a graphical input program. Roof type definition requires roof perimeter information only. Output includes roof type library layouts, roof drawings and quotations

References

Availability

Language

Computer

1159

Roof Wind Uplift *Redland Construction Software Limited*
A module to interface with roof tile estimating program or run independently. Performs analysis to produce fixing requirements for single lap roof tiles and fittings. Output gives the number of tiles in local area. The local area wind load and fixing specification can be combined to give one local area case or to give the wind load and fixing specification for Ridge, Verge, Eaves and Abutments separately

References

Availability

Language

Computer

1160

TB2 *Redpath Engineering Limited*
For automatic minimum weight design of trussed beam roof members. The trussed beam comprises a universal beam rafter with a central apex and a double channel battened tie underslung from the rafter with three internal struts of single channels. Output includes: member sizes of rafter, tie and struts; moments in rafter at each load point; axial forces in all members; actual and allowable stresses

References

Availability
Purchase

Language
Fortran

Computer
PDP11/70 ICL 1905F

1161

TRUS2DPC *Structural Software Systems*
Static analysis of a 2D truss by the Stiffness Method. The truss may be subjected to any combination of concentrated joint loads and support joint displacements. Support joints may be pinned or restrained by horizontal or vertical rollers. Output includes: joint displacements; support joint reactions; and member axial forces

References

Availability
Lease

Language
IBM BASIC
interpreter

Computer
IBM PC

Computer programs for the building industry

TRUS3DPC *Structural Software Systems*
Static analysis of a 3D truss by the Stiffness Method. The truss may be subjected to any combination of concentrated joint loads and support joint displacements. Support joints may be pinned or restrained by horizontal or vertical rollers. Output includes: joint displacements; support joint reactions; and member axial forces. There are no specific limitations on the number of joints and members for the structure to be analysed

References

Availability
Lease

Language
IBM BASIC interpreter

Computer
IBM PC

TRUSILPC *Structural Software Systems*
Computes the influence line ordinates for the member forces in a plane truss. Input consists of the truss geometry, the member and material properties, and the location and restraints for the support joints. No specific limitations on the number of joints and members for the truss which is being analysed

References

Availability
Lease

Language
IBM BASIC interpreter

Computer
IBM PC

ELPOR *Technical Services*
Handles the elastic analysis of single bay symmetrical portal frames to provide deflections and moments. Analysis by normal principles of statics and, in particular, the moment area method is used for estimating for estimating deflections. Input includes: frame geometry, member properties, type of steel, fixity of frame feet, and loads. Output includes moments at salient points on the frame together with reactions at the feet; deflections are output at eaves, crane beam level and apex. Output as a headed calculation sheet

References
Constructional Steelwork SWP

Availability
Purchase

Language
Extended Basic

Computer
Olivetti P6066 with 16K bytes

Plastic analysis of portal frame *Technical Services*
Analyses a symmetrical single bay portal frame using the plastic analysis techniques described in BCSA publications. Allows dead, snow, wind, crane and rafter loads to be considered, and four configurations of plastic hinges. The feet of the frame may be fixed or pinned. The program can handle multibay arrangements and frames having stanchion legs of differing lengths. Normal operation is as follows: enter geometry, design purlins, enter loads, estimate suitable sections for rafter and stanchion

References

Availability
Purchase

Language
Basic

Computer
Olivetti P6060, and P6066, 16K

Resolution of forces in a truss *Technical Services*
Calculates the forces in the members of any statically determinate pin-jointed truss. The truss is specified by entering the x and y coordinates of the nodes; the program then calculates and prints out all member lengths. Loading may be vertical and/or horizontal. When loads have been entered and reactions calculated, the resolution of forces proceeds from node to node in sequence. Results are output in the form of a calculation sheet

References

Availability
Purchase

Language
Basic

Computer
Olivetti P6060, and P6066, 16K

Roof truss design *TRADA*
Programs for producing load span tables for domestic truss and truss rafter constructions, and for industrial trusses, all jointed by nailed plywood gussets

References

Availability

Language

Computer

Span chart plotting *TRADA*
A number of programs for plotting span load charts in different forms for solid or built up timber beams and timber portals, and for other materials

References

Availability

Language

Computer

Timber portal frames *TRADA*
A number of programs for producing tables and designs for portal frames formed from uniform solid or ply web members, or with tapered members

References

Availability

Language

Computer

ABCONS *Associated British Consultants (Computers) Limited*
A system for the analysis, design and schedule detailing of reinforced concrete beam/slab structures to CP110. Analysis is available now. Design is in the development stage. The system allows extensive data check and screen editing facilities. Output includes shear and moment envelopes, and a summary of critical values

References

Availability
Purchase

Language
Basic

Computer
64K TRS80 Model 2

STEEL 1 *Associated British Consultants (Computers) Limited*
A program for the design of beams and stanchions to BS449. Contains screen editing facilities. Output includes moments, reactions and sections

References

Availability
Purchase

Language
Basic

Computer
64K TRS80 Model 2

1172

BEAMSCAN *Beamscan Computer Software*
Analysis of simply supported beams with a maximum span of 20m, with up to 30 combined loads. Selects suitable sections in both steel and timber in accordance with BS 449 and CP 112. Printout satisfies Local Authority requirements. A typical design is produced in under one minute. Output includes: all input loads and analysis results, reactions, bending moment, deflection etc, and section data and stresses

References
Sinclair User July 1983

Availability
Purchase

Language
Basic

Computer
BBC model B (32K)

1173

COMPB *British Olivetti Limited*
Designs and analyses composite beams to BS CP117. An interactive program for the design and analysis of composite beams for simply supported beams with uniformly distributed loads. On a minimum load factor requirement, the program selects the lightest section satisfying the design for the specified structural depth

References
Copyright: Roughton and Fenton

Availability
Purchase

Language
Basic

Computer
Olivetti minicomputer

1174

CDMBEAM *Cadsteel Limited*
Designs simply supported beams. Accuracy of deflection and bending moment results are achieved by numerical integration. Analysis and member sizing in accordance with BS 449. User can include up to 8 point loads, a UDL and 2 partial UDL's. Chooses section from comprehensive steel tables or checks a stated section. Output consists of calculation sheets for: load details, vertical reactions, distance to maximum BM and deflection, all maximum and permissible stresses, and section to be used

References
Constructional Steelwork SWP

Availability
Purchase

Language
Fortran IV

Computer
IBM mainframe
CP/M microcomputer

1175

CDMBRACE *Cadsteel Limited*
Designs pin-jointed ties and struts; sizes structural bracing members. Member design is to BS 449. Members are selected from CONSTRADO steel tables for equal/unequal angles, channels, universal beams and columns. Output in tabular form, is grouped into type of section required. For each member, stress and permissible stress are given together with individual and total weights

References
Constructional Steelwork SWP

Availability
Purchase

Language
Fortran

Computer
IBM mainframe
CP/M
microcomputers

1176

Plyweb Beam Design *Camutek*
Calculates stresses within a specified plyweb beam, whether it is a simply supported beam of any span subject to a uniformly distributed load broken into dead and live components, or merely an individual section subject to a given moment and shear force. The section properties are printed out and bending stresses, panel shear and rolling shear are checked, and the effects of joints are considered. The requirements of CP112 for full restraint is also printed out

References

Availability
From Camutek

Language
Basic

Computer
HP9835, 9845 Future:
HP 85 & 86

1177

Simply supported steel beam design *Camutek*
Designs steel beams in bending and deflection to BS449:1969. It chooses beam, column or channel sections from BS4:Part 1:1972 and BS4:Part 2:1969

References

Availability
From owner

Language
Basic

Computer
HP 9830 (2k) or (6k),
9831, 9835, 9845
Future: HP85, 86

1178

Single span beam analysis *Camutek*
Gives the shear forces, bending moments, slope and deflection of a single span beam. It also includes fixed ends or end moments

References

Availability
From owner

Language
Basic

Computer
HP 9830 (2k) or (6k),
9831, 9835, 9845
Future: HP85, 86

1179

CEPCON *CEP International*
Analyses beams and slabs spanning over a maximum of 11 supports in accordance with the requirements of CP110:Part 1:1972. Used for the design of reinforced concrete beams and slabs, including bending and shear envelopes, and the reinforcement required by these envelopes. Loads may be positive or negative. Either service or ultimate loads may be input

References

Availability
Purchase

Language
Basic

Computer
Commodore CBM
8032

1180

BMDES *Civil and Structural Computing (Northern) Limited*
Designs reinforced concrete beams in accordance with CP110, including reinforcement design, serviceability and shear checks. Input is either interactive or from previous analysis programs. Output is formatted suitable for submission to checking authorities

References
Bradshaw, Buckton and Tonge

Availability
Bureau service, time sharing, in-house

Language

Computer

1181

CNECT *Civil and Structural Computing (Northern) Limited*
Carries out the design of beam/column moment connections based on BS449. The program includes the design of plate thickness, bolt diameter and stiffeners. Connections are checked for the normal stability criteria which allows the designer to produce optimised designs

References
Bradshaw, Buckton and Tonge

Availability
Bureau service, time sharing, in-house

Language

Computer

GIRDER *Civil and Structural Computing (Northern) Limited*
Designs plate girders to BS449 including design of plates and welds. Web buckling, bearing and stress checks are included, and output is formatted suitable for submission to checking authorities

References
Bradshaw, Buckton and Tonge

Availability
Bureau service, time sharing, in-house

Language

Computer

1183

SBEAM *Civil and Structural Computing (Northern) Limited*
Designs steel beams subjected to various end conditions to BS449. Design selects from the standard BCSA Section Tables and carries out full stress checks, and display deflection criteria. Numerous load types may be allowed for including point loads, UDLs, trapezoidal and patch loading. Output is formatted suitable for submission to checking authorities

References
Bradshaw, Buckton and Tonge

Availability
Bureau service, time sharing, in-house

Language

Computer

1184

SHEREC *Civil and Structural Computing (Northern) Limited*
Analyses shear and connections for plate girders or universal sections subjected to various loading conditions. Analysis includes plate design and bolt setting-out criteria in accordance with BS449

References
Bradshaw, Buckton and Tonge

Availability
Bureau service, time sharing, in-house

Language

Computer

1185

VBEAM *Civil and Structural Computing (Northern) Limited*
Analyses beams of varying cross sections subjected to varying load conditions. Output includes bending moments, shear forces and displacements. The program caters for various support conditions

References
Bradshaw, Buckton and Tonge

Availability
Bureau service, time sharing, in-house

Language

Computer

1186

CRANE *Civil and Structural Computing (Northern) Limited*
Makes an analysis of a simply supported span for a moving load train composed of up to three electric overhead travelling cranes. The program determines maximum horizontal and vertical bending moments for the span; the maximum beam shear; maximum reactions to the supporting structure and also the out of balance load to the support; and maximum coexistent reactions to the supporting structure

References
Bradshaw, Buckton and Tonge

Availability
Bureau service, time sharing, in-house

Language

Computer
Hewlett Packard
9800
and others

1187

CANTILEVER BEAM *Civil-Ware (USA)*
Calculates forces at and between supports due to a uniformly distributed loading. Moments are determined at the cantilevered support and location and magnitude of the maximum moment in the inside span. Shear forces are determined at the supports. Maximum deflections are calculated for the cantilevered end and the inside span

References

Availability
Purchase

Language
Applesoft

Computer
Apple II+ (48K)

1188

WOOD BEAM *Civil-Ware (USA)*
Determines physical requirements of a simply supported wood beam with a uniform distributed loading. Deflection criteria, allowable stress increase due to snow loading and repetitive member in compliance with the Uniform Building Code are also accommodated. Output gives required cross-section area, section modulus, and moment of inertia of four different species of wood. Can be modified to include any wood species

References

Availability
Purchase

Language
Applesoft

Computer
Apple II+ (48K)

1189

BEMDES *Civilsoft (USA)*
For selection of structural beams. Input includes type of beam support and whether the loads are point loads, uniformly distributed loads or a combination of both loads. Output consists of selected beam size according to the AISC handbook, total load on beam and total load including beam.

References
ASCE, Building Construction Digest

Availability
Purchase

Language
8080 or 8088/86

Computer
8-bit with 64K or
16-bit with 128K
memory

1190

HETENYI *Computel Limited*
A program for the general analysis of a beam on an elastic foundation

References
GEOCOMP

Availability

Language

Computer

1191

Beam on Elastic Foundation *Computer Design*
Part of the COSPACK package. Determination of bending moments and shear forces for a beam resting on a bed of independent springs, using a finite element technique

References
Sirius Computing, January 1983

Availability
Purchase, lease

Language
Basic

Computer
ACT Sirius 1 256K.
Plotter

Computer programs for the building industry

1192

Plane Grid Analysis *Computer Design*
Part of the COSPACK package. Provides static analysis of plane grids with any beam arrangement using the displacement method

References
Sirius Computing, January 1983

Availability
Purchase, lease

Language
Basic

Computer
ACT Sirius 1 256K. Plotter

1193

BEAM DEFLECTIONS *Computrav (UK) Limited*
From data provided on end moments, end cantilevers, span, generalised loads and section moment of inertia, this program will display bending moment and shear force diagrams, plus rotations and deflections at all critical points in the length of the member

References
Approved by ACT Sirius

Availability
Purchase

Language
Basic

Computer
Minimum 32Kb on 8 and 16-bit micros under CP/M

1194

PSC SHEAR *Computrav (UK) Limited*
Calculates the shear capacity of a prestressed concrete section at intervals of half the effective depth over the half span of a beam. Result is compared with actual shear calculated for point and distributed load. Reinforcing links are designed by the program. Positions the load for maximum moment or shear; can give critical shear effects due to interaction between them. A table of shear reinforcement is produced. PSC ONE SHEAR allows the user to specify data for one particular section at a time

References
Approved by ACT Sirius

Availability
Purchase

Language
Basic

Computer
Minimum 32Kb on 8 and 16-bit micros under CP/M

1195

STEEL BEAM *Computrav (UK) Limited*
From data provided on end moments, end cantilevers, span and generalised loads, the program will display the eight most suitable standard steel sections for the three BS steel grades. For a chosen section, the program continues to calculate rotations and deflections at all critical points in the length of the member

References
Approved by ACT Sirius

Availability
Purchase

Language
Basic

Computer
Minimum 32Kb on 8 and 16-bit micros under CP/M

1196

Beam 110 *R J Crocker and Partners*
Analyses and designs reinforced concrete continuous beams, slabs, plate floors, and moment distribution, in accordance with CP110 and CP114. Beams may be up to 12 spans, and rectangular or T-shaped in profile. Column profiles are considered. Output includes details of the bending moment envelope and the shear force envelope, the support reactions and information concerning the shear reinforcement. Related programs are: Slab 110, Plate 110, Beam 114, Slab 114, Dist 110, Dist 114

References
DOC Evaluation Report No 2 (for Beam 110 only)

Availability
Bureau service from United Computing Services Limited

Language
Fortran

Computer
Sigma

1197

SCIA: 2D BEAM Structures *Eclipse Associates Limited*
The basic version covers the static elastic analysis of arbitrary 2D beam structures, ie various loadings and loading types. Extensions to the system include: stress control for steel structures; limit load analysis for steel structures following the theory of plasticity, and including second order effects (instability); limit analysis of concrete structures; graphical input and output program for graphic screen and/or plotter

References

Availability
Purchase, bureau service (SCIA SV, ST DATA APS)

Language
Wang Extended Basic, HP Basic

Computer
Wang mini and microcomputers

1198

SCIA: 3D BEAM Structures *Eclipse Associates Limited*
The basic version handles static electric analysis of arbitrary 3D beam structures, including eccentric and elastic connections and internal hinges. A related version covers 3D trusses, hinged bars, loads at the nodes and automatic deadload, temperature loading and imposed displacements

References

Availability
Purchase, bureau service (SCIA SV, ST DATA APS)

Language
Wang Extended Basic, HP Basic

Computer
Wang mini and microcomputers

1199

PD-1. Prestressed concrete beam *Ecom Associates, Inc*
Analyses and designs pre-tensioned, simply supported concrete beams with cantilevers according to ACI 318-77. The constant cross-section may be composite. Portions of strands may be slipped. Strands may have depression points. Mild steel reinforcement at release is displayed. Given a stranding, the flexural and shear stresses, moment capacity, web reinforcement, and deflection are calculated

References

Availability
Purchase

Language
M Basic

Computer
HP200, 9845

1200

SD-1. Steel beam design *Ecom Associates, Inc*
Selects highest sections for each of several section depths. Output includes moment capacity, shear stress ratio, end reactions, maximum moments, centreline and cantilever deflections

References

Availability
Purchase

Language
M Basic

Computer
HP, DEC, Wang, Apple, Tandy TRS-80, IBM PC

1201

SD-3. Composite steel beam design *Ecom Associates, Inc*
Designs or checks simple span beams of composite steel and concrete construction. Loads may be concentrated or uniform. No provision for continuity or end moments. Includes data files for AISC Steel Construction Manual. Any steel strength can be considered. All calculations are made in accordance with AISC specifications

References

Availability
Purchase

Language
M Basic

Computer
HP, Wang

BEAMS 1 *ESDU International Limited*
An interactive program with graphics; estimates the stresses in a curved beam.
Alternatively it allows investigation of the effect that each of the governing parameters has
on the transverse stresses and on the loss of efficiency induced by radial movement of the
free edges of the flange(s)

References

Availability
Licence

Language

Computer
Tektronix 4051,
4052, 4054

1203

SECTIONS 1 *ESDU International Limited*
A fully interactive program which calculates section constants for extruded and fabricated
beams. All geometrical variables can be controlled on input. Output includes illustrations
with annotation and results

References

Availability
Lease

Language
Tektronix and HP
Basic

Computer
Tektronix 4050, HP
9845 B

1204

CPSFA *Facet Limited*
Analyses continuous beams, portals and sub-frames as required by the CP110 clauses
3.2.1 for characteristic vertical loads. Envelopes of shear and bending moment are
calculated for each span, and may be redistributed as requested by the user. Members
may be of rectangular, L, T or I-shaped cross-section. An option is available for plotting
the design envelopes to any user-defined scale

References

Availability
Bureau service, or under licence

Language

Computer
Prime, Norsk Data,
Harris,
CP/M 8-bit micros

1205

ELDES *General and Engineering Computer Services*
Calculates the minimum weight elastic design of steel beams and columns in accordance
with BS449. Geometry and applied loads are input direct via VDU (interactive). Output of
paginated A4 calculations includes bending, shear, web buckling, web crushing and
deflection calculation

References
DOC Publications

Availability
Purchase

Language
Basic

Computer
Commodore PET,
Apple II, HP9845,
or any CP/M micro

1206

Steel beam-column analysis *Hilbern Engineering Software, USA*
An interactive program to aid the selection of steel members. Written in accordance with
the latest (8th) edition of the AISC Manual of Steel Construction. Menu arrangement leads
the user through major axis bending analysis, minor axis bending analysis, column analysis,
or beam-column analysis

References

Availability
Purchase

Language
Basic

Computer
Apple II, CP/M-80

1207

Steel beam/column design (plastic) *Hydro Systems (USA)*
Selects the lightest W-section from the standard table, for a beam/column or axially loaded
column, given end moments, end shear and axial load. Other W-sections may be examined
for adequacy

References

Availability
Purchase

Language

Computer
48K RAM minimum

1208

Steel beam design (elastic) *Hydro Systems (USA)*
Selects the lightest W-section from the standard table, which is stored in memory, for a
beam, given end moments, maximum interior moments, and shear. Outputs approximate
deflection. Analysis uses the AISC code.

References

Availability
Purchase

Language

Computer
48K RAM minimum

1209

Steel beam design (plastic) *Hydro Systems (USA)*
Selects the lightest W-section from the standard table, for a beam, given span condition,
geometry and loading. Prints brace interval required to produce full plastic moment of
section. Outputs approximate deflection for service load. Other W-sections may be
examined for adequacy

References

Availability
Purchase

Language

Computer
48K RAM minimum

1210

Ultimate strength design *Hydro Systems (USA)*
Designs singly reinforced concrete beams and slats using ultimate strength design. Various
sections may be examined for steel and concrete requirements, and strength parameters.
Examines development lengths and adequacy of various combinations of bars

References

Availability
Purchase

Language

Computer
26K RAM minimum

1211

Design of roof support steelwork for circular storage tanks *John Booth and Sons (Bolton)
Limited*
Provides design of layout and section sizes for steel beams used to support the roof
plating of circular storage tanks. Input required: overall roof dimensions, minimum and
maximum spacing of roof members, loading, and parameter relating to intermediate lateral
restraints. Output consists of: input data, chosen layout, section design, and tensile force in
curb member

References
Constructional Steelwork SWP

Availability
Contact Mr J Banks of John Booth
and Sons

Language
Algol

Computer
Burroughs 6700

Computer programs for the building industry

1212

Beams *Lancaster Computing*
Aids the design of simple span beams in timber, steel or concrete. It is not intended for complex situations. The program caters for spans of 0.6m up to 6m. For timber, grades are selectable; for concrete, only one mix is included; in the case of steel, the computer selects from the 12 available sections

References

Availability
Purchase

Language

Computer
Apple II

1213

Sub-decide *Lancaster Computing*
This is a series of 14 inter-connecting programs to aid the design of reinforced concrete to CP110. These are: simply supported beam, subframe, continuous beam, service, detail, shear, slab, slender column, output, copy, status, title. Operation is interactive (by answering displayed questions). Questions are asked until there is enough information for a solution. Output on screen or printer

References

Availability
Purchase

Language

Computer
Apple II

1214

BEAMCALC *Lowe Electronics*
Produces calculation sheets verifying the use of steel beams in small works engineering. The sheets are produced in type style format using standard engineering conventions, and are fully acceptable to building inspectors and local district surveyors

References
'Computing' July 23, 1981

Availability
Purchase

Language
Basic

Computer
Genie III Business Computer 64K

1215

Beam Analysis *Microsoft Structural Control Systems Limited*
Carries out the analysis of a single span beam subjected to any combination of common load types

References
Personal Computing with Apple

Availability

Language
Applesoft Basic

Computer
Apple II

1216

Steel Beam Design *Microsoft Structural Control Systems Limited*
Calculates the maximum bending moment and shear force for a simply supported beam, then selects the optimum steel section from the given range. Output includes: maximum bending moments, reactions, deflection coefficients and points of contraflexure; complete calculation for the chosen section giving design parameters, slenderness ratio, section depth to flange thickness ratio, permissible stress, working stress, total deflection, and value of span divided by 360

References

Availability
Purchase

Language
Applesoft Basic

Computer
48K Apple II

1217

AP103: Elastic beam analysis *Oasys Limited*
Features include: pinned, fixed or cantilever ends; columns; constant or variable E1 within spans; point, uniformly distributed, trapezoidal or triangular loading; case loading patterns; enveloping of load case results; moment redistribution; deflections; summary or detailed tabular output, graphical output

References

Availability
Purchase

Language
Basic

Computer
HP 9845 HP 85/87

1218

ELDES *Power Plus Engineering and Computer Services Limited*
Elastic Design of Steelwork to BS 449:1969; deals with design of steel beams and columns. Bending moments, deflections and shear forces are calculated according to normal elastic theory. Steel section properties are selected from tables published by BCSA. Permissible stresses are selected from tabulated values and formulae specified in BS 449. Used to design rolled steel joists, and universal beam and/or column sections under action of specified applied loads

References
Constructional Steelwork SWP

Availability
Purchase, lease

Language
Basic

Computer
DTC Micro 210 and MkX, PET, Apple II, HP85, HP9845

1219

ABDUL *Property Services Agency, Directorate of Civil Engineering Services*
Analyses and designs reinforced concrete beams to meet CP110:Part 1:1972 requirements. Factored load combinations are automatically generated with bending moment and shear force envelopes produced for each span. Output includes selected sizes and spacing for main and shear reinforcement

References
PSA program library

Availability

Language
Fortran

Computer
UCS DEC 10

1220

UBM/1 *Quest GENESYS Limited*
This sub-system enables a designer to calculate the ultimate bending moment of reinforced and prestressed concrete sections of any shape, which may be subject to both tensile and compressive loads. The section may or may not be restrained to the plane of bending. All calculations are to CP110:Part 1:1972

References
GENESYS program library

Availability
Bureau service, hire

Language
Gentran

Computer
DEC 20, Honeywell, IBM, ICL, PE, Philips, others

1221

Analysis of Structures by Finite Elements *Reading Computer Services Limited*
Based on the established program SAP (University of California). Element types include 3D and 2D beams, boundary elements, plane stress and plane strain. Data is prepared using a pre-processing program which assists the user to specify the problem accurately. More than 300 nodes (and any number of elements) can be included

References

Availability

Language

Computer
CP/M Microcomputer

Design of Beam Cross-Sections for Elastic Bending *Reading Computer Services Limited*
The section properties of beams of any cross-section can be described by the user. The beam may be homogenous, or a composite of two or more materials, and it may be prestressed. One option allows the user to interactively change the cross-section to resist specified moments, whereas another assists the user to obtain the lowest cost combination to resist a specified criteria

References

Availability

Language

Computer
CP/M Microcomputer

Design of Prestressed Beams *Reading Computer Services Limited*
Using a table of section properties, the program automatically chooses the most economical beam selection for the applied loading, together with the prestress requirements. Many options exist giving the user flexibility in specifying the problem

References

Availability

Language

Computer
CP/M Microcomputer

Autofab Estimating Programs *Redpath Engineering Limited*
A suite of three programs: ESTX determines the economic number of plates to order for a given size and quantity of girder, and provides detailed costs for materials and production. EST4 allows the use of the same plates for producing different sizes of girder. EST5 is used to simplify the estimates for groups of girders which have the same section size but different lengths. There is automatic inclusion of all BSC price extras for all structural steels to BS4360, apart from the rebate which is put in manually

References

Availability
Purchase

Language

Computer

LAT 4 *Redpath Engineering Limited*
For the automatic minimum weight design of statically determinate plane lattice girders of arbitrary geometry. Input includes node coordinates, member incidences and group codes, choice of section types for each group, loading components on each joint, local bending moments, lateral restraint and load combination information. Output consists of section size for each group, forces, actual stresses and allowable stresses for each member; central deflection

References

Availability
Purchase

Language
Fortran IV

Computer
PDP11/70

PG8 *Redpath Engineering Limited*
An interactive program for design of plate girder sections with equal or unequal flange sizes. Input includes selection of minimum weight or cost, analysis routine, position and magnitude of each load, lengths of restraint on flange or section, deflection limit, choice of stiffener layout, maximum and minimum values for each cross-sectional dimension. Output consists of section size and properties, actual and allowable stresses, minimum fillet weld sizes, weld stresses, and stiffener details

References

Availability
Purchase, bureau service

Language
Fortran IV

Computer
PDP11/70 ICL 1905F

STAAD-III *Research Engineers, Inc, USA*
A comprehensive structural analysis and design program serving almost all the structural engineer's requirements. Input and capability similar to STRUDL, but faster. Analysis includes all types of beam and column members as well as finite element capability; also includes P-DELTA effect. Design of steel is based on AISC-80 code and that of concrete is based on ACI-78 code

References

Availability
Bureau service, purchase

Language
Fortran

Computer
DEC VAX, Prime, IBM, HP, CDC, Pixel

FERMO *RIB*
Provides calculation of the stress resultants and deformations of prestressed, precast girders with subsequent in-situ reinforced concrete slab accounting for effects due to creep and shrinkage

References

Availability
Purchase

Language
Fortran IV

Computer
CPU 64K

BEAMDET, COLDET *SIA Computer Services*
Used for the design and detailing of reinforced concrete beams and columns

References

Availability
Bureau service

Language
High level

Computer
Control Data, IBM, Prime

CONBEM *SIA Computer Services*
Used for structural analysis, this is an interactive beam analysis program

References

Availability
Bureau service

Language
High level

Computer
Control Data, IBM, Prime

PREBEM *SIA Computer Services*
Used in civil engineering for pre-tensioned reinforced concrete beam analysis

References

Availability
Bureau service

Language
High level

Computer
Control Data, IBM, Prime

1232

QUEST *SIA Computer Services*
A program for box girder finite element analysis

References

Availability
Bureau service

Language
High level

Computer
Control Data,
IBM, Prime

1233

BEAMS *Structural Members Users Group, USA*
Calculates the deflection, slope, bending moment and shear force of beams for static and steady state conditions. Natural frequencies and node shapes are computed for free transverse vibrations. The beam can be formed of uniform segments with any loading, in-span supports, foundations and boundary conditions. The user can include any or all of bending, shear deformation, and rotary inertia effects

References
Book published by McGraw Hill, 1978

Availability
Purchase

Language
Fortran IV

Computer
CDC, IBM, Univac,
VAX, Prime

1234

Torsion of thin-walled beams *Structural Members Users Group, USA*
Angles of twist, bimoments, warping shear and internal twisting moments are calculated, as well as unstable loads and natural frequencies

References
Book published by McGraw Hill, 1978

Availability
Purchase

Language
Fortran IV

Computer
CDC, IBM, Univac,
VAX, Prime

1235

Steel Beam Design *Technical Services*
The program chooses a steel section to sustain a stated bending moment and shear force. Calculations for section size and weight are performed according to BS449 Part 2(1969). The span, effective span coeffient, applied bending moment and applied shear force are input. The program calculates the allowable bending stress according to Table 3a in BS449, and checks the value of section modulus required. The allowable deflection and the shear stress are checked

References

Availability
Purchase

Language
Basic

Computer
Olivetti P6060,
and P6066, 16K

1236

Span tables for timber beams *TRADA*
A number of programs for producing span tables, in various forms, for simply supported, uniformly loaded beams of rectangular section of any timber. Also, programs for laminated, ply web and stressed skin constructions and for tabulating the properties of rectangular sections

References

Availability

Language

Computer

1237

RETWAL *UCC (Great Britain) Limited*
For a cross-sectional, elastic analysis of retaining walls. The program will consider a maximum of 7 reinforcement bands. Output gives the minimum dimensions of each band and associated reinforcement and a full listing of input data

References
Developed by the computer branch of the DoE (Highway Engineering)

Availability
Bureau service

Language
Fortran

Computer

1238

SLADE *Building Computer Services Limited*
Analyses and designs continuous one way spanning slabs which must be of prismatic section throughout, but which may differ in thickness, for different spans. Input data should include support type and width, span type and length, slab thickness, loading, and depth to steel. Outputs (in tabular form) give moments and steel requirements for maximum moments, support reactions, warnings and failure indicators

References

Availability
Bureau service, hire, sale

Language
Fortran

Computer
DEC

1239

FLATS *Civil and Structural Computing (Northern) Limited*
Carries out the design of reinforced concrete flat slabs to CP110, including various normal reinforcement and serviceability checks

References
Bradshaw, Buckton and Tonge

Availability
Bureau service, time sharing, in-house

Language

Computer

1240

SLAB *Civil and Structural Computing (Northern) Limited*
Designs two-way spanning slabs to CP110. Design includes reinforcement and serviceability checks, and output is formatted suitable for submission to checking authorities

References
Bradshaw, Buckton and Tonge

Availability
Bureau service, time sharing, in-house

Language

Computer

1241

CD-3. Flat slab analysis and design *Ecom Associates, Inc*
Flat slabs may have drop panels at columns. Columns may have capitals. Either ultimate strength or working stress methods may be used. Design is for a one-bay wide strip using the equivalent frame analysis method and may be up to 10 spans. The strip may have cantilevers. Beams parallel to the direction of moments are not permitted

References

Availability
Purchase

Language
M Basic

Computer
HP, DEC, Wang,
Apple, Tandy
TRS-80, IBM PC

AP105: Continuous slab analysis *Oasys Limited*
This program has particular facilities for dealing with one-way slabs. It may be used on its own to produce summarised or detailed output for hand design of the slab, or it may be linked to DP105 or DP106 to produce a complete, automatic reinforcement design for solid slabs and ribbed slabs respectively

References

Availability
Purchase

Language
Basic

Computer
HP 9845 HP 85/87

AP112: Flat slab analysis *Oasys Limited*
This may be used as a self contained program to produce summarised or detailed output for hand design of the slab or, in conjunction with DP112 or DP113, to produce a complete, automatic, reinforcement design for solid slabs and coffered slabs respectively

References

Availability
Purchase

Language
Basic

Computer
HP 9845 HP 85/87

DP105: Continuous slab design *Oasys Limited*
Produces a reinforcement design for a solid one-way slab in accordance with CP110. Must be run in conjunction with AP105. The program produces a design which handles all relevent criteria, and which is complete within the design constraints. Further design refinements may be produced by adjusting the design parameters and cycling through the program to produce an optimum design

References

Availability
Purchase

Language
Basic

Computer
HP 9845 HP 85/87

DP106: Ribbed slab design *Oasys Limited*
Must be run in conjunction with AP105. The resultant design takes into account tension and compression required steel area, local bond, bar spacing, anchorage lengths, etc. Output includes main bars, links for a single rib with curtailment dimensions and a span/depth check. Mid-span top bars and links may be suppressed by the designer

References

Availability
Purchase

Language
Basic

Computer
HP 9845 HP 85/87

DP107: Flat slab shear check *Oasys Limited*
This program is for the design of shear reinforcement around concentrated loads and columns in flat slabs, in accordance with CP110. May be used as an aid to initial sizing of flat slabs, and for final detailed design of shear reinforcement

References

Availability
Purchase

Language
Basic

Computer
HP 9845 HP 85/87

DP112: Flat slab design *Oasys Limited*
Must be run in conjunction with AP112. The resulting design takes into account all the interactions between the various sections within a span and across supports. Interaction may occur between the user and the program, to change various design parameters such as preferred bar sizes or section dimensions

References

Availability
Purchase

Language
Basic

Computer
HP 9845 HP 85/87

DP113: Coffered slab design *Oasys Limited*
Must be run in conjunction with AP112. Output is reinforcement for a typical rib in the column and middle strips, with curtailment dimensions and a span/depth check. The automatic design takes into account tension and compression required steel area, local bond, bar spacing, anchorage lengths, etc. The finished design considers all interactions within and between spans

References

Availability
Purchase

Language
Basic

Computer
HP 9845 HP 85/87

FLAT-SLAB/1 *Quest GENESYS Limited*
This sub-system enables an engineer to design and detail a reinforced concrete building, including bar schedules, which incorporates flat slabs in accordance with CP110:Part 1:1972. There is no limit to the number of elements to be considered. The size of structure to be analysed is limited only by the size and type of computer used

References
GENESYS program library

Availability
Bureau service, hire

Language
Gentran

Computer
DEC 10, Honeywell, IBM, ICL, PE, Philips, others

LEAPWA *SIA Computer Services*
Used in civil engineering. A program to handle slab and beam reinforcement

References

Availability
Bureau service

Language
High level

Computer
Control Data, IBM, Prime

ORTHOP *SIA Computer Services*
A program for the harmonic analysis of slabs

References

Availability
Bureau service

Language
High level

Computer
Control Data, IBM, Prime

1252

2-WAY SLABS (CP110) *Technical Services*
Calculates positive and negative bending moments and maximum shear force in 2-way spanning slabs from the coefficients in Table 13 of CP110. The coeffients are on disk and interpolation between tabulated values is automatically carried out. Values of 1 x and 1 y are entered together with characteristic dead and imposed loads. Output consists of ultimate moments in each direction, top and bottom, together with maximum shear force and loads onto supporting beams

References

Availability
Purchase

Language
Basic

Computer
Olivetti P6060, and P6066, 16K

1253

BRICK *Amplix Services Limited*
Features include: design of unreinforced masonry structures to BS5628 Part 1; piers, single leaf, cavity and pier supported combinations of walls; calculation of vertical load resistance of design subject; calculation of wall strength in 2 planes under the action of wind and static vertical loads; calculation of resisting forces to sliding and shear stress on units; calculation of return wall dimensions

References

Availability
Purchase

Language
Commercial (SMB)
Cobol, Fortran

Computer
CP/M or MP/M
Microcomputer

1254

WALL *Camutek*
A program for the design of laterally loaded wall panel to BS5628: Part 1. Calculates the maximum allowable wind load which may be applied to a two-way spanning wall panel. The wall may be of one or two skins and the properties of each may be specified individually

References

Availability
from Camutek

Language
Basic

Computer
HP 9835, 9845
Future: HP 85 & 86

1255

SA-1. Shear wall analysis *Ecom Associates, Inc*
Analyses structures supported by shear walls for wind and seismic loads. The shears and moments are evaluated for the structure and for each wall element in each direction at every floor level. Seismic forces are determined using the provisions of the Uniform Building Code

References

Availability
Purchase

Language
M Basic

Computer
HP

1256

WALLS *Tony Gee and Partners*
A program for use by structural engineers. Provides design charts relating to the lateral strength of 6 different types of wall under various support conditions. Generally in accordance with BS 5628 Part 1, but includes walls with bed reinforcement. Each design chart displays a limiting line for various heights and lengths of a wall panel under a given wind load. Input includes variables for brick and block thickness and strength, single or double skin, bed reinforcement and wind load. Output is in graphical form

References

Availability
Purchase

Language
HP Enhanced Basic

Computer
Hewlett-Packard
HP9845 B/C

1257

CIRCTANK/1 *Quest GENESYS Limited*
This sub-system enables an engineer to analyse a circular tank wall with fixed, free or partially fixed ends. Provision can be made for prestressing hoops

References
GENESYS program library

Availability
Bureau service, hire

Language
Gentran

Computer
DEC 10, Honeywell,
IBM, ICL, PE, Philips,
others

1258

SHEARWALL/1 *Quest GENESYS Limited*
This sub-system enables an engineer to analyse shear stress in wall structures, by means of an idealised elastic stiffness frame, a method described by MacLeod. Structures comprising several interconnected walls may be analysed. The size of the problem to be handled is limited only by the size and type of computer used

References
GENESYS program library

Availability
Bureau service, hire

Language
Gentran

Computer
DEC 20, Honeywell,
IBM, ICL, PE, Philips,
others

1259

SHEWALS *SBI*
Provides an elastic analysis of a uniform shear wall building subjected to static and earthquake loadings. The term 'uniform' means that all storeys have the same structural layout, and that all walls are parallel with either of two horizontal axes perpendicular to each other. Buildings with up to 70 walls can be handled, irrespective of the number of storeys

References
Danish Building Research Institute
Abstract 48 11 303

Availability
Bureau service

Language
Fortran

Computer
Any with 260K

1260

Masonry Wall Design *Richard Twinch Design Limited*
For use by architects and designers. Input consists of spans, lengths and vertical loadings. The printouts should be checked by a structural engineer/building control. Provides all the options for blockwork in walls to meet Parts F, FF and G of the Building Regulations (thermal and sound), together with CP111, CP121 and CP3 (structural). Output includes the thickness of block VS K value, density and crushing strength. All three options are given simultaneously. Calculations are broken down for checking

References
Recommended by Apple. RIBA
Journal, July 1981

Availability
Purchase

Language
Basic 2.3,
Pascal and CP/M

Computer
Apple II 48K

1261

CDMSTAN *Cadsteel Limited*
An interactive program for the design of uncased stanchions. User can choose from UC, UB, RSJ or RSC sections. Design includes stanchions with and without base plates or just base plates. Output includes calculation sheets for: 3 alternative sections for each stanchion; bending stress for each alternative stanchion; compressive stress for each alternative stanchion; design criteria for base plate; size of base plate

References
Constructional Steelwork SWP

Availability
Purchase

Language
Fortran IV

Computer
IBM mainframe
CP/M microcomputer

Steel column design *Camutek*
This program designs steel columns to BS449:1969

References

Availability
From owner

Language
Basic

Computer
HP 9830 (2k) or (6k),
9831, 9835, 9845
Future: HP85, 86

Symmetrically reinforced concrete columns *Camutek*
This program designs reinforced concrete columns to CP110:1972

References

Availability
From owner

Language
Basic

Computer
HP 9830 (2k) or (6k),
9831, 9835, 9845
Future: HP85, 86

BECOL *Civil and Structural Computing (Northern) Limited*
Carries out the elastic design of members in steel to BS449 when subjected to combinations of axial loading and bi-axial bending. It is therefore suitable for the design of either beam or column elements of a structure. The program can be run in an interactive mode, allowing the engineer to make pertinent decisions, or automatically, when it will select the most efficient section based on minimum weight

References
Bradshaw, Buckton and Tonge

Availability
Bureau service, time sharing, in-house

Language
Basic, Fortran

Computer
Hewlett Packard
DEC, Prime

PLATE *Civil and Structural Computing (Northern) Limited*
Makes an analysis of a column baseplate, the plan dimensions and bolt configurations of which have been input by the engineer. Up to 6 loadings may be applied and each load can consist of a column in axial tension or compression, a major axis moment and a horizontal shear

References
Bradshaw, Buckton and Tonge

Availability
Bureau service, time sharing, in-house

Language

Computer
Hewlett Packard
9800
and others

FOOTING (1 and 2 Columns) *Computrav (UK) Limited*
FOOTING (1 Column) designs a rectangular reinforced concrete pad footing for one column in accordance with CP110. FOOTING (2 Columns) designs an inverted T beam footing for 2 columns and draws shear force and bending moment diagrams

References
Approved by ACT Sirius

Availability
Purchase

Language
Basic

Computer
Minimum 32Kb on 8
and 16-bit micros
under CP/M

COLUMN and BI-COLUMN *Computrav (UK) Limited*
The COLUMN program designs columns of rectangular section in accordance with CP110, taking into account additional moment due to deflection if the column is slender. The whole section may be designed or the steel area calculated for a given section. Sections are designed for direct load plus moment in one plane. Numbers and sizes of reinforcing bars are given. BI-COLUMN performs similar operations to COLUMN, but uses two moments in planes at right angles to each other

References
Approved by ACT Sirius

Availability
Purchase

Language
Basic

Computer
Minimum 32Kb on 8
and 16-bit micros
under CP/M

COL110 and COL114 *R J Crocker and Partners*
These programs are used for the design of rectangular columns subjected to axial and bending in one or two directions

References

Availability
Bureau Service

Language
Fortran

Computer
Sigma

CD-2. Reinforced concrete column design *Ecom Associates, Inc*
Designs or checks column capacity in accordance with ACI 318-77, with bending in either or both directions. Slenderness effects are evaluated according to moment magnification method. Output includes reinforcement data, allowable load and moment, moment magnification factor, spiral size and pitch, and eccentricities

References

Availability
Purchase

Language
M Basic

Computer
HP, DEC, Wang,
Apple, Tandy
TRS-80, IBM PC

SD-2. Steel column design *Ecom Associates, Inc*
Designs or checks wide flange, tube or pipe steel sections subjected to axial loads with or without bending moments applied about axes of the column. Moments can be applied to either or both ends of the column. Selects lightets section for a specified depth. Pin-ended column base plates can also be designed. Base plate dimensions can be established for special built-up column shapes. Includes data files for AISC Steel Construction Manual

References

Availability
Purchase

Language
M Basic

Computer
HP, DEC, Wang,
Apple, Tandy
TRS-80, IBM PC

BIAX *Facet Limited*
This program performs an elastic analysis of a column section in combined axial loading and biaxial bending to determine section stresses. A solution is achieved by iteration, ie neutral axis positions are tried until the internal stresses and applied forces are in equilibrium, with concrete areas in tension being neglected. The concrete section is defined by points connected by straight lines. Facilities exist for the automatic generation of rectangular and circular sections

References

Availability
Bureau service, or under licence

Language

Computer
Prime, Norsk Data,
Harris,
CP/M 8-bit micros

1272

1969 AISC-AISI steel column design *A M Kinney, Inc*
The program selects steel columns for axial load plus end moments about major and/or minor axis per the allowable stress provisions. Output for each column begins with an input echo printout. Column selections for each of the 3 input loading conditions are indicated together with the sum of the terms in the combined stress formulas, the length factors and yield stress. Finally, the lightest column shape that is adequate for all loading conditions is printed

References

Availability

Language
Fortran

Computer
IBM 1130 and 370

1273

Steel Stanchion Design *Microsoft Structural Control Systems Limited*
Designs a cased or uncased steel stanchion to BS449. For the specified loadings and design parameters, the chosen range of sections is examined in order of increasing weight until a suitable section is found. Output includes: height and maximum slenderness ratio; effective loadings and lengths; serial size chosen; permissible axial and bending stress; resultant moment about X and Y axes; value of the unity factor

References

Availability
Purchase

Language
Applesoft Basic

Computer
48K Apple II

1274

AP123: Irregular column analysis *Oasys Limited*
For the analysis of irregular section columns in accordance with CP110. The program examines up to ten load cases, calculates and compares the moment capacity for each, with the resultant applied moment. Features include rectoparabolic stress block for concrete and steel strains; definition of voids in column as part of concrete outline; graphical output

References

Availability
Purchase

Language
Basic

Computer
HP 9845
HP 85/87

1275

DP103: Rectangular column design *Oasys Limited*
A design and analysis program for columns, in accordance with CP110; may be used with AP102. Includes: automatic reinforcement design; reinforcement design based on user specified bar groups; analysis of columns with symmetrical bar groups of varying diameter; plotting of graphs

References

Availability
Purchase

Language
Basic

Computer
HP 9845 HP 85/87

1276

DORIC *Quest GENESYS Limited*
Analysis and design of reinforced concrete columns monolithic with concrete beams and subject to axial loading with one or two way bending. Columns may be rectangular or circular and be subject to axial or biaxial bending and/or wind loading. Results include design solutions considered, and solution adopted, including number and size of both main steel and links

References

Availability

Language
Gentran

Computer

1277

COL 1 *Redpath Engineering Limited*
For automatic minimum weight design of compound crane columns comprising a roof leg with either two crane legs or an external back leg and a crane leg. Input consists of geometry and type of column, several different loading cases, lengths of lateral restraint to main members, load combination data. Output includes: sizes of main members, bracing and base plates; forces, actual and allowable stresses; deflections at eaves and crane rail, pressures beneath base plates; optimum centroid position for foundation

References

Availability
Purchase

Language
Fortran IV

Computer
PDP11/70

1278

BEST *RIB*
Provides buckling analysis and design for columns commonly found in high-rise buildings, particularly in precast concrete constructions. The column can be subjected to bi-axial bending with axial compression. Cross- section properties and reinforcements varying from storey to storey are allowed for. The various static systems during transport, construction and operation are examined

References

Availability
Purchase

Language
Fortran IV

Computer
CPU 64K

1279

COLDES *SIA Computer Services*
A program for reinforced concrete column optimum design

References

Availability
Bureau service

Language
High level

Computer
Control Data, IBM, Prime

1280

Rotating shafts *Structural Members Users Group, USA*
For a shaft with unbalanced forces, the displacements, internal forces and bearing forces are calculated. For this unbalanced response analyses, the bearings can be modelled with a spring, dashpot, mass system. The critical speeds are found for damped or undamped shaft systems. For all analyses the shaft system can be formed of lumped or continuous segments with supports, foundations and any boundary conditions

References
Book published by McGraw Hill, 1978

Availability
Purchase

Language
Fortran IV

Computer
CDC, IBM, Univac, VAX, Prime

1281

Thin-walled cylinder *Structural Members Users Group, USA*
The response variables are found for axisymmetric motion of axisymmetric, thin-walled circular cylinders. The displacement, slope, bending moment and shear force are radially oriented. Static, stability and natural frequency analyses are performed

References
Book published by McGraw Hill, 1978

Availability
Purchase

Language
Fortran IV

Computer
CDC, IBM, Univac, VAX, Prime

Torsional Systems *Structural Members Users Group, USA*
For static and steady state torsional loads, the angle of twist and the twisting moment of a shaft are calculated. The natural frequencies and mode shapes are found for torsional vibrations. The torsion system can be a bar formed of uniform segments with any loading, gears, branches, foundations and boundary conditions

References
Book published by McGraw Hill, 1978

Availability
Purchase

Language
Fortran IV

Computer
CDC, IBM, Univac, VAX, Prime

Steel Stanchion Design *Technical Services*
The value of P c is calculated from the formula given in Appendix B of BS449. The value of P bc is calculated from Table 3a of BS449, which is held in the machine. After calculating this factor, the program compares it with unity. The disk contains all Universal beam sections, joists, and Universal column sections. Values of the actual, direct and bending stresses are calculated; values of section modules, size and weight, D/T ratio, etc, are copied from the disk

References

Availability
Purchase

Language
Basic

Computer
Olivetti P6060, and P6066, 16K

ABC4 *Associated British Consultants (Computers) Limited*
Performs a complete elastic analysis and provides the necessary calculations, fixing instructions and schedules for an in-situ reinforced concrete building. It can deal with solid and hollow tile floors, spanning one or two ways, and with beams and columns. Quantities of materials for shuttering, concrete and reinforcement are given for each element and summarised for the whole structure. The design is in accordance with CP114

References

Availability
Bureau service, including preparation of input data, etc

Language
Fortran IV

Computer
Univac 1108

CDMTREST *Cadsteel Limited*
For design and weighting of support trestles and gravity take-up towers. The program sizes each member and base plate, then calculates total weight of steelwork for cost estimate purposes. Results are produced in tabular form including: forces in each bay of the tower; section size of each member; length and weight of each member; total weight of structure

References
Constructional Steelwork SWP

Availability
Purchase

Language
Fortran IV

Computer
IBM mainframe
CP/M
microcomputers

Reinforced concrete design *Camutek*
This program designs reinforced concrete sections in bending or shear. It checks for deflection to CP110:1972

References

Availability
From owner

Language
Basic

Computer
HP 9830 (2k) or (6k), 9831, 9835, 9845
Future: HP85, 86

STAIRWAY DESIGN *Cheshire County Council*
Enables the user to analyse his building type and obtain the stairway design parameters, together with the preferred or optimum dimensions as recommended in BS5395. By entering floor to floor heights or preferred riser height, the system will print a set of complying solutions for 'straight' or spiral staircases. For use by architects from sketch design stage

References

Availability

Language
APL

Computer
Microcomputer

Civil Engineering Analysis and Design *Datron Micro Centre*
A series of programs designed to assist in the analysis and design of concrete slabs, beams, sub-frames, plastic portal frames, plane frames, and masonry panels. Where applicable, the programs conform to standards required by CP110, 1972

References

Availability
Purchase

Language
Basic

Computer
64K microcomputer

BUCKLE 1 *ESDU International Limited*
An interactive program, with graphics, for estimating the shear and direct loads, which, acting either singly or in combination, cause buckling of a flat rectangular orthotropic or isotropic plate with clamped edges. Sketches are used to help define the parameters. Isometric sketches can be displayed to illustrate the wave form of the buckled plate

References

Availability
Licence

Language

Computer
Tektronix 4051, 4052, 4054

BUCKLE 2 *ESDU International Limited*
An interactive program, with graphics, for estimating the shear and direct loads, which, acting either singly or in combination, cause buckling of a flat rectangular orthotropic or isotropic plate with 2 opposite edges simply supported and the other 2 clamped. Sketches are used to help define the parameters. Isometric sketches can be displayed to illustrate the wave form of the buckled plate

References

Availability
Licence

Language

Computer
Tektronix 4051, 4052, 4054

BUCKLE 3 *ESDU International Limited*
An interactive program, with graphics, enabling an accurate estimate to be made of the shear and direct loads which, acting either singly or in combination, cause buckling of a flat, rectangular, orthotropic or isotropic plate with clamped edges. Sketches are used to help define the parameters. Isometric sketches can be displayed to illustrate the wave form of the buckled plate

References

Availability
Licence

Language

Computer
Tektronix 4051, 4052, 4054

Computer programs for the building industry

1292

PLATE BUCKLING 1 *ESDU International Limited*

Calculates both the compressive load that will make a rectangular panel or plate buckle, and the shear load or combination of tensile, compressive and shear loads that will cause buckling. The idealised edge supports to the plate may be simply supported or clamped, or a combination of two simply supported and two clamped. The material of the plate may be isotropic, such as mild steel, or orthotropic, such as corrugated sheet or many modern sandwich materials

References

Availability
Licence

Language
Fortran IV
Basic

Computer
Minicomputer
Mainframe

1293

PLATE BUCKLING 2 *ESDU International Limited*

For estimating stresses and deflections in buckled, flat, rectangular, orthotropic plates. Related to PLATE BUCKLING 1

References

Availability
Purchase

Language
Fortran

Computer
Most mini and
mainframe computers

1294

PLATE-S 1 *ESDU International Limited*

An interactive program with graphics, enabling the user to make an accurate estimate of the stresses and deflections at various positions in a structural plate when its geometry, material and loading are known. Alternatively the thickness of such a plate may be determined in order to keep stresses and/or deflections below specified limits

References

Availability
Licence

Language

Computer
Tektronix 4051,
4052, 4054

1295

PLATE-V 1 *ESDU International Limited*

A fully interactive program for estimating natural frequencies of vibration of rectangular plates with various edge conditions. Input includes geometry, material and edge conditions. Output is in the form of graphics plus numerical screen

References

Availability
Lease

Language
Tektronix or HP
Basic

Computer
Tektronix 4050, HP
9845B

1296

PLATE CHECK *Flint and Neill Partnership*

For the analysis of unstiffened plate panels under both service and collapse conditions. Input data includes: plate dimensions and material properties; the constant, bending and varying stresses in the two directions; plate shear stress; imperfections required; residual stresses. Output contains the following results: number of 1/2 wavelengths in panel; factor against buckling; effective plate and critical stresses; effective stress required to cause yield in plate surface; ultimate effective stress which plate is capable of carrying

References
Constructional Steelwork SWP

Availability
Purchase

Language
Basic

Computer
HP9830 with
8Kb storage

1297

STEDE *General and Engineering Computer Services Limited*

Can be used in conjunction with P-FRAP. STEDE provides computer aided design of structural steelwork in accordance with BS449. Input includes structure geometry, loads, effective length, material type, and user defined cost data. Output includes reduced column axial loads (CP3), permissible stresses, actual/permissible stress ratios, and material cost of structure

References
DOC publication 'Computer Programs
for Structural Steelwork'

Availability
Purchase

Language
Fortran IV

Computer
Prime minicomputer

1298

CABLE *Grist Business Services Limited*

Analyses cable or wire arrays, using an interactive Galerkin residual method on the potential energy of the system. The analysis is non-linear and the member forces in this case are the wire element tensions. Output includes: member loads, consisting of bending moments and horizontal and vertical forces at each node point for each member; node point displacements for each node

References

Availability
Purchase

Language
Fortran

Computer
Apple II 48K

1299

Computer aided fire escape design *R C Jenkins & Son*

The coordinates of all doors, landings or windows involved are stored and relevant regulations selected; standard set of stock materials can be inspected and amended. The screen is used to sketch overall approach, then plan and elevation views of landings for detailed analysis. Performs full SI calculations of bending moments, point loads, etc. After analysis, a list is produced of materials needed, total weight and cost for inclusion in a quotation

References

Availability
Purchase or hire from Microcore
Limited

Language
Basic

Computer
Apple II 68K

1300

CP38 *National Research Council of Canada*

Simulates a stair-shaft pressurisation system in multistorey buildings

References
C Y Shaw, D M Sander & G T Tamura

Availability

Language
Fortran IV

Computer

1301

GLADYS *Oasys Limited*

Performs various calculations for structural engineering design. The system comprises a master program and sub-systems covering the following topics: analysis and design of concrete beams, slabs and flat slabs; design of rectangular or circular columns and irregular sections; calculation of irregular section properties; design of pad footings and pilecaps; design of rc plates or in plan forces and moments; dynamic analysis (of 'cantilever' models); statistical analysis of extreme value wind data

References
DOC Bulletin, March 1976.
Recommended by GECS and Facet
Limited

Availability
Bureau service or purchase

Language
Fortran

Computer
DEC (various), Prime,
Data General,
Norsk Data

BARD *Quest GENESYS Limited*
A computer based method of producing reinforced concrete detail drawings. Self standing programs for beam, column and all types of slab. A3 detail drawings include both the element drawing and a bar bending schedule on the same sheet

References

Availability

Language
Gentran

Computer

CP114 Programs *Quest GENESYS Limited*
An integrated program for the design and detail of in-situ reinforced concrete framed structures, to CP114. Flexibility to design one or many components in one computer run. Elements available include beams, columns and one and two-way spanning solid slabs. The program produces calculations to satisfy independent checking and detail schedules for bar bending and fixing. General arrangement drawings may be produced by the RC-PLOT program

References

Availability

Language
Gentran

Computer

Steel Chimney Design *Redpath Engineering Limited*
Designs mild steel (grade 43) chimneys to BS4076, which are self supporting and of circular cross-section. May include a lower cone section with an increased base diameter. Wind loading is calculated to CP3 chapter 5, and may incorporate a shielded height. Chimney sections are defined by a regular section spacing. Checks each section for axial and bending stresses, increasing plate thickness where necessary; calculates deflection of top of chimney. If critical, computer modifies the design

References

Availability
Purchase

Language

Computer
PDP11/70

KERN *RIB*
Provides analysis of the structural components of high-rise buildings which provide stiffening against horizontal loading

References

Availability
Purchase

Language
Fortran IV

Computer
CPU 64K

HETOP-32 *Shade (Computer Services) Limited*
For the design of timber structures. Runs under the control of a real time, multi user operating system. The hub of this system is a database on the disc which is access by a database management system. Input is from the architect's plan drawing, together with details of the structure's exterior finish, its location, shape, etc. and processing more sophisticated, than for the smaller systems, and includes the calculation of load points and loading values.

References

Availability
Purchase

Language
Fortram 77+

Computer
32-bit minicomputer with 512K

Thick cylinder *Structural Members Users Group, USA*
The radial displacement, radial stress, tangential stress and axial stress are found for static and steady state conditions. The natural frequencies and mode shapes are calculated for radial vibrations. The theory is based on a plane strain assumption, with either isotropic or orthotropic material. The loadings and responses are axially symmetric

References
Book published by McGraw Hill, 1978

Availability
Purchase

Language
Fortran IV

Computer
CDC, IBM, Univac, VAX, Prime

Thick sphere *Structural Members Users Group, USA*
The radial displacement, radial stress and tangential stress are computed for static and steady state loading. The natural frequencies and mode shapes are given for radial vibrations. The sphere may be isotropic or orthotropic. The loading and responses are spherically symmetric

References
Book published by McGraw Hill, 1978

Availability
Purchase

Language
Fortran IV

Computer
CDC, IBM, Univac, VAX, Prime

CONSAS *Structures and Computers Limited*
A general purpose, finite element program, suitable for the analysis of plane trusses, space trusses, plane frames, space frames, plane grillages, plated grillages, plane membranes, space membranes, plates, ribbed plates, folded plates, box girders and shells. Used in the analysis stage of the building design process

References

Availability
Purchase

Language
Fortran IV

Computer
256K

Laminated arch design *TRADA*
A program for the design of glue laminated portal arches

References

Availability

Language

Computer

COLDES *UCC (Great Britain) Limited*
Using the linear elastic design theory, this program analyses and designs reinforced concrete sections subjected to bi-axial bending and axial loading. Output plots crack widths, gives steel and concrete stresses, cost of materials and formwork, and includes a full listing of input data

References
Developed by the computer branch of the DoE (Highway Engineering)

Availability
Bureau service

Language
Fortran

Computer

Computer programs for the building industry

1312

PREBEM *UCC (Great Britain) Limited*
Used to design prestressed and pre-tensioned single spans of constant inertia. Output gives stresses, strand arrangements, shear steel and end block requirements, and a full listing of input data

References
Developed by the Midland Road Construction Unit

Availability
Bureau service

Language
Fortran

Computer

1313

UMIST structural steelwork system *UMIST*
Details end plate connections in structural steel frames consisting of beams and columns. Calculations are carried out to BS449:1969. When automatic detailing fails, bolt clashes and excessive stresses are noted. Correction is interactive

References

Availability
Contact NRDC

Language
Fortran

Computer
CDC 7600, Cyber 72

1314

ASAS *United Information Services Limited*
For general stress analysis of finite elements of all forms of structure under varying load conditions, including thermal and dynamic. Associated programs give graphic displays of the structure, indicating displacement, etc

References

Availability
Bureau service, time sharing

Language
Fortran IV

Computer
Honeywell Sigma 9

Pipework, ductwork and sound control

Pipework
Ductwork
Sound control

1315

RCSECT *United Information Services Limited*
This program analyses the stresses in a reinforced concrete member of any section

References

Availability
Bureau service, time sharing

Language
Basic

Computer
Honeywell
Sigma 9

1316

PIPEWORK-PIPES *ABS Oldacres Computers Limited*
Used at the pre or post-contract stage to produce priced estimates of mechanical
engineering pipework installations

References

Availability
Purchase

Language
M Basic

Computer
CP/M 64K

1317

DOWSE *Amplix Services Limited*
Features include: the design of cold water pipes for a multistorey building with multiple
consumer outlets served by a header tank or reservoir; user defined outlets and
consumptions; pipe diameters to BS2871

References

Availability
Purchase

Language
Commercial (SMB)
Cobol, Fortran

Computer
CP/M or MP/M
Microcomputer

1318

Piping (MO1P) *APEC Executive Office*
Provides all basic information required for the design of a piping system. The program
uses a 'nodal description' system with a pipe 'link' between every two nodes. Velocity
criteria is used for sizing based on the type of pipe being used

References

Availability
Doris J Wallace, Exective Director,
APEC

Language
Fortran

Computer
IBM/370
CDC Cyber 175

1319

$PS1 *Building Service Design*
Calculates the sizes of steel pipes (from six inches to ten feet in diameter) for carrying
water at given flow rates. The flow rate (lb/h or gal/min) together with the desired water
velocity (ft/sec) is input. A pipe size is selected which will give a velocity just below that
required. The pipe diameter, pressure loss and velocity are also output. The same
information is supplied for pipes one size larger, and two sizes smaller

References

Availability
Bureau service, time sharing

Language
Basic

Computer
Honeywell Sigma 7,
Sigma 9

1320

HPIPE *Civil and Structural Computing (Northern) Limited*
Determines pipe sizes and pressure loss in a hot water system, using data and equations
from the IHVE Guide. Pipes can be of predetermined size, and limits can be placed on the
minimum pipe sizes to be chosen and/or the maximum pressure loss/m in the pipes.
Heatloss from lagged or unlagged pipes is calculated to determine the system heatloss.
The system can be proportioned to adjust the temperature drop to a specified value. Can
also be used to analyse cold water systems

References
Bradshaw, Buckton and Tonge

Availability
Bureau service, time sharing, in-house

Language

Computer

1321

DARCY *Civilsoft (USA)*
Gives the solution for headloss in a single pipe. Input includes the pipe diameter, length
and size of a roughness element in the pipe. Uses the Darcy-Weisbach equation and
computes the friction factor. Solution includes total headloss in feet and psi. Resuls
displayed on creen and on printer

References
ASCE, Building Construction Digest

Availability
Purchase

Language
8080,8088/86

Computer
8-bit with 64K. 16-bit
with 128K

1322

PSA 5 *Compeda Limited*
A suite of programs to provide stress analysis calculations for pipework subjected to
thermal, gravitational, wind and seismic loadings. Stresses can be presented according to
a wide choice of design codes in power generation, chemical, oil, gas and petroleum
processing, and ship/rig building. A graphics moduie allows data to be displayed as
isometric line drawings or as a full 3D picture with hidden lines removed, either on screen
or in plotted form

References

Availability

Language

Computer

1323

PIPENET *Computational Mechanics Consultants Limited*
For the linear and non-linear analysis of pipe networks. The network is visualised as a
series of elements (the pipes) connected at a specific number of nodes (the joints). Pipe
sizes, geometric dimensions of the network and consumptions or pressure heads at nodes
are input as data. The system is then solved for the remaining pressure heads at each
node; this yields the discharges at the remaining nodes and flow rates in all the pipes.
Available methods of solution are based on formulas of Pouseuille and Hazen-Williams

References

Availability
Licence

Language
Fortran IV

Computer
Microcomputer

1324

HEATLOSS 4 *Contract Computer Software Limited*
A pipe sizing program for hot and cold water services, incorporating static head analysis.
Based on CIBS methods. Includes data storage, error recovery and printout facilities. For
use by professional and clerical staff

References
Building Products journal

Availability
Purchase

Language
8-bit CP/M
16-bit CP/M86,
MS-DOS

Computer
Micro, min 64K

HEATLOSS 3 *Contract Computer Software Limited*
A versatile pipe sizing program. In accordance with CIBS standards, the program covers any fluid in any pipe material at any temperature, and includes load proportioning option and index run analysis. Full data storage is provided together with error recovery and printout facilities. For use by professional and clerical staff

References
Building Products journal

Availability
Purchase

Language
8-bit CP/M
16-bit CP/M86,
MS-DOS

Computer
Micro, min 64K

1326

Homogeneous heat pipe design code *COSMIC*
Facilitates parametric performance evaluation of heat pipes in a lightweight heat rejection system. Limited to the analysis and design of homogeneous wick heat pipes, although an annular heat pipe program is included as part of the heat pipe radiator sub-routine

References
CAL TECH/Jet Propulsion Laboratory

Availability

Language
Fortran IV

Computer
Univac 1100 series

1327

Piping system parameter calculation *COSMIC*
Allows mechanical and control engineers to rapidly analyse complex piping systems. Input is by punched cards. Output includes: the Kw and c values associated with each circuit component; computes L/gA, pipe volume and other data. Three individual flow rates can be input; the pressure drop existing across each individual component is then calculated. All output variables can be summed up at any time during calculation. The final system c, Kw and pressure drop data is tabulated

References
Aerojet-General Corporation

Availability

Language
Fortran IV

Computer
IBM 360 series

1328

PASS *Daverman/SP Group*
Analyses the flow of fluid through a pipework system. Pipe sizes, pressure, temperature, and size of expansion tank and pump required are calculated. Several types of fluid may be examined, and the pipework and insulation may be of one of several materials

References

Availability
Time sharing

Language

Computer
CDC Cyber

1329

Compaid *Davy Computing Limited*
For pipework detailing, purchasing and isometric production. Metric and Imperial standards, shop and site material splits, complicated and repeated piping configurations, and staggered material deliveries. Output includes estimates and material costs for projects, standard material control reports, automatic selection of correct part number then preparation of accurate bills of materials for each isometric, and information on lines which can or cannot be fabricated or erected

References

Availability
Bureau service

Language

Computer
Univac 1100/81

1330

$PIPES *Dewco Programming and Computer Services*
Produces the most economical design for two pipe hot water systems. It gives a detailed list of piping and fittings required for installation. The program operates with metric or Imperial units

References

Availability
Bureau service, remote batch,
purchase

Language
Fortran

Computer
Honeywell 6000

1331

FLOW 1 *ESDU International Limited*
An interactive program which estimates pressure changes in pipes carrying two phase flow, including those in boilers and condensers. Used in SI units and intended for application to single component mixtures. Any fittings must be accountable in terms of additional lengths of straight pipe

References

Availability
Licence

Language

Computer
Tektronix 4051,
4052, 4054

1332

PISCES *Facet Limited*
Sizes all the components in hot or chilled water circuits. It accounts for single or two-pipe systems, reverse return systems, or any mixture of these types. Detailed calculations are provided of pressure and temperature losses throughout the system. The program allows circuits to be balanced using valves only, or by resizing non-index paths in the network. Velocity limits can be defined and any pipes in the system can be fixed in size

References

Availability
Bureau service, or under licence

Language

Computer
Prime, Norsk Data,
Harris,
CP/M 8-bit micros

1333

Pipe and Duct Networks *Haden Central Engineering*
A suite of four programs containing: 3A Pressure drop, equivalent length and velocity of a series of flow rates of any fluid at any temperature in a range of sizes of any type of pipework. 3B Sizing or checking single pipe loops to a series of radiators. 3C Comprehensive ventilation duct analysis. 3D Duct library creation, amendment and printout for use in 3C

References
Recommended by The Technical
Software Centre, Cranfield, Bedford

Availability
Purchase

Language
Fortran IV

Computer
4032 and 8032 PET,
Apple II

1334

PC PLOD *Haden Central Engineering*
Comprehensive closed circuit pipe analysis and sizing for any fluid at any temperature range (usually heating/chilled water). The program gives pipe sizes, pressure drops and totals, balancing valve settings, pump duty, list of quantities, etc. Used at the detailed design stage through to commissioning

References

Availability
Licence

Language
Fortran IV and F77

Computer
Any minicomputer
with 128K/16-bit

Computer programs for the building industry

1335

PIPDAT *Haden Central Engineering*
Calculates the pressure drop, equivalent length and velocity for a series of flow rates for any fluid at any temperature in a range of sizes for any type of pipe

References

Availability
On application

Language
Basic, Fortran

Computer
Apple II
PET, Tandy II

1336

Pipe dimensions (central heating systems) *Hansen, Carlsen & Frolund A/S*
Gives dimensions for a two pipe central heating system with given radiator performance. Division of quantity of water, pressure loss, pump performance, resistance to regulation for adjustment of valves, total quantity of water and total length of piping in each size are also calculated. A maximum of 1000 radiators per system can be handled

References
Danish Building Research Institute
Abstract 48 15 002

Availability
Bureau service from CE-data

Language

Computer

1337

EMIT *Hevacomp Limited*
Calculates the heat emission from bare or insulated pipework, for steel or copper tubing. The program uses basic heat transfer equations

References

Availability
Purchase

Language

Computer
Any 64K
microcomputer

1338

EXPIPE *Hevacomp Limited*
Computes friction losses in an existing pipe system, given the pipe sizes and flow rates. It is useful when examining pressure drops in an existing system which is to be extended

References

Availability
Purchase

Language

Computer
Any 64K
microcomputer

1339

HPIPE *Hevacomp Limited*
Sizes two pipe heating systems on a section by section basis, automatically computing mains heat emission. The index run is sized first and the results stored on disk. Branches off the index can subsequently be sized independently, using the stored index run data. Maximum velocity and/or pressure drop is used as sizing constraint. The program uses basic fluid mechanics equations

References

Availability
Purchase

Language

Computer
Any 64K
microcomputer

1340

PIPE *Hevacomp Limited*
Handles basic pipe sizing for steel, copper or galvanised pipework, containing water at any temperature. Friction losses are computed on a section by section basis, using maximum velocity and/or pressure drop as a sizing constraint

References

Availability
Purchase

Language

Computer
Any 64K
microcomputer

1341

PIPEX *Inatome and Associates*
This interactive program calculates stresses in linear steel or copper piping systems using the general method for square corner systems outlined in the Kellog Handbook. The program handles single end, multi plane pipe systems with no intermediate restraints or branches

References

Availability
Time sharing

Language
Fortran IV

Computer
CP/M microcomputer

1342

Gas deliverability study *A M Kinney, Inc*
Predicts the annual rates at which gas is produced from a reservoir, and provides allowable options common to the industry. Collecting line pressure can be single pipeline. It will predict up to 30 years of gas flow and provide economic information for 30 years. Four decrements to the pipeline pressure are allowed. Allowable taken can be specified either as a fraction of the absolute open flow or as a fixed rate

References

Availability

Language
Fortran

Computer
IBM 1130 and 370

1343

Hardy-Cross water distribution through a network of pipes *A M Kinney, Inc*
Calculates water distribution through a network of pipes by means of the Hazen and Williams equation. The program handles up to 150 pipes and 70 loops. Input data required: pipe number, size and length; assumed flow in magnitude and direction; Hazen and Williams coefficient C; primary and secondary loop number. Output includes: discharge through each pipe in gpm; head loss in feet; pipe diameter and length; tolerance of head loss specified in input data

References

Availability

Language
Fortran

Computer
IBM 1130 and 370

1344

Pipe flexiblity analysis *A M Kinney, Inc*
Handles very complex piping systems, including multiple closed loops, and any type of restraint, such as a rigid restraint or stop, a restraining force, or spring-loaded restraint. Limited to 15 branch points or 25 branches. No restriction to number of loops or anchors. Output includes computation of forces, moments and expansion stress at all numbered points of piping system; maximum stress and its location are computed and listed; cold-to-hot translations and rotations for each membered point on the point system

References

Availability

Language
Fortran

Computer
IBM 1130 and 370

Piping friction losses *A M Kinney, Inc*
Calculates piping head losses due to friction, using the Darcy-Weisbach formula. Evaluation of all factors, affects the loss, and also covers a wide range of real pipe fluid over rough and small boundaries. Used to compute head loss for non-circular conduits, such as rectangular air ducts. Darcy's equation for circular pipes may be used by the hydraulic radius concept. Tabulation of inside diameter, relative roughness, velocity, Reynolds number, friction factor, velocity head in psi, and pressure drop in psi/100ft

References

Availability

Language
Fortran

Computer
IBM 1130 and 370

Power and process pipe sizing *A M Kinney, Inc*
Computes the pipe minimum wall thickness from Ansi pressure piping code plus a bending allowance for every outside diameter, then checks it to determine if it is a standard size. Output consists of outside diameter, calculated minimum and standard wall thickness, inside diameter, pipe weight in pounds/ft, fluid flow in pounds/hour, velocity of fluid in feet/minute, Reynolds number, friction factor, velocity head in pounds/square foot, and pressure drop in pounds/square foot/hundred feet of pipes

References

Availability

Language
Fortran

Computer
IBM 1130 and 370

Surface condenser sizing *A M Kinney, Inc*
By assuming the condenser surface, the program will calculate the circulating water flow, temperature rise, range, vacuum temperature, friction losses for condenser tubes and water boxes, and the terminal temperature difference. For design, by assuming the vacuum, the program will interpolate non-linearly the saturation temperature, then the temperature rise, range, circulating water flow, condenser surface, terminal difference and friction losses for condenser tubes and water boxes

References

Availability

Language
Fortran

Computer
IBM 1130 and 370

NETPLOT *Microcomp*
A screen plotting program which will plot the network on the screen of the Apple II computer. Coordinate data is appended to the rest of the network data using NETIN. This enables the user to see a plot describing how the system will appear to the computer during the numerical solution. The program plots the pipes and the pipe numbers, together with nodes and node numbers

References

Availability
Purchase

Language

Computer
Apple II, and most microcomputers using CP/M

NETWK *Microcomp*
For pipe network analysis, used for systems up to 100 pipes, 100 nodes, including 5 source pumps and 5 reservoirs. Allows up to 10 loops with up to 20 pipes per loop. Flows can be in CFS or GPM and either Hazen-Williams or Darcy-Weisbach friction factors may be used. Output includes all necessary information to design or analyse a complete water system. A user-friendly utility program, NETIN, prompts the user for necessary data which may be easily edited and stored on disk

References

Availability
Purchase

Language

Computer
Apple, and most microcomputers using CP/M

MULPIP *National Bureau of Standards, Washington*
Calculates heatlosses and gains of underground pipes buried together. Heat transfer to and from each pipe is calculated, taking into account temperature, thermal insulation, depth, ground temperature and thermal properties of the soil

References
Underground Heat and Chilled Water Distribution Systems, NBS Building Science Series, Number 66

Availability
Dr Tamami Kusuda, at NBS

Language
Fortran V

Computer
Univac 1100

PIPE 1 *Oasys Limited*
Given details of heating/cooling units, their connections and the flow and return mains, this program will calculate the pipe sizes required and the maximum pressure loss through the network. Output gives total emissions, mass flows, excess pressures, maximum pressure loss, diameter and length of each pipe run, and water volumes. The IHVE 1970 method is used

References

Availability
Bureau service

Language
Fortran

Computer
DEC 10

BP112: Pipe sizing *Oasys Limited*
A program for central heating or chilled water pipe systems. Given details of units and their connections to flow and return pipes, the program calculates the pipe sizes required, and the maximum pressure losses throughout the pipe network

References

Availability
Purchase

Language
Basic

Computer
HP 9845 HP 85/87

Heating pipe resistance, simple *Ontwerp-en Adviesbureau Ing The J MUL BV*
Calculates the internal resistance of pipework for symmetrical two pipe heating or cooling systems. The program has been modified for application in houses, flats and offices where most pipework branches are the same and only radiator outputs differ

References
Simplified version of 'two pipe' program

Availability
Bureau service, purchase

Language
Basic

Computer

Heating pipe resistance, two pipe *Ontwerp-en Adviesbureau Ing Thu J MUL BV*
Calculates the internal resistance of pipework for any symmetrical two pipe heating or cooling system. The program calculates the overall pressure for each branch pipe and each radiator in the system. Details are given in the output of total length of pipe, insulation and number of appliances, and all totals are priced

References

Availability
Bureau service, purchase

Language

Computer

Computer programs for the building industry

1355

Pipe resistance, Tiggelmann *Ontwerp-en Adviesbureau Ing Th J MUL BV*
Calculates the internal resistance of any pipework system, with any given pipe dimensions, according to the Tiggelmann system

References

Availability
Bureau service, purchase

Language

Computer

1356

Water pipe resistance *Ontwerp-en Adviesbureau Ing Th J MUL BV*
Calculates the internal resistance of pipework for hot and cold water supply in domestic premises, and sizes the pipes for a given flow of water. Output prints and prices the total length of pipes, including insulation if required, and the number of valves, check valves and water meters

References

Availability
Bureau service, purchase

Language

Computer

1357

LPHW-PIPES/1 *Quest GENESYS Limited*
This sub-system enables an engineer to calculate the pipe sizes for any two pipe heating system. Design may be for minimum cost or specific water velocities

References
GENESYS program library

Availability
Bureau service, hire

Language
Gentran

Computer
Dec 20, Honeywell, IBM, ICL, PE, Philips, others

1358

PIPE-SCHEDULE/1 *Quest GENESYS Limited*
Produces pipe measurement schedules for pipe runs of different types, diameters, groups and reference names. Data can be input as tabular information, or digitised from long section drawings of pipe runs. Output includes a tabular presentation of all pipes required, sorted and measured

References

Availability

Language
Gentran

Computer

1359

Isolation *Technies Rekencentrum Polybit bv*
Estimation of the optimum for relationship of isolation to thickness of pipes

References

Availability
Bureau service, remote batch, time sharing, purchase

Language
Fortran

Computer
Cyber 750

1360

SPAN *UCC (Great Britain) Limited*
Used to analyse the flexibility of multiple branch, closed loop pipe systems, taking into account thermal expansion, weight effects, pressure effects, imposed movements and loads and various types of constraint. Stresses at each point, deflections, anchor loads and constraint forces can be calculated

References

Availability
Bureau service

Language

Computer

1361

PANP *United Information Services Limited*
This CIRIA program is for the analysis of large scale pipe networks including pressure reducing valves and pumps

References

Availability
Bureau service, time sharing

Language
Fortran

Computer
Honeywell
Sigma 9

1362

PSA 5 *United Information Services Limited*
This Whessoe pipe stress program is available with interactive aids for data checking and results interrogation

References

Availability
Bureau service, time sharing

Language
Fortran

Computer
Honeywell
Sigma 9

1363

DONKEY LM102 *The Association for Computer Aided Design*
Determines the sizes of duct networks, performs acoustical analysis on the basis of the selected sizes; determines quantities for costing, in the form of weight of ductwork and fabrication, erection, and shop drawing man hours. Applicable to air-conditioning duct systems including those handling heated and/or cooled air, or systems that just ventilate occupied space. It does not have application in sawdust extraction systems and other specialised waste disposal systems in which the air stream carries soil waste material

References

Availability
Contact ACADS

Language
Fortran IV

Computer
Univac 1108
Prime 750, 400

1364

SUPER-DUCT II *APEC Executive Office*
An improved version of the SUPER-DUCT program. The engineering methodology includes the total pressure concept. The program uses three methods for sizing ducts (constant velocity, constant friction, static regain), and will also handle previously sized duct systems. It determines the longest run of duct from a pressure viewpoint and it calculates metal gauge required based on SMACNA and ASHRAE methodology. The program has been enhanced to size supply, return and exhaust air ducts

References
81 Licences plus Public Access

Availability
Doris J Wallace, Executive Director, APEC

Language
Fortran

Computer
IBM/370
CDC Cyber 175
TRS-80 Model II

DS/DN *Bahco Ventilation Entreprenad AB*
Sizes and/or calculates duct systems. Friction losses, leakage, losses in fittings, etc, are taken into account; settings of registers and balancing dampers are presented, as well as selection data for the fan. An extension of the program calculates sound generation and attenuation in the ducts, and gives the dB values at each outlet/inlet

References

Availability
By arrangement with Bahco

Language
Fortran V

Computer
Data General

1366

VDUCT *Civil and Structural Computing (Northern) Limited*
Determines duct sizes and pressure loss in a ventilation system using data and equations from the IHVE Guide. Duct sizes may be calculated by the program using specified minimum diameter, maximum velocity and maximum pressure loss/m of duct. Alternatively, sizes may be predetermined, rectangular or circular, for calculation of actual pressure loss. Quantities may be output if required

References
Bradshaw, Buckton and Tonge

Availability
Bureau service, time sharing, in-house

Language

Computer

1367

DADDS *Daverman/SP Group*
For sizing ductwork. Pressures, temperatures and quantities of material are calculated for each design. One of two methods can be used for calculating sizes (equal friction or static regain). As an option, the program can re-calculate air quantities and duct sizes to compensate for heatgains of the ducting, and can analyse the system for noise

References

Availability
Time sharing

Language

Computer
CDC Cyber

1368

$DUCT *Dewco Programming and Computer Services*
Sizes ventilating or extraction duct systems to determine pressure losses and velocities. Facilities are available to achieve balanced air flows and to determine the effects of damping. The program operates for standard ducting as approved by the HVCA

References

Availability
Bureau service, remote batch, purchase

Language
Fortran

Computer
Honeywell 6000

1369

EPS-DUCTS *DHSS (Department of Health and Social Security)*
Ducts can be applied to existing or proposed designs to simulate the performance of ventilation ductwork. After comparison with the requirement, the design can be changed accordingly until the simulated performance is suffiently close to the requirement. This is not a duct sizing program, but it allows a design to be hypothesised, then simulated so that its physical performance can be predicted. This allows potential problems to be identified and design changes effected to obviate such problems

References

Availability
Purchase

Language
Fortran

Computer
SEL

1370

Commercial Estimating (DV2) *Estimation Limited*
For sheet metal contractors. Covers rectangular, round, spiral and flat/oval ductwork. Ductwork measured item by item or by over measurement of fittings. Rectangular and circular ductwork is included from a design, manufacture and erection aspect, whilst spiral and flat/oval is included on the basis of brought in components. Joints, supports and stiffeners on manufactured ductwork are automatically taken off; provision for manual entry. Full summary, tender and automatic bill of quantities available

References

Availability
Purchase

Language

Computer

1371

'Duct Magic' Fabrication - Basic *Estimation Limited*
A shop fabrication program providing mathematics and graphics. Computes a detailed list of accessories on each fitting. Offers visual layout of each blank size. Provides a drawing of each sheet of metal showing exact cut through points. Labels for fitting identification can be colour coded for easy assembly on the job site or in the shop. By using colour coding the operator can separate and identify the job by area, floor, etc

References

Availability
Purchase

Language

Computer

1372

'Duct Magic' Fabrication - Drop Cheek Option *Estimation Limited*
When using T's, cheeks can both rise, both drop, or one rise and one drop, or remain flat while wrapper also changes. When using elbows, cheek can rise or drop out of plane while wrapper size also changes. This fitting can be entered as a 90° elbow or a non 90° elbow by simply expressing degree of turn. This program requires the 'Duct Magic' - Basic program

References

Availability
Purchase

Language

Computer

1373

INDUS *Facet Limited*
Sizes open-ended air duct networks and calculates all pressure losses and air temperatures in the system; deals with supply and extract systems; it can size ducts by constant friction, constant velocity, or static regain. By any combination of circular, rectangular and flat-oval ductwork, allows any mixture of duct materials and air temperatures. Accounts for supply systems, duct heat pick up and volume flow changes. The system can be balanced using dampers only, or by resizing non-index runs

References

Availability
Bureau service, or under licence

Language

Computer
Prime, Norsk Data, Harris, CP/M 8-bit micros

1374

LK003 *Flakt Installator AB*
For sizing ducts in high velocity systems. Creates designs for both circular and rectangular ducts to achieve the smallest total pressure difference between units in a supply or exhaust systems and economy in the amount of metal used. The results include dimensions, air flow and velocity, and fall in total pressure for each section. A parts list of components for the ducting is also included

References

Availability
By arrangement. Available in UK from Flakt Limited or Control Data Limited

Language
Fortran IV

Computer
Cyber 175

Computer programs for the building industry

1375

DUCTS *Focus Software consultants*
Facilities: Ventilation and extra duct sizing data input/amendment; calculate duct sizes, fan duty and heater battery duty. Both ventilation and extract ductwork systems may be sized by this module, using regular, flat oval or circular ductwork. Both mains and branch maximum velocity and pressure drop constraints may be stated for a network as may the maximum duct height available for installation purposes

References

Availability
Purchase

Language

Computer
CP/M or MS DOS

1376

DUCTSIZE *Haden Central Engineering*
This program provides comprehensive duct sizing, pressure drops, damper settings, flows, velocities, etc. For any supply or extract ventilation system, either for a whole network, up to 250 ducts, or just for an index circuit

References

Availability
On application

Language
Basic, Fortran

Computer
Apple II
PET, Tandy II

1377

DUCT *Hevacomp Limited*
This program computes the friction losses in a duct system when the system has been pre-sized and air flow rates are known (or, alternatively, in an existing system). Ductwork can be circular, rectangular or flat oval

References

Availability
Purchase

Language

Computer
Any 64K
microcomputer

1378

PRESS *Hevacomp Limited*
Sizes ductwork on a section by section basis and calculates pressure drop through ductwork and fittings. Ductwork can be circular (galvanised or spirally wound), rectangular or flat oval. Duct sizes can be either exact, HEVCA standard, or to the nearest 25mm. Sizing is constrained by a given maximum duct pressure drop and a maximum velocity. Duct losses are computed iteratively using basic fluid mechanics equations

References

Availability
Purchase

Language

Computer
Any 64K
microcomputer

1379

STATIC *Hevacomp Limited*
Sizes ductwork using static regain between sections. It operates on a section by section basis, allowing the static regain factor for a T to be specified, and it sizes the subsequent section so that its friction loss is equal to the static regain at the preceding junction. Losses in other fittings can be handled. Sizing can optionally be carried out on a maximum velocity basis for any section

References

Availability
Purchase

Language

Computer
Any 64K
microcomputer

1380

VELO *Hevacomp Limited*
This program sizes ductwork as for PRESS, except that it uses a maximum velocity constraint only

References

Availability
Purchase

Language

Computer
Any 64K
microcomputer

1381

DUCT *Oasys Limited*
Sizes low velocity, low pressure supply and extract air duct systems by static regain, constant pressure drop and velocity method: also analyses existing duct systems and calculates outflow and total pressure drop. Each section is defined by dimensions, materials, fittings, air flow rates, velocities and required pressures. For each section, output gives air velocity, total pressure drop, size, surface area and weight. For the whole network, it gives totals for surface area, weight, air flow and pressure drop

References

Availability
Bureau service

Language
Fortran

Computer
DEC 10

1382

Air duct calculation *Ontwerp-en Adviesbureau Ing Th J MUL BV*
Calculates changes in air velocity in ventilation ductwork due to friction and dynamic loss or regain. Suitable for supply or exhaust systems with ductwork of round or square section. Roughness factors may be introduced for various materials. Output gives total air volume and external resistance as well as, for round ducts, overall length and, for square ducts, total area of sheet metal for any given thickness

References

Availability
Bureau service, purchase

Language

Computer

1383

Air duct system *Technies Rekencentrum Polybit bv*
Aids design of air duct systems for air-conditioning installations with high and low velocity, round and rectangular ducts, for inlet and extraction. Pressure losses for duct systems may also be calculated

References

Availability
Bureau service, remote batch, purchase

Language
Fortran

Computer
Cyber 750

1384

Air slit *Technies Rekencentrum Polybit bv*
Dimensioning of a duct with air slit for a uniform air flow

References

Availability
Bureau service, remote batch, time sharing, purchase

Language
Fortran

Computer
Cyber 750

VariTrane duct program *The Trane Company*
Used at the design stage to make the best use of, and balance, variable air volume ductwork using VariTrane boxes of the shut off type. It uses static regain to minimise pressure variations in the system and generally reduces operating static pressure through the system. Output includes a report showing predicted static pressure along the trunk system, selected boxes with predicted room noise levels and a complete bill of materials.

References

Availability
Bureau service

Language
Fortran

Computer
IBM 370

NOIZ and RAYTR *COSMIC*
Assists the acoustical engineer in overcoming problems of noise level prediction. NOIZ is an interactive system which calculates predictions in rooms with many sources and receivers, and moderately complex geometry. RAYTR is used to obtain detailed prediction of noise levels in critical areas of the room. This program uses geometric acoustics and bases noise level predictions on actual sound transmission paths rather than the reverberant field concepts

References
Virginia Polytechnic Inst

Availability

Language
Fortran IV

Computer
IBM 370 series

NOISE *Cymap Limited*
The program deals with noise levels at grilles and in rooms. It is used in conjunction with DUCTSIZE. Part 1 gives SPL at each grille: dampers, attenuators and other noise sources can be included. Part 2 compares the SPL for each octave at a chosen point in a room against a maximum permissible value

References

Availability
Purchase (under licence)

Language
Microsoft Basic

Computer
Most CP/M based microcomputers, 8 and 16-bit, 64K

Reverberation Time *Grootenhuis Allaway Associates*
Calculates reverberation times for a room at eight frequencies, from 63Hz to 86Hz, by the formula of Eyring. Each category of room surface (walls, floor and roof) may have up to 20 sub-areas or absorptive finishes; this also applies to the room contents and volume. Approximately 100 stored sound absorption spectra for common finishes and contents. Facility for direct entry of other spectra. Output includes lists of reverberation time/octave; absorption coefficients and total absorption

References

Availability
Purchase

Language
Basic 4.0

Computer
CBM 4032, 32K

Acoustic program *Pilkington Brothers Limited*
Calculates internal noise levels (octave or 1/3 octave spectra) and subjective levels (dBA and NRC) that result from given external noise spectra, or using figures for typical aircraft or road traffic noise stored in the program. Using window and room sizes, and the absorption of room surfaces, the program evaluates the effect of any glazing design

References

Availability
Used only to advise customers. Not for sale

Language

Computer

Heating, ventilation and air-conditioning

Heat and cooling loads
Systems analysis and design
Energy use
Solar energy
Shading
Air-cleaning
Other

1390

TEMPER *The Association for Computer Aided Design Limited*
Operates in one of two modes 1: LOAD - calculates, as a function of time, the heating or cooling load required to maintain a building at a specified air temperature 2: TEMP - calculates the building internal air temperature for a specified cooling or heating effect. The program consists of a heat transfer analysis on a building which is subjected to a specified external climatic environment, together with an internal loading according to building usage and occupancy

References

Availability
Contact ACADS

Language
Control Data Fortran

Computer

1391

HCC-III (Heating Cooling Calculation Level 3) *APEC Executive Office*
Calculates design heating and cooling loads utilizing ASHRAE methodology, using the room as the basic level of calculation. Heating load calculations consist of conventional transmission loss analyses involving areas, U-factors, and temperature differences. Infiltration is calculated on an input or master factor basis. The maximum glass solar heat gain for the specified winter month is calculated and its effect on the heatloss for the room is determined together with lighting and occupant heatgain

References
194 Licences plus Public Access

Availability
Doris J Wallace, Executive Director, APEC

Language
Fortran

Computer
CDC Cyber 175
IBM/370
TRS-80 Model II

1392

HCCL-I *APEC*
Calculates design heating and cooling loads using ASHRAE steady state method. A thermostatically controlled room is used as a basic level of calculation for: conventional transmission loss analysis involving areas, U-factors and temperature differences; infiltration; cooling load on an hourly basis over a 24-hour period; glass, wall and roof loads, separated into transmission and solar components; shading devices

References
68 Licences plus public access

Availability
Doris J Wallace, APEC

Language
Fortran

Computer
Machine independent

1393

VOK *Bahco Ventilation Entreprenad AB*
Calculates air temperatures as well as heating and cooling loads within one room. Heat transmission due to temperature gaps and to solar radiation through walls, roof and glazing are taken into account, as well as heat storage in building materials

References

Availability
By arrangement with Bahco

Language
Fortran V

Computer
Data General

1394

THERM *British Gas Corporation*
Simulates the thermal behaviour of buildings; predicts loads, temperatures and humidities at hourly intervals over a specified period. Heating/cooling loads and seasonal consumption can be obtained. It can be used at the design stage, at the plant design stage or at the plant management stage. It contains the weather data of major British cities for the last twenty years. Provides: temperatures and heat loads at each time step throughout the building; a summary at the end of simulation

References
IGE Communication 1007

Availability
Bureau service - Geisco

Language
Fortran

Computer
Univac 1106
65K minimum

1395

BS1 *Building Service Designs*
Calculates heatgains and losses in rooms, and the air flow rates required from air-conditioning plant in order to maintain specific temperatures in summer and winter. The program will also create a preliminary lighting design. Calculations for each room may be summarised in one line or printed out in greater detail. Heat gain and loss calculations are based on the IHVE Guide (1970)

References

Availability
Bureau service, time sharing, remote batch

Language
Basic

Computer
Honeywell Sigma 7, Sigma 9

1396

HG2 *Building Service Designs*
Calculates heatgains through external glazing, in shade, throughout a design day. External air temperature, diffuse radiation incident on the glass, shading coefficient, thermal transmittance, internal air temperature and window area are input. The heatgains in Btu/h, per square foot of glass or per window, are produced as an hourly value for each of the 24 hours

References

Availability
Bureau service, time sharing

Language
Basic

Computer
Honeywell Sigma 7, Sigma 9

1397

HG3 *Building Service Designs*
Calculates heatgains through horizontal roofs from sol-air temperatures. In addition to the sol-air temperatures, internal air temperature, decrement factor, time lag and U value of the wall structure are input. Heat gains in Btu/h are produced as hourly values for each hour throughout a design day

References

Availability
Bureau service, time sharing

Language
Basic

Computer
Honeywell Sigma 7, Sigma 9

1398

HG4 *Building Service Designs*
Calculates heatgains through external walls from sol-air temperatures. These values must be supplied, over 24 hours, for each elevation and a wall in shade. Additional inputs are internal air temperature, decrement factor, time lag and U value of the wall structure. Heat gains through walls in shade and for each elevation are produced as hourly values in Btu/h/ft^2. Sol-air temperatures may be derived from program HG5

References

Availability
Bureau Service, time sharing

Language
Basic

Computer
Honeywell Sigma 7, Sigma 9

1399

HG5 *Building Service Designs*
Calculates the sol-air temperatures for a design day from total direct and diffuse solar intensities. In addition, diurnal variation, maximum temperature and surface absorption coefficient are input, together with correction factors for height above sea level, sky clarity and ground reflectance. Sol-air temperatures for 8 wall orientations and for a horizontal surface are produced in degrees Fahrenheit and Celsius

References

Availability
Bureau service, time sharing

Language
Basic

Computer
Honeywell Sigma 7, Sigma 9

Computer programs for the building industry

HG7 *Building Service Designs*
This is an optional addition to program HG5. It produces printout of air temperatures calculated by that program. These are calculated for each of the 24 hours and are expressed in degrees Fahrenheit and Celsius. No additional input data is required other than that used by HG5

References

Availability
Bureau service, time sharing

Language
Basic

Computer
Honeywell Sigma 7, Sigma 9

HEATGAIN *Building Services Software*
Predicts cooling loads for a series of rooms using the procedures described in the CIBS guide. Calculations take into account specific latitude, orientation of building, thermal characteristics of construction and internal gains. Output includes: solar position and radiation; surface/glazing gains; ventilation, occupancy, equipment and lighting gains; latent gains; room, zone and building hour by hour cooling loads

References

Availability
Licence

Language

Computer
Commodore Series PET 3/4/8000

LAMSAC Application code 32065126170A *Cardiff City Council, Architect's Department*
Calculates heatlosses. Slow peripheral units used are a card reader and line printer

References
LAMSAC

Availability

Language
ICL extended Fortran

Computer
ICL 1904S
9K core

Heating and Cooling Load Calculations *Computair*
For the calculation of heatgains and/or losses for buildings. All data has been compiled from the IHVE guide

References

Availability

Language

Computer
Commodore PET

Refrigeration Equipment and Cold Rooms *Computair*
Calculates heatgain, direct usage and product load for cold rooms. A mixmatch selection of cooler and condensing units would be made. The design of refrigeration coils can also be accommodated

References

Availability

Language

Computer
Commodore PET

HEATSOFT 2 *Contract Computer Software Limited*
Calculates heatlosses for a single room, or anything up to a multistorey office block. Suitable for a wide range of applications and providing error recovery, full data storage and printout facilities. For use by professional and clerical staff

References
Building Products journal

Availability
Purchase

Language
8-bit CP/M
16-bit CP/M86,
MS-DOS

Computer
Micro, min 64K

BASE *Cymap Limited*
This is a combined data entry for all the thermal load programs. It greatly reduces data entry time when data has been entered for, say, a Heatgain calculation, Heatloss and Summertime temperatures, as these can be output without further data entry. Information is entered for the overall buildings and material parameters, and for data on each room

References

Availability
Purchase (under licence)

Language
Microsoft Basic

Computer
Most CP/M based microcomputers,
8 and 16-bit, 64K

HEATGAIN - Cooling loads *Cymap Limited*
Calculates the total cooling load (heatgains) for a series of rooms in a building as in the CIBS guide. Calculations are carried out for each hour of a selected day for the specified latitude, size and material orientations, exposed materials and internal gains for the rooms, which can be grouped in up to 10 zones. The program will summarise the room peaks, zone peaks and building totals

References

Availability
Purchase (under licence)

Language
Microsoft Basic

Computer
Most CP/M based microcomputers,
8 and 16-bit, 64K

HEATLOSS - Heatlosses *Cymap Limited*
Suitable for assessing the heatlosses for a series of rooms in a complete dwelling, which itself forms part of a larger block, or just separate rooms in a building. Corrections are included for intermittent plant operation, the relative percentages of corrective and radiant heating, and the hours of preheating

References

Availability
Purchase (under licence)

Language
Microsoft Basic

Computer
Most CP/M based microcomputers,
8 and 16-bit, 64K

RADS - Radiator selection *Cymap Limited*
Used in conjunction with HEATLOSS to aid the selection of radiators. Radiators from any source can be used. Any height or length restrictions are entered for each room with the preferred number of radiators. The program outputs a bill of quantities with selection for each room

References

Availability
Purchase (under licence)

Language
Microsoft Basic

Computer
Most CP/M based microcomputers,
8 and 16-bit, 64K

1410

BA4 *Laboratoriet for Varmeisolering*
Calculates, for one room, half hour values of temperatures. Calculates heating and cooling loads, taking into account sun radiation, fixed and movable shading devices, varying ventilation and infiltration, electric lighting and other heat sources in the room, etc. Uses weather data from a Test Reference Year, or from Design Day. Results presented: with a few values for each day, with detailed description for single days, or for each of the twelve months and for the whole year, sums, mean values, frequencies or fractiles

References
Program BA4, Users Guide, Report no 44, Thermal Insulation Laboratory

Availability
Source, bureau service

Language
Fortran

Computer
IBM 370 or 3033
104K

1411

SOLIND *Laboratoriet for Varmeisolering*
Calculates hourly values of solar radiation in clear weather incident on facades, roofs and through windows with one or more layers of glazing. Direct, diffuse and ground reflected radiation for a given date, latitude, inclination, orientation, glazing and shading

References

Availability
Source

Language
Fortran

Computer
IBM 360,370,3033

1412

BLESS *Daverman/SP Group*
Calculates cooling loads for each hour during summer months, and heating loads during the winter. Calculations are based on the method described in the Carrier handbook. The program is interactive. Input errors may be corrected as they occur and values changed to allow repeated re-processing

References

Availability
Time sharing

Language

Computer
CDC Cyber

1413

GAINS *Dewco Programming and Computer Services*
Determines cooling loads for a whole building and zones within it. Calculates both sensible and latent component gains and thermal balance temperature. It operates in metric or Imperial units with simulated weather conditions for any climate over a typical month. Shadowing effects of other buildings can be considered

References

Availability
Bureau service, remote batch, purchase

Language
Fortran

Computer
Honeywell 6000

1414

HEAT *Ekono*
Calculates indoor temperatures and heating or cooling loads in buildings. Heat balance in outer walls is calculated using the response factor method. A number of different types of window can be defined for use with the program. Heat balance is calculated at half hour periods over 24 hours, or at hourly intervals over four days

References

Availability
Bureau service

Language
Fortran

Computer
VAX-11

1415

Saddle Design Load Calculation *Estimation Limited*
A comprehensive cooling and heating load calculation based on ASHRAE published standards for residential and commercial structures. The program provides information for equipment selection and HVAC system design; also allows the user to evaluate optimum possibilities for load reduction, and permits analysis of partial loads for system design, operation and control. Consideration is given to differing geographic locations

References

Availability
Purchase

Language

Computer

1416

ENPRO *Facet Limited*
Calculates zone heating and cooling loads during an average year, and estimates the energy consumption of the HVAC plant and miscellaneous equipment such as lights and machinery. The required climate of each zone may be affected by various psychrometric processes. These may be analysed, covering different heating and air-conditioning systems. The energy requirements of these systems are calculated to give total plant energy demand

References

Availability
Bureau service

Language

Computer
Prime, Norsk Data, Harris, CP/M 8-bit micros

1417

FELP *Facet Limited*
Analyses the heatlosses of both individual rooms and their combined zones, whether they are heated by radiant or convective systems. FELP is easy to use and incorporates a number of automatic data checks to ensure that reasonable values are used in calculations; the results are presented in a report format

References

Availability
Bureau service, or under licence

Language

Computer
Prime, Norsk Data, Harris, CP/M 8-bit micros

1418

VENTAC *Flakt Installator AB*
Calculates the actual 'achieved' temperature or required heating and cooling capacities in a room with regard to the actual system for ventilation, heating and cooling. Also assists selection of main components - central unit, cooling and heating installation - and energy consumption per hour, month and year. Capacities are calculated for allowed room temperature swing within defined limits; method allows for variation in heat transfer and long wave radiation coefficients. Also analyses compound room structures

References

Availability
Flakt Limited or Control Data Limited

Language
Fortran IV

Computer
Cyber 175

1419

HEATLOSS *Focus Software Consultants*
Used for: U value calculations, heatloss/gain data input/amendment and calculations. U values may be calculated from component fabrics for walls, floors, roofs and intermediate ceilings. CIBS tables are displayed for guidance. Heat losses and gains are calculated for each room within a building by CIBS formulae. Maximum of 1000 rooms may be stored in a building file. Room losses are calculated individually and a document produced detailing room information and losses, and the integral building losses

References

Availability
Purchase

Language

Computer
CP/M or MS DOS

Computer programs for the building industry

Heat Gains Calculations *Haden Central Engineering*
A suite of four programs containing: 1A Determination of U value, admittance, time lag and decrement factor for any specified multi-layer wall or roof. 1B Heat gains and cooling load calculations for a series of rooms/modules. Follows CIBS recommended procedure, can be run for a series of dates, and can include shading, etc. 1C As above, but for summer temperatures in rooms which are not air-conditioned, using CIBS Section A8. 1D Shading diagrams plotting any point in plan view or on any vertical face from adjacent buildings

References
Recommended by The Technical Software Centre, Cranfield, Bedford

Availability
Purchase

Language
Fortran IV

Computer
4032 and 8032 PET
Apple II

Heat Loss Calculations *Haden Central Engineering*
A suite of four programs containing: 2A Prediction of possible occurrence of interstitial condensation in multi-layer walls and roofs. 2B Heat loss calculations for a series of rooms, following CIBS Sections A3 and 5 for convective or radiative systems. 2C selection of single or >double panel radiators for heatlosses calculated. User inserts information from manufacturer's literature. 2D Radiator schedules and list of quantities from selection made in 2C

References
Recommended by The Technical Software Centre, Cranfield, Bedford

Availability
Purchase

Language
Fortran IV

Computer
4032 and 8032 PET,
Apple II

CD11 *Haden Central Engineering*
Calculates heatgains and losses for a series of rooms using the CARRIER method. The program is run for a series of months to find peak module loads and overall building totals. Used during the early and middle stages of project design. Output provides confirmation of all input data and detailed results, giving component breakdowns of gains for each hour of each month considered, for each room, plus total building summation

References

Availability
Licence

Language
Fortran IV and F77

Computer
Any minicomputer
with 128K/16-bit

CIBSGAIN *Haden Central Engineering*
Calculates heatgains and losses for a series of rooms using the CIBS 1970 method. It is run for a series of months to find peak module loads and overall building totals. Other information provided includes internal room temperatures without air-conditioning. The program is used during the early and middle stages of project design

References

Availability
Licence

Language
Fortran IV and F77

Computer
Any minicomputer
with 128K/16-bit

HLOSS *Hevacomp Limited*
Calculates the design heatlosses from a building on a room by room basis. The program uses environmental temperature methods and takes into account the radiative/convective characteristics of heat emitters. Any number of rooms may be defined and all information is stored on disk, allowing subsequent changes (eg using double glazing) to be performed easily

References

Availability
Purchase

Language

Computer
Any 64K
microcomputer

UVAL *Hevacomp Limited*
Calculates the thermal transmittance, or U value, for any layer wall, intermediate floor or roof, solid ground floor, internal wall, pitched roof or submerged basement

References

Availability
Purchase

Language

Computer
Any 64K
microcomputer

ACLD2 *Inatome and Associates*
Calculates the maximum heating and cooling loads for each room in a building and for the building itself, based upon design data. The required amount of air to be supplied to each area, and energy required for reheating it, if necessary, are also calculated

References

Availability
Time sharing

Language
Fortran IV

Computer
GE 630, PDP 10
CP/M microcomputer

PSYCH *Inatome and Associates*
Used for psychrometric analysis of moist air. A table of psychrometric properties is produced, together with an analysis of cooling loads, including dewpoint of apparatus and by-pass factor calculations, and a complete analysis of the air-conditioning cooling cycle

References

Availability
Time sharing

Language
Fortran IV

Computer
CP/M microcomputer

QDOT1, QDOT2 *Inatome and Associates*
QDOT1 evaluates the costs of using the TRU-70 heat pipe, manufactured by the Q-DOT Corporation, over a period of use. Immediate savings on costs of equipment are subtracted from initial costs to give a net cost. The annual savings from reduction of expenses for utilities are divided into the net cost to give the period over which initial costs may be justified. QDOT2 evaluates initial and continuing cost savings over a given amortization period

References

Availability
Time sharing

Language
Basic

Computer
CP/M microcomputer

BA4(L) *Lysteknisk Laboratorium*
Calculates half hour values for a room during a whole year of room temperatures, utilising a simplified method. Also calculates heating and cooling loads, taking into account sun radiation, fixed and movable sun shading devices, varying ventilation and infiltration, electric lighting and other heat sources in the room, etc. Average illumination is then calculated. The calculations utilise the weather data from the Danish Reference Year

References
With the permission of the Technical University of Denmark, Thermal Insulation Laboratory

Availability
Purchase

Language
Fortran IV

Computer
HP 1000

1430

LAMSAC Application code 32063126070A *Mid-Glamorgan County Council, Architect's Department*
This program calculates heatloss in buildings. Slow peripheral units used are a card reader and lineprinter

References
LAMSAC

Availability

Language
Fortran

Computer
ICL 1904S
5K core

1431

NBSLD *National Bureau of Standards, Washington*
Calculates the hourly heating and/or cooling load in a building. The thermal response factor is used to calculate transient heat conduction through walls and roofs. The program includes a sub-routine which can calculate the temperature of rooms with little or no air-conditioning or natural ventilation

References
Algorithms for Building Heat Transfer Sub routines, ASHRAE Bulletin, 1975

Availability
Purchase

Language
Fortran V

Computer
Univac 1100

1432

CP33 *National Research Council of Canada*
Calculates Z-transfer functions for the calculation of transient heat transfer through walls and roofs

References
G P Mitalas & J G Arseneault

Availability

Language
Fortran IV

Computer

1433

CP43 *National Research Council of Canada*
Simulates the cooling and dehumidifying Einned-Tube multi-row heat exchangers

References
A H Elmahdy & G P Mitalas

Availability

Language
Fortran IV

Computer

1434

STAST *Norwegian Building Research Institute*
Solves numerically the differential equation of 2D stationary heat flow. Structures of any shape may be analysed. The structure may be made up of different materials with different properties combined in orthogonally anisotropic patterns, and may also have internal sources of heat. The program is based on the finite element method. The structure to be analysed may be modelled by a combination of triangular (three nodes) and square (four nodes) elements

References

Availability
Purchase, bureau service

Language
Fortran IV

Computer
Univac 1100

1435

COOL *Oasys Limited*
Calculates the maximum instantaneous heatgains for individual rooms, for rooms grouped into zones and for the whole building. The program uses the CIBS (1970) method. Output is either in the form of tables of heatgains for 24 hours x 12 months, or easily read calculation sheets that identify the time and value of peak loads and the time and value of constituent loads to these peaks

References

Availability

Language
Fortran IV

Computer
IBM 1130
CDC 6400

1436

HEAT *Oasys Limited*
Calculates the heatlosses from rooms and complete buildings using either radiant or convective heating systems. A detailed description is entered, room by room, which may run to 99 separate room types and up to 999 incidences of each room type. Heat losses from individual rooms are calculated and combined to give the total heatlosses from the section or building. The program uses the IHVE 1970 method

References

Availability
Bureau service

Language
Fortran

Computer
DEC 10

1437

SOLAIR *Oasys Limited*
Calculates in deg C the equivalent temperature differences through walls at any latitude and altitude. The program will consider walls of any colour, uninsulated or insulated (internally or externally). Details of position, climate, room dimensions and temperatures are entered and the output gives tabulations for one or more months. Values are given for total incident solar radiation, sol-air temperatures, solar altitudes and azimuths

References

Availability
Bureau service

Language
Fortran

Computer
DEC 10

1438

THERMAL *Oasys Limited*
A suite of three programs: HEAT, COOL and ENERGY. HEAT is used for steady state heat loss calculations. COOL provides maximum instantaneous cooling loads calculations using cyclic weather data. ENERGY provides analysis using recorded weather data and simulation techniques for both the performance of the building fabric and building services. The suite can be used with building data for up to 100 different room types. Programs have a common file structure allowing data to be used with any of the programs

References

Availability
Bureau service

Language

Computer
DEC 10

1439

Cooling load *Ontwerp-on Adviesbureau Ing Th J MUL BV*
Calculates the total cooling load imposed by a building due to internal and external influences, eg solar radiation, building occupants, light fittings and machines. The program will take into account daily temperature range, latitude, building orientation and the storage effect of various materials. The program is especially useful for discovering the effects of screening or shading

References

Availability
Bureau service, purchase

Language

Computer

Heat load and radiator selection *Ontwerp-en Adviesbureau Ing The J MUL BV*
Calculates the heatlosses of a building, based upon the method described in DIN 4701:1959. If required, the dimensions of suitable radiators for each space in the building can also be calculated

References

Availability
Bureau service, purchase

Language
Basic

Computer
Wang, HP, Philips P2000

Air-conditioning program *Pilkington Brothers Limited*
Calculates total heatgains or losses for an air-conditioned building, thereby gauging the effect of a large number of successive days of radiation. It will take into account solar radiation gains and conduction gains and losses through the windows, as well as fabric, internal and ventilation gains (latent and sensible). Printouts give hourly and peak cooling loads for each mode of heatgain in each zone, or the whole, of the building

References

Availability
Used only to advise customers. Not for sale

Language
Fortran

Computer

ANT5 *Pilkington Brothers Limited*
This interactive program calculates the thermal performance of buildings with air-conditioning. Outputs include, for a given space, air-conditioning loads during a day in a specified month and annual energy consumption. Any design may be modified until an acceptable thermal performance is achieved in terms of energy consumption and air-conditioning requirements

References

Availability
Used only to advise customers. Not for sale

Language
Fortran

Computer

ANTI *Pilkington Brothers Limited*
This interactive program calculates the thermal performance of buildings without air-conditioning. Outputs include room temperatures for a given day in a specified month and annual energy consumption for a given space. Any design may be modified until an acceptable thermal performance is achieved in terms of energy consumption and susceptibility to summer overheating

References

Availability
Used only to advise customers. Not for sale

Language
Fortran

Computer

Multiple glazing program *Pilkington Brothers Limited*
Calculates the transmission characteristics of various combinations of glass and blinds when subject to solar radiation. The window is defined by the reflection, absorption and transmission values of each of the glass and blind surfaces, and the degree of exposure by the heat transfer coefficients

References

Availability
Used only to advise customers. Not for sale

Language
Fortran

Computer

Design point requirements *Ross F Meriwether and Associates*
This program groups various zones into areas to be served by a given air handling unit, to find totals of air supplied and coil requirements

References
Meriwether analysis series

Availability
Bureau service, purchase

Language

Computer
Univac 1108

Zone thermal loads *Ross F Meriwether and Associates*
Calculates heating and cooling loads on a zone by zone basis, using 24 hours of weather and solar data per month

References
Meriwether analysis series

Availability
Bureau service, purchase

Language

Computer
Univac 1108

HOT STUFF *Soft Option*
For comparison of heatlosses, solar gains and net space heating loads for each month of the year. Any shape of zone may be modelled provided that it can be approximated by a horizontal roof and floor with vertical walls orientated north, south, east and west. Output includes surface reference, type code, gross and percentage transfer rates. External losses, solar gains and inter-zonal losses can be output as well as net space heating demand for one month, or the year

References

Availability
Purchase

Language
Sinclair ZX Basic

Computer
Sinclair ZX Spectrum or ZX81

EDIT ROOM *TCL Software*
This is a program specially designed for architects and engineers, to handle heatloss calculations

References

Availability
Purchase

Language

Computer
CP/M

Composite wall *Technies Rekencentrum Polybit bv*
Calculates variable heat flow through homogeneous and composite walls and roofs/ceilings

References

Availability
Bureau service, remote batch, time sharing, purchase

Language
Fortran

Computer
Cyber 750

Computer programs for the building industry

1450

Cooling load *Technies Rekencentrum Polybit bv*
Calculates inner temperatures or cooling loads of a building, and also design information for air-conditioning systems. The amount of energy required annually for heating and cooling is also calculated

References

Availability
Bureau service, remote batch, purchase

Language
Fortran

Computer
Cyber 750

1451

Radiant temperatures *Technies Rekencentrum Polybit bv*
Calculates the mean radiant temperature for any point in a room

References

Availability
Bureau service, remote batch, time sharing, purchase

Language
Fortran

Computer
Cyber 750

1452

Solar radiation *Technies Rekencentrum Polybit bv*
Calculates the direct and diffuse solar radiation for all periods of the year for every degree of latitude

References

Availability
Bureau service, remote batch, purchase

Language
Fortran

Computer
Cyber 750

1453

Thermal comfort *Technies Rekencentrum Polybit bv*
Estimates a suitable radiant or air temperature for thermal comfort in a room

References

Availability
Bureau service, remote batch, time sharing, purchase

Language
Fortran

Computer
Cyber 750

1454

ATKOOL *United Information Services Limited*
A suite of programs to evaluate cooling and heating loads in buildings. Comprehensive interactive facilities are provided, including investigating temperature swings, shadow effects and effect of plant size

References

Availability
Bureau service, time sharing

Language
Fortran

Computer
Honeywell
Sigma 9

1455

ESP-II *APEC*
(Energy Simulation Program - Level 2). Simulates HVAC system performance. Uses a thermal loads program to build an architectural model, and subjects it to actual weather data. Also simulates a HVAC system, of specific design within the model. Allows for scheduling of lights, equipment, people, systems and building temperature. Includes economiser cycles, heat reclaim capability and system capacity resets

References
87 Licences plus public access

Availability
Doris J Wallace, APEC

Language
Fortran

Computer
IBM 370
CDC Cyber 175

1456

SYSTEM *British Gas Corporation*
Simulates the thermal performance of central heating systems using water; predicts the water temperatures throughout the system every few seconds. A heat balance is provided at regular intervals, comprising heat input, heat emissions, boiler surface losses, flue losses, heat stored and amount of hot water drawn off. This enables efficiencies, fuel consumption and recovery times to be computed. Provides heat outputs and temperature throughout the system at each time step

References
IGE Communication 1007

Availability
Bureau service

Language
Fortran

Computer
Univac 1106
65K minimum

1457

DEWPOINT *Building Services Software*
Calculates the U value of a wall or roof composite, plus an assessment of the condensation risk due to water vapour transfer. Factors considered include description of wall or roof elements as solid, air-spaces or surface coatings/films. These in turn are broken down into relevant descriptive features. Graphics plots of temperatures and vapour/saturation pressure profiles through the structure are produced on the video screen, in addition to tabulated hardcopy output

References

Availability
Licence

Language

Computer
Commodore Series
PET 3/4/8000

1458

HEATLOSS *Building Services Software*
Calculates the steady state design heatloss from a building. A room is described by up to 10 faces, with 3 surfaces per face, and each surface specified by 2 dimensions. No limit to number of rooms. Output includes: surface fabric heatloss; face fabric heatloss; room fabric, ventilation and total loss; room loss per unit volume; zone heatloss; building heat loss; average U value of perimeter wall and building; building loss per unit volume; building loss per unit temperature difference

References

Availability
Licence

Language

Computer
Commodore Series
PET 3/4/8000

1459

BTEMP *Civil and Structural Computing (Northern) Limited*
Used to perform three types of calculation: solar intensity and window shading; summertime temperature; heatgain

References
Bradshaw, Buckton and Tonge

Availability
Bureau service, time sharing, in-house

Language

Computer

Heating and Cooling Coil Design *Computair*
A range of programs which include: the design of heating and cooling coils given the required conditions with all commonly used heat transfer media; optimum selection of coils; back selection of coils to enable the engineer to predict performance of a known coil block; runaround coil design for use in heat reclaim systems; surplus heat rejection coils (air blast water coolers). Comprehensive pricing structures can be interfaced to provide a complete quotation package, including dimensioned drawings where required

References

Availability

Language

Computer
Commodore PET

MICROHEAT *Comsoft Associates*
Produces estimates for the installation of home heating systems. Provides: heatloss calculations for each room; calculation of pipe runs and heatlosses from pipework; boiler selection and sizing; semi-automatic radiator selection; calculates installation time and total cost for over 1000 radiators and components. Heating components are totally under user control. Reports provide: list of radiators showing manufacturer's code, size, BTU output, and price; printed estimate; list of heating components

References

Availability
Purchase

Language
Basic

Computer
Commodore CBM 8000

HEATLOSS 5 *Contract Computer Software Limited*
A pipe sizing and system analysis program dealing with compressible flow. In accordance with CIBS methods, the program covers most gases and compressed air. Also includes steam pipe sizing with full pressure drop analysis and condense line sizing. Data storage, error recovery and printout facililties provided. For use by professional and clerical staff

References
Building Products journal

Availability
Purchase

Language
8-bit CP/M
16-bit CP/M86, MS-DOS

Computer
Micro, min 64K

CIRC *Cymap Limited*
Used in connection with PIPESIZE, this program permits the inclusion of a circulating arrangement in a hot water system with towel rails if included. It gives pump duty and pressure drops and pipes sizes on the secondary system

References

Availability
Purchase (under licence)

Language
Microsoft Basic

Computer
Most CP/M based microcomputers, 8 and 16-bit, 64K

DEMAND *Cymap Limited*
Analysis includes: fabric and ventilation gains and losses, solar gains, hot water requirements, lighting, other electrical plant, and people gains. These are related to plnt system efficiencies to give the total demand for energy in a planned or existing building over a year. This demand can then be compared against target figures

References

Availability
Purchase (under licence)

Language
Microsoft Basic

Computer
Most CP/M based microcomputers, 8 and 16-bit, 64K

DUCTSIZE *Cymap Limited*
For supply or extract ventilation ductwork; sizes the system and gives pressure drops, velocities, flows and damper pressure drops for a range of inlet velocities. It can accommodate most fitting types, and pre-fixed duct sizes, oval, rectangular or circular. Excess pressures at terminals can be given, or the system can be balanced using dampers or by allowing the velocities in non index circuits to rise. Also calculates budget cost for the system

References

Availability
Purchase (under licence)

Language
Microsoft Basic

Computer
Most CP/M based microcomputers, 8 and 16-bit, 64K

LOOP *Cymap Limited*
This program allows single pipe loops with heaters connected in a variety of ways to be included in the circuit analysed using the PUMPSIZE program

References

Availability
Purchase (under licence)

Language
Microsoft Basic

Computer
Most CP/M based microcomputers, 8 and 16-bit, 64K

MATS *Cymap Limited*
Calculates the U value, admittance, decrement factor and time lag for a slab of up to 20 layers. Determines whether interstitial condensation or ice formation may occur and where. A number of materials are stored in the program, but others may be added. It also calculates infiltration rates on a room by room basis, including pressure difference due to stack and wind effects

References

Availability
Purchase (under licence)

Language
Microsoft Basic

Computer
Most CP/M based microcomputers, 8 and 16-bit, 64K

PIPESIZE *Cymap Limited*
Calculates the pipe sizes in a hot or cold water system, either gravity or pressurised, with diversity of usage in the summated circuit flow using the CIBS demand units and pipe data. The program may be used to size the distribution pipework on the basis of its carrying capacity, and indicate the head required for the index circuit with the excess heads and at all other loads given; the program can also be used to balance the system by increasing or reducing pipe sizes

References

Availability
Purchase (under licence)

Language
Microsoft Basic

Computer
Most CP/M based microcomputers, 8 and 16-bit, 64K

PUMPSIZE *Cymap Limited*
Heating pipes sizing for hot water systems using any type of heater in any configuration of flow and return pipes. Balancing is achieved by regulating valves. Proportioning of heat losses is carried out automatically. Standard data for six pipe types in the CIBS Guide, but any type of pipe can be balanced by reducing the pipe sizes on non-index circuits

References

Availability
Purchase (under licence)

Language
Microsoft Basic

Computer
Most CP/M based microcomputers, 8 and 16-bit, 64K

SUMPTEMP *Cymap Limited*
Calculates the internal summertime air or DRT temperatures as in the CIBS Guide. Temperatures are evaluated for each hour for the specified orientations, exposed materials and internal gains; if the peak temperature exceeds a specified value, a mechanical ventilation rate can be calculated to achieve this value. A summary includes for each room the maximum temperature for every date calculated

References

Availability
Purchase (under licence)

Language
Microsoft Basic

Computer
Most CP/M based microcomputers, 8 and 16-bit, 64K

1471

HEVACOMP *DHSS (Department of Health and Social Security)*
A suite of microcomputer programs for the design of building services. Facilities include: heating and energy, cooling, ducting, piping, lighting, finance and statistics. These facilities are available on separate discs. Calculations are largely based on CIBS methods

References

Availability
Purchase

Language
M Basic 80

Computer
SEL, Prime

1472

SECAD *DHSS (Department of Health and Social Security)*
A suite of microcomputer programs for the engineering design office, offering facilities for: LPHW Heating (including heatlosses), CWS and HWS pipe sizing and simulation, duct sizing, and interstitial condensation. Individual programs can be made available and facilities provided for storing project details and making interactive design changes. Methods follow closely the formulae and algorithms in the CIBS guide

References

Availability
Purchase

Language
M Basic 80

Computer
64K microcomputer

1473

SCIA: Design for central heating, air-conditioning and sound transmission *Eclipse Associates Limited*
This program provides a choice of minimum installation and transmission, and gives a choice of radiators, piping and air heating

References

Availability
Purchase, bureau service (SCIA SV, ST DATA APS)

Language
Wang Extended Basic, HP Basic

Computer
Wang mini and microcomputers

1474

SPECALC *Ecotech*
Part of the SCRIBE system. Produces calculation either from design model data, or from dimensions put in from keyboard, of lengths, areas, or volumes of coded elements. The program caters for input of specification from keyboard or diskette, and produces calculation of total cost, total heatloss and seasonal consumption estimates by degree day method, with facilities for interactive checks and changes

References
RIBA Journal, June 1982 Architects' Journal, June 23 and 30 1982

Availability
Purchase

Language
Compiled binary code

Computer
Apple II +

1475

SPIEL/D *Ecotech*
Part of the SCRIBE system. This handles a 10 node thermal network of daily simulation of: hourly temperatures, heatloss, backup heating, wild gains, solar gains and thermal storage. The program has facilities for simulating different thermostat and time switched zones; it produces graphs of temperatures, and incorporates a solar and wild gains facility for changing buildings and weather data for comparisons to be made

References
RIBA Journal, June 1982 Architects' Journal, June 23 and 30 1982

Availability
Purchase

Language
Compiled binary code

Computer
Apple II +

1476

SPIEL/S *Ecotech*
Part of the SCRIBE system. This is a seasonal version of SPIEL, similar to SPIEL/D, but it involves continuous simulation of the number of days per month and the number of months input by the user; generating sequence of days of differing radiation and temperature varying systematically around the mean for local data input by the user, or chosen from localities stored on diskette. The program produces a summary of seasonal totals and mid-monthly daily means

References
RIBA Journal, June 1982 Architects' Journal, June 23 and 30 1982

Availability
Purchase

Language
Compiled binary code

Computer
Apple II +

1477

SPIELCALC *Ecotech*
Part of the SCRIBE system. Covers calculation from design data of fabric quantities, input of thermal specification, facility for assigning coded elements to nodes and boundaries between nodes; it summarises conductances, night insulation, capacitances, glazing areas, volumes. It is stored on diskette in format for input to SPIEL dynamic simulation modules

References
RIBA Journal, June 1982 Architects' Journal, June 23 and 30 1982

Availability
Purchase

Language
Compiled binary code

Computer
Apple II +

1478

Heating and Cooling Load Calculation *Estimation Inc*
Based on ASHRAE published standards for residential and commercial structures. Provides information for equipment selection and HVAC systems design. The system allows the operator to evaluate the optimum possibilities for load reduction, and permits analysis of partial loads as required for system design, operation and control. Consideration is given to differing geographic locations

References

Availability
Purchase

Language

Computer

1479

SMIRFS *Facet Limited*
This program can be used to assess the relative benefits of various smoke control schemes in buildings. It accommodates four levels of complexity in the creation of the fire model. This allows the user to balance the accuracy of the simulation and the computer processing time used. The four levels of analysis are: steady state, constant pressure-variable stack, variable pressure-variable stack, and full dynamic simulation

References

Availability
Bureau service, or under licence

Language

Computer
Prime, Norsk Data, Harris, CP/M 8-bit micros

SWIFIB *Facet Limited*
Calculates air flows through a building envelope, and can be used for predicting ventilation rates, or as a pre-processor to the smoke movement program SMIRFS. The program considers the building in terms of a flow network, with the room represented by nodes, and the cracks and ventilation ducts represented by the branches. The program caters for effects due to stack, wind pressures, and mechanical ventilation

References

Availability
Bureau service, or under licence

Language

Computer
Prime, Norsk Data, Harris, CP/M 8-bit micros

HEAT *Focus Software Consultants*
Facilities: heater sizing data input/amendment; size heaters; LPHW pipe sizing data input amendment; calculate LPHW pipe sizes, pump duty, and boiler size. Room heat requirements entered from the heatloss module. Different pipe materials may be used and maximum velocity and pressure constraints may be stated. Boiler and pump duties are also calculated and individual pipe sizes may be changed. Sized heating systems' boilers and pump duties may also be assessed from the sized pipe network

References

Availability
Purchase

Language

Computer
CP/M or MS DOS

WATER *Focus Software Consultants*
Facilities: domestic hot water service and circulation pipe sizing, tank and mains cold water service pipe sizing. Tap flow requirements stated by a mixture of both volume flow and simultaneous demand units to cater for a wide range of sanitary fittings and equipment. Individual pipe branch data is entered. Pipe network is sized as a whole and the results stored. All domestic hot and cold water service design programs allow simple data entry; input and calculated data stored and altered as required

References

Availability
Purchase

Language

Computer
CP/M or MS DOS

CAPS *Grundfos Pumps Limited*
A program designed for quick, accurate selection of the right pump to suit a customer's requirements. Input information includes: the type of pump, eg booster, liquid transfer, boiler feed, etc; required flow rate; working head; power system; operating temperature, etc. The program then computes and displays the performance curve of the selected pump, the desired duty point being plotted against the performance curve, giving a clear visual comparison of actual duty against required pump duty

References

Availability

Language

Computer
Apple II

CIBSGAIN *Haden Central Engineering*
Calculates heatgains for a series of rooms using the CIBS 1970 Guide. Can be run for a series of months to find the peak module loads and overall building totals. Used during the early and middle stages of project design. Relates to programs SHADOW and SUMMER

References

Availability
On application

Language
Basic, Fortran

Computer
Apple II
PET, Tandy II

HEATLOSS *Haden Central Engineering*
Calculates heatlosses in a series of rooms in a building, in accordance with the CIBS Guide. Relates to programs RADSIZE and RADQUANT

References

Availability
On application

Language
Basic, Fortran

Computer
Apple II
PET, Tandy II

RADQUANT *Haden Central Engineering*
Produces radiator schedule and a quantities list from the selections made by the program RADSIZE. Also related to HEATLOSS

References

Availability
On application

Language
Basic, Fortran

Computer
Apple II
PET, Tandy II

RADSIZE *Haden Central Engineering*
Selects single or double panel radiators from any manufacturer's range, to meet room heat loss. Relates to programs HEATLOSS and RADQUANT

References

Availability
On application

Language
Basic, Fortran

Computer
Apple II
PET, Tandy II

SPLOOP *Haden Central Engineering*
Used for sizing or checking of single pipe loops to a series of radiators for heating. Output includes a breakdown of all calculation steps, giving temperature, surface areas, etc, for radiators

References

Availability
On application

Language
Basic, Fortran

Computer
Apple II
PET, Tandy II

SUMMER *Haden Central Engineering*
Provides evaluation of internal summertime temperatures in a series of rooms in a building. It is run for a series of dates to find the maximum for each room to assess if air-conditioning is necessary. Used at the assessment stage of a project. Output provides detailed results giving component breakdowns of gains for each hour of each month; also gives graphs of temperature against time. Relates to programs SHADOW and CIBSGAIN

References

Availability
On application

Language
Basic, Fortran

Computer
Apple II
PET, Tandy II

Computer programs for the building industry

1490

ADMIT *Hevacomp Limited*
Computes the admittance decrement factor, time lag and surface factors of exposed and internal walls and roofs. Any number and combination of solid layers and air gaps can be handled

References

Availability
Purchase

Language

Computer
Any 64K
microcomputer

1491

CONDEN *Hevacomp Limited*
This program examines the moisture flow through any wall or roof, and determines whether condensation of solid layers, air gaps and vapour barriers can be handled

References

Availability
Purchase

Language

Computer
Any 64K
microcomputer

1492

INSUL *Hevacomp Limited*
Analyses the thermal performance of various methods of insulation and the financial aspects of the installation. Suitable insulation strategies can be examined for buildings so that ineffective, under- insulation, can be avoided. Up to 21 different schemes can be handled. The key output is energy saving, cost saving and payback period

References

Availability
Purchase

Language

Computer
Any 64K
microcomputer

1493

RLOSS *Hevacomp Limited*
Sizes radiators using the information from the HEATLOSS program. Radiator data for many commercial emitters are provided on disk, and any manufacturer's range can be added as required. Radiator type, height and maximum length can be specified. A radiator schedule is produced

References

Availability
Purchase

Language

Computer
Any 64K
microcomputer

1494

DUCTS *Inatome and Associates*
Calculates the horsepower of fans and the static pressure required to operate a ducted air-conditioning system. It also determines the static and total pressures at any point so that the system may be balanced when installed. Supply and return ductwork may be handled separately or simultaneously

References

Availability
Time sharing

Language
Fortran IV

Computer
CP/M microcomputer

1495

CONDX *Inatome and Associates*
This program matches air cooled condensing units with direct expansion freon cooling coils. The design for each is selected at the point where their respective capacity curves intersect. These curves are generated by assuming that suction temperature and ambient temperature are constant

References

Availability
Time sharing

Language
Fortran IV

Computer
CP/M microcomputer

1496

CWCOIL *Inatome and Associates*
Used for sizing chilled water coils. Calculations are based on the by-pass factor method as developed by Dr W Carrier. Trane coils are selected, although the program can easily be adapted to select other coils

References

Availability
Time sharing

Language
Fortran IV

Computer
CP/M microcomputer

1497

DXCOIL *Inatome and Associates*
Used for sizing direct expansion cooling coils. Calculations are based on the by-pass factor method as developed by Dr W Carrier. Trane coils are selected, although the program can easily be adapted to select other coils

References

Availability
Time sharing

Language
Fortran IV

Computer
CP/M microcomputer

1498

HWCOIL *Inatome and Associates*
Used for sizing hot water heating coils. Calculations are based on the by-pass factor method as developed by Dr W Carrier. Trane coils are selected, although the program can easily be adapted to select other coils

References

Availability
Time sharing

Language
Fortran IV

Computer
CP/M microcomputer

1499

STCOIL *Inatome and Associates*
Used for sizing steam coils. Calculations are based on the by-pass factor method as developed by Dr W Carrier. Trane coils are selected, although the program can easily be adapted to select other coils

References

Availability
Time sharing

Language
Fortran IV

Computer
CP/M microcomputer

Trane cooling water coil selection *A M Kinney, Inc*
Selects a water cooling coil to determine the capacity of a special coil at any given condition, such as entering wet and dry bulb, water inlet temperatures, air and water velocities, etc. It provides a simple means to select coils that will minimise piping, pump and pump operating costs. The output lists suitable coils, together with fin series, required gpm, Delta T, leaving air temperature, and the air and water pressure drop required for each coil

References

Availability

Language
Fortran

Computer
IBM 1130 and 370

1501

Trane fan selection *A M Kinney, Inc*
Selects the optimal size of fan based on space limitations, operating efficiency, sound power level, and capacity modulation capability. The types of fan available are centrifugal, model Q and utility. Output handles the results of the fan size selection, such as type and class, fan speed in rpm, static pressure and efficiency brake horsepower, maximum horsepower, and the motor size

References

Availability

Language
Fortran

Computer
IBM 1130 and 370

1502

Trane hot water coil selection *A M Kinney, Inc*
Selections are in accordance with ARI Standard 410-64. The program has an option of selecting the multiple coils up to six different coils (3 each with and without tabulators) for each input condition. The output consists of fin type and row type selected, coil length and width, face velocity, gpm, water temperature and pressure drop, etc

References

Availability

Language
Fortran

Computer
IBM 1130 and 370

1503

CP9 *National Research Council of Canada*
G-15 program to calculate the best 2-lump equivalent thermal circuit for building sections

References
G P Mitalas

Availability

Language

Computer

1504

RADZON *Pilkington Brothers Limited*
This interactive program calculates air radiation temperatures in winter for a room with one external wall and a given pattern of windows and radiators. By modifying the input and therefore the design, the effects of altering various parameters can be assessed. Output values are shown on a grid. As part of the service, an environmental engineer runs the program with the client until a suitable size and position of radiator is determined

References

Availability
Used only to advise customers. Not for sale

Language
Fortran

Computer

1505

TEMPFO4 *SBI*
Calculates indoor temperatures in buildings. The quality of the indoor climate and energy consumption of the heating and air-conditioning systems can also be examined. Calculations are carried out on an hourly basis over a period of one year. Sun screening and artificial lighting within the building are taken into account

References
Danish Building Research Institute
Abstract 48 14 001

Availability
Bureau service

Language

Computer

1506

Transmission and radiator choice *Technies Rekencentrum Polybit bv*
Estimates the heatlosses in a central heating system. Suitable radiators, of one of several makes, are selected for use in the system

References

Availability
Bureau service, remote batch, time sharing, purchase

Language
Fortran

Computer
Cyber 750

1507

Optimised equipment selection *The Trane Company*
Selects equipment to meet specified duty conditions and provides multiple selections of heating, cooling and refrigerant coils, fans and air handling units. Output data on coils includes type, flow rate and pressure drop information. Output data on fans includes efficiency and sound power information by octave band for each fan selected. Output data on air handling units includes multiple selections for each set of conditions

References

Availability
Free service

Language
Fortran

Computer
IBM 370

1508

TRACE (Trane Air Conditioning Economics) *The Trane Company*
Analyses the energy requirements and economic viability of various heating, ventilation and air-conditioning alternatives. Output includes data for analysis of the system, monthly energy usage, utility bills, operating costs and depreciation for up to four alternative designs. An appendix contains peak heatgains and losses, profiles of loads on the system in operation and the usage by month of each piece of equipment

References

Availability
Bureau service, time sharing

Language
Fortran with Assembler I/0. Edit in PL/1

Computer
IBM 370

1509

CENTRAHEAT *Walters Computer Systems Limited*
Produces estimates for installation of home heating systems. Features: heatloss calculations for each room, including air changes, design temperatures, temperature differences and U values; calculates pipe runs and heatlosses from pipework; boiler selection and sizing; radiator selection; calculates installation time and total cost. Pipe options, pipe runs, and radiators in ascending price order within BTU bands. Reports include a list of radiators, a printed estimate, and a list of heating components

References
Heating and Ventilating, August 1982

Availability
Purchase

Language

Computer
Commodore 8000

Computer programs for the building industry

1510

STD90 (Standard 90-75) *APEC*
Designed to facilitate the evaluation of a building 'envelope', as defined by, and as compared to, limitations established by Section 4 'Exterior envelope requirements' of ASHRAE Standard 90-75 'Energy conservation in new building design'

References
98 Licences plus public access

Availability
Doris J Wallace, APEC

Language
Fortran

Computer
IBM 370
CDC Cyber 175
TRS-80 Model II

1511

ENERGY *Building Services Software*
Predicts annual energy consumption of a building which is not air-conditioned, using the degree day method from Section B18 of the CIBS Guide. The program considers: the steady state design temperatures and heatloss; the climate (degree days); the building thermal mass; internal gains; the type and pattern of occupancy; the response of the heating plant

References

Availability
Licence

Language

Computer
Commodore Series
PET 3/4/8000

1512

DES Design Note 17 *Cheshire County Council*
Assists the architect to meet the recommendations set out in Design Note 17 'Guidelines for environmental design and fuel conservation in educational buildings'. The program computes the annual energy cost and annual energy consumption in accordance with Part D of Note 17 from project data supplied by the architect

References

Availability

Language
APL

Computer
IBM 3767

1513

Extensions to Fuel monitoring system *Cheshire County Council*
This system has been designed to assist in monitoring fuel consumptions in all the major County owned buildings. The actual consumptions are checked against devised or theoretical values for each building. The original system was devised for batch operation. The extensions enable data from this system to be handled interactively either for straightforward reading or for use with small sub-routines written by the engineers

References

Availability

Language
APL

Computer
IBM 3767

1514

FFCHECK *Cheshire County Council*
(Building Regulations Part FF.) Provides an arithmetical check for compliance with the Building (First Amendment) Regulations 1978, Part FF; Conservation of fuel and power in buildings other than dwellings. The program assists the designer to comply with a project that does not meet the straightforward tests against the schedules of permitted glazed areas and U values. The system is used in conjunction with the RIBA guide to the Building Regulations

References

Availability

Language
APL

Computer
IBM 3767

1515

FMS (Cheshire) *Cheshire County Council, Department of Construction Services*
Compares the calculated theoretical usage of hot water heating with the actual consumption, records the consumption of gas and electricity and calculates the energy usage per m². For an individual building, it stores building and plant information, calculates monthly theoretical heat consumption, taking into account hourly external temperatures, building situation, plant efficiency, usage, type of controls and mains losses

References

Availability
Chief Engineer, Department of Construction Services

Language
PL1 in OS

Computer
IBM 3031 mainframe

1516

Tariff checking *Cheshire County Council*
This is a system to check whether a County building is on the correct electricity tariff. Figures for electricity consumptions are input and the program computes the costs based on the alternative tariff structures which can apply

References

Availability

Language
APL

Computer
IBM 3767

1517

Building structure thermal properties *CIBS*
For calculating thermal transmittance of a composite structure. Used in calculations for composite structures of any number of layers: thermal transmittance (U values), thermal admittance (Y values), surface factor, decrement factor, time lags/leads, and modified values for internal walls. The package includes a summary of calculations, together with a description of methods and flow chart of procedure, a program listing for the TI59, and pre-programmed magnetic cards

References

Availability
Purchase

Language

Computer
Texas Instruments
TI59, PPC

1518

U values of ground floors *CIBS*
Enables engineers to compute required data to their own specifications. Calculates U values of solid floors in contact with the earth, and for suspended floors directly above the ground. All fixed values needed to compute U values are included, but some may be altered if required. The package includes a summary of calculations, description of calculation methods, flow chart of calculation procedure, program listing for the TI59, and the method of use of the card programs

References

Availability
Purchase

Language

Computer
Texas Instruments
TI59, PPC

1519

HEATSOFT 1 *Contract Computer Software Limited*
A comprehensive U-value program suitable for domestic, commercial and industrial applications. Incorporates full data storage, error recovery, printout and calculation facilities. For use by professional and clerical staff

References
Building Products journal

Availability
Purchase

Language
8-bit CP/M
16-bit CP/M86,
MS-DOS

Computer
Micro, min 64K

ECP-JPL Energy Consumption Program *COSMIC*
Simulates a building's thermal performance on an hourly basis for a full year; for the study and design of heating/cooling systems. Evaluates: heatloss and gain; heating and cooling loads imposed on plant; energy input to components; weather data; physical and architectural characteristics of the building; primary equipment performance. The unit cost of thermal and electric forms of energy, from a utility or generated on site, is used to compute the monthly and yearly cost of energy

References

Availability
Purchase

Language
Fortran IV

Computer
UNIVAC 1100

ESEA *COSMIC*
A flexible, analytical tool used for the rank ordering of alternative energy systems. The program estimates costs of purchasing, installing and operating an energy system, excluding transmission and distribution costs. The ESEA analysis may be run for several energy systems so that comparisons may be made

References

Availability
Purchase

Language
Fortran IV

Computer
Univac 1100

OPERATE *Cymap Limited*
The installation, running, maintenance and replacement costs can be compared to determine, for example, the payback period for measures to conserve energy, or the cost implications of plant type choices

References

Availability
Purchase (under licence)

Language
Microsoft Basic

Computer
Most CP/M based microcomputers, 8 and 16-bit, 64K

ESP *DHSS (Department of Health and Social Security)*
This program dynamically simulates energy transfers within a room or building and takes into account shading, internal gains, eg lighting, occupancy, equipment, etc. It predicts energy requirements, internal temperatures, etc. The user can define a building or room's geometry and its thermal properties to sufficient accuracy to permit a detailed assessment of the thermal performance. Interactive facilities allow rapid design changes to be made and their effects evaluated

References

Availability
Purchase

Language
Fortran

Computer
SEL, Prime

BEEP *The Electricity Council*
Estimates seasonal energy demands in buildings, and provides comparisons of energy consumption and cost for various heating systems and fuel. U values are calculated from information concerning the structure. Design heatlosses and gains per zone, and for the building as a whole, are estimated against inside and outside design temperatures. A monthly heating and cooling energy analysis is produced for a typical year

References

Availability
From area Electricity Boards in the UK and the Electricity Council. For suitable projects, the service is free

Language
Fortran based

Computer
IBM 370

F-LOAD *F-Chart Software*
Calculates monthly heating energy use in buildings, the life cycle cost of heating, and the design heating load for residential and light commercial buildings. Passive heating features as well as conventional heating systems. Detailed specification of building shape, construction, orientation and locations. Analysis includes cost of heating to include fuel inflation rates, mortgage and market discount rates, and energy credits. Determines the energy savings and economic benefits of conservation measures

References
F-LOAD, WA Beckman, JA Duffie, SA Klein and JW Mitchell, ASHRAE Trans. Vol 88 pt 2 1982

Availability
Purchase

Language
Basic, Fortran 77

Computer
Apple, TRS-80, CP/M or mainframe

CREAM *Haden Central Engineering*
Calculates the risk of condensation in walls and roofs, together with the U value, admittance, time lag and decrement factor for CIBS heatgain calculations. Used during the early design stage. The program outputs detailed results giving a breakdown of all calculations, and a graph section through the structure

References

Availability
On application

Language
Basic, Fortran

Computer
Apple II
PET, Tandy II

ENDSOP *D J Hardy*
A suite of standalone programs which access a common database. Used for calculating all aspects of the thermal performance of buildings, from U value to energy consumption. Incorporates weather tapes, shading and plant characteristics. Also sizes and simulates pipe networks. Output on line printer and plotter

References
South Bank Polytechnic. IHE Annual Conference, May 1982

Availability
Purchase, bureau service via South Bank Polytechnic

Language
Fortran IV
Algol 68

Computer
16-bit minicomputer with 64K

ENERGY *Hevacomp Limited*
Enables the annual heating energy consumption of a building, and annual full costs to be computed, using the degree day method. Intermittent heating factors, thermal weight and occupancy are calculated and corrected. Degree days are used with building heatlosses to compute annual energy. Plant efficiencies and fuel costs enable the annual heating costs to be calculated

References

Availability
Purchase

Language

Computer
Any 64K microcomputer

GAIN *Hevacomp Limited*
Handles heatgain calculations for any number of rooms, using the CIBS Guide method. Results for each hour of the design day are printed in terms of solar, convective, fabric, casual and latent gains. Total building loads are accumulated and printed. Data is prepared and stored on a disk file for subsequent heatgain calculations. The program includes the amendments in the new Section A5 and A9 of the Guide

References

Availability
Purchase

Language

Computer
Any 64K microcomputer

1530

LCOST *Hevacomp Limited*
This program enables the life cycle costing of energy conservation measures to be evaluated. It allows several energy sources to be examined with differing escalation rates. The program produces the net present value of savings due to energy conservation

References

Availability
Purchase

Language

Computer
Any 64K microcomputer

1531

SUMMER *Hevacomp Limited*
Enables summertime temperatures in buildings which are not air-conditioned to be computed. The program uses CIBS Guide methods to predict summertime temperatures at each hour of the specified design day. The effect of increased daytime infiltration (eg by opening windows) may be examined

References

Availability
Purchase

Language

Computer
Any 64K microcomputer

1532

CADAM *Holec Energy*
An energy management system which controls the functions of: heating, temperature and electrical energy controls, air-conditioning systems, boilers and chillers, lighting, and maintenance. High resolution graphic facilities present trend information. Alarms advise of any plant failures and the system provides full information on energy usage to identify the next area for conservation. The system is usable by building services and works engineering staff without specialist computer knowledge

References

Availability
Purchase

Language
Extended Basic CP/M

Computer
Hewlett-Packard HP87

1533

EDX Energy Conservation *IBM Corporation, USA*
A fully automated control system which aids the reduction of energy usage. Allows separate strategies for 4 day types: holidays, weekends, weekdays and one user-defined type. Allows for 9 time of day segments for each device. Compares actual and desired usage, and takes corrective action when projected usage exceeds targets; action consists of cycling off or off-loading selected devices for short time intervals. Used to reduce electrical demands and consumption, and for reduced fuel adjustments and tax charges

References

Availability

Language

Computer
IBM 4952

1534

Energy Management for Supermarkets *IBM Corporation, USA*
An automated energy control program which can reduce energy usage by way of lower electrical consumption and reduced fuel adjustment and tax charges. Secondary savings occur with fuel oil and natural gas

References
Developed at Spartan Stores, Byron Center, Michigan

Availability

Language

Computer
IBM 4952C

1535

GPAX *IBM Corporation, USA*
The general purpose automation executive program provides a basis for the implementation of energy management and facilities automation in a cost effective manner. Aids in conserving energy and maintaining environmental conditions. Also used for general purpose, sensor based process automation and control. Can be used to control heating, ventilating and air-conditioning equipment

References

Availability

Language

Computer
IBM 4978 and 4979

1536

HUDACS *IBM Corporation, USA*
The Howard University Distributed Automation and Control System. Used in conjunction with GPAX for energy management and facilities control. Remote controllers can be dispersed around a large facility, eg a university, or be situated at remote locations. The program is used to control chillers, air handlers, heating systems, domestic hot water systems, and has a central power plant for generation and distribution of steam to different buildings

References
Howard University

Availability

Language

Computer
IBM 4955

1537

INSUL *Inatome and Associates*
Calculates comparative costs in use for a given roof or wall assembly with different thicknesses of insulation. The best thickness for insulation is calculated, together with the incremental and cumulative savings on heat requirements over each area of 10 000 square feet of surface. Reduction in refrigeration loads is also calculated if air-conditioning is taken into consideration

References

Availability
Time sharing

Language
Fortran IV

Computer
CP/M microcomputer

1538

Tas° *Jones Cassidy Mellor Limited*
This is a system to simulate building energy use. It minimises building capital and running costs through the detailed analysis of all energy related factors, including: building thermal mass, shape and detail; heating and cooling system and size; mechanical plant control details; occupancy and equipment use details. Used from earliest sketch design through to planning remedial measures for existing buildings. Used in planning for energy related trouble-shooting

References

Availability
Licence or consultancy

Language
Fortran 77 or IV

Computer
DEC: RSX11M VAX VMS Prime: others

1539

Electric bill saving via power factor correction *A M Kinney, Inc*
Computes savings to be made by the installation of capacitors to improve power factor. Applicable only to rate formulas based on kVA demand. The program will also compute the monthly cost for no power factor correction, and for various increments of power factor correction. Output contains capacitors in kVAR, annual savings in dollars, capacitor cost, payoff period, and incremental payoff period

References

Availability

Language
Fortran

Computer
IBM 1130 and 370

TARIFF *Lancashire County Council*
For checking the tariff being used for any building and to advise if a cheaper tariff could reasonably be used. Keeps account of savings made by changes over any given period. Input includes property energy consumption details, tariff rules and rates, control parameters. Output consists of analysis of energy used and cost, statement of potential savings if tariff change is made, statement of savings made in a given period, and statement of outstanding changes requested but not effected

References

Availability
From Lancashire County Council, Architects Department

Language
Fortran

Computer
ICL 2976

Adhoc *Lancaster Computing*
A suite of programs to aid the rapid calculation of heatlosses from individual rooms or from whole buildings. The protected program disk runs in drive 1, and a data disk in drive 2 stores information produced by the operation of the program as well as the data input. Results calculated for each room can be displayed on the screen, one room at a time, or as a continuous printout. The output includes infiltration, room fabric loss, total room loss, loss per unit volume, and total building heatloss

References

Availability
Purchase

Language

Computer
Apple II

Arch-u-Val *Lancaster Computing*
Assists architects and engineers to assess the thermal and vapour transfer performance of building structures. The thermal transmittance coefficient (U value) can be calculated for 9 different types of structure, including solid and suspended floors, and internal and external multilayer wall, floor, roof and ceiling structures, including pitched roofs of any angle up to 70 degrees. The thermal conductivity or thermal resistance of 64 structural elements have been incorporated into a data bank within the program

References

Availability
Purchase

Language

Computer
Apple II

NECAP *NASA, Construction Engineering Branch*
Used for the analysis of energy consumption in a building. Economic comparisons are also produced. Simplified output is available

References

Availability
Bureau service through COSMIC

Language
Fortran IV

Computer
CDC 6400, 6600

CP25 *National Research Council of Canada*
Calculates radiant energy interchange factors

References
G P Mitalas and D G Stephenson

Availability

Language
Fortran IV

Computer

CP2 *National Research Council of Canada*
A program to evaluate overall interchange factors for radiant heat

References
G P Mitalas

Availability

Language

Computer

CP34 *National Research Council of Canada*
Calculates absorption and transmission of thermal radiation by single and double-glazed windows

References
G P Mitalas & J G Arseneault

Availability

Language
Fortran IV

Computer

CP42 *National Research Council of Canada*
A program concerned with a roof insulation study in Saskatoon

References
S S Tao

Availability

Language

Computer

CP47 *National Research Council of Canada*
A program to calculate net heatgains through windows

References
S A Barakar

Availability

Language
Fortran IV

Computer

ENCORE *Norwegian Building Research Institute*
Calculates the energy consumption of residential buildings. These may be of any shape or type, and have any arrangement of interior divisions. Real weather data is used (magnetic tape from weather bureau) and combined with internal heatgains and thermostat settings. The program uses the 'Z-transfer' or 'weighting factor' method, as described in the ASHRAE Handbook

References

Availability
Purchase, bureau service

Language
Fortran IV

Computer
Univac 1100
ND-100, ND-500
minicomputer 32K,

Computer programs for the building industry

1550

ENERGY *Oasys Limited*
Calculates the energy consumption for each hour of a complete year using models of the plant and building fabric, a description of the way the building is used, and recorded weather data. User can define room and central plant system, and capacities. Output can be hour by hour or summaries of energy consumption on a daily, weekly, monthly, quarterly or annual basis. Test weeks and other reduced records can also be run

References

Availability
Bureau service

Language
Fortran

Computer
DEC 10

1551

BP101: Heat losses *Oasys Limited*
Calculates heatlosses from a building. It can also calculate the annual fuel consumption and cost. The program allows assembly of various arrangements of surface glazing types and operating zones. Heat losses are provided for each room type, zone type and the building total. Calculations for heatlosses are based on the dry-resultant temperature, and the annual fuel consumption is found by using the degree day method

References

Availability
Purchase

Language
Basic

Computer
HP 9845

1552

BP111: Thermal performance of elements *Oasys Limited*
This program predicts the thermal behaviour of composite elements formed from multiple layers of various materials. Facilities include: calculation of thermal transmittance (U value); costing for economic thickness of insulation; thermal gradient through element; calculation of quantities of water vapour condensing at each interface; graphical presentation of thermal and vapour pressure gradient

References

Availability
Purchase

Language
Basic

Computer
HP 9845 HP 85/87

1553

RIBA E2 Energy Package *RIBA Publications Limited*
A suite of seven programs providing: calculations for heatlosses; three methods of calculating heating energy consumption; calculation of Peak Internal Temperature. Also provided are U value calculations and the attendant condensation risk for structures of up to 8 layers

References

Availability
Purchase

Language

Computer
TI 59
Calculator

1554

Energy requirements estimate *Ross F Meriwether and Associates*
Calculates thermal and electrical loads for a building on an hourly basis. The operation of the air distribution system is simulated in meeting these loads

References
Meriwether analysis series

Availability
Bureau service, purchase

Language

Computer
Univac 1108

1555

Energy-systems and analysis series *Ross F Meriwether and Associates*
This is a series of 17 programs for hour by hour calculation of the annual energy consumption of various types of air handling system and mechanical plant. Local utility rate schedules are applied to consumption. These costs are combined with other owning and operating costs for year by year cashflow projections

References

Availability
Bureau service, purchase

Language

Computer
Univac 1108

1556

Equipment Energy Consumption/B *Ross F Meriwether and Associates*
This program simulates the operation of various pieces of an air distribution system, to find monthly and annual energy consumption

References
Meriwether analysis series

Availability
Bureau service, purchase

Language

Computer
Univac 1108

1557

DEROB *Solenco Inc*
Dynamic Energy Response of Buildings. This program provides the simulation of heat flow in complex structures. It can be applied at any stage of design or building. Input includes: various wall planes and their construction; building shape; orientation; location. Output reflects all input data and temperature at the various user selected probe locations during the test period

References
List available from Source

Availability
Purchase

Language
Fortran

Computer
Control Data,
Cyber 750

1558

Total energy *Technies Rekencentrum Polybit bv*
This system aids the design of electricity generating plant in which heat released is to be utilised to the maximum extent. Demands for electric energy and for heat are coordinated, and an energy balance is calculated for every hour of the year, together with the power required to produce this

References

Availability
Bureau service, remote batch, purchase

Language
Fortran

Computer
Cyber 750

1559

Energy/1 Thermal Insulation and Condensation *Richard Twinch Design Limited*
Used throughout the design process by architects and designers. Calculates U values from a database holding up to 300 materials with their relevant K value and vapour resistivity. The program gives options for thermal insulation, together with costs. Information conforms with Parts F and FF of the Building Regulations BRE Digest 108 and 110. Provides a condensation risk assessment by numeric and graphic methods

References
Recommended by Apple. RIBA Journal, April 1982

Availability
Purchase

Language
Basic 2.0,
Pascal and CP/M

Computer
Apple II 48K

Computer programs for the building industry

SHACSAC-1 *The Charles Stark Draper Laboratory, Inc*
A program for solar heating and cooling simulation, and costs system. This handles design optimisation based on costs, for commercial buildings with a 2-pipe unitary heat pump system. The program was specifically developed for short execution time, allowing repetitive simulations with varied parameters

References

Availability
Negotiable with CSDL

Language
Fortran IV

Computer
IBM 370

SUNFAX *Colt Solar Control Limited*
Provides data on the effects of solar radiation incident to, and through, glazed facades of buildings situated at any latitude and orientation on the Earth's surface. Printout shows: position of sun in relation to each surface; make up and total of incident solar radiation; solar heatgain and/or cooling load attributes to solar radiation transmitted through window glass. Input includes latitude and height of proposed building, and angle, tilt and orientation of each surface

References

Availability
Contact Colt (limited availability)

Language

Computer

HEAP-HEAT *COSMIC*
An energy analysis program to predict the thermal behaviour of solar receivers. HEAP has the capability to solve any general heat transfer problem. It also has specific features, custom-made, for analysing solar receivers; it can predict their performance under varying solar flux, ambient temperature and local heat transfer rates; furthermore, it can detect the locations of hot spots and metallurgical difficulties and predict performance sensitivity of neighbouring component parameters

References

Availability
Purchase

Language
Fortran IV

Computer
Univac 1100

F-CHART for microcomputers *F-Chart Software*
An interactive program used for designing solar heating and domestic hot water systems using liquid or air as the heat transfer fluid. Passive direct gain and collector storage (Trombe) wall, industrial process and pool heating systems can also be analysed. Weather data can be added to the database of 244 cities. The program includes a complete life cycle cost option. F-Chart is an implementation of methods developed at the University of Wisconsin Solar Energy Laboratory

References
'Solar Heating Design by the F-Chart Method' Beckman WA, Klein SA, and Duffie JA. J Wiley & Sons NY 1977

Availability
Purchase

Language
Basic

Computer
Apple, TRS-80 CP/M with Microsoft Basic

ICARUS *Facet Limited*
Handles the analysis and design of active solar systems, matching the time-varying incident solar radiation with the space heating and domestic hot water load. Models of simple or complex systems can be built up from descriptions of their component parts and the manner in which they are connected together. The program then uses standard hourly meteorological data and calculates the temperatures and energy flows within the system. Results are printed out or plotted, as required

References

Availability
Bureau service

Language

Computer
Prime, Norsk Data, Harris, CP/M 8-bit micros

BP102: Solar cooling loads *Oasys Limited*
The program allows various arrangements of surface and glazing types and operating zones to be assembled, modified and tested. Selected heatgain types are output in tabular form, for any period of months during the year

References

Availability
Purchase

Language
Basic

Computer
HP 9845

BP103: Summertime temperatures *Oasys Limited*
Calculates the hourly environmental temperature, in a room or building which is not air-conditioned, due to solar and casual heatgains. Each room or building is described by entering the physical and thermal properties of each surface. A detailed output shows solar heatgains through each external surface, and the internal gains and resulting environmental temperature

References

Availability
Purchase

Language
Basic

Computer
HP 9845

SOLAR 2 *University of California*
A passive solar design program to show the consequences of designing various sized fins and overhangs on windows orientated in different directions. The program shows how the design performs in any month, by plotting the resulting sunlight patterns hour by hour across the floor of a room. Calculates a table of direct solar radiation gains. The user inputs details of latitude, orientation, geometry of the window and its sun controls. Allows the user to interactively re-design the window or its sun controls

References

Availability
Purchase

Language
Fortran

Computer
Tektronix Plot/10

SOLAR 3 *University of California*
An opaque building envelope performance package. Calculates, on an hour by hour basis, surface temperature, heat flow/gain/loss, solar gain, etc. Plots up to 5 of these attributes for any month, or will give an annual plot of any attribute showing all 12 values. The user can interactively re-design and re-analyse the building element until a satisfactory performance is reached

References

Availability
Purchase

Language
Fortran

Computer
Tektronix Plot/10

FCHART *University of Wisconsin Solar Energy Laboratory*
Used for designing solar heating systems which use either liquid or air as the heat transfer medium. It treats the area of the collector as the main variable, but also takes into account the capacity of the storage unit. It determines the fraction of monthly and annual loads to be carried by solar energy. An interactive version of this program may be used to give the thermal and economic performance of the solar system

References
Solar heating design by the FCHART Method, Beckman, Klein & Duffie, J Wiley, NY 1977

Availability
Purchase

Language
Fortran II

Computer

1570

TRNSYS (Transient system simulation) *University of Wisconsin Solar Energy Laboratory*
Used to simulate the operation of various solar energy systems. Models for components such as collectors, controls, storage tanks, heat exchangers, furnaces, building loads and integrators can be selected. When detailed loads are not required, a 'degree day' or 'degree hour' model is used. For a more exact determination, 'wall', 'roof' and 'room' transfer functions can be assembled to model almost any structure

References
A method of simulation of solar processes. Solar Energy, Vol 17, pp 29-37

Availability
Purchase

Language
Fortran

Computer

1571

OBSTRUCT - Obstructing buildings *Cymap Limited*
This program section is used to include the effect of shading from other buildings, or the building itself if L-shaped, on the solar gain for each room in the HEATGAIN calculation. Obstructing buildings can be divided into a number of separate blocks. The height within each block can be allowed to vary

References

Availability
Purchase (under licence)

Language
Microsoft Basic

Computer
Most CP/M based microcomputers, 8 and 16-bit, 64K

1572

SHADOW *Haden Central Engineering*
Shows the extent of shadows on vertical building faces, caused by adjacent buildings, for different times of the year. It provides detailed results showing front elevations of each building face for any hour in the year, showing the extent of shading, if any. Relates to programs CIBSGAIN and SUMMER

References

Availability
On application

Language
Basic, Fortran

Computer
Apple II
PET, Tandy II

1573

COE *Koolshade Corporation*
Used to compare the relative efficiency of various combinations of glazing and shading devices, taking into account the amount and cost of air-conditioning required in each case

References
ASHRAE solar heatgain factors, shading coefficients and U values. Climatic data for the US and Canada

Availability
Koolshade contractors and distributors

Language
Basic

Computer
Hewlett-Packard 200F

1574

Obstructional shading *Pilkington Brothers Limited*
Calculates, for each hour of the day that the sun is above the horizon, the shadows due to obstructions falling onto a facade. The effects of shading on the cooling load by other parts of the building, or by adjacent buildings, may thus be determined. The program can be used in conjunction with the air-conditioning program

References

Availability
Used only to advise customers. Not for sale

Language
Fortran

Computer

1575

RSHADOW *University of Sydney*
Creates and draws, in colour, shadows falling on ground surfaces and adjacent buildings for any hour of any day in any location

References

Availability

Language
Fortran 77

Computer
CDC NOS-based computer

1576

CAMEL LM101 *The Association for Computer Aided Design Limited*
An air-conditioning method for estimating cooling loads. The program calculates the hourly cooling load in a building, including storage effects, the peak heating load excluding storage effects, and the associated psychrometrics. Provides for analysis of conventional by-pass systems, evaporative cooling plant, packaged plant and supply/exhaust air heat exchangers. Output summary includes cooling and heating load, air quantities, coil data and check figures

References
Carrier International Corporation 'Handbook of Air Conditioning System Design'

Availability
Contact ACADS

Language
Fortran IV

Computer
Univac 1108
Prime
DEC 10

1577

Air Handling Units *Computair*
Handles the design of any type of air handling unit, eg multi-zone, dual duct, draw through single deck, blow through single deck, etc. Incorporates all standard components associated with: air handling units, filters, humidifiers, plenums, access sections, mixing boxes, exhaust/fresh air mixing boxes, exhaust and supply fans, silencers, heating and cooling coils, gas burners, electric heaters, weather louvres, face and bypass dampers, moisture eliminators, etc. Comprehensive pricing structure and schematic drawings

References

Availability

Language

Computer
Commodore PET

1578

COLO *Facet Limited*
For the design of air-conditioning. Calculates the instantaneous heatgain and cooling loads in every room at each hour of the day. Makes allowance for the thermal storage effect of the building, and for intermittent plant operation. Takes into account gains due to occupancy, lighting, ventilation, infiltration, machinery, and solar radiation on glazing, walls and roofs. Can include effects of shading due to local projections and other parts of the building. Calculates latent loads resulting from ventilation and casual gains

References

Availability
Bureau service, or under licence

Language

Computer
Prime, Norsk Data, Harris,
CP/M 8-bit micros

1579

NODDIE *Haden Central Engineering*
Provides comprehensive duct analysis for any supply or extract ventilation system. It can be used at various times throughout the design process. Related programs are Savaloy and Hyena. Output includes confirmation of all input data, and a detailed results printout giving all sizes, quantities, sound levels, etc

References

Availability
Licence

Language
Fortran IV and F77

Computer
Any minicomputer with 128K/16-bit

EXHAU *Inatome and Associates*
Calculates capacity and capabilities of an industrial exhaust duct system. Flow velocity, accumulated air quantity, losses in pressure and the static pressure required at the exhaust fan are calculated

References
Heating, piping and air-conditioning, September 1968

Availability
Time sharing

Language
Fortran IV

Computer
CP/M microcomputer

1581

Cooling load determination *A M Kinney, Inc*
Determining cooling load requirements for individual rooms, or floors, or for an entire building, prior to installation of individual air-conditioning units, a central station air-conditioning system, or an evaporation cooling system. Used for all air systems and dual duct systems. Output includes: heatgain for each room, maximum conductive load for rooms with outside wall and/or outside glass; summation of conductivity loads by time, transmission, equipment, infiltration, occupancy, heat factors, area, volume, etc

References

Availability

Language
Fortran

Computer
IBM 1130 and 370

1582

Selection of Trane central station air handlers *A M Kinney, Inc*
Selects two unit sizes, each with three heating coil options and five cooling coil options, both with and without turbulators. Output is the result of selection for proper sizes of heating and cooling coils, air handling unit, and the fan, to suit the input conditions

References

Availability

Language
Fortran

Computer
IBM 1130 and 370

1583

CP35 *National Research Council of Canada*
A program to simulate air movement in multistorey buildings

References
D M Sander & G T Tamura

Availability

Language
Fortran IV

Computer

1584

CP37 *National Research Council of Canada*
A program to calculate air infiltration in buildings

References
D M Sander

Availability

Language
Fortran IV

Computer

1585

CP45 *National Research Council of Canada*
Calculates smoke concentrations in a multistorey building

References
H Yoshida, C Y Shaw & G T Tamura

Availability

Language
Fortran IV

Computer

1586

HEAT TRANSFER PACKAGE *Celtip Star Microcomputers*
Analyses steady state heatloss through a plane wall with temperature dependent conductivity. Used in furnace design or other situations where a wide temperature range is involved. Input includes details of hot face temperature, emissivity and atmosphere. Output is by screen and printer

References

Availability
Purchase

Language
Basic

Computer
Apple II or III
Commodore 4000 or 8000

1587

Fan Selection *Computair*
Suitable for use with any centrifugal fan. For a given duty, volume versus pressure, the program selects a single fan or a complete range of fans to do the duty, giving details of fan speed, total efficiency, static efficiency, sound power spectrum analysis, horsepower absorbed and motor to be fitted. Fan run-up time is also available, as is a pricing structure to enable finished quotations to be prepared, and pulley and belt selections

References

Availability

Language

Computer
Commodore PET

1588

Psychrometric Viability *Computair*
This program checks air-on, air-off and coolant conditions against a theoretical cooling curve and will adjust, as necessary, either the requested off-coil condition or the coolant temperatures. The air conditions can be entered in a variety of forms, dry bulb and wet bulb, dry bulb and relative humidity, etc

References

Availability

Language

Computer
Commodore PET

1589

Standard Product Selection *Computair*
Programs are available for the selection of standard products such as fan coils, unit heaters, air cooled condensers, product coolers, skirting heating, etc

References

Availability

Language

Computer
Commodore PET

Computer programs for the building industry

1590

PIPENET MK III *Computer Aided Design Centre (UK)*
Calculates pressure drops for gas or liquid flow through pipe or duct networks. Used for the design of fire protection systems: water sprinkler, halon and carbon dioxide systems

References
Recommended by UCC (Great Britain) Limited

Availability
Bureau Service via UCC (Great Britain) Limited

Language
Fortran

Computer

1591

GLASS ORDER PROCESSING *Conosil Systems Limited*
Deals with annealed, tempered or laminated single panel and sealed units of all types and thicknesses of glass and spacers, together with any extras such as stepped units, leaded, Georgian, holes, etc. Orders are sorted into delivery/ manufacturing date order priority. Produces acknowledgements, delivery notes and non-optimised glass cutting lists, labels, etc. Includes stock maintenance

References

Availability
Purchase

Language

Computer

1592

UPVC, ALUMINIUM OR TIMBER WINDOWS AND DOORS *Conosil Systems Limited*
A manufacturer's production control system for customers' orders. Includes details of style number, width, height, and vent width/height, etc. Style includes plain, thermal clad or thermal break, alternative outer frames, vents and transoms, alternative finishes, subframes and extras of all types. Includes batching, editing, handling of orders, pricing, stock, etc.

References

Availability
Purchase

Language
CP/M

Computer

1593

CRKFLO *DHSS (Department of Health and Social Security)*
An air leakage calculation program for fire protection. Predicts ventilation rates and direction of air flow in buildings for natural and mechanically induced air flow. The program includes the study of the natural ventilation performance of buildings, the influence of natural infiltration on mechanical ventilation systems, and the movement of smoke in the event of a fire

References

Availability
Purchase

Language
Fortran

Computer
SEL, Prime

1594

HYDCALCS *Haden Central Engineering*
Provides full hydraulic calculations for an extra high hazard sprinkler system in accordance with the FOC, NFPA or FM rules with either single end feed, looped or griddled arrangements. A very flexible program which can cope with any valid network, including balancing to a pump curve. Also used for gaining approval by an insurance company

References

Availability
Licence

Language
Fortran IV and F77

Computer
Any minicomputer with 128K/16-bit

1595

Window Design *Micro Applecations Limited*
For design of windows involving double glazing. Produces a cutting list and ancillary parts for 32 frame styles. Includes length reduction parameters, costing, and materials usage

References
Personal Computing with Apple

Availability
Purchase

Language

Computer
Apple II

1596

Replacement Window System *Missing Link Computers Limited*
Provides: accurate cutting list calculations and costing; immediate revision of price lists reflecting material and labour cost changes; measurement of the effect of wastage, manufacturing times, overheads, etc, on prices and profit, design and cost calculation of new window styles. The system can be expanded to handle accounting, word processing, payroll, mailing lists, etc

References

Availability
Purchase

Language

Computer
4000 CBM and 8000 CBM

1597

The Window Manager *Missing Link Computers Limited*
Covers most aluminium and upvc profiles; caters for the following types of double glazed windows: turn and tilt, side hung, bottom hung, top hung, and fixed. Available functions are: production of works order, report summaries, window/door prices, parts lists user-definable window/door styles. Steel reinforcement sections, reverse-butt welds, mitre joints, notched (birdsmouth) joints, etc, are all handled by the program

References

Availability
Purchase

Language

Computer
4000 CBM and 8000 CBM

1598

PSYCHR *National Bureau of Standards, Washington*
This program generates, in tabular form, values determining the thermodynamic properties of partially saturated and dry air. Exact statistical mechanics calculations are used as developed by Goff and Gratch

References
Algorithms for Psychrometric Calculations, NBS Building Science Series, 1970

Availability
Purchase via Dr Tamami Kusuda, NBS

Language
Fortran V

Computer
Univac 1100

1599

RESPTK *National Bureau of Standards, Washington*
Calculates response factors for various heat conduction systems. Utilises the superposition principle, so that the overall thermal response in a building at one time is the sum of many preceeding responses

References
ASHRAE Transactions, Volume 5, 1969

Availability
Dr Tamami Kusuda, National Bureau of Standards

Language
Fortran IV

Computer
Univac 1100

Computer programs for the building industry

CP32 *National Research Council of Canada*
Analyses the behaviour of fire in an enclosure

References
Y Tsuchiya

Availability

Language

Computer

CP36 *National Research Council of Canada*
Calculates sizes and venting capacities of smoke shafts

References
C Y Shaw & G T Tamura

Availability

Language
Fortran IV

Computer

CP44 *National Research Council of Canada*
A program for use on a pocket calculator to derive spatial separations to deter fire spread

References
G Williams-Leir

Availability
Purchase

Language

Computer
Pocket calculator

Double glazing manufacture *Orion Microware Limited*
A series of programs for the manufacture of replacement windows and doors in aluminium and upvc. Standard packages can be modified to meet the user's requirements. Programs cover the design of standard and non-standard window styles in any type of extrusion. Can also assist in production of leadlighted windows and panes, rectangular, diamond or Georgian. Also assesses cost

References

Availability
Purchase

Language

Computer
Apple IIE

Glazing Industry Computer System *Sourcecode Limited*
Features: integrated stock system; stock levels and other updates can be adjusted by the user; prepares glass and parts order from different suppliers; full cutting list, including workshop drawing; job costing; stock and price reports; over 1100 styles can be held on one floppy disc; stores over 200 different types of glass; 30 different components assigned to any window type

References

Availability
Purchase

Language
Basic

Computer
Act Sirius 1, others

Sum-Glaze *Sumlock Calculating Services Limited*
A suite of costing and estimating programs for fabricators in the replacement window/door industry. User inputs aperture measurements, style, glass pattern and thickness. Computer outputs a works order showing the window design together with a cutting list for frames, glass and accessories; included is a list of individual extrusion measurements plus a total meterage for each extrusion. Labour and material costings are also calculated. The program also provides price listing

References

Availability
Lease

Language

Computer
Triumph-Adler
Alphatronic
microcomputer

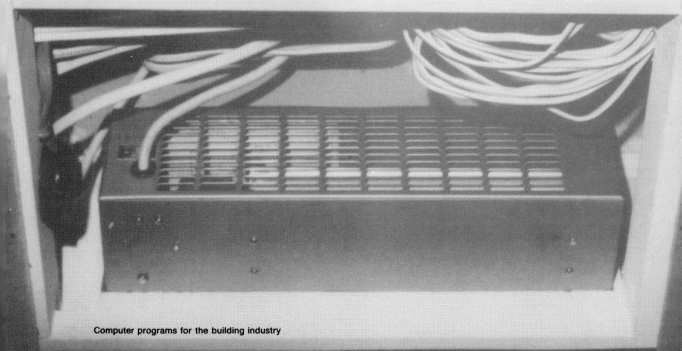

Lighting
Electrical services
Other

1606

NATLIT *ABACUS Services, Department of Architecture and Building Science*
This conversational program computes the Daylight Factors in a rectangular room at user specified points, or at points on a user specified grid. The program is based on the CIE Standard Overcast Sky approach, incorporating an exact analytical solution of the daylight factor integral for rectangular windows. The BRE split-flux method is used for the calculation of the reflected component

References
DOC

Availability
See DOC Report No 3

Language
Fortran

Computer
Univac 1108

1607

Natural Lighting (Version 1.1) *ABACUS Services, Department of Architecture and Building Science*
Computes the daylight factor in a rectangular room at user specified points, or at points on a user specified grid. It is based on the CIE Standard Overcast Sky approach, incorporating an exact analytical solution of the daylight factor integral. The split-flux method is used for the calculation of the reflected component

References
DOC Evaluation Report No 3

Availability

Language
Univac Fortran V

Computer
Univac 1108 (Under EXEC-8)

1608

GLIM *ARC Limited*
Determines quantitatively and accurately the way light (internal or external) will affect the internal environment of proposed buildings. Ascertains internal reflection patterns, from natural or artificial light. The program then decides how this light is scattered about predetermined enclosed areas, including the calculation of glare levels. Output is to a line printer producing greytones with character combinations. More extensive graphics require an optional graphics post-processor

References

Availability
Purchase

Language
Fortran

Computer
IBM 360, 370
Prime, VAX

1609

L/1, 2, 3 and 4 *Blandfold Limited*
For the design of fluorescent lighting schemes for internal areas. Calculates and tabulates four nearest solutions for the user - proposed luminaires with their resulting lux levels (two for singles, two for twins on programs L/1 and L/2; triples and quads on L/3 and L/4). Gives minimum number recommended due to space-height ratio. Menu allows design optimisation. Printout facility. Use when floor plans and ceiling heights are available

References

Availability
Purchase

Language
Basic

Computer
Sinclair, Apple II,
Commodore 64

1610

Daylighting *Cheshire County Council*
Assesses natural daylighting in a building. The system accommodates the effects of windows and rooflights with reveals, and of overhanging eaves. Output is in the form of a matrix of daylight values on a horizontal plane selected by the user

References

Availability

Language
APL

Computer
IBM 3767

1611

FLDLT *Civil and Structural Computing (Northern) Limited*
Calculates horizontal direct lighting intensity in lux at a specified matrix of points on the working plane from given types and arrangements of luminaires. Data on standard luminaires is stored in a separate data file and others can be easily added if the flux zones and total lumen output are known

References
Bradshaw, Buckton and Tonge

Availability
Bureau service, time sharing, in-house

Language

Computer

1612

DAY *Cymap Limited*
Calculates the total daylighting factors on the working plane of a rectangular room from a standard CIE overcast day, using the BRS 'split flux' method. The sum of sky, internally reflected and externally reflected is the total daylighting factor. Windows may be in any of 4 walls, or horizontal on the ceiling, and can be obstructed by shading devices or other buildings. Rooflights can be included

References

Availability
Purchase (under licence)

Language
Microsoft Basic

Computer
Most CP/M based microcomputers, 8 and 16-bit, 64K

1613

ILLUM *Cymap Limited*
Lighting and glare calculations for rooms using various types of lighting fittings for specified service illuminance level. It can compare the different sizes and number of tubes or discharge lamps for any specified fitting. It follows the normal 'Lumen' method and the IES glare indices to give a running cost for each arrangement with a schedule of quantities for the fittings and lamps used, and the installation costs

References

Availability
Purchase (under licence)

Language
Microsoft Basic

Computer
Most CP/M based microcomputers, 8 and 16-bit, 64K

1614

PTP *Cymap Limited*
Carries out lighting calculations on a point to point basis using fittings with symmetrical light distribution. The fittings can be symmetrically or randomly arranged, and have varying heights. The rooms must be rectangular. The printout is a grid with the direct lighting intensities given at regular intervals over the room. Data for any type of fitting with filament or discharge lamps can be used, if the polar curves are known

References

Availability
Purchase (under licence)

Language
Microsoft Basic

Computer
Most CP/M based microcomputers, 8 and 16-bit, 64K

1615

AISLE *Daverman/SP Group*
This program (ASHRAE and IES Standard for Lighting Energy) determines the maximum power limit for the lighting of interior spaces. Based on the lighting power budget determination procedure (EMS-1) recommended by the Illuminating Engineers Society (IES) and adopted by the American Society of Heating, Refrigerating and Air Conditioning Engineers (ASHRAE) in its Standard 90-75. Program users need to understand Section 9 of the Standard

References

Availability
Time sharing

Language

Computer

Computer programs for the building industry

TASK LT *DHSS (Department of Health and Social Security)*
A program for task lighting and background calculation. Determines the direct illuminance pattern produced by a fluorescent luminaire sited above a working plane. The illuminance levels can then be calculated for a grid of discreet points over this area. It enables illuminance levels to be calculated at any particular point within a room, enabling the designer to check levels at exact points in the room

References

Availability
Purchase

Language
M Basic 80

Computer
64K microcomputer

FLOOD *Facet Limited*
Calculates the illumination levels at equally distributed grid points over the working plane, taking into account the direct and the internally reflected components. The program uses an elliptical interpolation technique for the evaluation of illuminance from point sources. The aspect factor method is used for the evaluation of illuminance from linear fittings. The user is able to define a fitting with any given rotation or beam direction

References

Availability
Bureau service, or under licence

Language

Computer
Prime, Norsk Data,
Harris,
CP/M 8-bit micros

IDLE *Facet Limited*
A program for calculating the daylight factors at equally distributed grid points over the working plane, due to any combination of vertical rectangular windows. The direct sky component and the internally reflected component are both taken into account. Calculations are based on the assumption of the CIE standard overcast sky

References

Availability
Bureau service, or under licence

Language

Computer
Prime, Norsk Data,
Harris,
CP/M 8-bit micros

LUGL *Facet Limited*
Performs a lumen method calculation for a given room and specified lamp/luminaire type. The program calculates the number of fittings required to attain a design illuminance, the spacing details, and the actual illuminance and load resulting from the installation of a number of fittings. The glare indices for either two orientation modes (point source), or four orientation modes (linear fittings) may also be calculated

References

Availability
Bureau service, or under licence

Language

Computer
Prime, Norsk Data,
Harris,
CP/M 8-bit micros

LUMEN 2 *Facet Limited*
Performs lighting design calculations for a given room and specified lamp/luminaire types. The program suggests fitting arrangements on the basis of both illuminance and spacing criteria. The details of regularly used fittings can be stored in a lighting database and recalled with the program whenever they are needed. Printed output from the program includes a line by line description of each room and its lighting arrangement so that, even if a large number of rooms are analysed, the output is neat and manageable

References

Availability
Bureau service, or under licence

Language

Computer
Prime, Norsk Data,
Harris,
CP/M 8-bit micros

SPIEL *Facet Limited*
Uses the natural and artificial illumination calculation procedures of IDLE and FLOOD to provide a base to evaluate the potential monthly energy savings of a lighting control system. Luminaires are divided into a number of controller groups; each group is controlled by one of the control options, including on/off switching, automatic dimming and set point dimming. Tabulated values of predicted energy savings are produced for each control group and summed for a bar chart showing total savings

References

Availability
Bureau service, or under licence

Language

Computer
Prime, Norsk Data,
Harris,
CP/M 8-bit micros

LIGHT *Focus Software Consultants*
Facilities: artificial lighting requirements data input/amendment; calculate number of: lighting fittings; print lighting schedule. Room data may be entered to the computer or be produced automatically from the heatloss module. Lighting requirements are entered interactively and may be changed at any time to produce alternative results. Lighting schedules include individual room schedules and schedules of the total building lighting fittings and lamps

References

Availability
Purchase

Language

Computer
CP/M or MS DOC

Electrical Lighting *Haden Central Engineering*
A suite of three programs containing: 4A Library creation, amendment and printout for fluorescent luminaires, using manufacturers' data. 4B Lighting and glare calculations in a room using the lumen method and CIBS code. 4C Distribution of direct and reflected lighting intensities within a room from defined arrangement of fluorescent luminaires

References
Recommended by The Technical
Software Centre, Cranfield, Bedford

Availability
Purchase

Language
Fortran IV

Computer
4032 and 8032 PET,
Apple II

ASPECT *Haden Central Engineering*
Used for the distribution of direct and reflected lighting intensities at a grid of points on the working plane of a room from a defined arrangement of fluorescent luminaires

References

Availability
On application

Language
Basic, Fortran

Computer
Apple II
PET, Tandy II

DAYLIGHT *Haden Central Engineering*
Calculates the distribution of the daylighting factor in a room from vertical windows and rooflights. Follows the BRE split flux method allowing for sky, internally reflected and externally reflected components, onto a grid of points on the working plane in a defined room

References

Availability
Licence

Language
Fortran IV and F77

Computer
Any minicomputer
with 128K/16-bit

1626

FLOOD *Haden Central Engineering*
Calculates the distribution of lighting intensity on the ground from a defined arrangement of specific floodlighting luminaires. Output consists of a grid of points showing the variation of lighting intensity over an area

References

Availability
Licence

Language
Fortran IV and F77

Computer
Any minicomputer with 128K/16-bit

1627

LUMEN *Haden Central Engineering*
Provides lighting and glare calculations in a room using the lumen method and CIBS Guide. Used for any fluorescent luminaire in the library, with photometric data taken from manufacturers' catalogues. The program can determine the number and spacing of fittings, as well as checking an existing system

References

Availability
On application

Language
Basic, Fortran

Computer
Apple II
PET, Tandy II

1628

DAY *Hevacomp Limited*
This program handles daylight factors in a room, on a grid of up to 10 x 10 points. It takes into account sky, and externally and internally reflected components. It allows for any number of windows and up to 16 glass types. Facilities exist for: external obstructions, recess or external shading, variable working plane height, maintenance factor and seven types of roof light

References

Availability
Purchase

Language

Computer
Any 64K microcomputer

1629

LEN *Hevacomp Limited*
Computes the annual electrical energy consumption by an artificial lighting system. It allows top-up and on/off lighting control to be specified, together with daylight factors

References

Availability
Purchase

Language

Computer
Any 64K microcomputer

1630

LUMEN *Hevacomp Limited*
Computes the number of artifical lighting fittings required in rooms, using files of light fittings which are stored on disk. Tube wattage and colour can be defined (as can Hi-bay fittings). Room reflection factors can be selected, together with a maintenance factor. Fittings can be suspended from ceilings. The program uses the BZ method to compute transfer factors and coefficients of utilisation. The manufacturer's recommended spacing is also checked

References

Availability
Purchase

Language

Computer
Any 64K microcomputer

1631

LIGHTS *Lancashire County Council*
Analyses artificial lighting systems and calculates optimum layout for minimum energy consumption. Variables that can be controlled on input include: length, breadth and height of room; height of lamp and working plane; type of bulb or tube to be used; reflective factors; illumination required. Output consists of: a printout giving layout details and energy required plus details of the optimum layout if different; a plot of the selected layout

References

Availability
From Lancashire County Council, Architects Department

Language
Fortran

Computer
ICL 2976

1632

BEYS *Lysteknisk Laboratorium*
A general purpose program with a variety of applications, such as interior lighting, daylighting and design of luminaires, louvres, skylights, window shadings, etc. A room with its lighting system is simulated by a number of surfaces which are luminous, diffuse reflecting, specular reflecting or directly transmitting. The results are luminance and illuminance on relevant surfaces, and/or light intensity distribution of the construction. Related to ISPOR, BEKON and GLAR

References
Report No 15, Lysteknisk Laboratorium, 1977 (The Danish Illuminating Engineering Laboratory)

Availability
Purchase

Language
Fortran IV

Computer
HP1000

1633

SPORT, POoo7 *Lysteknisk Laboratorium*
Calculates the lighting intensity originating from a haphazard lighting system, on a rectangular area; particularly useful for sports installations. Intensity can be calculated at points on a horizontal plane, and through two vertical sections to a certain height above the horizontal. SPORT calculates cylindrical lighting intensity (lighting intensity on a vertical half-cylinder): POoo7 calculates lighting intensity on plan

References
Danish Building Research Institute Abstract 48 14 01

Availability
Purchase

Language
Fortran IV

Computer
Hewlett-Packard 1000

1634

VIVAB *Lysteknisk Laboratorium*
Calculates transmittance and reflectance of light for windows with up to five layers of obscure or clear glazing. The Gauss-Seidel iterative technique is used for calculation of transmitted, reflected and absorbed rays in individual layers of glazing. Heat gains in the glazing and inside the building can also be calculated

References
Danish Building Research Institute Abstract 48 14 013

Availability
Purchase

Language
Fortran IV

Computer
Hewlett-Packard 1000

1635

BP104: Lighting-area sources *Oasys Limited*
Calculates the illuminance on a plane surface parallel to uniform diffusing rectangular light sources. The direct and indirect illuminance can be calculated over any area described by a rectangular grid of points

References

Availability
Purchase

Language
Basic

Computer
HP 9845 HP 85/87

BP105: Lighting-point sources *Oasys Limited*
Calculates the illuminance on a plane surface from point source luminaires. The illuminance can be calculated over any area described by a rectangular grid of points. The aiming angles of spotlights can be specified and adjusted. Both indirect and direct illuminances are calculated by the split flux formula and inverse square law, respectively

References

Availability
Purchase

Language
Basic

Computer
HP 9845 HP 85/87

BP107: Illuminance level and glare index calculation *Oasys Limited*
Calculates the direct and indirect illumination on principal room surfaces. Rooms described by: dimensions, surface reflections, mounting height, work surface height, illumination level and mid-point ratio. Fittings chosen by type, name, BZ number, coefficient of utilisation, maintenance factor, downward flux ratio, flux fraction ratio, light output and spacing along and across the room; illumination levels and ratios are calculated

References

Availability
Purchase

Language
Basic

Computer
HP 9845 HP 85/87

Philips Lighting *Philips Electronics, Lighting Division*
Based on CIBS TM5. Calculates the number of luminaires required for a specified flux level, the number of rows needed either for a square array or widespread installation, and spacing details. Luminaire data is input from a bar code via a bar code reading pen. Calculation includes energy loading per square metre and installation costs

References

Availability
Purchase

Language

Computer
HP41CV

INTLITE *Philips Lighting*
Calculates the number of luminaires necessary to obtain a certain illuminance level in a room. From light distribution characteristics of the luminaire, the room dimensions and reflective properties of surfaces, the utilisation factor is found. Calculations are made using the CIBS method

References

Availability
Purchase

Language

Computer
Hewlett-Packard type 41CV

ANL1 *Pilkington Brothers Limited*
This interactive program calculates the provision of daylight in a room. Outputs include daylight at points on a grid representing the room. Results at intermediate stages in the calculation, isolating the contribution of various heatgains and losses to the final results, may also be obtained. As part of the service, an environmental engineer runs the program with the client until a design is arrived at which will give satisfactory thermal performance

References

Availability
Used only to advise customers. Not for sale

Language
Fortran

Computer

ANNEX *Environmental Advisory Service, Pilkington Brothers Limited*
Computes the daylight factors in a rectangular room, at points on a 5x5 or 10x10 grid. It uses the Seshadri method in connection with the CIE Standard Overcast Sky for calculating the sky component. The internally reflected component calculation is based on the Pilkington method. The program is part of a suite of environmental programs

References
DOC Evaluation Report No 3

Availability
Used only to advise customers. Not for sale

Language
Fortran IV, Basic

Computer
Honeywell Mk III

PSA DAYLIGHT *Property Services Agency, Directorate of Civil Engineering Services*
Computes the daylight factors in a rectangular room at user specified points or on a user specified grid. It is based on the CIE Standard Overcast Sky. The Hopkinson analytical solution of the daylight factor integral is used for the calculation of the sky component, and the BRE split flux method for the calculation of reflected components

References
DOC Evaluation Report No 3

Availability

Language
Fortran IV

Computer
UCS DEC 10

Illumination level *Technies Rekencentrum Polybit bv*
This program is for the design of lighting installations in rooms. The illumination levels of the direct and indirect (average and at points) are calculated. Extensions provide for dispersion of light and variable height of fittings

References

Availability
Bureau service, remote batch, purchase

Language
Fortran

Computer
Cyber 750

Daylighting and supplementary artificial lighting *Technisch Rekencentrum*
Deals with the design of position, dimensions and types of glazing in windows placed in outside walls, and/or roofs, in relation to the access of daylighting. The energy consumption of artificial lighting is also calculated. In the early design stages, the program can be used in balancing the energy use of a building

References

Availability
Hire

Language
Fortran IV, Basic

Computer

EDP-I *APEC*
(Electrical distribution program - Level 1) Aids the electrical engineer in the design of an entire low voltage power distribution system. Provides schedules to be used on contract documents. Organises and simplifies data gathering and presentation. Covers: branch circuit panelboards, power panels, switchboards, transformers, motors, motor control centres, motor starter panels, automatic transfer switches, feeders, overcurrent protective devices

References
43 Licences plus public access

Availability
Doris J Wallace, APEC

Language
Fortran

Computer
IBM 370
CDC Cyber 175
TR8-80 Model II

1646

OCP-1 *APEC*
Overcurrent protection coordination - Level 1. Provides the electrical engineer with a broad choice of coordination curves for a low voltage distribution system circuit, with up to 15 overcurrent protection devices. Output includes operating characteristic curves for selected circuit breakers and Bussman fuses to assist the engineer to coordinate an electrical design system

References
37 Licences plus public access

Availability
Doris J Wallace, APEC

Language
Fortran

Computer
IBM 370
CDC Cyber 175
TRS-80 Model II

1647

$LAMSAC Application code 32125121140A *Bradford City Council, Architect's Department*
Produces schedules for the maintenance of electrical batteries, for emergency lighting, etc. The slow peripheral unit used is a lineprinter. The program was first used in 1977

References
LAMSAC

Availability

Language
Cobol

Computer
ICL 1904A
10K core
3 magnetic tape units

1648

IEE-15 *Building Services Computer Service*
Enables the electrical design engineer to design all the final circuits from a distribution board and the submains cable serving the distribution board or switchgear location. Any amendment to the design parameters results in fast, accurate recalculation of the circuit date. Output includes schedule of: detail circuit chart for distribution board installation; full design data as required by IEE Wiring Regulations; sub-mains details plus phase load summaries

References
Electrical Review, May 1983

Availability
Purchase

Language
Compiled Basic + machine code

Computer
Commodore, ACT
Sirius I, IBM PC

1649

GEO 17 *Computel Limited*
A program for the generation of resistivity curves

References
GEOCOMP

Availability

Language

Computer

1650

Documenting complex wiring *COSMIC*
An electrical engineering package for documenting the wiring interconnections in complex electrical systems. The characteristics and functions of each conductor in the electrical system are input. Each component is given a unit number, and a sequential signal number identifies all conductors from each unit. Output tabulations include each conductor with both termination points. Wire lists show the origin of each conductor, its destination, cable designation number and the electrical characteristics of the circuit

References
NASA Lewis Research Center

Availability

Language
Fortran IV

Computer
IBM 7000 series

1651

CABLE *Cymap Limited*
Selects the most economical cable sizes for all types of copper and aluminium cable in any single or 3-phase distribution system within or between buildings. Includes corrections for temperature and bunching and automatically increases cable sizes to keep all circuits below the required volt drop. Cables automatically paralleled; voltages at each load given and volt drops for each cable. Sizes, fuses and cables and produces budget costing. Calculation of 3-phase symmetrical short circuit fault levels

References

Availability
Purchase (under licence)

Language
Microsoft Basic

Computer
Most CP/M based microcomputers,
8 and 16-bit, 64K

1652

Compels *Davy Computing Limited*
For electrical engineers and designers engaged in industrial AC power system design. Given the overall power system design criteria, cable lengths and loads, Compels will size power cables, calculate system performance and generate high quality switchboard and cable schedules. Design and scheduling changes can be accommodated throughout the duration of a project, with revised outputs being available on demand

References

Availability
Bureau service

Language

Computer
Univac 1100/81

1653

C SIZE *Haden Central Engineering*
Calculates sizing, volt drop and fault level for sub-mains cables feeding different types of loads

References

Availability
Licence

Language
Fortran IV and F77

Computer
Any minicomputer with 128K/16-bit

1654

CP1 *Institution of Electrical Engineers*
This electrical program is concerned with accurate root locus, including the effects of pure time delay. It is used for producing diagrams

References
IEE program library

Availability
Photocopies available on request.
Price: £8.50

Language
Algol

Computer

1655

CP21 *Institution of Electrical Engineers*
Used for the general analysis of electrical control systems, employing an operational array technique

References
IEE program library

Availability
Photocopies available on request.
Price: £6.65

Language
Algol

Computer
English Electric KDF9

CP23 *Institution of Electrical Engineers*
Calculates the transient response of lumped linear systems from their frequency response

References
IEE program library

Availability
Photocopies available on request.
Price: £6.35

Language
Algol

Computer
ICL 1905F

CP29 *Institution of Electrical Engineers*
This program enables the dynamic simulation of electrical control systems to be made, using a symbolic array technique

References
IEE program library

Availability
Photocopies available on request.
Price: £8.30

Language
Algol

Computer
English Electric KDF9

CP4 *Institution of Electrical Engineers*
Enables an assessment of security to be made in electrical distribution systems

References
IEE program library

Availability
Photocopies of program supplied on
request: Price: £12.25

Language
Fortran IV

Computer

Cable pulling tension for insulated electric wire in conduit or duct system *A M Kinney, Inc*
Computes cable and wire pulling tensions at various points in a conduit system, minimum bending radius of bends to prevent side wall pressure from crushing insulation, and maximum allowable tensions as determined by conduit fill and method of pulling. Output includes tensions at exit and entrance at each bend, tension at pulling end, unreeling tension, and all minimum radii of curvature

References

Availability

Language
Fortran

Computer
IBM 1130 and 370

Electric distribution system short circuit calculations *A M Kinney, Inc*
Calculates short circuit currents at various points on distribution system, symmetrical and asymmetrical amperes for 3-phase and ground faults, including the effect of motor contribution and half winding faults on single phase 120/240 volt transformers. Output includes bus number, kVA, ampere, voltage, and the ratio of X over R for 3-phase faults, and the symmetrical and asymmetrical for ground faults

References

Availability

Language
Fortran

Computer
IBM 1130 and 370

Electric power system fault study *A M Kinney, Inc*
The program determines, for a 3-phase fault, total fault (per unit), volt amperes, and contributions and, as an option, total fault and contributions when each line is connected to the faulted bus is opened successively. Input data includes load flow, generation impedance and fault bus data. Output consists of the fault, bus number, and its current at the bus line and in the generator

References

Availability

Language
Fortran

Computer
IBM 1130 and 370

Electrical distribution system analysis *A M Kinney, Inc*
Computes voltages and current in all line and load segments of a radial electric distribution system, the effect of motor starting amperes on system voltage, the effect of adding capacitors on system voltage and amperes, or simply computing voltages and amperes in all segments under steady state loading. Output contains load and line current components, and line impedances for motor current equal to full load ampere, full voltage starting ampere, or zero

References

Availability

Language
Fortran

Computer
IBM 1130 and 370

IBM 1130 Electric power system load flow *A M Kinney, Inc*
Computes the results of a performance calculation on an electric power system under load. Results include the power and reactive flow in transmission lines and other facilities. The output calculates and reports the power and reactive flows and other quantities of physical significance. Large power systems are solved in a small core environment; several cases may be run together; no data manipulation is required for a particular case; no judgement of mathematical performance of power systems is necessary

References

Availability

Language
Fortran

Computer
IBM 1130 and 370

Sag and tension calculations *A M Kinney, Inc*
Computes sags and tensions for transmission and distribution lines for unloaded or loaded conductors for varying temperature conditions, including design limiting conditions for heavy, medium or light loading districts. Output consists of temperature range, weather condition, the value of (S)(W)/T, sag factor, sag span in feet, and tension in pounds

References

Availability

Language
Fortran

Computer
IBM 1130 and 370

Selection of economical conductor size *A M Kinney, Inc*
Calculates present worth of total annual costs for any four conductor sizes, and prints these costs for each year for a period not exceeding 20 years, on a 1000 wire-foot basis. Information required includes: installed costs, resistances, load forecast, and unit loss costs. The output contains the annual charge rate and cumulative costs for each conductor in tabular form which may be easily transferred to a graph

References

Availability

Language
Fortran

Computer
IBM 1130 and 370

1666

Transmission losses and penalty factors *A M Kinney, Inc*
Will calculate the generated power, transmission losses, and receive power for any system for which the B-constants are known. Also calculates the penalty factor at each entry point to the system. Input includes the size of B-constant matrix, a set of B-constants, and the real power at each axis in megawatts. Output consists of system generation, power losses, received power in mw, axis number and its respective power in mw, and the penalty factor

References

Availability

Language
Fortran

Computer
IBM 1130 and 370

1667

Unbalanced loading of 3-phase electric distribution system *A M Kinney, Inc*
The program utilises symmetrical component for calculating unbalanced voltages in electrical distribution systems caused by unbalanced loads. Output includes: impedance table used; unbalanced load per unit volts from phase to neutral, and between lines; percentage of voltage drop for values with and without Delta-Wye transformer phase shift

References

Availability

Language
Fortran

Computer
IBM 1130 and 370

1668

BP109: Electrical fault levels *Oasys Limited*
Calculates 3-phase symmetrical short circuit fault levels and voltage drops for 3-phase balanced loads. Input entails a description of the network in terms of nodes and elements, a specification of the fault level locations, and the base energy level to which the percentage impedance of all components is referred. Output consists of a summary of the input data, with results of the analysis

References

Availability
Purchase

Language
Basic

Computer
HP 9845 HP 85/87

1669

Electrical distribution in buildings *Technisch Rekencentrum*
Calculates the electrical distribution system for buildings and building complexes. Optimalisation is selected on a basis of investments and of exploitation costs. Output includes: calculated cable diameters, lengths and installation costs; investment costs (transformers, switchgear, etc); exploitation costs; cable losses

References
Smit, Tranformaturen Nymegen (Netherlands)

Availability
Hire

Language
Fortran IV

Computer

1670

ESP (Environmental System Performance) *ABACUS studies*
This package allows a rigorous appraisal at the 'building performance/energy consumption/plant strategy of operation' interface. It provides information on the thermal, lighting and acoustic performance of any enclosure. Graphic output gives variation, over any specified time, of temperatures, energy loadings, natural lighting levels, shadow patterns, daylight factor contours and wall temperature variations

References
ABACUS Occasional Paper No 48

Availability
Purchase, hire, interactive bureau service

Language
Fortran IV

Computer
Univac 1108
Tektronix graphics terminal

1671

SERNET *ABACUS studies*
Appraises the interdepartmental service requirements of a whole hospital complex. Input comprises three files: scheme file, providing a description of the buildings' geometry; pipe file, giving various pipe sizes, costs and other characteristics; and network file, showing the coordinates of a pipe network throughout the building. The program may be run with the first two only

References
PHASE, ACTNET. ABACUS Occasional Paper No 36 (PHASE)

Availability
Purchase, hire, interactive bureau service

Language
Fortran IV

Computer
Univac 1108
Tektronix graphics terminal

1672

Heat exchanger design (HTEX2) *A M Kinney, Inc*
Computes design parameters of heat exchangers for 3 cases: no phase change; condensing a vapour from a noncondensable gas; pure condensation. The program applies to horizontal and vertical condensers. Output consists of shell surface area, log mean temperature, heat transfer coefficients, total fluid in, and fluid condensed on, shell side and tube side, pressure drops, velocities, channel side and shell side factors, shell and tube side characteristics

References

Availability

Language
Fortran

Computer
IBM 1130 and 370

1673

Heat exchanger design (HTEX4) *A M Kinney, Inc*
Computes design parameters of heat exchangers for 2 cases: miscible condensate and immiscible condensate. The preliminary guess (area) is based on the overall design heat transfer coefficient

References

Availability

Language
Fortran

Computer
IBM 1130 and 370

1674

Methanol synthesis loop material balance *A M Kinney, Inc*
Computes, for a given feed composition, the methanol synthesis material balance. Output contains information on the compositions of feed, recycle, feed plus recycle, reacted, dissolved, and vent

References

Availability

Language
Fortran

Computer
IBM 1130 and 370

1675

Solvent recovery-carbon unit *A M Kinney, Inc*
Computes design parameters for a solvent recovery-carbon unit. Options include SLA cooler and heater, humidifier, condenser, decanter and storage tank. Output contains general specifications of the unit, and adsorber, condenser, decanter, tank and blower specifications

References

Availability

Language
Fortran

Computer
IBM 1130 and 370

Stress in horizontal pressure vessels on two saddle supports *A M Kinney, Inc*
Computes approximate stresses that exist in cylindrical vessels supported on two saddles at various locations. The program will also compute design parameters for wear plates and ring stiffeners. Output consists of design parameters (input and output), and a tabulation of calculated and allowable stresses

References

Availability

Language
Fortran

Computer
IBM 1130 and 370

CP41 *National Research Council of Canada*
A GPSS program to simulate the use of washroom facilities

References
D Henning, D P McPhie & L M Webster

Availability

Language

Computer

Lifts
Internal communications
External communications

Transport and communications

1678

LIFTS *ABACUS studies*
Used to demonstrate the operation of a lift system. Input data includes: number and height of storeys; number of occupants per floor; number, size and speed of lifts; and duration of demonstration. It produces total and average times for passenger waiting and journeys, lift parking time and average passenger waiting time per floor

References

Availability
Purchase, hire, interactive bureau service

Language
Fortran

Computer
Univac 1108
Tektronix graphics terminal

1679

LIFTS *Dewco Programming and Computer Services*
This program selects the best lift system by relating performance for peak loading conditions to installed cost

References

Availability
Bureau service, remote batch, purchase

Language
Fortran

Computer
Honeywell 6000

1680

FILDER *Facet Limited*
The design of lift systems involves the iterative evaluation of the Round Trip Time formula to establish the Handling Capacity and Interval factors. The user-defined description of the building, population and lift door characteristics are used to calculate the number of passengers required per trip. This determines the size and number of lifts required. The program compares the performance of program-suggested standard lift car arrangements and also allows the user to specify additional options

References

Availability
Bureau service, or under licence

Language

Computer
Prime, Norsk Data, Harris, CP/M 8-bit micros

1681

LISI *Facet Limited*
Analyses a specified lift system, giving average waiting times and queue lengths at the end of each specified period. The program simulates lift systems operated by interconnected, directional-collective group control. Passenger arrivals are generated by the program at random intervals according to a normal distribution curve. The arrival and destination floors are also chosen according to distributions given by the user

References

Availability
Bureau service, or under licence

Language

Computer
Prime, Norsk Data, Harris, CP/M 8-bit micros

1682

LIFT 2 *Oasys Limited*
The LIFT program offers the following facilities: up peak or two way lift system; selection of lifts or analysis of the performance of a given lift installation; 1-3 lift zones; 1-3 entrances; simple or complex assignment of lifts from different zones to different entrances; three methods of specifying lift zones or floor populations

References

Availability
Bureau service

Language
Fortran

Computer
DEC 10

1683

Elevators *Technies Rekencentrum Polybit bv*
Determines the most economical system of vertical transport in buildings. Lift installations are compared. That which requires minimum investment and costs in use, and gives maximum capacity, is selected. Waiting periods are calculated with various control systems and traffic programs

References

Availability
Bureau service, remote batch, purchase

Language
Fortran

Computer
Cyber 750

1684

ACTNET *ABACUS studies*
Appraises the performance of a whole hospital complex. Input consists of a description of the geometry of the buildings and the circulation system, ie stairs, lifts and corridors. Graphic output displays the buildings' geometry with departmental entrances located. Tabular output gives the shortest route, in terms of time taken, for any set of critical journeys between pre-specified departments

References
PHASE, SERNET. ABACUS Occasional Paper No 35 (PHASE)

Availability
Purchase, hire, interactive bureau service

Language
Fortran IV

Computer
Univac 1108
Tektronix graphics terminal

1685

AIR-Q *ABACUS studies*
Appraises a proposed design involving the movement of objects. It is time based, and indicates areas where congestion and queues may arise. A description of the object system (which may be graphical) to be simulated is input as a network. The network includes average time for utilisation for each activity and the links between the activities represent the possible direction of movement through the network

References

Availability
Purchase, hire, interactive bureau service

Language
Fortran IV

Computer
Univac 1108
Tektronix graphics terminal

1686

LOCAL *ABACUS studies*
Used to solve location/allocation problems. It can be used for such problems as locating a set of required service centres, so that demand points are served most effectively, eg by reducing travel distance or time to a minimum

References

Availability
Purchase, hire, interactive bureau service

Language
Fortran

Computer
Univac 1108
Tektronix graphics terminal

1687

NETSYS *DHSS (Department of Health and Social Security)*
The movement of any or all groups of people and goods on one or more links of a hospital communication network can be seen in tabular or graphical output. Used in conjunction with TRAM. Various options include one or two-way traffic and the closing-off of any routes to any of the traveller types. A digitising table will ease the input; for high quality output a plotter is necessary

References

Availability
Purchase

Language
Fortran IV

Computer
SEL, Prime

TRAM *DHSS (Department of Health and Social Security)*
This program deals with traffic modelling between hospital departments, predicting the loading and capacity of each department in terms of patient throughput in an average 24 hour day. It also gives a matrix of trips between departments, and histograms of movement from each department by time of day

References

Availability
Purchase

Language
Fortran IV

Computer
SEL, Prime

1689

Pneumatic tube systems *Technies Rekencentrum Polybit bv*
Selects the best postal pneumatic tube system by simulation. Various tube systems are compared and the installation which would service the internal mail at minimum cost is selected

References

Availability
Bureau service, remote batch, purchase

Language
Fortran

Computer
Cyber 750

1690

ROADWAY *Scicon*
A suite of programs for traffic modelling which contains facilities for survey analysis, trip end estimation, trip distribution, and network analysis. The suite can process data extracted from the Regional Highway Traffic Model produced by the Department of Transport

References

Availability
Bureau Service

Language

Computer
UNIVAC 1100/62

1691

ENVPLAN *Scott Wilson Kirkpatrick and Partners*
A suite of linked programs with varying levels of sophistication, designed for transport modelling which is interactive with land use planning. Sub-routines are available for analysis of rural, urban and city transport

References

Availability
Purchase, lease

Language
Fortran

Computer
VAX/VMS

Mathematics
Statistics
Other

1692

CIRCLE *The Association for Computer Aided Design Limited*
Part of suite GCP1. Calculates stresses, strains and displacements in a homogenous, elastic half space, subject to loading applied to a circular area on the surface of the half space. Ten different types of loading can be analysed, including uniform and linear vertical stress, uniform shear stress, linear radial and torsional shear stresses, and the analogous displacement defined loads. The linear elastic material in the half space can be isotropic or cross-anisotropic

References

Availability
Contact ACADS

Language
ANSI Fortran IV

Computer

1693

CIRCLY *The Association for Computer Aided Design Limited*
Analyses multi-layered, anisotropic medium subject to multiple circular loads. Load types considered include horizontal and vertical forces, moments about horizontal and vertical axes and shear stress of a self-cancelling nature. All the load types involve polynomial type, contact stress distributions, enabling complex load distributions to be realistically modelled. Special provision has been made for a vertical load with rough contact

References

Availability
Contact ACADS

Language
ANSI Fortran IV

Computer
Control Data
Cyber

1694

CRALAY *The Association for Computer Aided Design Limited*
Part of Suite GCP1. Calculates stresses, strains and displacements in a system of horizontal layers, subject to a uniform vertical stress or inward shear stress, applied to a circular area on the upper surface. The linear elastic materials in each of the layers may be cross anisotropic or isotropic

References

Availability
Contact ACADS

Language
ANSI Fortran IV

Computer

1695

CRLAY *The Association for Computer Aided Design Limited*
Calculates stresses, strains and displacements in a system of horizontal layers subject to a uniform unidirectional shear stress or linear torsional shear stress applied to a circular area on the upper surface. The linear elastic materials in each of the layers may be cross-anisotropic or isotropic

References

Availability
Contact ACADS

Language
ANSI Fortran IV

Computer

1696

PLANE *The Association for Computer Aided Design Limited*
Part of Suite GCP1. Calculates stresses, strains and displacements in a homogenous, linear, elastic half space, due to loading applied to an infinite strip on the surface. Twelve types of loading can be analysed, including uniform and linear vertical stress, uniform and linear lateral shear stress, and the analogous displacement defined loads. The material in the half space may be orthorhombic, cross- anisotropic or isotropic

References

Availability
Contact ACADS

Language
ANSI Fortran IV

Computer

1697

PSLAY *The Association for Computer Aided Design Limited*
Part of Suite GCP1. Calculates stresses, strains and displacements in a system of horizontal layers subject to a uniform vertical stress or uniform lateral shear stress, applied to an infinite strip on the upper surface. The linear elastic materials in each layer may be orthorhombic, cross anisotropic or isotropic

References

Availability
Contact ACADS

Language
ANSI Fortran IV

Computer

1698

LAMPS *CAP Scientific Limited*
A general purpose system for the efficient solution of large mathematical programming problems. Features: production or selection of raw materials, then blending and processing into products; transport of materials; allocation of production resources to achieve a production plan; selection between alternative paths used in plan. Many problems can be formulated using only linear constraints; for problem solution a primal algorithm is used. Alternatively, the program incorporates a range of integer and non-linear facilities

References
Developed by Advanced Mathematical
Software Limited

Availability
Purchase

Language

Computer
32-bit minicomputers

1699

BES093 *Centre de Recherches Routieres*
A set of three fast sub-routines for evaluating the Bessel functions J0, J1 and J2 of an arbitrary argument. These sub-routines, based on a polynomial and trigonometrical approximation, are accurate to the seventh place

References

Availability
Contact owner

Language
Fortran

Computer
GE235
CDC Cyber
TI 990

1700

EXP093 *Centre de Recherches Routieres*
An iterative program for least square fitting of a series of exponentials, with an optional linear term to an experimental increasing curve with downward curvature, or to a decay curve. Exponents are in a geometrical progression. The program operates by the collocation method

References

Availability
Contact owner

Language
Basic

Computer
GE235

1701

REG093 *Centre de Recherches Routieres*
A general least square regression program for two variables, handling unlimited series of data. Regression coefficients are calculated (with standard deviation) between two user defined functions respective of the input data. Correlation coefficients and confidence intervals are produced. A row of ten choices of functions can be handled for the same data in a single run

References

Availability
Contact owner

Language
Basic

Computer
GE235
CDC Cyber

Computer programs for the building industry

STEIN *Computel Limited*
For the general solution of Steinbrenner elasticity equations for a rigid layer, at depth, overlaid by a material with increasing or constant modulus with depth

References
GEOCOMP

Availability

Language

Computer

1703

NAL (Numerical Algorithms Library) *Computer Design*
A structural collection of computer sub-routines designed to solve mathematical and statistical problems in science and engineering. Includes: eigensolutions, matrix operations including inversion, linear equations, determinants, complex algebra, differential equations, curve fitting, special functions, basic statistics, random numbers, distribution functions, sorting, etc

References

Availability
Purchase, hire

Language
Fortran 77

Computer
ACT Sirus 1
Also, all micros with
Fortran compiler

1704

FITTER *Computrav (UK) Limited*
This program finds the best polynomial to a given set of X,Y data. For users developing ad hoc programs, this is an effective method of supplying tabular data in a program

References
Approved by ACT Sirius

Availability
Purchase

Language
Basic

Computer
Minimum 32Kb on 8
and 16-bit micros
under CP/M

1705

DEVI *Facet Limited*
This program is used to calculate the mean and standard deviation from a set of user-defined data

References

Availability
Bureau service, or under licence

Language

Computer
Prime, Norsk Data,
Harris,
CP/M 8-bit micros

1706

SOLAR *Hevacomp Limited*
This program computes the altitude and azimuth angles of the sun, for any latitude, on any day of the year

References

Availability
Purchase

Language

Computer
Any 64K
microcomputer

1707

Numerical analysis *Hilbern Engineering Software, USA*
Contains routines for numerical integration using adaptive integration techniques with the Romberg and an adaptive method not available elsewhere. The third routine is a cubic spline fit which can be used to interpolate, differentiate and integrate tabular data

References

Availability
Purchase

Language

Computer
TRS-80, Apple II, IBM
PC

1708

Polynomial Root Finder *Hilbern Engineering Software, USA*
Deals with finding the roots of a polynomial and lets the user solve for the roots of a polynomial with constant coefficients. Used for numerical problems in engineering and science

References

Availability
Purchase

Language
Basic

Computer
Osborne, HP85,
TRS-80, IBM PC

1709

Mathemagic *International Software Marketing*
A number processing package designed for the manipulation of data in business, engineering, science and education. The data disk contains over 50 formulae for industry, finance and education. Features include: easy creation of personalised arithmetic expressions up to 240 characters, including standard maths functions, stored variables and stored formulae; interface with Graphmagic for graphical representation of results; automatic retention of variable for use in chain calculations, etc

References

Availability
Purchase

Language

Computer
Apple II
IBM PC
CP/M 2.2

1710

Curve fitting program *A M Kinney, Inc*
1 Lagrangian polynomial curve fit: produces empirical equation of a curve using data from an existing curve plotted on rectangular coordinated graph paper or from tabulated values.
2 Exponential curve fit: produces an exponential equation of a curve using data selected from an existing curve plotted on semilogrithmic graph paper, or from tabulated values. 3 Logrithmic curve fit: calculates a set of constants A and B, based on data from an existing curve plotted on log-log graph paper, or from tabulated values

References

Availability

Language
Fortran

Computer
IBM 1130 and 370

1711

Solution of a real polynomial equation *A M Kinney, Inc*
Computes the real and complex roots of a real polynominal. Newton-Raphson iterative method is used for the solution. The program may solve up to the maximum of 36th order of a real polynomial. Floating-point overflow may occur for high order polynomials, but will not affect the accuracy of the results

References

Availability

Language
Fortran

Computer
IBM 1130 and 370

Computer programs for the building industry

1712

Solution of simultaneous equations *A M Kinney, Inc*
Solves up to 40 unknowns with 40 equations. The inverse of matrix method is used to obtain the solution. Output includes a printout of the inverse of A- matrix and the product of inverse of matrix times the original matrix (or identify matrix). Accurancy of substituting solution matrix into original A- matrix. The relative errors between computed values and actual values are checked and printed

References

Availability

Language
Fortran

Computer
IBM 1130 and 370

1713

COGO *Microcomp Limited*
Designed to solve engineering coordinate geometry problems, such as traverse adjustment and vertical and horizontal curve fitting. Applications include land surveying, subdivision work, highway design and constructional layout. Facilities for more general application include location of points from distances and angles, or intersections of lines, arcs and spirals. Areas with either straight or circular boundaries can be computed, and distances along circles and spirals, calculated

References

Availability
Licence

Language
Basic

Computer
Apple II 48K

1714

CP10 *National Research Council of Canada*
A computer method for the solution of biharmonic equation

References
A S Krausz

Availability

Language

Computer

1715

CP14 *National Research Council of Canada*
A Bendix G-15 Algo program for calculating the steady temperature under arbitrary areas on the surface of a semi-infinite solid

References
W G Brown

Availability

Language

Computer

1716

CP17 *National Research Council of Canada*
An Algo program to process weather observations

References
G P Mitalas

Availability

Language

Computer

1717

CP29 *National Research Council of Canada*
A program to calculate the dynamic response by fast fourier transform

References
J H Rainer

Availability

Language

Computer

1718

MP101: Solution of simultaneous equations *Oasys Limited*
Apart from performing routine tasks, this program provides additional facilities in data entry, copying, checking and data storage, which greatly reduce the effort in obtaining a solution. A check on the accuracy of the solution is also provided

References

Availability
Purchase

Language
Basic

Computer
HP 9845 HP 85/87

1719

Mathematical and Statistical routines *Reading Computer Services Limited*
A total of 29 statistical and 37 mathematical routines to undertake the most common requirements of a design office

References

Availability

Language

Computer
CP/M Microcomputer

1720

DIAGNOSE *S D Micros Limited*
Allows the user to produce a mathematical diagnosis of current status of completion on construction projects. In addition, the program calculates the spend rate over the contract

References

Availability
Purchase

Language
Basic

Computer
48K Apple,
and others

1721

SERIES *Computel Limited*
A series of statistical programs

References
GEOCOMP

Availability

Language

Computer

TABX and XT suite *Data and Research Services Limited*
This suite of programs is used for cross-tabulating, and analysing statistically, data and stock files. Data can also be derived from origin/destination and similar fact gathering surveys. Data fields may be combined, named, weighted and operated on in various other ways. Tabulations may be filtered, and percentages and averages arrived at on various bases. Twelve column headings and 100 row headings are permitted in any table

References

Availability
Bureau service

Language
Fortran

Computer
PDP 11/60

1723

QUANAL *Hutton + Rostron*
For analysing data obtained from questionnaire and similar surveys. Boolean and numerical data is summed and output in the form of simple totals and totals for any specified combination of answers. The data can be interrogated interactively and printed out in the form of totals, percentages, histograms or graphs. Comments made by respondents can be coded and sorted into significant groups using SORT

References
Surveys on employment of architects and advertising by architects published in The Architects' Journal

Availability
Bureau or purchase

Language
PAL8

Computer
DEC PDP8

1724

Statistical analysis *A M Kinney, Inc*
These programs can rapidly screen large amounts of data and evaluate the relationships. The use of statistics in analysis of test results, reduces the probability of error by organisation of the experimental results, and points out the essentials of replication and randomisation in testing procedures

References

Availability

Language
Fortran

Computer
IBM 1130 and 370

1725

STATISTICS *Marcus Computer Systems*
Analyses and calculates deviation; gives a correlation matrix for specified variables; plots a scattergram of 2 variables; two-way tabulation of 2 frequency variables; lists values of residuals; groups values of a variable into specified class; extracts subset of the observations; auto correlation analysis of specified variable; lists data

References

Availability
Purchase

Language

Computer
CPM 86, MS-DOS, CPM 2.2

1726

AP125: Statistical analysis of concrete cubes *Oasys Limited*
Analyses concrete cube crushing strengths in accordance with CP110. Features include: statistical results in tabular and graphical form; intermediate results after every 40 cubes

References

Availability
Purchase

Language
Basic

Computer
HP 9845 HP 85/87

1727

Statistical Analysis *Tandy Corporation*
Programs for descriptive statistics, graphic histogram, frequency distribution, one and two-way analysis of variance, one-way analysis of covriance, correlation matrix, chi-square analysis, time series analysis, multiple regression, random data samples and item analysis and test/survey scoring

References

Availability
Purchase

Language

Computer
TRS-80
Model II

1728

Linear regression scatter *TRADA*
A program for producing a complete scatter diagram with regression line and 98 per cent lower confidence line (straight)

References

Availability

Language

Computer

1729

GENSTATS *United Information Services Limited*
An interactive program for general statistical analysis. It can calculate basic statistics, such as mean and standard deviations, compute correlations, regressions and T-tests, and perform data transformations, all under the user's control. It also has a general file handling section

References

Availability
Bureau service, time sharing

Language
Fortran

Computer
Honeywell
Sigma 9

1730

TENSILE DATA SYSTEM 1 *Heyden & Son Limited*
Used with most tensile testing machines. Provides automatic calculation and report generation. Plots stress against strain; plots stress against displacement or time. Calculates to BS 18 and IS082: ultimate tensile stress, elastic modules, proof stress, percentage elongation and reduction in area. Produces reports, graphs and statistical data

References

Availability
Purchase

Language

Computer

1731

Rank Statistics *Hilbern Engineering Software, USA*
Two programs for statistical analysis based on ranked data sets. The tests are Friedman's Test and Spearman's Correlation test. The tests are distribution independent and can be applied to data that is ranked on the basis of non-quantative factors

References

Availability
Purchase

Language
Basic

Computer
IBM, CP/M, TRS-80, Max-80

Computer programs for the building industry

Hardware directory

3M (UK) Plc
9th Floor, 3M House
PO Box 1
Bracknell
Berkshire
RG12 1JU
0344 58300

Abacus Computers Limited
62 New Cavendish Street
London
W1M 7LD

Able Computer Support Centre
287 London Road
Newbury
Berkshire
RG13 2QJ
(0635) 32125
848715

ABS Computers
Multibus House
Station Approach
Woking
Surrey
GU22 7UZ
Woking 70516
859143

Ace Computers
Wolsey Hall
Oxford
(0865) 54233

Ace Microsystems Limited
Challenger House
125 Gunnersbury Avenue
London
W3 8LH
01–993 5036

ACI Calapine
12 & 13 Sheep Street
Wellingborough
Northants
(0933) 229292

ACT (Sirius) Limited
ACT House
111 Hagley Road
Birmingham
West Midlands
337007

ADDS (UK) Limited
137–141 High Street
New Malden
Surrey
KT3 4BH
01–949 1272

Adler Business Computers Limited
140–154 Borough High Street
London
SE1 1LH
01–407 3191
887349

Advanced Data Communications
116 Cleveland Street
London
W1P 5DP
01–387 7930
295788

Advent Data Products Limited
Merlin Way
Bowerhill
Melksham
Wiltshire
NS12 6TJ
(0225) 706289
449469

AES Data (UK) Limited
170 Windmill Road
Sunbury on Thames
Middlesex
TW16 7HH
(09327) 88342

Alberta Limited
70 Park Street
St Albans
Herts
0727 74361/2

Allegro Computer Services Limited
Abbey Mill
Bishops Waltham
Southampton
SO3 1DH
Bishops Waltham (04893) 6266

Almarc Data Systems Limited
Great Freeman Street
Nottingham
(0602) 52657
37407

Alper Systems Limited
35 Impington Lane
Histon
Cambridge
0220 234452

Altos Computer Systems
Index House
Ascot
Berks
SL5 7EU
(0602) 52657
849426

AM Admel Limited
Brooklands Road
Weybridge
Surrey
KT13 0RL
Weybridge 47212

AM Programmers Limited
Bridge House
Broad Street
Teddington
TW11 8QT

Amber Controls Limited
Central Way
Andover
Hants
SP10 5AL
Andover 65951
477048

American Microcomputers Limited
IDA, Unit 20
Pearse Street
Enterprise Centre
Dublin 2
0001–717 477

Amida Systems
71 St Peters Street
St Albans
Herts
AL1 3ED
0727 34251

Anagram Systems
Kingston House
Stephenson Way
Three Bridges
Crawley
Sussex
RH10 1TN
0293 26494

Apple Computer UK Limited
Eastman Way
Hemel Hempstead
Herts
HP2 7PS
Hemel Hempstead 60244
825834

Applicon UK
Regent House
Heaton Lane
Stockport
SK4 1DA
061–429 7227
668697

Applied Computer Systems Limited
51 Garamonde Drive
Wymbush Industrial Estate
Milton Keynes
MK8 8DD
(0908) 567933

ARC Limited
4 Jesus Lane
Cambridge
CB5 8BA
(0223) 65015
851153

Asolv Limited
12–14 Church Street
Basingstoke
Hampshire
RG21 1QH
(0256) 795 746

Autosystems Limited
Crosland Hall
Netherton
Huddersfield
HD4 7DZ
0484 665111
517165

B & W Micro Computers
Hollingworth Court
Turkey Mill
Ashford Road
Maidstone
Kent
ME14 5PN
0622 675471/4

BDP (Word Processing) Limited
Hill House
Clock Tower Road
Isleworth
Middx
TW7 6DT
01–560 7905
895513

Beam Microqwest
Richmond House
12–13 Richmond Buildings
Dean Street
London
W1V 5AF
01–434 3933

Bell & Howell Business Equipment Div
33–35 Woodthorpe Road
Ashford
Middx
TW15 2RJ
Ashford (07842) 51234
266119

Bencom Communications
190 Petersham Road
Richmond
Surrey
TW10 7AD
01–940 1386
8954102

Berrys of Holborn
37–39 High Holborn
London
WC1V 6BG
01–405 6231

Bonsai Limited
112–116 New Oxford Street
London
WC1A 1HJ
01–580 0902
28905

Briarstar Limited
Regency House
Churchtown
Belton
Nr Doncaster
DN9 1PA
Epworth (0427) 873008

Britannia Computers Limited
12 Castle Hill
Dudley
West Midlands
(0384) 233433

British Olivetti Limited
Olivetti House, PO Box 89
86—88 Upper Richmond Road
London
SW15 2UR
01—785 6666

British Telecom
ME Publ 121
3rd Floor, Seal House
Swan Lane
London
EC4R 3TH
01—357 3701

Building Design Software
3 Sandileigh Drive
Hale
Cheshire
WA15 8AS
061—928 3021
665275

Burroughs Machines Limited
Heathrow House
Bath Road
Cranford
Middx
01—679 1533

Busicomputers Limited
Polebrook Hall
Peterborough
5LN PE8
Oundle (0832) 72052

Business Computer Systems PLC
The Pagoda
Theobald Street
Borehamwood
Herts
WD6 4RT
01—207 3344
8813195

Business Computers (Systems) Limited
North Street
Portslade
Brighton
Sussex
BN4 1ER
0273 420565
87488

Byteshop Computerland
324 Euston Road
London
NW1
01—387 0505

Bytronix Microcomputers Limited
83 West Street
Farnham
Surrey
GU9 7EN
Farnham 726814

C/WP Computers
108 Rochester Row
London
SW1
01—828 900/01—630 7444

CalComp Limited
Cory House
The Ring
Bracknell
Berks
RG12 1ER
Bracknell 50211
848949

Calma (UK) Limited
Beech House
373/399 London Road
Camberley
Surrey
GU15 3HP
(0276) 682021
858216

Canon (UK) Limited
Waddon House
Stafford Road
Croydon
Surrey
01—680 7700

The Carter-Parratt Group Limited
VISIrecord House
Kimpton Road
Sutton
Surrey
SM3 9QD
01—644 4355
943959

Case Office & Computer Systems
Caxton Way
Watford Business Park
Watford
WD1 81X
(0923) 33500
298807

CBS Consultants
75 Watery Lane
Birmingham
B9 4HW
021—772 8181

Chatterbox Computers Limited
Whitechaple Technology Centre
75 Whitechaple Road
London
E1
01—377 9341

Chernikeeff Telecommunications
Limited
Pumping Station Road
Chiswick
London
W4 2SN
01—994 6685

Chubb Cash Limited
Crowhurst Road
Hollingbury
Brighton
East Sussex
BN1 8AQ
0273 558441

Cifer Sytems Limited
Avro Way
Bower Hill
Melksham
Wiltshire
SM12 6TP
0225 706361

City Microsystems Limited
65 London Wall
London
EC2M 5TU
01—588 7272

Cleno Computing Systems Limited
Crown House
18 Gipsy Hill
London
SE19 1NL
01—670 4202
8954102

CMG (UK) Limited
Sunley House
Bedford Park
Croydon
CR0 2AP
01—686 8251

Colt Computer Systems Limited
Fairfield Works
Fairfield Road
Hounslow
Middx
TW3 1UY
01—577 2686

Comart Limited
Little End Road
Eaton Socon
St Neots
Huntingdon
Cambridgeshire
PE19 3JG
0480 215005
32514

Commodore Business Machines (UK)
Limited
818 Leigh Road
Trading Estate
Slough
Berks
0753 74111
848403

Commodore Information Centre
675 Ajax Avenue
Slough
Berks
SL1 4BG
Slough (0753) 79292

Compucorp Limited
Barnet House
120 High Street
Edgware
Middx
HA8 7EL
01—952 7860
923421

Compuquant Limited
Witbridge House
Derby
(0332) 44924

Computational Mechanics
125 High Street
Southampton
SO1 0AA
0703 21397

Computeam Technology Limited
Stone Rede
Stansted
Sevenoaks
Kent
TN15 7PS
0732 822460

Computer Ancillaries Limited
64 High Street
Egham
Surrey
TW20 9EY
Egham 36455
934598

Computer Automation Limited
Hertford House
Maple Cross
Rickmansworth
Herts
WD3 2XB
09237 71211

The Computer Centre
39 Sidbury
Worcester
WR1 2NU
0905 26108

Computer Information Centre Limited
Spirella Building
Bridge Road
Letchworth
Herts
0426 79466

Computer programs for the building industry

Computer Products (International)
Limited
Westbourne House
159 Oldham Road
Ashton-under-Lyne
Lancs
OL7 9AR
061—339 8747

Computer Technology Limited
Eaton Road
Hemel Hempstead
Herts
HP2 7LB
0442 3272
825052

Computervision
1040 Uxbridge Road
Hayes
Middx
UB4 0RJ
01—561 2626
8954125

Comway Microsystems Limited
Market Street
Bracknell
Berks
RG12 1JU
Bracknell 55333
847201

Control Data Limited
179—199 Shaftesbury Avenue
London
WC2H 8AR
01—240 3400
267656

Couhlson Heron Associates Limited
1,2 & 3 Angel Court
Market Harborough
Leicestershire
(0858) 63902

Counting House Computer Systems
Limited
Fornham House
Fornham St Martin
Bury St Edmunds
Suffolk
(0284) 68921
817078

CPS (Data Systems) Limited
Arden House
1102 Warwick Road
Acocks Green
Birmingham
B27 6BH
021 707 3866
312280

CPT (UK) Limited
48 Berners Street
London
W1P 3AD
01—741 9050

CSL Business Systems Limited
Bijoli House
Icknield Way
Letchworth
Herts
SG6 4AB
0426 73991

CTS Recognition Limited
32 Saville Row
London
W1X 1AG
01—734 8826

Cullinane Computer Pictures Limited
150 Southampton Row
London
WC2
01—408 1612

Cyber (UK) Limited
426—428 Cranbrook Road
Gants Hill
Ilford
Essex
IG2 6HW
01—518 1414
897311

Dacoll Group
Dacoll House
Gardeners Lane
Bathgate
West Lothian
EH48 1TP
(0506) 56565

Data and Control Equipment Limited
DCE House
Bessemer Crescent
Rabans Lane
Aylesbury
Bucks
0296 32971

Data Efficiency Limited
Maxtel Road
Maylands Avenue
Hemel Hempstead
Herts
HP2 7LE
0442 57137
825554

Data General Limited
Hounslow House
724—734 London Road
Hounslow
Middx
TW3 1PD
01—572 7455
935364

Data Logic Limited
29 Marylebone Road
London
NW1
01—486 7288
888103

Data Recall Limited
Diamond House
Bookham Industrial Park
Church Road
Bookham
Surrey
(0372) 58911
892414

Data Recording Equipment Limited
Hawthorne Road
Staines
Middx
TW18 3BJ
0784 51388
263156

Data Terminals & Communications
The Genesis Centre
Birchwood Science Park
Warrington
Cheshire
WA3 7BH
(0925) 824645
628761

Data Text
White Hart House
London Road
Blackwater
Camberley
Surrey
GU17 9AD
Camberley (0276) 32923
848980

Data Type Systems Limited
Unit 23
Elliott Road
West Howe Industrial Estate
Bournemouth
BH11 8JZ
02016 6561
497906

Datalect Limited
33—35 Portugal Road
Woking
Surrey

Datapoint (UK) Limited
Park House
191 London Road
Isleworth
Middx
TW7 5BO
01—560 5445

Dataword Equipment Limited
Park House, 1st Floor
The South Bank Business Centre
140 Battersea Park Road
London
SW11 4NB
01—627 0388
918820

Davy Computing Limited
Moorfoot House
2 Clarence Lane
Sheffield
S3 7UZ
(0742) 71201
54184

Decision Graphics UK Limited
Gatwick Road
Crawley
West Sussex
RH10 2UN
0293 543675
877471

Design Plus
2—4 Canning Street Lane
Edinburgh
EH3 8ER
031—228 2181
727893

Desktop Computing Limited
2—4 Bridge Street
Warrington
WA1 2QW
0925 415415

The Dictaphone Company Limited
Regent Square House
The Parade
Leamington Spa
Warwickshire
CV32 4NL
0926 38311
312327

Digico Limited
Arena House
46 The Broadway
Letchworth
Herts
Letchworth 78172
825508

Digital Building Systems Limited
Orient House
Granby Row
Manchester
M1 7AN
061—236 3396
666380

Digital Data Electronics Limited
Clarks House
Pump Lane
Hayes
Middx
01—573 8854

Digital Equipment Co Limited
PO Box 53
DEC Park
Reading
RG2 0TW

Digital Systems Limited
Fitzherbert Road
Farlington
Portsmouth
Hants
PO6 1RU
0705 324934
86883

Digitus Limited
Lading House
10–14 Bedford Street
Covent Garden
London
WC2E 9HE

Domain-Apollo Computer (UK) Limited
Bulbourne House
Gossoms End
Berkhamsted
Herts
HP4 3LP
(04427) 75026
825357

Dragon Data Limited
Queensway
Swansea Industrial Estate
Swansea
SA5 4EH

DRG Business Machine
5th Floor
Kingsway House
103 Kingsway
London
WC2B 6QW
01–242 0621

Duport Computer Services Limited
Sedgley Road East
Tipton
West Midlands
DY4 7RT
021–557 4922

Ego Computer Systems Limited
Bennett House
1 High Street
Edgware
Middx
HA8 7HR
01–951 0744
261215

EMG National Microcentres
2 Fleming Way Industrial Centre
Gatwick
Crawley
West Sussex
(0293) 519211
878124

Encotol Systems Limited
7 Imperial Way
Croydon Airport Industrial Estate
Croydon
Surrey
CR0 4RR
01–686 9687
8951921

Engineering Computer Services
Limited
Piccadilly
Tamworth
Staffs
B78 2ER
(0827) 873300
341687

Engineering Graphic Applications
Limited
52 Sutherland Square
London
SE17

Entex Limited
Entex House
High Street
Merstham
Redhill
Surrey
RH1 3EA
Merstham 2727
926395

Epson (UK) Limited
Dorland House
388 High Road
Wembley
Middx
01–900 0466

Equinox Computer Systems Limited
Kleeman House
16 Anning Street
New Inn Yard
London
EC2A 3HB
01–739 2387
27341

ESDU (Engineering Sciences Data Unit)
251–259 Regent Street
London
W1R 7AD
01–437 4894
266168

Estimation Limited
Highlands Road
Shirley
Solihull
West Midlands
B90 4NL
021–704 3221
338018

Euro-Calc Limited
224 Tottenham Court Road
London
W1
01–636 8161

Evets Computers Limited
123–125 Green Lane
Derby
DE1 1RZ
(0332) 363981
377106

The Exchange Telegraph Company
Limited
Extel House
East Harding Street
London
EC4P 4HB
01–739 2041
27595

F International Limited
The Bury
Church Street
Chesham
Bucks
HP5 1LB
02405 4999
837213

Ferguson Computers Limited
Ground Floor, Wellington House
New Zealand Avenue
Walton-on-Thames
Surrey
KT12 1PY
Walton-on-Thames (09322) 41692/7

Ferranti Cetec Graphics Limited
Bell Square
Brucefield
Livingston
West Lothian
EH54 9BY
0506 411583
727898

Ferranti Computer Systems Limited
Gwent House
Town Centre
Cwmbran
Gwent
NP4 1PL
06333 67761
497636

Ferranti Computer Systems Limited
Wythenshawe Division
Simonsway
Manchester
M22 5LA
061–499 3355

FI-Cord International Limited
Didsbury
Manchester
M20 0RD
061–4457716
668914

Five Technology Limited
Britannia Way
Lichfield
Staffs
WS14 9UY
Lichfield (05432) 57701
335836

Flexiform
16 Duncan Terrace
London
N1 8BZ
01–278 0671

Formscan Limited
Apex House
West End
Frome
Somerset
BA11 3AS
0373 61446

Fortune Systems Limited
52 Bedford Square
London
WC1
01–631 3383
262658

Fully Integrated Business Systems
Limited
30 Spring Lane
Erdington
Birmingham
B24 9BX
021–382 8414

Future Computers Limited
PO Box 306
Purley
Surrey
01–689 4341

Future Technology Limited
Britannia Way
Lichfield
Staffs
WS14 9UY
Lichfield (05432) 57701

GBM (Goodknoll) Limited
3 Harpton Parade
Yateley
Surrey
Yateley 875335

GEC Computers Limited
Elstree Way
Borehamwood
Hertfordshire
WD6 1RX
01–953 2030
22777

Gecas Microcomputers Limited
Freepost
London
W1E 3UZ
01–629 3758

Geest Computer Services Limited
Carr Road Industrial Estate
Royce Road
Peterborough
PE1 5YB
(0733) 51231

Geisco Limited
114—118 Southampton Row
London
WC1B 5AB
01—242 5725

General Computer Systems (UK)
Limited
12 Mount Road
Hanworth
Feltham
Middx
01—898 5251

Gestetner Duplicators Limited
PO Box 23
Gestetner House
210 Euston Road
London
NW1 2DA
01—387 7021
22153

Geveke Electronics Limited
RMC House
Vale Farm Road
Woking
Surrey
GU21 1DW
Woking (04862) 26331
859531

GMW Computers Limited
Castle Mill
Lower Kings Road
Berkhamsted
Hertfordshire
04427 5481
825797

GNT Automatic (UK) Limited
Suffolk House
High Street
Sunningdale
Berkshire
Ascot 26156

Gould Bryans Instruments Limited
Willow Lane
Mitcham
Surrey
CR4 4UL
01—640 3490
946097

Grafox Limited
35 St Clements
Oxford
OX4 1AB
(0865) 242597

Graphic Information Systems Limited
1 High Street
Blairgowrie
Perthshire
PH10 6ET
(0250) 3166

Grundy Business Systems Limited
Science Park
Milton Road
Cambridge
CB4 4BH
(0223) 350355
818849

H B Computers Limited
22 Newland Street
Kettering
Northants
0536 520910

Hadland Graphic Arts
Newhouse Road
Bovingdon
Hemel Hempstead
Herts
HP3 0EL
(0442) 832525
82344

Michael Haines
55 Addington Road
West Wickham
Kent
BR4 9BN
01—462 5875

Robert Harding TV Limited
63 London Road
Brighton
Sussex
BN1 4JE
Brighton 608444

Harper and Tunstall Limited
CADD Systems Division
Denington
Wellingborough
Northamptonshire
(0933) 71166
31690

Hartley Reece & Company
Building One, GEC Estate
East Lane
Wembley
Middx
HA9 7PY
01—908 2577

Hasler Limited
Commerce Way
Croydon
Surrey
CR0 4XA
01—680 6050

Hawk Computers Limited
Park House
88—102 Kingsley Park Terrace
Northampton
(0604) 710522

Haywood Electronic Associates Limited
Electron House
Leeway Close
Hatch End
Pinner
Middx
HA5 4SE
01—428 0111
896819

Held Products
16 Station Parade
Harrogate
Yorks
HG1 1UE
0423 504772

Hevacomp
25 Byron Road
Sheffield
Yorks
S7 1RY

Hewlett Packard Limited
Fourier House
257—263 High Street
London Colney
Herts
AL2 1HG
0727 24400

Thos Hill International Limited
Hill House
142 Clock Tower Road
Isleworth
Middlesex
TW7 6DT
01—847 1881

Hitachi Sales (UK) Limited
Computer Products Division
Hitachi House
Station Road
Hayes
Middx
UB3 4DR
01—848 8787
933611

Holec
Station Road
Horsham
West Sussex
RH13 5EU
0403 69612
877784

Honeywell Information Systems Limited
Great West Road
Brentford
Middx
TW8 9DH
01—568 9191

Hoskyns Group Limited
Africa House
64 Kingsway
London
WC2
01—242 1951

Hotel Information Services Limited
387 High Road
Willesden
London
NW10 2JR
01—451 3888
8813089

Hovat Limited
88 Main Road
Sundridge
Sevenoaks
Kent
TN14 6ER
0959 64443

Hytec Microsystems Limited
9 West Way
Oxford
OX2 0JB
(0865) 726644
837875

IBM United Kingdom Limited
PO Box No 218
40 Basinghall Street
London
EC2P 2DY
01—628 7700
884382

IBM United Kingdom Limited
Marketing & Services Communications
PO Box 32
Alencon Link
Basingstoke
Hants
PO9 6BD
(0256) 56144
858043

IBM United Kingdom Limited
101 Chiswick High Road
London
W4

IBR Microcomputers Limited
Unit 57
Suttons Industrial Park
Earley
Reading
Berks
RG6 1AZ
Reading (0734) 664111

Icarus Computer Systems Limited
Deane House
27 Greenwood Place
London
NW5 1NN
01—485 5574
264209

Impetus Computer Systems
Classic offices
Hendon Central
London
NW4 3NN
01—202 2726

Imtech Limited
170 Honeypot Lame
Stanmore
Middx
HA7 1LB
01—204 8355
924574

Informer International Inc
PO Box 91054
Los Angeles
California 90009
(213) 649 2030
910—328 6544

Intergraph (Great Britain) Limited
Albion House
Oxford Street
Newbury
Berks
RG13 1JG
0635 49044
848831

International Computers Limited
ICL House
Putney
London
SW15 1SW
01—788 7272
22971

International Research and
Development
Fossway
Newcastle-upon-Tyne
NE6 2YD
(0632) 650451
537086

Internet Limited
43 West Street
Dorking
Surrey
RH4 1BU
Dorking (0306) 886 442

Interscan Communication Systems
Limited
39 Montrose Avenue
Slough
Berks
SL1 6BS
Slough 70821

Intertec Data Systems
2300 Broad River Road
Columbia
SC 29210
803 798 9100
810 666 2115

IO Technology PLC
4 Playhouse Yard
Blackfriars Lane
London
EC4V 5EX
01—248 4876

Isher Woods Computer Systems Group
110/112 Leagrave Road
Luton
Beds
LU4 5HX
Luton 416204
825562

Itek Internatinal Corporation
Itek House
Mora Street
London
EC1V 8BT
01—253 3080
883060

J R Micros (Anglia) Limited
76 Rose Lane
Norwich
Norfolk
NR1 1RT

Jarogate Limited
197—213 Lyham Road
Brixton
London
SW2 5PY
01—671 6321

JEL Energy Conservation Services
Limited
Edgeley Road Industrial Estate
Cheadle Heath
Stockport
Cheshire
SK3 0XE
061—477 4165
665131

Jenson Computer Systems
30 Queen Square
Bristol
Avon
BS1 4ND
0272 297341
449721

Johnson Microcomputers
Johnson House
75—79 Park Street
Camberley
Surrey
GU15 3XE
Camberley 20446

Kalamazoo Limited, Micro Computer
Div
Northfield
Birmingham
B31 2RW
021 475 2191
336700

Kardex Systems (UK) Limited
2 Dyers Buildings
Holborn
London
EC1N 2JT
01—405 3434
27585

Keen Computers
5 Giltspur Street
London
EC1A 9DE
01—236 5682

Kendal Computer Group
Kendal House
700 Great Cambridge Road
Enfield
Middx
EN1 3PN
01—366 1411

Kent Automation Systems Limited
Hunting Gate
Hitchin
Herts
Hitchin 54801
82321

KGB Micros Limited
14 Windsor Road
Slough
Berks
SL1 2EJ
Slough 38310
847777

Kienzle Data Systems
224 Bath Road
Slough
SL1 4DS
Slough 33355
848535

Kodak Limited
PO Box 66
Hemel Hempstead
Herts
HP1 1JU
0442 61122 Ex 206

Kode Limited
Station Road
Calne
Wiltshire
0249 813771

Langton Information Systems Limited
133 Oxford Street
London
W1R 1TD
01—434 1031
21766

Lanier Business Products Inc
Rennell House
40a Mill Place
Kingston
Surrey
KT1 2RL
01—549 8741

Leterite Microtext Limited
Highland House
18—24 John Street
Luton
Beds
LU1 2JE
Luton 418819
826801

LMR Computer Services
54—57 Moorbridge Road
Maidenhead
Berks
SL6 8BN
0628 37123
847112

Logic Box Limited
31 Palmer Street
London
SW1
01—222 1122

Logica VTS Limited
64 Newman Street
London
W1A 4SE
01—637 9111
27200

Logitek (EIC Electronics Limited)
Logitek House
Bradley Lane
Standish
Greater Manchester
WN6 0XQ
0257 426644
677354

Lombard Services Limited
241 Field End Road
Eastcote
Ruislip
Middlesex
HA4 9NJ
01—868 0942

London Computer Centre Limited
43 Grafton Way
London
W1P 5LA
01—388 5721

Lowe Electronics
Bentley Bridge
Chesterfield Road
Matlock
Derbyshire
DE4 5LE
(0629) 2817
377482

LSI Computers Limited
Copse Road
St Johns
Woking
Surrey
GU21 1SX
Woking 23411
859592

Lucas Logic Limited
Welton Road
Wedgnock Industrial Estate
Warwick
CV34 5PZ
0926 497733

Lundy-Farrington Limited
3 Belmont Chambers
Baker Road
Uxbridge
UB8 1RG
0895 54623
86579

MAI UK Limited
Black Arrow House
2 Chandos Road
London
NW10 6NF
01-965 9731

Mannesmann Tally Limited
7 Cremyll Road
Reading
RG1 8NQ
Reading 580141
847028

Margaux Controls Limited
York House
199 Westminster Bridge Road
London
SE1 7UT
01-633 0866
919642

Master Systems Limited
100 Park Street
Camberley
Surrey
GU15 3NY
0276 28527

MBS Data Systems Limited
Aldwych House
Madeira Road
West Byfleet
Surrey
KT14 6BA
Byfleet 53151
847777

McAuto (UK) Limited
Crown Life House
Woking
Surrey
GU21 1XW
Woking (04862) 26761
859521

MCS Mini Computer Systems Limited
Park House
Park Street
Maidenhead
Berkshire
SL6 1SL
0628 71411

Measurement Control & Displays
Limited
8 North Street
North Square
Guildford
Surrey
GU1 4TD
Guildford (0483) 574659

Mediatech Business Systems Division
Woodside Place
Alperton
Wembley
Middx
HA0 1XA
01-903 4372
8814541

Mellordata
Woodgates Road
East Bergholt
Colchester
Essex
(0206) 298181
988764

Memory Computers (UK) Limited
Britannia House
960 High Road
London
N12 9RY
01-445 6614
291340

MGB Business Systems
Edmonds Chambers North
Marlowes
Hemel Hempstead
Herts
0442 212511

Micro Five
Britannia Way
Litchfield
Staffs
WS14 9UY
(05432) 57701
335836

MicroAPL Limited
19 Catherine Place
Victoria
London
SW1E 6DX
01-834 2687/8
914505 NODE

Microbits
346 London Road
Blackwater
Camberley
Surrey
GU17 9AA
Camberley 34044
858893

MicroComputer Land
1 Princes Street
The Square
Richmond
Surrey
TW9 1EB
01-948 6411

Microcomputers for Business Limited
Thameside Computer Centre
Ferry Works
Summer Road
Thames Ditton
Surrey
KT7 0QJ
01-398 2464

Microflex Limited
Worton Hall
Worton Road
Isleworth
Middx
TW7 6ER
01-568 6281
933432

Microscope Limited
Mill Lane
Taplow
Maidenhead
Berks
SL6 0AA
Maidenhead 72047

Microsense Computers Limited
Finway Road
Hemel Hempstead
Herts
HP2 7PS
Hemel Hempstead 48151
825554

Microsystem Services
PO Box 37
Lincoln Road
Cressex Industrial Estate
High Wycombe
Bucks
HP12 3XP
(0494) 41661
837187

Microwriter Limited
31 Southampton Row
London
WC1
01-831 6801

Midas Computer Services Limited
2 High Street
Steyning
Sussex
0903 813913
877886

Midlectron Limited
Midlectron House
Nottingham Road
Belper
Derby
DE5 1JQ
Belper 6811
377879

Millbank Computers Limited
Millbank House
Amyard Park Road
Twickenham
TW1 3HN
01-891 4691

Mini-computer Systems Limited
Park House
Park Street
Maidenhead
Berks
0628 71411
849434

Missing Link Computers Limited
Abacus House
53-55 Ballards Lane
London N3
01-349 4711

Mitsu Computers Limited
Oakcroft Road
Chessington
Surrey
KT9 1SA
01-397 5111
929929

Monotype Communications Limited
14-16 Cockspur Street
London
SW1Y 5BL
01-930 1323
917125

Mountford & Laxon Co Limited
20 Anchorage Road
Sutton Coldfield
West Midlands
B74 2PL
021-354 5389

Multicomputer Limited
24 Windmill Road
Brentford
Middx
TW8 0QA
01-568 5272
8812541

NBI Limited
Brummel House
33—39 Savile Row
London
W1X 1AG
01—434 3521

NCR
206 Marylebone Road
London
NW1 6LY
01—723 7070

NEC Business Systems (Europe)
Limited
164—166 Drummond Street
London
NW1 3HP
01—388 6100
261914

Newbury Laboratories Limited
68 Regent Street
Cambridge
CB2 1DP
0223 64862

Nexos Office Systems Limited
Centre Point
New Oxford Street
London
WC1A 1QA
01—240 5795
8952779

Nine Tiles Information Handling
Limited
Beach House
25 Greenside
Waterbeach
Cambridge
CB5 9HW
Cambridge (0223) 862125
861030

Nixdorf Computer Limited
125—135 Staines Road
Hounslow
Middx
01—570 1888

Nokia (UK) Limited
York House
Empire Way
Wembley
Middx
01—900 0421
8814680

Norrie Hill Limited
Sullivan House
493 London Road
Camberley
Surrey
GU15 3JE
Camberley 61175

Norsk Data Limited
Strawberry Hill House
Bath Road
Newbury
RG13 1NG
Newbury (0635) 35544
849819

Northern Ireland Computer Centre
Limited
4 High Street
Holywood
Co Down
BT18 9AZ
(02317) 6548

Oceanic Limited
95—97 Fenchurch Street
London
EC3M 5JB
01—488 9751
8951066

Office and Electronic Machines Plc
140—154 Borough High Street
London
SE1
01—407 3191

Office International Group
International House
Windmill Road
Sunbury on Thames
Middx
TW16 7HR
Sunbury on Thames 85666
889219

Office Technology Limited
Walkden House
3—10 Melton Street
London
NW1 2EB
01—388 6561

Olympia Business Machines
203 Old Marylebone Road
London
NW1 5QS
01—262 6788

Onyx Computers Limited
Chanctonbury House
Church Street
Storrington
West Sussex
RH20 4LZ
09066 5432
87213

Optim Computers Limited
Lawford House
427—429 Harrow Road
London
W10 4RE
01—969 6768

Osborne Computer Corporation (UK)
Limited
38 Tanners Drive
Blakelands North
Milton Keynes
Buckinghamshire
MK14 5BW
0908 615274
825220

Pafec Limited
Strelley Hall
Nottingham
NG8 6PE
(0602) 292291
377494

Panasonic Business Equipment (UK)
Limited
9 Connaught Street
London
W2 2AY
01—262 3121
28492

Perkin-Elmer Data Systems Limited
227 Bath Road
Slough
Berks
SL1 4AX
(0753) 34511
847376

Petalect Electronic Services Limited
32 Chertsey Road
Woking
Surrey
GU21 5JE
Woking 23637

Philips Business Systems
Elektra House
Colchester
Essex
0206 575115

Plessey Microsystems Limited
Water Lane
Towcester
Northamptonshire
NN12 7JN
Towcester (0327) 50312
31628

Plessey Peripheral Systems Limited
3 Harrowden Road
Brackmills
Northampton
NN4 0EB
Northampton (0604) 65151
312254

Plexus Computers Inc
Langley House
Langley Mill
Nottinghamshire
NG16 4AN
07737 66141
377985

Plus Business Systems Limited
Ashton Lodge
Ashton Road
Dunstable
Bedfordshire
LU6 1NP
Dunstable 666661

Polaroid Limited
Ashley Road
St Albans
Herts
AL1 5PR
St Albans 59191
263246

Polebrook Management Systems
Limited
Polebrook Hall
Peterborough
PE8 5LN
Oundle (0832) 72052/73049

Positron Computers Limited
Unit 16
Deacon Trading Estate
Newton-le-Willows
Lancs
WA12 9XQ
(09252) 29741

Poulter Computervision Systems
Poulter House
2 Burley Road
Leeds
LS3 1NJ
(0532) 469611
556339

PPM
Hermitage Road
St Johns
Woking
Surrey
GU21 1TZ
Brookwood 80111
858893

Prime Computers (UK) Limited
6 Lampton Road
Hounslow
Middx
TW3 1JL
01—572 7400
938371

Project Universe
Information Technology Division
Department of Industry
29 Bressenden Place
London
SW1E 5D
01—213 6526

Pye TMC Limited
Marketing Division
Swindon Road
Malmesbury
Wiltshire
SN16 9NA
Malmesbury 2861
44208

Q1 Europe Limited
Collingwood House
Nelson Gate
Southampton
SO1 0GX
0703 37226
477134

Quantum Computer Systems Limited
60—62 The Balcony
Merrion Centre
Leeds
(0532) 458877

Quest CAE
Quest House
Princes Road
Ferndown
Dorset
BH22 9HQ
(0202) 891010
41358

Quest Genesys Limited
Lisle Street
Loughborough
Leics
LE11 0AY
0509 39185
341747

R & H Systems Limited
Oxford House
Oxford Street
Wellingborough
Northants
NN8 4HG
Wellingborough (0933) 227477
311898

Racal-Milgo Limited
Landata House
Station Road
Hook
Hants
RG27 9JF
Hook (O25672) 3911
858294/5 and 858054

Racal-Redac Limited
Tewkesbury
Glos
GL20 8HE
(0684) 294161

Radan Computational Limited
19 Belmont
Lansdown Road
Bath
Avon
BA1 5DZ
(0225) 318483

Rair Limited
Wellington House
6—9 Upper St Martins Lane
London
WC2H 9EQ
01—836 6921
298452

Randaro Computer Systems
Daro Systems Services
Root End Road
Oldbury
Warley
West Midlands
B68 8SF
021—552 3092
337354

Rank Xerox
Bridge House
Oxford Road
Uxbridge
Middx
UB8 1HS
0895 51133

Raytheon Company
141 Spring Street
Lexington
Massachusetts 02173

Rediffusion Computers Limited
4th Floor, Holborn Hall
Holborn Hall
100 Gray's Inn Road
London
WC1 8AL
01—404 0066
28716

Redifon Computers Limited
Kelvin Way
Crawley
Sussex
0293 31211
877369

Research Machines Limited
Mill Street
Botley Road
Oxford
OX2 0BW
(0865) 49866
83703

Rhone Poulenc Systems Limited
High Street
Houghton Regis
Bedfordshire
LU5 5QL
0582 605551

Riva Terminals Limited
9 Woking Business Park
Albert Drive
Woking
Surrey
GU21 5JY
Woking (04862) 71001
859502

Robinson Ford Associates
The Chapel
5 Salisbury Street
Cranborne
Dorset
BH21 5PU
Cranborne (07254) 566

Rostronics Limited
115 Wandsworth High Street
London
SW18
01—870 4805
8813089

Rotring UK
Building One
GEC Estate
East Lane
Wembley
Middx
HA9 7PY
01—908 2577

Sanyo Marubeni (UK) ltd
8 Greycaine Road
Watford
Herts
Watford 46363

Satchwell
57 Westow Hill
London
SE19
01—761 1422

Scope Data Systems Limited
Cranfield Lodge
33 Crook Log
Bexleyheath
Kent
DA6 8ED
01—301 0660

Scotia Office Machines Limited
2—4 Castle Terrace
Edinburgh
EH1 2DP
031 229 2261

Scribe Computers Limited
Eagle House
High Street
Wimbledon
London
SW19 5EF
01—946 5357

Semaphore Computer Systems Limited
Borden House
Borough Road
Godalming
Surrey
GU7 2AE
04868 5631

Sension Limited
Denton Drive Industrial Estate
Northwich
Cheshire
CW9 7LU
Northwich 44321
666468

Shape Data Limited
All Saints Passage
Cambridge
CB2 3LS
(0223) 316673

Sharp Electronics (UK) Limited
Sharp House
Thorpe Road
Manchester
M10 9BE
061—205 2333
668380

Shelton Instruments Limited
22—26 Copenhagen Street
London
N1 0JD
01—278 6273

Siemans Limited
Siemans House
Windmill Road
Sunbury on Thames
Middlesex
TW16 7HS
09327 85691

Sintrom Electronics
1 Arkwright Road
Reading
Berks
RG2 0LS
Reading 875464
847395

SISCO (Small Information Systems Co
4 Moorfields
London
EC2
01—920 0315

Small Business Computer Systems
Limited
25 Church Road
Teddington
Middlesex
0784 63891

Socius Computer Systems (UK)
Limited
Samuel House
6 St Alban's Street
Haymarket
London
SW1Y 4SQ
01—930 4214
296885

Solitaire Business Systems Limited
580—586 Chiswick High Road
London
W4 5RP
01—995 3573

Sony (UK) Limited
Pyrene House
Sunbury-on-Thames
Middx
TW16 7AT
Sunbury 81211
266371

Sperry Univac Centre
Stonebridge Park
North Circular Rd
London
NW10 8LS
01—965 0511
8951141

Star Computer Group PLC
64 Great Eastern Street
London
EC2A 3QR
01—739 7633
892544

Sumlock Bondain Limited
263—269 City Road
London
EC1V 1JX
01—250 0505
299844

Summagraphics Limited
3—4 Winchcombe Road
Newbury
Berks
(0635) 32257

Supabeam Computer Services
4 The Bishopric
Horsham
Sussex
(0403) 61647

Syscom Computers Limited
Kelvin House
The Broadway
Dudley
West Midlands
DY1 4PY
Dudley 236701
335001

Systime Limited
Millshaw Park
Leeds
0532 702277
556283

TABS Limited
Sopers House
Chantry Way
Andover
Hants
SP10 1PE
0264—58937

Tally Limited
Tally House
7 Cremyll Road
Reading
RG1 8NQ
Reading 580141
847028

Tandata Marketing Limited
Wells Road
Malvern
Worcestershire
W1 14PA
06845 68421

Tandy Corp (UK Branch)
Tameway Tower
Bridge Street
Walsall
West Midlands
WS1 1LA
(0922) 648181
339423

TDI Limited
29 Alma Vale Road
Clifton
Bristol
BS8 2HL
(0272) 742796

Techex Limited
5B Roundways
Elliott Road
West Howe Industrial Estate
West Howe, Bournemouth
Dorset
BH11 8JJ
02016 71181
41437

Tektronix UK Limited
PO Box 69
36—38 Coldharbour Lane
Harpenden
Herts
AL5 4UP
(05827) 63141
25559

Telecom Gold Limited
42 Weston Street
London
SE1 3QD
01—403 6777

Telema Business Computer Systems
Bruntwood Hall
Schools Hill
Cheadle
Cheshire
SK8 1JD
061—491 1295
667067

Terodec Limited
Unit 58
Suttons Park Avenue
Earley
Reading
Berkshire
RG6 1AZ
0734 664343
849758

Tetra Data Systems Limited
Tetra House
14—16 Temple End
High Wycombe
Bucks
HP13 5DR
0494 448773

Texas Instruments
Manton Lane
Bedford
MK41 7PA
(0234) 67466
82178

Thorncroft Manor Services Limited
Thorncroft Manor
Dorking Road
Leatherhead
Surrey
KT22 8JB
Leatherhead 76756
929333

TKT Computer Services Limited
Cockell House
Penrith
Cumbria

Torch Computers Limited
Abberley House
Great Shelford
Cambridge
CB2 5LQ
0223 841000

Touchstone Computers Limited
319 City Road
London
EC1V 1JL
01—278 5708

Transdata Limited
11 South Street
Havant
Hants
PO9 1BU
Havant 486556
86806

Transmitton Limited
Smisby Road
Ashby-De-la-Zouch
Leicestershire
LE6 5UG
05304 5941
342284

Transtec Computers
13a Small Street
Bristol
BS1 1DG
(0272) 277462

Transtel Communications Limited
Station Road
Langley
Slough
Berks
0753 44222

Trend Communications Limited
Knaves Beech Estate
Loudwater
High Wycombe
Bucks
06285 24977

Triumph Adler (UK) Limited
27 Goswell Road
London
EC1M 7AJ
01—250 1717
897772

Trivector Commerce Limited
Sunderland Road
Sandy
Beds
SG19 1RB
Sandy (0767) 82222
825478

Turnkey Software Limited
12 Clifton Street
Chalfont St Giles
Bucks
02407 5995

Tycom Corporation
8—12 New Bridge Street
London
EC4V 6AL
01—583 2755
8955766

Ultronic Data Systems Limited
31—33 Park Royal Road
London
NW10 14E
01—965 5744

Unilever Computer Services Limited
PO Box 110
Watford
Herts
WD1 1SA
Watford 47911

Unit C Limited
Dominion Way West
Broadwater
Worthing
West Sussex
0903 212114

Universal Computers Limited
23 Paradise Street
London
SE16 4QD

Universal Computers Limited
23 Paradise Street
London
SE16 4QD
01—232 1155
8955698

Vector Graphic
Vector House
William Street
Windsor
Berks
SL4 1BA
(07535) 69375
848558

Vega Computers Limited
10 Essex House
George Street
Croydon
CR0 1PH
01—680 4484

Ventek Limited
112 North Acton Road
London
NW10 6QH
01—965 8722

Videcom Limited
Newtown Estate
Reading Road
Henley-on-Thames
Oxon
RG9 1HG
04912 78427

Vitel Limited
Vitel House
Albert Road
Hendon
London
NW4 2SH
01—203 6161

Volker-Craig (UK) Limited
William Olds Estate
Tolpits Lane
Watford
Herts
WD1 8XL
Rickmansworth (0923) 771378
8956082

Vydec
Exxon Information Systems
Borax House
Carlisle Place
London
SW1P 1HT
01—834 9070

Wang (UK) Limited
661 London Road
Isleworth
Middx
01—486 0200
8954350

Westward Micro Systems Limited
Alexandra Way
Ashchurch Industrial Estate
Tewkesbury
Glouchestershire
GL20 8NB
0684 298600
437239

Widefine Limited
41 London Road
Slough
Berks
SL3 7RP
Slough 35400

Wilkes Computing Limited
Bush House
72 Prince Street
Bristol
BS1 4QD
Bristol (0272) 25921
449205

Wimpey Group Services Limited
27 Hammersmith Grove
London
W6 7EN
01—748 2000
25666

Wootton Jeffreys & Partners
Cemetery Pales
Brookwood
Woking
Surrey
GU24 0BL
(04867) 80033
859589

Wordnet UK Limited
Buckingham Court
London
SW1
01—222 0592/5

AES Wordplex Limited
Excel House
De Montford Road
Reading
Berks
Reading (0734) 584141

Jonathan Wright & Ptns
Unit 16
Ongar Road Industrial Estate
Great Dunmow
Essex
CM6 1EU

Xtec Limited
High Street
Hartley Wintney
Hants
RG27 8PB
025 126 4222

Zenith Data Systems
Bristol Road
Gloucester
GL2 6EE
0452 29451
43179

Zenith Plan Limited
Shropshire House
2—10 Capper Street
London
WC1E 6JA
01—636 5364
24902

Zilog (UK) Limited
Zilog House
Moorbridge Road
Maidenhead
Berks
SL6 8PL
(0628) 39200
848609

Zynar Limited
122/3 High Street
Uxbridge
Middlesex
UB8 1JT
Uxbridge 59831

Databases

Computer programs for the building industry

219

ACOMPLINE

This is the catalogue of the GLC Research Library: books, journal articles, reports, pamphlets, etc. It takes an industrial library approach to urban information ranging from industrial relations, employment, public safety, to housing and pollution. Can compare with other more specialised databases in specific fields. The file originated in 1973 and now serves all departments in the GLC. It has absorbed libraries in the fields of mechanical and electrical engineering; scientific research; and, since 1980, architecture and construction
Records: 80,000
Growth rate per annum: 6,000
Greater London Council Research Library
The County Hall
London SE1 7PB
United Kingdom
Tel: 01—633 6482
Telex: 919443
Availability: On-line: via ESA-IRS
Also via a TTY-compatible terminal and telephone;
via video-text terminal

ALIS

ALIS is an on-line system for catalogue search combined with circulation control developed as a public service by the National Technological Library of Denmark (DTB) and I/S Datacentralen. It contains monographs and dissertations held by DTB and other Danish technological university libraries from 1968; Scandinavian union catalogue of conference proceedings accessed by Scandinavian technological university libraries; covers the period 1975 to date, updated monthly
Records: 115,000
Growth rate per annum: 12,000
I/S Datacentralen of 1959
Retortvej 6—8
DK—2500 Valby, Copenhagen
Denmark
Tel: (451) 4681 22
Telex: 27122
Availability: Magnetic tape
On-line
Direct call/Scannet/DTH.Net/and Euronet
Free of charge

API

The Architectural Periodicals Index provides a unique service to librarians, architects, researchers, students, art and architectural historians, and all those connected with the built environment. It covers 529 international journals and is produced by computer on a quarterly basis, in cooperation with Hutton + Rostron. The API includes a names index, a topographical index and an up to data bibliography of articles on building types, materials etc
Records: 63,000
Hutton + Rostron
Netley House
Gomshall, Surrey
GU5 9QA
Tel: 048—641 3221
Telex: 859167
Availability: Magnetic tape
Payable by subscription

ARIANE

Covers the fields of building technology and tools, i.e. construction techniques, thermal insulation, acoustics, equipments, materials etc; technical regulations concerning building in France; and building products: 10,500 manufacturers, 100,000 trademarks, 3,200 families of products. The data for the building industry carried covers the fields of over 70 trades. ARIANE was inaugurated in 1972, and is updated weekly
Records: 400,000,000 characters
Growth rate per annum: 50% of each year's total
ITBTP-CATED
9 Rue La Perouse
75784 Paris Cedex 16
France
Tel: (1) 720 10 20
Telex: FEDEBAT 611975
Availability: On-line
Payable by connect time

BCIS

A new database, launched in April 1984, which operates as a collaborative venture for the exchange of building cost information. User selects and retrieves information to store on their own microcomputer. Information can be manipulated by the user, with BCIS software
Records : 600 detailed, 2000 superficial information. 11,000 Index series
BCIS On-line
85—87 Clarence Street
Kingston-upon-Thames
Surrey
KT1 1RB
Tel: 01—546 7554
Availability: On-line
Payable by subscription

BSI

A catalogue of current and withdrawn British Standards Specifications, Codes of Practice, Drafts for Development and Provisional Documents covering the whole field of British Standards Institution's activities. The file is current at date of issue and is revised monthly. It is proposed to extend the database to include the names and addresses of firms approved under quality assurance schemes
Records: approximately 12,000
Growth rate per annum: approximately 2000 records
Hutton + Rostron
Netley House
Gomshall
Nr Guildford
GU5 9QA
Tel: 048 641 3221
Telex: 859167
Availability: Magnetic tape. Building industry
standards available through Contel Viewdata service

BUILDING RESEARCH ESTABLISHMENT

BRE's abstract database is likely to become publicly accessible on-line this year. The database covers the international journal, report and book literature on various aspects of building science
Records: approximately 100,000
Mr Peter Elvin, Librarian
Building Research Establishment
Garston, Watford
WD2 7JR
Tel: (0923) 674040

CECILE

This database covers the fields of industrial design, visual communication, architecture, and space planning, with a historical perspective over the 19th and 20th centuries. More specifically, the file on architecture includes; architectural design, history of contemporary architecture, industrial archaeology, research and forecasting, architectural education, building and architectural professional practice, and interior design. The database was created in 1973, and is updated monthly
Records: 15,000
Telesystemes-Questel
40 Rue du Cherche Midi
75006 Paris
France
Tel: (1) 544 3813
Telex: 204594
Availability: On-line
Payable by connect time

CIM

This database covers international bibliographic documentation concerning hydraulic bindings, cements, lines, plasters and related fields. It covers the period 1969 to date, and is updated monthly
Records: 13,000
Telesystemes-Questel
40 Rue du Cherche Midi
75006 Paris
France
Tel: (1) 544 3813
Telex: 204594
Availability: On-line
Payable by connect time

COMPENDEX

This is the computerised version of Engineering Index which summarises and indexes worldwide literature on civil, electrical, mechanical engineering and electronics. It covers subjects such as construction materials; water and waterworks engineering; materials properties and tests; thermodynamics; engineering physics etc. The literature scanned includes technical reports, professional and trade journals, conference proceedings and papers, books and documents having a limited distribution; it dates from 1969 to present
Records: 950,000
Growth rate per annum: c.100,000
ESA-IRS
Via Galileo Galilei
00044 Frascati
Italy
Tel: 06 94011
Telex: 610637 ESRIN I
Availability: On-line
Payable by connect time

CONTEXT

A Viewdata Service operated by AVS Intext; provides information on product supplies and trade names, together with British Standards bibliographical information, details on computer programs and a variety of practical information. A similar service, specifically for builders, will be established in September 1984
AVS Intext
145 Oxford Street
London, W1R 1TB
Tel: 01–434 2034
Availability: On-line
Payable by subscription

CRONOS-EUROSTAT

This is a time-series databank; it covers the fields of economy, products, production and trade, in the European Community, about 200 developing countries and USA and Japan. The subject areas range from monthly trade statistics, the iron and steel industry, to research and development, production and external trade. The information covers the time period from 1955 to date.
Records: 700,000 time series
Datacentralen af 1959
Retortvej 6–8
DK–2500 Valty, Copenhagen
Denmark
Tel: (451) 4681 22
Telex: 27122
Availability: On-line
Magnetic tape
Payable by connect time
Following: DKR5

EABS

The EABS database contains references to the published results of scientific and technical research programs wholly or partly sponsored by the commission of the European Communities. It covers a wide range of subject areas (e.g enviromental research, nuclear research). It covers material from 1966 onwards, and is updated monthly
Records: 25,000 citations
ECHO Customer Service
15 Avenue de la Faiencerie
Luxembourg
Tel: 352 20764
Telex: 2752 EURODUC LU
Availability: On-line
Free of charge

EDF-DOC

The subjects covered include Material properties and resistances; electrical material; Environment: waste; pollution; Electric applications (lighting, heating, air-conditioning). The file dates from 1972, and is updated monthly
Records: 208,800
Telesystemes-Questel
40 Rue du Cherche Midi
75006 Paris
France
Tel: (1) 544 3813
Telex: 204594
Availability: On-line
Payable by connect time

ENREP

The ENREP Database is an on-line directory of Enviromental Research Projects in the Member States of the European Communities, collected on a national basis by focal points under the management of the Commission of The European Communities. The research projects cover all aspects of the enviromental field, and date from 1980 onwards; regularly updated
Records: 17,000 research projects
ECHO Customer Service
15 Avenue de la Faiencerie
Luxembourg
Tel: 352 20764
Telex: 2752 EURODUC LU
Availability: On-line
Free of charge

EPOIS

The European Patents Office (EPO) is entrusted with the task of providing the public with register information in respect of the published European patent applications and patents. Register information can be obtained by direct access, and will display the most up-to-date state of the European Patent register
Records: 65,000 publications 10,000 patents
Growth rate per annum: 27,000 publications per year 8,000 patents
European Patents Office
P.B. 5818 Patentlaan, 2
2280 HV Rijswijk (2H)
Netherlands
Tel:70 906789
Telex: 31651
Availability: On-line: Publications telephone net. /EURONET
Payable by subscription

EUROCOPI

Eurocopi Database has been established to collect and disseminate information on scientific and technical computer programs. It covers areas such as computer sciences, physics, chemistry, engineering, management sciences, social sciences. Sources include libraries, software producers
Records: 2000
Growth rate per annum: 2000
Commission of the European Communities
Joint Research Centre
I–21020 Ispra (Va)
Italy
Tel: (0332) 780131/780271
Telex: 380042/380058 EUR 1
Availability: On-line
No charge during test phase (until end 1983)

EURODICAUTOM

This is an on-line terminology databank, containing scientific and technical terms, contextual phrases, and abbreviations in most of the official European Community languages. It is invaluable for those looking for translations for particular terms, and also for those needing up-to-date translations of scientific and technical terms which may not yet be available in printed form. Updated monthly
Records: 200,000 terms and contextual phrases 20,000 abbreviations
Growth rate per annum: 24,000
ECHO Customer Service
15 Avenue de la Faiencerie
Luxembourg
Tel: 352 20764
Telex: 2752 EURODUC LU
Availability: On-line
Free of charge

Geomechanics Abstracts

This is a bibliographic database consisting of documents pertaining to rock mechanics, soil mechanics and engineering geology. Subjects covered include tunnelling, support, foundation engineering, slope stability and site investigation. From 1977, updated bimonthly
Records: 7,500
Growth rate per annum: 1,500
Pergamon InfoLine Limited
12 Vandy Street
London EC2A 2DE
United Kingdom
Tel: 01 377 1225
Telex: 8814614
Availability: On-line
Payable by connect time

HSELINE

Produced by the Health and Safety Executive, Library and Information Services. Contains citations, with abstracts, to worldwide literature on occupational safety and health. Covers all UK Health and Safety Commission and H & S Executive publications as well as a wide range of periodicals, books, conference proceedings, reports and legislation. Includes all relevant areas of science and technology, with particular emphasis on engineering, manufacturing, agriculture, mining, nuclear technology, explosives and occupational hygiene.
Updated by approximately 800 records per month
Records : 27,000 references
The Online Information Centre
3 Belgrave Square
London, SW1X 8PL
Tel: 01—235 1732 (Direct line)
01—235 5050 (Aslib)
Telex: 23667
Availability: On-line
Payable by connect time

IBSEDEX

This database includes all forms of literature to provide a comprehensive coverage of the field of building services: heating, cooling, lighting, plumbing, air conditioning, electrical, solar, insulation, etc. The file dates from 1977.
Records: 22,000
Growth rate per annum: 5,000
Building Services Research and Information Association
Old Bracknell Lane
Bracknell
Berkshire RG12 4AH
United Kingdom
Tel: (0344) 25071
Availability: On-line
Magnetic tape
Payable by connect time outright purchase

INSPEC

A comprehensive information service covering physics, electrical engineering, electronics, computing and communications. Abstracts are provided for published literature, conference proceedings, journals, etc
Records: Over 2 million
INSPEC Marketing Division
Station House
Nightingale Road
Hitchin, Hertfordshire
SG5 1RJ
Tel: Hitchin (0462) 53331
Telex: 825962
Availability: On-line
Payable by connect time

LCMARC

This is the compilation of books catalogued by the Library of Congress in all subject areas, including all aspects of the building industry, since 1968
Records: 1,380,000
Growth rate per annum: 240,000
BLAISE
2 Sheraton Street
London W1V 4BH
United Kingdom
Tel: 01—636 1544
Telex: 21462
Availability: On-line
Magnetic tape
Payable by subscription connect time

LEXIS

A computer assisted legal research service which is available to British lawyers. Thought to be the largest database of its kind. Provides a research facility which is thorough, fast, economical and up to date. LEXIS is a large and rapidly expanding database of both English and European Communities law
Butterworth (Telepublishing) Limited
4—5 Bell Yard
London, WC2A 2JR
Tel: 01—404 4097
Telex: 95678
Availability: On-line
Payable by subscription or connect time

Meteorological Office

Data collected from some hundreds of Climatological stations, 130 Meteorological Office stations, 50 Aeolographic stations and some 5000 rain gauges since 1970 on a range of measurements from daily maximum and minimum ground temperatures to three-second gusts. Records of wind speeds, rainfall, air and ground temperatures, sunlight, incidence of snow, hail and fog can be obtained for selected stations throughout the United Kingdom
Growth rate per annum: not applicable
Climatological Services
Meteorological Office
London Road
Bracknell
Berkshire
RG12 2SZ
Tel: 0344 420242 extension 2279
Telex: 849801
Availability: Magnetic tape for specified stations and data

MINSYS

This is a databank covering the field of international mining and minerals, which includes the subject of construction materials
Records: 750,000
Growth rate per annum: 200,000
Geosystems
PO Box 1024
Westminster
London SW1
United Kingdom
Tel: 01—222 7305
Telex: 051 915771
Availability: On-line
Magnetic tape

NTIS

The NTIS database covers research, development and engineering reports from over 250 U.S federal government agencies and comprises 22 subject categories including electronics and electrical engineering; materials; mathematical sciences; mechanical, industrial, civil engineering; ordnance; physics. It covers business and economic data as well as scientific and technical report literature
Records: 750,000
Growth rate per annum: 60,000
ESA-IRS
Via Galileo Galilei
00044 Frascati
Italy
Tel: 06 94011
Telex: 610637 ESRIN I
Availability: On-line
Payable by connect time

NTIS

This database comprises abstracts of journals, reports etc of a technical nature on engineering, technology etc. Data-Star is the on-line information service of Radio Suisse S.A, based in Switzerland and marketed through offices in the UK, West Germany and France
Records: 700,000
Growth rate per annum: 25,000
DATA-STAR
199 High Street
Orpington BR6 0PF
United Kingdom
Tel: (0689) 38488
Telex: 898239
Availability: On-line
Magnetic tapes
Other machine-readable format
Payable by connect time

PASCAL and PASC 73

These two databases have a multi disciplinary subject coverage which includes: physics; chemistry; engineering science, i.e. mechanical engineering, building industry, public works, metallurgy. PASC 73 covers the period 1973—1976, and PASCAL, the period 1977 to date, updated monthly
Records: 1,700,000 PASC 73
2,600,000 PASCAL
Telesystemes-Questel
40 Rue du Cherche Midi
75006 Paris
France
Tel: (1) 544 3813
Telex: 204594
Availability: On-line
Payable by connect time

PICA

Property Services Agency Information on Construction and Architecture is a new database which corresponds to the Property Services Agency Library catalogue. Contains references and abstracts to most types of literature on building and architecture. Includes computer aided architectural design, interior design and all aspects of construction (fireproofing, ventilation, plumbing, energy conservation, health and safety regulations, etc)
Mr Richard Searle, Room C102
Property Services Agency
Whitgift Centre
Wellesley Road
Croydon, Surrey
CR9 2LY
Tel: 01—686 8716 ext 4483
Availability: On-line

PINCCA

The PINCCA databank provides a comprehensive set of accurate up-to-date price index numbers for current cost accounting. PINCCA applications also include: revaluing fixed assets; updating prices in line with national trends; econometrics analysis, modelling and forecasting; inflation analysis and research. Currently PINCCA includes over 280 price index time series, including indices for public and private housing and non-housing construction. Historical coverage consists of monthly data from 1968 for most series, and quarterly data from 1956 for most series. Updated monthly
SIA Computer Services
Ebury Gate
23 Lower Belgrave Street
London SW1 0NW
United Kingdom
Tel: 01—730 4544
Telex: 916635
Availability. On-line

PREDICASTS PROMT

This database comprises abstracts from trade journals across the world on industries, companies, technology, and markets. Data-Star is the on-line information service of Radio Suisse S.A, based in Switzerland and marketed through offices in the UK, West Germany and France
Records: 406,000
Growth rate per annum: 140,000
Data-Star 199 High Street Orpington BR6 0PF United Kingdom Tel: 0689 38488 Telex: 898239
Availability: On-line
Magnetic tape
Payable by connect time

RAPRA

The RAPRA abstracts database covers all commercial and technical information on polymer materials, processing and products. It covers the world's polymer literature, including journals, conference proceedings, books, specifications, reports and trade literature. Patents were included from 1978—80. The file covers the period 1972 to date, and is updated bi-weekly
Records: 154,000
Growth rate per annum: 24,000
Pergamon Infoline Limited
12 Vandy Street
London EC2A 2DE
United Kingdom
Tel: 01—377 1225
Telex: 8814614
Availability: On-line
Payable by connect time

SOFI

Contains descriptions (in German) of computer programs according to DIN 66230. Research; planning; laws; administration; the chemical, physical and biological aspects of construction; architecture; landscaping; mechanics; engineering; high and low-rise technology; surveying; foundations and supports; installation and finishing; materials and parts; light and water; transportation. The file covers the period 1981 to date and is updated continually; it is chiefly concerned with Federal Republic of Germany. In German
Records: 310
Informationszentrum RAUM und BAU
der Fraunhofer-Gesellschaft (IRB)
Nobelstrasse 12
D—7000 Stuttgart 80
West Germany
Tel: (0711) 6868—500
Telex: 7255 167
Availability: On-line
Payable by subscription

TED (Tender Electronic Daily)

The office for Official Publications of the European Communities publishes invitations to tender (ITTs) for millions of pounds worth of contracts, in its daily supplement $_S$ to the $_o$fficial Journal. This publication has been placed on-line and is available on the morning of its publication date. This makes immediate access possible to a wide range of ITTs for work and supply contracts, published in all seven Community languages
Growth rate per annum: 20—40 ITTs daily
Saarbrucker Zeitung
Verlag und Druckerei GmbH
Gutenbergstrasse 11—23
6600 Saarbrucken
Federal Republic of Germany
Tel: (0681) 502468
Telex: 4421262
Availability: On-line
Payable by
subscription
connect time

TEXTLINE

Textline provides access to constantly updated information on industries, companies, markets and products, with coverage of current economic data, attitudes, trends and forecasts. It uses as sources national newspapers, business journals, press releases, news tapes, corporate financial reports, etc; published in English, French, German, Italian, Japanese and Spanish. All are translated
Records: 230,395
Growth rate per annum: 140,000
Finsbury Data Services
68—74 Carter Lane
London EC4V 5EA
United Kingdom
Tel: 01 236 9771
Telex: 892520 FINDAT G
Availability: On-line
Payable by
subscription
connect time

UKMARC

This is the catalogue of British books in the British Library in all subject areas, including all aspects of the building industry, since 1950
Records: 800,000
Growth rate per annum: 40,000
BLAISE
2 Sheradon Street
London W1V 4BH
United Kingdom
Availability: On-line magnetic tape
Payable by subscription connect time

URBAMET

The coverage by this database is of scientific, technical, economical and legal information related to town planning, environment and transport. More specifically, the file includes town, country and land planning; housing and architecture; urban sociology; group building; local budget, local authority. It dates from 1976, and is updated monthly
Records: 40,000
Telesystemes-Questel
40 Rue du Cherche Midi
75006 Paris
France
Tel: (1) 544 3813
Telex: 204594
Availability: On-line
Payable by connect time

Indexes

Computer programs for the building industry

Index to terms

0904 alignments highway design
0902 alignments highways design
0905 alignments highways earthworks analysis
0477 allocations projects resource forecasts
1706 altitude azimuth angles
1603 aluminium UPVC manufacture windows doors
1597 aluminium UPVC windows double glazed
0727 analyse design 3D models production
0750 analyse graphs fire resistance
0182 analyse supply equipment hire utilisation
1298 analyses cable wire arrays
0353 analyses statements management invoices
0359 analysis accounting brought forward
1190 analysis beam elastic foundation
0773 analysis bridge deck grillage
0088 analysis control construction projects
0725 analysis dynamics graphical
0382 analysis income expenditure
0136 analysis information bill quantities
0671 analysis mapping network
0824 analysis pile loads elastic theory
0316 analysis project estimate
0823 analysis sheet piled walls cofferdams
1251 analysis slabs
0807 analysis structural piling
0749 analysis structural steelwork drawings
0758 analysis system finite element
0826 anchored retaining walls stress analysis
0707 angle distance survey points
1234 angles twist warping unstable loads
1693 anisotropic circular loads polynomial
0602 annotation graphics drawing
0820 applied moments pile group analysis
0927 aquifer well
0587 architect design/draughting geometric construction
0144 architect engineer billll quantity surveyor
0263 architect engineer surveyor specification clauses
0589 architect perspectives isometric projections
0631 architects 2 1/2D draughting design
0567 architects 2D 3D drawings model CAD
0647 architects 2D draughting package
0616 architects 2D symbolic drawings
0613 architects 3D model building design production
0350 architects accounting job costing
0632 architects bills estimates quantity surveyors
0125 architects bills quantities
0135 architects bills quantities
0153 architects bills quantities
0166 architects bills quantities
0599 architects builders 3D model design graphics
0226 architects builders merchants property management
0531 architects commitments account
0117 architects drawings bill quantities dimensions
0285 architects drawings register design
0633 architects engineers hatching 2D drawing
0429 architects fee control
0459 architects job analysis costing system
0463 architects management accounts analyses
0155 architects quantity surveying
0551 architectural design housing sites
0572 architectural draughting drawing 2D CAD
0566 architectural drawings design work symbols
0663 architectural drawings draughting
0591 architectural drawings interactive production
0555 architectural planning drawing 3D models
0330 architectural practice book-keeping accounting
0585 architecture CAD 2D draughting
0696 area conversions trigonometry surveying coordinate
0730 area position section properties rectangles
1098 area section properties
0167 areas takes-off plans maps
1474 areas volumes heat loss consumption lengths
0681 areas zone maps mapping information
1709 arithmetic expressions mathematics
0035 arrow networks cost critical path/resource
0019 arrow precedence networks
0027 arrow precedence PERT system CPM
0028 arrow project planning critical path
1630 artificial lighting rooms light fittings
0721 artificial excitation tests graphical
1629 artificial lighting daylight energy
1631 artificial lighting energy illumination
1622 artificial lighting fittings
0416 assets liabilities income/expenditure accounts
0177 assets management plant accounting depreciation
0333 assets values depreciation
0538 assignment problems transport
0334 audit management job cost trial balance
0419 audit trail accounting creditors control
0373 audit trail management accounting contractor
0360 audit trail trial balance accounting
0421 audit trails accounting analysis
0420 audit trails accounting VAT analysis

0414 audit trails trial balance budget
1130 axial forces deflection non-linear stability
1272 axial load end moments steel columns
1270 axial loads bending moments designs steel sections
1122 axial loads displacement force bar
1281 axisymmetric circular cylinders
0735 axisymmetric orthotropic well seepage temperature
0734 axisymmetric shells loads material properties
0635 axonometric views 3D presentation perspective
1706 azimuth angles altitude
0701 azimuth slope angles intersection coordinates
0700 azimuths traverse coordinates bearings
0936 backwater curve analysis flow channel
0527 bank details
0393 bank reconciliation invoices purchase ledger
0394 bank reconciliations statements
1122 bar axial loads displacement force
1095 bar bending schedules reinforced concrete
0657 bar chart plotting graphs
0091 bar charts CPM draw
0646 bar charts line graphs pie charts numeric
0595 bar charts monitoring graphics display
0545 bar charts performance sketch designs
0679 bar charts statistics graphs histograms
1124 bar cross-sectional properties
1247 bar design sections span
1245 bar design tension compression steel
0623 bar pie charts maps 3D charts graphics
0198 bar reinforcement bending schedules
1249 bar schedules flat slabs reinforced concrete
1112 bar schedules reinforcement quantities
1118 bar schedules weight steel reinforcing bars
0789 bar sizes design beams flexural reinforcement
1125 bar stresses cross section
1261 base plates uncased stanchions
1230 beam analysis structural analysis
1216 beam bending moment shear force
1191 beam bending moments shear forces
0799 beam cantilever reinforced concrete
1181 beam/column moment connections designs
1302 beam column reinforced concrete drawings
0755 beam/column steel detailing drawings
1227 beam column structural analysis design
1207 beam/column weight
1192 beam displacement method plane grids
1190 beam elastic foundation analysis
0992 beam elements plane grid simply supported
0768 beam finite elements concrete bridge slab
1215 beam load types single span
1188 beam loading deflection stress wood
1049 beam plane frame 2D
1231 beam pre-tensioned reinforced concrete
1194 beam prestressed concrete section
1160 beam rafter trussed beam roof members
1250 beam reinforcement slab
1283 beam sections joists column sections
1223 beam selection loading section properties
1178 beam shear forces bending moments slope deflection
1170 beam/slab structures reinforced concrete
1039 beam string column lifts frames
1208 beam weight W-section
1209 beam weight W-section
0796 beams analysis design
1229 beams columns design reinforced concrete
1218 beams columns elastic design steelwork
1313 beams columns end plate steel frames
0808 beams columns foundations design
1201 beams composite steel concrete
1222 beams cross-section section properties
1185 beams cross sections load conditions
1174 beams deflection bending moment
1233 beams deflection slope bending moment
1006 beams elastic analysis plates ribs
0789 beams flexural reinforcement bar sizes design
1219 beams load combinations reinforced concrete
1288 beams portal frames concrete slabs
1276 beams reinforced concrete columns
1203 beams section constants
1180 beams shear reinforced concrete
1179 beams slabs analysis
0964 beams slabs columns reinforced concrete
1171 beams stanchions design
1172 beams steel timber simply supported
1236 beams timber span tables
1212 beams timber steel concrete simple span
1016 beams trusses grids frames
0832 bearing capacity analysis footings
1280 bearing forces shaft displacements
0853 bearing pressures rectangular base loading
0848 bearing pressures steel resistance moment
0700 bearings azimuths traverse coordinates
0693 bearings distances plan points coordinates
0703 bearings survey rectangular coordinates

1177 bending deflection steel beams
1271 bending elastic analysis column section loading
1264 bending elastic design members steel loading
1174 bending moment beams deflection
1233 bending moment beams deflection slope
1220 bending moment concrete sections loads
1020 bending moment plane frame structural analysis
1216 bending moment shear force beam
1235 bending moment shear force section steel
0971 bending moment strength concrete section
0802 bending moments continuous beam
0804 bending moments continuous beams
1270 bending moments designs steel sections axial loads
0765 bending moments reinforced concrete column
1252 bending moments shear force slabs
1191 bending moments shear forces beam
0786 bending moments shear forces continuous beam
0787 bending moments shear forces continuous beam
1178 bending moments slope deflection beam shear forces
0198 bending schedules bar reinforcement
0121 bending schedules bills quantities concrete
1095 bending schedules reinforced concrete bar
1114 bending schedules weight reinforcement
1286 bending shear reinforced concrete sections
1699 bessel functions polynomial trigonometrical
1714 biharmonic equation
0142 bill contractor quantity surveyor
0164 bill cost analysis take-off
0149 bill electrical contractors cost labour
0148 bill estimating
0139 bill interim certificate cost
0278 bill materials estimating steel fabrication
0307 bill materials quantity surveys stock control
0308 bill materials quantity surveys stock control
0146 bill preparation quantity surveyors taking-off
0136 bill quantities analysis information
0163 bill quantities civil engineering
0271 bill quantities construction industry estimate
0456 bill quantities cost material estimating
0117 bill quantities dimensions architects drawings
0168 bill quantities estimates materials
0173 bill quantities estimators building
0147 bill quantities job management quantity surveyors
0141 bill quantities labour materials cost job
0299 bill quantities metals roofs labour
0151 bill quantities plumbing contractors estimate
0162 bill quantities quantity surveyor pricing
0152 bill quantities quantity surveyors contractors
1409 bill quantities radiators room
0133 bill quantities reconciliations
0134 bill quantities reconciliations
0150 bill quantities schedule rates valves material
0137 bill quantities subcontractors construction
0143 bill quantities taking-off
0171 bill quantity estimating valuations
0213 bill quantity heating plumbing electrical
0157 bill valuations accounts costs
0144 billll quantity surveyor architect engineer
0632 bills estimates quantity surveyors architects
0645 bills materials 2 1/2D CAD/CAM 3D mesh
0070 bills materials drawing project management
0590 bills materials graphics design/draughting
0124 bills quantities
0125 bills quantities architects
0135 bills quantities architects
0153 bills quantities architects
0166 bills quantities architects
0130 bills quantities civil engineering
0121 bills quantities concrete bending schedules
0368 bills quantities construction management estimating
0170 bills quantities cost analysis estimates
0161 bills quantities cost analysis NEDO
0145 bills quantities NEDO calculations
0118 bills quantities prices cost data building
0169 bills quantities pricing cost analysis
0119 bills quantities quantity surveyors
0138 bills quantities quantity surveyors
0160 bills quantities quantity surveyors
0158 bills quantities quantity surveyors cost
0122 bills quantities rectangular ductwork fittings
0140 bills quantities resource estimating
0315 bills quantities resources estimating
0154 bills quantities resources estimator
0159 bills quantities surveyor
0128 bills quantities taking-off data
0126 bills quantities tender cost analysis
0131 bills quantities tender forecasts
0172 bills quantities tenders
0127 bills quantity building estimators
0132 bills quantity civil engineering
0123 bills quantity valuations
0174 bills valuations building contracts
0872 bishop equation safety method slices

1260 blockwork walls spans building control
1331 boilers condensers estimates pressure changes pipes
1265 bolt configurations column baseplate
0761 bolt group geometric layout design
1033 bolt/weld layout steel connections
0990 bolted column/beam column/rafter
0330 book-keeping accounting architectural practice
1723 boolean numerical data
0422 bought ledger remittance advice accounts
1029 boundary element 2D gradients
1111 boundary element static deformation
0737 boundary element stress analysis elasticity
0736 boundary element stress analysis engineering
1221 boundary elements pre-processing 3D 2D beams
0678 boundary tract parcel maps
1232 box girder finite element
0775 box structure bridge analysis
1140 bracing elements portal frames design
1141 bracing gable frames
1175 bracing members pin-jointed ties struts
0835 brick/block piers sections wall
0771 bridge analysis
0775 bridge analysis box structure
0773 bridge deck grillage analysis
0770 bridge design finite element loading
0769 bridge design influence lines
0777 bridge finite element concrete
0774 bridge frame long span
0698 bridge geometry geometry highway design surveying
1128 bridge joints welded frames
0776 bridge programs library
0768 bridge slab beam finite elements concrete
0772 bridge structures finite strip
0963 bridges buildings design library roads
0767 bridges continuous beams elastic supports
1002 bridges elastic analyses 2D structures trusses
0781 bridges erection conditions finite element
0973 bridges nuclear engineering offshore structures
0766 bridges steel concrete stresses highway
0359 brought forward analysis accounting
0358 brought forward statistics nominal ledger
1080 buckling 3D scaffolding frame analysis
1278 buckling analysis
1037 buckling loads compression members steel
1291 buckling plate graphics estimate loads
1290 buckling plate graphics estimating loads
0414 budget audit trails trial balance
0425 budget forecasting cash flow time expense
0428 budget profit accounts costs sales value
0454 budget profitability cost contract
0371 budgeted costs stock payroll accounting
0464 budgeting cashflow forecasts financial modelling
0111 budgeting data planning
0375 builder contractor accounting
0599 builders 3D model design graphics architects
0332 builders accounting system
0396 builders accounting word processing
0107 builders management
0076 builders management company accounts
0272 builders merchants accounting stock control
0397 builders merchants invoicing purchase ordering
0379 builders merchants invoicing stock control
0226 builders merchants property management architects
0526 builders system estimating
0550 building 3D model perspective design
0654 building 3D wire-frame model
1450 building air-conditioning energy cooling loads
1390 building air temperature heating cooling load
0173 building bill quantities estimators
0118 building bills quantities prices cost data
0010 building civil engineers CPM project planning
0267 building construction estimating schedules
0563 building construction thermal
0431 building contract interim valuations cashflow
0304 building contract NEDO evaluating
0174 building contracts bills valuations
0275 building contracts NEDO price adjustments
0280 building contracts NEDO valuation
0205 building contracts price adjustment formula
1260 building control blockwork walls spans
0261 building cost insurance cover
0465 building cost labour material
0432 building cost plan
1511 building degree day energy consumption
0630 building design draughting system
0544 building design outline proposal evaluating
0613 building design production architects 3D model
1284 building elastic analysis reinforced concrete
1516 building electricity tariff check
1543 building energy consumption
1540 building energy consumption tariff
1438 building energy heat loss cooling loads
1510 building envelope energy conservation

1480 building envelope ventilation air flows	0625 CAD scaling library graphics
0127 building estimators bills quantity	1297 CAD structural steelwork
1572 building faces shadows vertical	0598 CADD interior planning 2D 3D data
1551 building fuel cost heat losses	0637 CAE 3D design modeller
1528 building heating energy consumption	0638 CAE 3D wire framing piping cabling CAD
0351 building industry accounting job costing	0611 CAE heating ventilating 3D geometric modelling
0355 building industry accounting payroll	0302 calculate NEDO building valuation
0565 building industry design drawing production	0867 calculates coeffeicient permeability
0610 building latitude sunpath diagram	0870 calculates percentage soils
1096 building loading element	1386 calculates predictions rooms noise level
0372 building management accounts materials	0264 calculates repairs expenditure
0557 building modelling design sketch plan	0873 calculates specific gravity
0561 building natural infiltration rates	0688 calculating plotting survey paths
0547 building planning diagrammatic layout	1253 calculation design masonry structures
0452 building prices	0291 calculations analysis estimators prices
0062 building projects management	1217 cantilever columns spans loading patterns
1440 building radiators heat losses	0847 cantilever earth pressures sheet pile wall design
0086 building regulations	0799 cantilever reinforced concrete beam
1514 building regulations fuel power buildings	0828 cantilever retaining wall analysis stability
0562 building regulations wall roof constructions	0816 cantilever retaining wall reinforced concrete
1458 building room heat loss	0844 cantilever retaining walls abutments stability
1424 building room temperature heat losses	1200 cantilever section shear stress
1439 building screening shading cooling load	0821 cantilever wall footing reinforced concrete
1503 building sections thermal circuit	0838 cantilever walls soils gravity
1471 building services heating cooling energy	1187 cantilevered forces supports
0558 building sites cut fill	0825 cantilevered retaining walls sheet pile
0553 building sizing planning space programming	0827 cantilevered sheet pile retaining walls
0282 building specifications payroll accounts	0794 cantilevers continuous frames columns slab
1413 building thermal balance cooling loads	1199 cantilevers designs concrete beams
1554 building thermal electrical loads	1024 cantilevers loads structure geometry continuous frame
1431 building thermal response heating cooling load	1195 cantilevers span loads end moments
1287 building type stairway design	1193 cantilevers span shear force end moments
0302 building valuation calculate NEDO	1539 capacitors power factor savings
1550 building weather energy consumption plant	1580 capacity exhaust duct system
0506 building work DOE indices cost	0013 capital allowance cost management
1443 buildings air-conditioning energy thermal	0711 card coding survey data
1442 buildings air-conditioning loads energy thermal	0619 cartography graphics wire frame land
0548 buildings appraisal performance	0385 cash flow forecast valuation data
1514 buildings building regulations fuel power	0364 cash flow subcontractors management contracts
1454 buildings cooling heating loads	0425 cash flow time expense budget forecasting
1524 buildings cost heating U values energy	0431 cashflow building contract interim valuations
0321 buildings design estimates	0498 cashflow construction
0963 buildings design library roads bridges	0461 cashflow forecast subcontracts cost control
0540 buildings design stage models	0510 cashflow forecasting resource aggregating
0747 buildings estimates modes vibrations	0464 cashflow forecasts financial modelling budgeting
1479 buildings fire model smoke control	0466 cashflow project forecasts
1513 buildings fuel consumptions	0537 cashflow projects forecasting
1557 buildings heat flow energy response	0962 cement aggregates concrete mix
1403 buildings heat gains	1336 central heating radiator performance water pressure
1430 buildings heat loss	1506 central heating radiators heat losses
1394 buildings heating/cooling loads thermal behaviour	0284 central heating servicing records
1525 buildings heating energy	1352 central heating water pipe connections flow
1575 buildings hour day shadows	1587 centrifugal fan duty volume pressure
0569 buildings plan drawing timber framed	1113 centroid area moments sections components
0199 buildings programme maintenance work	0424 certificate/surveyors valuations contracts
0054 buildings project design location environment	0875 chamber pressures stress pore pressure
1538 buildings simulate energy management	0936 channel backwater curve analysis flow
1571 buildings solar gain heatgain shading	0916 channel flow capacity
1561 buildings solar radiation glazed facades	0937 channel hydrograph flow hydraulics floods
1414 buildings temperatures heating cooling loads	0575 charts graph numerical data
1520 buildings thermal heating/cooling energy	0576 charts graphs numerical data
1492 buildings thermal performance insulation	1168 charts timber beams plotting span load
1527 buildings U value energy thermal performance	1372 cheeks elbows ducts
1542 buildings U value thermal vapour transfer	1496 chilled water coils by-pass factor
1593 buildings ventilation fire protection	1304 chimneys mild steel
1549 buildings weather data energy consumption	0560 CIBS energy code design building
1531 buildings windows summertime temperatures	0731 circuit layouts piping diagrams graphic draughting
0075 buildings works information management maintenance	1281 circular cylinders axisymmetric
0188 business management stock control accounting	1693 circular loads polynomial anisotropic
0097 business planning corporate modelling	1374 circular rectangular sizing ducts high velocity
0099 business planning financial reporting data	0857 circular slip failure slope stability
1496 by-pass factor chilled water coils	1257 circular tank wall prestressing hoops
1497 by-pass factor cooling coils designs	1347 circulating water flow temperature condenser
1498 by-pass factor hot water heating coils	0090 circulation periodicals libraries
1499 by-pass factor steam coils sizes	1684 circulation system route hospital
1669 cable costs electrical distribution	0163 civil engineering bill quantities
1651 cable sizes copper aluminium electrical	0130 civil engineering bills quantities
1298 cable wire arrays analyses	0132 civil engineering bills quantity
1659 cable wire conduit system electrical	0094 civil engineering construction management estimating
0638 cabling CAD CAE 3D wire framing piping	0276 civil engineering NEDO price adjustment
0585 CAD 2D draughting architecture	0874 civil engineering safety method slices
0567 CAD architects 2D 3D drawings model	0010 civil engineers CPM project planning building
0572 CAD architectural draughting drawing 2D	0402 client billing project costing timesheet
0638 CAD CAE 3D wire framing piping cabling	0071 client records professional practices
0645 CAD/CAM 3D mesh bills materials 2 1/2D	0392 client retention payment certification
0629 CAD/CAM system 3D	0867 coeffeicient permeability calculates
0675 CAD drawings 2D pipework electrical	0823 cofferdams analysis sheet piled walls
0655 CAD drawings draughting structural steelwork	1445 coil requirements air handling
0627 CAD drawings symbols dimensioning	1500 coil temperatures velocities water cooling
0661 CAD geometric constructions graphics	1496 coils by-pass factor chilled water
0658 CAD graphics 2D	1507 coils fans air handling heating cooling
0908 CAD highway engineering road plan	1502 coils water temperature pressure drop
0568 CAD plant layout 3D modelling drawings	1404 cold rooms condensing units heat gain

1317 cold water pipes design multistorey building	0866 consolidation continuous void permeability
1570 collectors components solar energy	1708 constant coefficients numerical polynomial
1700 collocation method exponentials geometrical	1360 constraint stresses pipe systems thermal expansion
1265 column baseplate bolt configurations	0667 constructing 2D drawings
0839 column bases sizing reinforcement	0137 construction bill quantities subcontractors
0765 column bending moments reinforced concrete	0498 construction cashflow
1269 column capacity slenderness effects designs	0380 construction company management
1248 column design spans reinforcement	0503 construction cost estimating
0822 column footing steel load conditions	0474 construction costs evaluation analysis
1039 column lifts frames beam string	0267 construction estimating schedules building
0819 column load design steel concrete pad	0383 construction industry accounting management
1279 column optimum design reinforced concrete	0405 construction industry accounting payroll
0990 column/rafter bolted column/beam	0508 construction industry accounts management
1213 column reinforced concrete continuous beam	0430 construction industry contract costing accounting
1271 column section loading bending elastic analysis	0524 construction industry costing financial management
1283 column sections beam sections joists	0271 construction industry estimate bill quantities
1276 columns beams reinforced concrete	0509 construction industry estimating
1007 columns continuous beams spans	0069 construction industry financial planners
1263 columns designs reinforced concrete	0481 construction industry payroll management
1246 columns flat slabs concentrated loads	0065 construction industry quantity surveyors control costs
1241 columns flat slabs drop panels	0249 construction industry stock perpetual inventory
0808 columns foundations design beams	0063 construction industry subcontractor accounting
1004 columns loads framed structure continuous beam	0399 construction industry valuation accounting
1274 columns moment capacity irregular section	0064 construction industry vehicle fleets management
1267 columns rectangular section deflection	0008 construction management CPM PERT precedence
0964 columns reinforced concrete beams slabs	0368 construction management estimating bills quantities
1266 columns reinforced concrete pad footing	0094 construction management estimating civil engineering
1275 columns reinforcement design analysis	0088 construction projects analysis control
0794 columns slab cantilevers continuous frames	0505 construction projects monitoring staff costs
1217 columns spans loading patterns cantilever	0468 construction sites planning cost control
1205 columns weight elastic design steel beams	1474 consumption lengths areas volumes heat loss
1560 commercial buildings solar heating cooling	0793 continous beam analysis multi-span
0531 commitments account architects	0790 continuous beam analysis loads
0076 company accounts builders management	0802 continuous beam bending moments
0390 company group location depreciation	0786 continuous beam bending moments shear forces
0742 component model pipes fittings drawings 3D	0787 continuous beam bending moments shear forces
0309 component project price	1213 continuous beam column reinforced concrete
0238 component structure manufacturing database	1004 continuous beam columns loads framed structure
0726 components 3D solid modelling	0974 continuous beam elastic analysis
1113 components centroid area moments sections	1057 continuous beam frame grid member loads
0600 components engineering assemblies	0791 continuous beam graphic multispan
0314 components products works orders	0795 continuous beam load
1173 composite beams design analysis	0785 continuous beam loading conditions analysis
1134 composite deck universal beams slab design	0788 continuous beam loadings supports
1552 composite elements thermal transmittance U value	0979 continuous beams 2D orthogonal frames
1101 composite section topping stress checks	0804 continuous beams bending moments
1201 composite steel concrete beams	0993 continuous beams calculates plane frame
1517 composite structure thermal transmittance	0800 continuous beams design reinforced concrete
0523 compound interest project discounted rate	0801 continuous beams design reinforced concrete
1037 compression members steel buckling loads	0767 continuous beams elastic supports bridges
1245 compression steel bar design tension	0797 continuous beams influence lines
0983 compression tension timber strut	0784 continuous beams load factors analysis
1292 compressive load plate buckle shear load	1038 continuous beams plane frames
0628 computer aided draughting system	1051 continuous beams plane framework frames
1050 concentrated forces grillages hydrostatic	1204 continuous beams portals sub-frames
1246 concentrated loads columns flat slabs	1196 continuous beams reinforced concrete
1199 concrete beams cantilevers designs	0966 continuous beams reinforced concrete design
1201 concrete beams composite steel	0803 continuous beams section properties
0121 concrete bending schedules bills quantities	0783 continuous beams slabs moment analysis
0777 concrete bridge finite element	1007 continuous beams spans columns
0768 concrete bridge slab beam finite elements	0792 continuous beams steel concrete timber
1726 concrete cube crushing statistical	0782 continuous beams steel reinforced structures
0234 concrete cube crushing test statistics	1024 continuous frame cantilevers loads structure geometry
0818 concrete footing design soil conditions	1010 continuous frame shears moments deflections
0960 concrete mix aggregate portland cement	0794 continuous frames columns slab cantilevers
0962 concrete mix cement aggregates	1023 continuous frames structure geometry
0961 concrete mix portland cement proportioning	0604 continuous rotation line perspectives projections
1093 concrete offshore structures steel	1238 continuous slabs steel requirements
0819 concrete pad column load design steel	0866 continuous void permeability consolidation
1086 concrete plane frames stress analysis	0685 contour mapping surface approximation
1194 concrete section beam prestressed	0680 contour maps isometric projections 3D
0971 concrete section bending moment strength	0692 contouring site reduced levels
1102 concrete section elastic design prestressed	0683 contouring survey surface modelling
1103 concrete section moment capacity prestressed	0682 contouring system survey surface modelling
1106 concrete sections elements properties	0454 contract budget profitability cost
1220 concrete sections loads bending moment	0445 contract cost analysis management
1212 concrete simple span beams timber steel	0455 contract cost ledger
1228 concrete slab stress precast girders	0401 contract cost valuation management accounting
1288 concrete slabs beams portal frames	0320 contract cost valuation quantity surveyors
0766 concrete stresses highway bridges steel	0476 contract costing
0792 concrete timber continuous beams steel	0430 contract costing accounting construction industry
1673 condensate design heat exchangers	0366 contract costing payroll purchases
1491 condensation moisture flow wall roof	0489 contract costing timesheets labour costs
1457 condensation risk U value wall roof	0457 contract costs materials purchasing
1526 condensation walls roofs U value	0536 contract instructions cost
1347 condenser circulating water flow temperature	0434 contract management costs
1589 condensers fan coils heaters	0052 contract management professional practices
1495 condensing units cooling coils air cooled	0375 contractor accounting builder
1404 condensing units heat gain cold rooms	0373 contractor audit trail management accounting
1672 condensing vapour heat exchangers	0512 contractor hours management personnel expenditure
1477 conductances insulation glazing areas thermal	0055 contractor payments fees jobs productivity
1659 conduit system electrical cable wire	0142 contractor quantity surveyor bill
1184 connections plate girders sections shear	0152 contractors bill quantities quantity surveyors

0190 contractors information storage retrieval
0209 contractors job summary
0387 contractors records labour pay
0364 contracts cash flow subcontractors management
0424 contracts certificate/surveyors valuations
0458 contracts costs calculation
0447 contracts financial monitoring
0471 contracts labour material stock
0436 contracts subcontractors payments
0311 control accounting production planning
0362 control accounting purchase ledger creditors
0093 control analysis manhours projects
1260 control blockwork walls spans building
0088 control construction projects analysis
0106 control contracts/projects expenditure progress sites
0472 control cost jobs
0065 control costs construction industry quantity surveyors
0098 control data input validation
0469 control job costs
0176 control plant labour invoicing documentation
0109 control project management
0011 control project planning
0033 control project planning
1533 control system energy usage
0002 controlling projects time resources cost planning
1436 convective heat losses rooms buildings radiant
1417 convective heat losses rooms radiant
1094 conveyor gantry steelwork sizes member
1588 coolant conditions air-on air-off
1675 cooler heater humidifier design
1495 cooling coils air cooled condensing units
1497 cooling coils designs by-pass factor
1560 cooling commercial buildings solar heating
1433 cooling dehumidifying heat exchangers simulates
1415 cooling heating load equipment selection
1576 cooling heating loads air-conditioning
1454 cooling heating loads buildings
1581 cooling load air-conditioning heat gain
1439 cooling load building screening shading
1407 cooling load heat gains rooms building
1420 cooling load U value time lag heat gains
1578 cooling loads air-conditioning heat gain
1450 cooling loads building air-conditioning energy
1438 cooling loads building energy heat loss
1413 cooling loads building thermal balance
1446 cooling loads calculates heating
1416 cooling loads energy HVAC plant zone heating
1427 cooling loads psychrometric analysis moist air
1401 cooling loads rooms
1412 cooling loads summer heating loads winter
0696 coordinate area conversions trigonometry surveying
0695 coordinate data traverses traverse surveys
1129 coordinate geometry
0715 coordinate geometry land surveying planning
0701 coordinates azimuth slope angles intersection
0700 coordinates bearings azimuths traverse
0693 coordinates bearings distances plan points
1299 coordinates doors windows analysis
0716 coordinates land survey point plotting traverse
0617 coordinates plotting survey
0729 coordinates points section plane area
0686 coordinates roads footpaths graphic site area
0706 coordinates staff position reduced level
0691 coordinates survey stations distance tacheometry
1651 copper aluminium electrical cable sizes
1337 copper steel heat emission pipework
1340 copper steel pipework water pipe sizing
1341 copper steel piping stresses linear
0097 corporate modelling business planning
0113 corporate modelling financial analysis planning
0096 corporate modelling management accounting
0186 corporate modelling project evaluation
0517 corporate planning financial analysis modelling
0533 corporate planning financial modelling
1701 correlation coefficients least square
1725 correlation matrix variables
0518 cost accounting depreciation
0216 cost accounts timesheet expenses projects
0036 cost analyses project management time resource
0462 cost analysis
0169 cost analysis bills quantities pricing
0126 cost analysis bills quantities tender
0170 cost analysis estimates bills quantities
0445 cost analysis management contract
0161 cost analysis NEDO bills quantities
0488 cost analysis payrolls
1226 cost analysis plate girder sections
0400 cost analysis quantity surveyors management
0164 cost analysis take-off bill
0313 cost appraisals projects estimate
0139 cost bill interim certificate
0158 cost bills quantities quantity surveyors
0506 cost building work DOE indices

0454 cost contract budget profitability
0536 cost contract instructions
0461 cost control cashflow forecast subcontracts
0468 cost control construction sites planning
0473 cost control house builders
0009 cost control network analysis resource allocation
0441 cost control project time accounting
0470 cost control timesheet analysis
0007 cost CPM motorway construction plant time
0024 cost critical path resource aggregation
0035 cost critical path/resource arrow networks
0118 cost data building bills quantities prices
0105 cost development project planning estimating
0257 cost efficient handling storage timber yard
1535 cost environment energy management
0460 cost estimates profitability retention
0503 cost estimating construction
0906 cost estimating road construction
0513 cost fees estimate mathematical
0053 cost finance profitability development
1551 cost heat losses building fuel
1524 cost heating U values energy buildings
0204 cost hospital design costs estimating
0261 cost insurance cover building
0472 cost jobs control
0149 cost labour bill electrical contractors
0465 cost labour material building
0455 cost ledger contract
1679 cost lift system loading conditions
0507 cost limits secondary education projects
0013 cost management capital allowance
0456 cost material estimating bill quantities
0318 cost optimiser fabrication windows doors
0432 cost plan building
0089 cost plan job developers budget viability
0444 cost plan non-constructional elements
0002 cost planning controlling projects time resources
0502 cost records management timesheet
0031 cost/resource project control PERT/cpm database
0085 cost scheduling employment production levels
0514 cost tasks personnel labour
0467 cost time analysis forecast
0449 cost time materials
0435 cost unit price profit
0367 costing accounting
0348 costing accounting stock control
0476 costing contract
1530 costing energy conservation
0345 costing estimates accounting
0524 costing financial management construction industry
0450 costing forecasting timesheets job
0437 costing job
0327 costing overheads profit price lists
0532 costing product process
1363 costing sizes duct networks acoustic analysis
0459 costing system architects job analysis
0270 costing window cutting stock control
1596 costing window styles cutting list
0301 costings window door frame cutting fitting
0157 costs bill valuations accounts
0458 costs calculation contracts
0065 costs construction industry quantity surveyors control
0434 costs contract management
0469 costs control job
1665 costs electrical conductor
1669 costs electrical distribution cable
1522 costs energy installation maintenance
1521 costs energy systems estimates
0754 costs estimate shopfronts cutting design
0204 costs estimating cost hospital design
0519 costs labour estimate plant materials
0197 costs material take-off project information
0457 costs materials purchasing contract
0451 costs project tender
0306 costs quantities valuation jobs
0428 costs sales value budget profit accounts
0453 costs time staff
0050 costs value analysis project
0004 CPA analysis
0027 CPM arrow precedence PERT system
0091 CPM draw bar charts
0007 CPM motorway construction plant time cost
0018 CPM network project
0008 CPM PERT precedence network construction
0023 CPM/pert techniques multiple projects
0010 CPM project planning building civil engineers
0029 CPM project planning network
0003 CPM project planning plans time resources
0020 CPM resource scheduling project planning
0016 CPM resources project planning management
0026 CPM utilisation planning network analysis
0864 cracks safety sliding soils
1277 crane columns roof leg weight design

0363 credit control sales analysis accounting
0344 credit control stock valuation accounting
0362 creditors control accounting purchase ledger
0419 creditors control audit trail accounting
0418 creditors control purchase analysis accounting
0037 critical path analysis
0028 critical path arrow project planning
0021 critical path plan project
0032 critical path project management
0005 critical path project management scheduling
0015 critical path project planning
0024 critical path resource aggregation cost
0035 critical path/resource arrow networks cost
0012 critical paths project management evaluation
1125 cross section bar stresses
1222 cross-section section properties beams
1237 cross-sectional elastic analysis retaining walls
1124 cross-sectional properties bar
1099 cross-sectional torsional properties section
0858 cross-sections earthwork cut fill
1185 cross sections load conditions beams
0859 cross-sections road earthwork
1117 cross-sections shear stresses section properties
0234 cube crushing test statistics concrete
0944 culvert design rc
0952 culverts design
0407 currency exchange conversions fluctuations
1092 current offshore steel jacket wave wind
0936 curve analysis flow channel backwater
1713 curve fitting land surveying geometry
0748 curve fitting line surface regression analysis
1202 curved beam graphics estimates stresses
0558 cut fill building sites
0858 cut fill cross-sections earthwork
0883 cut/fill ground model earth works calculate
0754 cutting design costs estimate shopfronts
0301 cutting fitting costings window door frame
1596 cutting list costing window styles
1605 cutting list fabricators window/door
1604 cutting list window type stock
1595 cutting list windows double glazing
0290 cutting lists double glazing drawings
0268 cutting optimisation sheet materials
0969 cutting optimisation steel stock
0281 cutting optimiser rectangular material 2D
0319 cutting schedules sheet materials optimiser
0317 cutting sheet glass plans estimates
0270 cutting stock control costing window
1156 cutting timber frame production drawings
1676 cylindrical vessels stresses
1345 Darcy-Weisbach formula piping head losses
1349 Darcy-Weisbach pipes reservoirs Hazen-williams
0099 data business planning financial reporting
0231 data dictionary information retrieval
0220 data file management retrieval
1718 data handling solution check
0098 data input validation control
0615 data management 3D graphics draughting
0066 data management programming
0103 data management project information
0202 data management system information retrieval
0229 data management system label printing
0111 data planning budgeting
0574 data plotting
0057 data preparation program operation energy
0079 data smoothing fourier transforms
0240 data stores records maths package
0187 database management records information retrieval
0365 database manager accounting multiple currencies
0081 databases information handling schedules
1629 daylight energy artificial lighting
1607 daylight factor room windows
0580 daylight factors perspective view
1641 daylight factors room sky component
1642 daylight factors room sky component
1606 daylight factors room windows
1628 daylight factors room windows
1618 daylight factors windows
1640 daylight room heat gains thermal
1610 daylighting building windows rooflights
1644 daylighting energy glazing windows
1612 daylighting factors room windows
1632 daylighting luminaires window lighting
1625 daylighting room windows rooflights
0571 definition scaling perspective drawing
0987 deflected forms portal frame plots
1174 deflection bending moment beams
1267 deflection columns rectangular section
1130 deflection non-linear stability axial forces
1233 deflection slope bending moment beams
1010 deflections continuous frame shears moments
0817 deflections sheet pile wall shears
1073 deformations joint displacements plane frame

1511 degree day energy consumption building
1433 dehumidifying heat exchangers simulates cooling
0177 depreciation assets management plant accounting
0333 depreciation assets values
0390 depreciation company group location
0518 depreciation cost accounting
0511 depreciation financial control
0522 depreciation project
0354 depreciation straight line double declining
1275 design analysis columns reinforcement
1173 design analysis composite beams
0552 design analysis engineer
0285 design architects drawings register
0796 design beams analysis
0808 design beams columns foundations
0789 design beams flexural reinforcement bar sizes
1171 design beams stanchions
0761 design bolt group geometric layout
0550 design building 3D model perspective
0560 design building CIBS energy code
0639 design change substructure structure
1256 design charts lateral strength wall
0590 design/draughting bills materials graphics
0587 design/draughting geometric construction architect
0577 design draughting piping layout
0565 design drawing production building industry
0321 design estimates buildings
1310 design glue laminated portal arches
0599 design graphics architects builders 3D model
0741 design kitchen 3D drawings
1254 design laterally loaded wall panel
0963 design library roads bridges buildings
0054 design location environment buildings project
0637 design modeller CAE 3D
0269 design optimisation accounting window
1318 design piping system
1144 design purlins side rails
1268 design rectangular columns
1229 design reinforced concrete beams columns
0800 design reinforced concrete continuous beams
0801 design reinforced concrete continuous beams
0812 design reinforced concrete pad foundations
0539 design secondary school
1247 design sections span bar
0557 design sketch plan building modelling
0540 design stage models buildings
0546 design stage models hospital
0583 design stage perspective
0559 design sun overshadowing solar orientation
1245 design tension compression steel bar
1300 design timber structures
0001 design tree diagram project management
0762 design weld pattern geometric layout
0566 design work symbols architectural drawings
0641 designers finite element thermal behaviour
1269 designs column capacity slenderness effects
1199 designs concrete beams cantilevers
1263 designs reinforced concrete columns
1262 designs steel columns
1270 designs steel sections axial loads bending moments
1273 designs steel stanchion
0708 detail points levels plotting station
0755 detailing drawings beam/column steel
0236 detailing projects steelwork fabrication
0581 details plans 2D draughting
0089 developers budget viability cost plan job
0044 development appraisal tenders land
0053 development cost finance profitability
0105 development project planning estimating cost
1705 deviation calculate mean standard
0956 dewatering systems analysis
0929 dewatering wells designs water supply
0547 diagrammatic layout building planning
0627 dimensioning CAD drawings symbols
1384 dimensioning duct air slit
0634 dimensioning road layout 2D draughting
0117 dimensions architects drawings bill quantities
0293 dimensions material quantities take-off
0606 direct diffuse reflected radiation slope
1637 direct indirect illumination rooms
0523 discounted rate compound interest project
0253 discrepancies/variances stock availability
1122 displacement force bar axial loads
1121 displacement force static loading
0997 displacement method 2D pin-jointed frameworks
1192 displacement method plane grids beam
0998 displacement method plane rigid-jointed frameworks
1032 displacement static deformation 2D finite element
1027 displacements 2D frame joints member types
1066 displacements 3D frames load conditions
1072 displacements 3D structures frame forces
1280 displacements bearing forces shaft
1692 displacements loading stresses strains

1696 displacements loading stresses strains
1108 displacements stresses finite element
1694 displacements stresses strains
1695 displacements stresses strains
1697 displacements stresses strains
0707 distance survey points angle
0691 distance tacheometry coordinates survey stations
0690 distance tacheometry plan coordinates survey stations
0693 distances plan points coordinates bearings
0073 distribution manpower levels
0217 distribution order entry sales marketing
0061 distribution vehicle fleet maintenance management
0092 document control project managers expediting
0060 document search retrieval word processing
0506 DOE indices cost building work
1509 domestic installation heating systems
1167 domestic truss rafter load span
0301 door frame cutting fitting costings window
0535 door frames staircases quotations window
0318 doors cost optimiser fabrication windows
1299 doors windows analysis coordinates
0354 double declining depreciation straight line
1597 double glazed aluminium UPVC windows
1595 double glazing cutting list windows
0290 double glazing drawings cutting lists
0938 drain analysis flow pipes storm
0918 drainage basin hydrograph
0697 drainage design triangular DTM survey highway
0924 drainage hydraulics analysis sewer
0925 drainage hydraulics analysis sewer
0914 drainage hydrograph foul surface water
0933 drainage hydrograph rainfall
0923 drainage hydrology watersheds design
0915 drainage network surface water
0907 drainage networks highway analysis design
0941 drainage networks storm pipes hydrograph flow
0935 drainage pipe foul surface water
0953 drainage schemes design pipes hydrograph
0912 drainage systems calculations hydraulic design
0922 drainage urban hydrograph rainfall
0928 drainfield water saturation waste disposal
0608 draughting 2D
0620 draughting 2D
0665 draughting 2D
0663 draughting architectural drawings
0585 draughting architecture CAD 2D
0731 draughting circuit layouts piping diagrams graphic
0615 draughting data management 3D graphics
0631 draughting design architects 2 1/2D
0634 draughting dimensioning road layout 2D
0572 draughting drawing 2D CAD architectural
0584 draughting drawings 3D graphic modelling
0579 draughting drawings perspectives isometrics
0668 draughting graphic symbols sketch plans
0659 draughting package 2D
0647 draughting package architects 2D
0577 draughting piping layout design
0597 draughting production 3D graphics
0655 draughting structural steelwork CAD drawings
0630 draughting system building design
0628 draughting system computer aided
0596 draughting system electrical mechanical lï
0648 draughting system geometry 2D mechanical
0091 draw bar charts CPM
0626 draw flow chart
0572 drawing 2D CAD architectural draughting
0555 drawing 3D models architectural planning
0605 drawing 3D projections
0649 drawing administrative routines 2D 3D
0602 drawing annotation graphics
0633 drawing architects engineers hatching 2D
0588 drawing graphics editing material take-off
0718 drawing graphics surveying field
0662 drawing management graphics
0565 drawing production building industry design
0070 drawing project management bills materials
0675 drawings 2D pipework electrical CAD
0742 drawings 3D component model pipes fittings
0584 drawings 3D graphic modelling draughting
0749 drawings analysis structural steelwork
1302 drawings beam column reinforced concrete
0755 drawings beam/column steel detailing
0568 drawings CAD plant layout 3D modelling
0667 drawings constructing 2D
0290 drawings cutting lists double glazing
0741 drawings design kitchen 3D
0655 drawings draughting structural steelwork CAD
0246 drawings information storage retrieval plans
0732 drawings isometrics perspective views 3D
0579 drawings perspectives isometrics draughting
0223 drawings project
0233 drawings project managers record
0222 drawings project specification

0285 drawings register design architects
0194 drawings register planning statistics maintenance
0627 drawings symbols dimensioning CAD
0582 draws sunlight perspective projections
1119 drilling rigs storage tanks force stress
1241 drop panels columns flat slabs
0294 drywall partitions suspended ceilings
1384 duct air slit dimensioning
1579 duct analysis ventilation system
1472 duct interstitial condensation heat losses pipe
1363 duct networks acoustic analysis costing sizes
1368 duct pressure losses velocities sizes ventilating
1366 duct sizes pressure loss ventilation system
1375 duct sizing installation ventilation
1376 duct sizing ventilation system
1377 duct system friction losses
1365 duct systems sizing friction losses leakage
1494 ducted air-conditioning fans horsepower
1372 ducts cheeks elbows
0652 ducts finite element 3D surface design
1374 ducts high velocity circular rectangular sizing
1364 ducts sizing calculates metal gauge
1370 ductwork fittings sheet metal
1382 ductwork friction air velocity ventilation
1380 ductwork maximum velocity sizes
1378 ductwork pressure drop sizes
1367 ductwork pressures temperatures quantities sizing
1369 ductwork simulate ventilation
1465 ductwork sizes system ventilation
1379 ductwork static regain sizes
1385 ductwork varitrane boxes air
0212 duplicate copies estimation master files
1062 dynamic analysis 2D 3D trusses frames
1081 dynamic analysis frame shell structures
1022 dynamic analysis plane frame node shapes
0640 dynamic analysis structural mass
0722 dynamic behaviour load conditions graphics
1131 dynamic loads earthquakes structures
1717 dynamic response fast fourier
0712 dynamic seismic analysis soil-structure
0725 dynamics graphical analysis
0834 earth embankment sliding slope stability
0871 earth embankment slip circle safety
0829 earth fill structures stress settlement
0846 earth pressures piles loads
0847 earth pressures sheet pile wall design cantilever
0884 earth slopes slip circle stability
0883 earth works calculate cut/fill ground model
0689 earthquake actions safety factors evaluation
1259 earthquake elastic analysis shear wall
0863 earthquake safety sliding slip surface
1131 earthquakes structures dynamic loads
1074 earthquakes wave 3D offshore structures
0859 earthwork cross-sections road
0858 earthwork cut fill cross-sections
0882 earthwork quantities
0901 earthwork volumes alignment road section
0905 earthworks analysis alignments highways
0900 earthworks design alignment road
0911 earthworks highway design alignment
0898 earthworks highways design
0903 earthworks road design alignment
1155 eaves tie load portal frame members
0588 editing material take-off drawing graphics
0080 editing retrieval managing text databases
1512 educational buildings energy fuel conservation
0549 educational policies spatial implications
1003 elastic analyses 2D structures
1002 elastic analyses 2D structures trusses bridges
1067 elastic analyses 3D structural systems
1197 elastic analysis 2D beam loadings
1271 elastic analysis column section loading bending
0974 elastic analysis continuous beam
1005 elastic analysis grid structures loadings
0753 elastic analysis isotropic finite elements linear
1061 elastic analysis plane frame geometry
0991 elastic analysis plane frames
1055 elastic analysis plane frameworks member forces
1006 elastic analysis plates ribs beams
1164 elastic analysis portal frames moments
0985 elastic analysis portal frames plastic design
1284 elastic analysis reinforced concrete building
1237 elastic analysis retaining walls cross-sectional
1259 elastic analysis shear wall earthquake
0744 elastic analysis strength walls excavations
1018 elastic analysis structural frames
1019 elastic analysis structural frameworks
0975 elastic analysis structures frame
0780 elastic analysis suspension bridges non-linear
0986 elastic deflection load portal frame
1154 elastic deflection steel portal frames
1264 elastic design members steel loading bending
1102 elastic design prestressed concrete section

0154 estimator bills quantities resources	1014 finite element Poissons ratio plane stress
0173 estimators building bill quantities	0756 finite element post-processing system
0291 estimators prices calculations analysis	0724 finite element pre− post-processing model
0283 estimators quantities pricing tender	1041 finite element static analysis elastic structure
1545 evaluate interchange factors radiant heat	1065 finite element stress 3D models steel
1428 evaluates heat pipe savings	1077 finite element stress analysis 2D 3D
0304 evaluating building contract NEDO	1127 finite element stress strain loads
0544 evaluating building design outline proposal	0723 finite element structural analysis heat transfer
0258 evaluating prepared timber order/sales	0763 finite element structural heat transfer
0474 evaluation analysis construction costs	1097 finite element structure loading
0012 evaluation critical paths project management	0641 finite element thermal behaviour designers
0689 evaluation earthquake actions safety factors	1309 finite element trusses frames grillages
0250 evaluation management information stock control	0996 finite elements 2D mesh plane shape
0556 evaluation planning health buildings	0768 finite elements concrete bridge slab beam
0939 excavation design pipe flow sewer calculated	0753 finite elements linear elastic analysis isotropic
0865 excavation slope stability multilayered soils	1314 finite elements load conditions stress analysis
0744 excavations elastic analysis strength walls	1105 finite elements structural design
1580 exhaust duct system capacity	0772 finite strip bridge structures
0074 existing buildings space management	1600 fire behaviour analysis
0092 expediting document control project managers	0811 fire collapse analysis portal frame
0181 expediting field management equipment project	1479 fire model smoke control buildings
0382 expenditure analysis income	1593 fire protection buildings ventilation
0264 expenditure calculates repairs	1590 fire protection pressure gas pipe duct
0512 expenditure contractor hours management personnel	0750 fire resistance analyse graphs
0106 expenditure progress sites control contracts/projects	1602 fire spread spatial separations
0475 expenditure resources project management	0195 firm word processing management accounting
0427 expense analysis job costing time	0412 fixed asset register accounts
0425 expense budget forecasting cash flow time	1159 fixing requirements roof tile estimating
0292 expenses overheads profit material labour	0972 flanges design analysis
0216 expenses projects cost accounts timesheet	1246 flat slabs concentrated loads columns
0395 expired certificates transactions retentions	1241 flat slabs drop panels columns
1710 exponential Lagrangian polynomial curve empirical	1239 flat slabs reinforced concrete
1700 exponentials geometrical collocation method	1249 flat slabs reinforced concrete bar schedules
1396 external glazing air temperature heat gains	0789 flexural reinforcement bar sizes design beams
1398 external walls sol-air temperatures heat gains	0913 flood hydrographs storm retarding basins
1115 fabricate welded tubular structures estimating	1626 floodlighting luminaires lighting intensity
0318 fabrication windows doors cost optimiser	0937 floods channel hydrograph flow hydraulics
1605 fabricators window/door cutting list	1135 floor design framed structures precast concrete
1589 fan coils heaters condensers	1132 floor elements plan production prefabricated
1501 fan size type	1133 floor framing supported beams loads stresses
1507 fans air handling heating cooling coils	0739 floor plan space planners stacking plans
1494 fans horsepower ducted air-conditioning	1425 floor roof thermal transmittance U value wall
1717 fast fourier dynamic response	1518 floors suspended solid U values
0429 fee control architects	0916 flow capacity channel
0513 fees estimate mathematical cost	1352 flow central heating water pipe connections
0055 fees jobs productivity contractor payments	0936 flow channel backwater curve analysis
0515 fees RICS scale quantity surveyors	0626 flow chart draw
0295 fibreboard pipe prices rectangular duct	0941 flow drainage networks storm pipes hydrograph
0718 field drawing graphics surveying	0764 flow heat transfer seepage groundwater
0181 field management equipment project expediting	1482 flow hot water pipe sizing volume
0180 field personnel schedule equipment project	0937 flow hydraulics floods channel hydrograph
0230 file maintenance information retrieval	1351 flow pipe sizes heating/cooling units
0220 file management retrieval data	0938 flow pipes storm drain analysis
0241 filing system storage retrieval	1328 flow pipework system sizes pressure temperature
0051 finance accounting marketing sales	0743 flow problem Poisson equation soil water
0053 finance profitability development cost	1333 flow rates fluid temperature pipework pressure drop
0352 financial accounting analysis/auditing	1338 flow rates friction losses pipe system
0517 financial analysis modelling corporate planning	1335 flow rates pipe pressure drop length velocity
0113 financial analysis planning corporate modelling	1319 flow rates sizes steel pipes water
0438 financial control analysis	0934 flow sewer calculates
0511 financial control depreciation	0951 flow sewerage network pipeline
0486 financial control payroll	0869 flow toughness liquidity plasticity
0059 financial forecasting modelling project	0931 flow wellfield waste disposal finite element
0524 financial management construction industry costing	0940 flows waterways surface profiles
0499 financial modelling analysis	0324 fluctuation quantity surveying NEDO
0464 financial modelling budgeting cashflow forecasts	1334 fluid heating/chilled water pipe analysis sizing
0533 financial modelling corporate planning	1325 fluid pipe material pipe sizing
0084 financial modelling management planning	1333 fluid temperature pipework pressure drop flow rates
0520 financial modelling mathematical functions	1616 fluorescent lighting illuminance pattern
0068 financial modelling plan monitor project management	1609 fluorescent lighting internal areas
0447 financial monitoring contracts	1627 fluorescent luminaire lighting glare room
0110 financial office management specifications	1623 fluorescent luminaires lighting glare
0069 financial planners construction industry	1624 fluorescent luminaires lighting intensities
0534 financial planning	1638 flux level energy loading luminaires
0099 financial reporting data business planning	0836 footing loads moments
1083 finite element 2D 3D space frames	0821 footing reinforced concrete cantilever wall
0995 finite element 2D trusses frames	0832 footings bearing capacity analysis
0652 finite element 3D surface design ducts	0805 footings slabs plate raft foundations
1100 finite element analysis structural engineering	0830 footings stress calculation settlement
0758 finite element analysis system	1122 force bar axial loads displacement
1232 finite element box girder	1121 force static loading displacement
0781 finite element bridges erection conditions	1119 force stress drilling rigs storage tanks
0777 finite element concrete bridge	1072 forces displacements 3D structures frame
1032 finite element displacement static deformation 2D	1166 forces members pin-jointed truss
1108 finite element displacements stresses	1187 forces supports cantilevered
0931 finite element flow wellfield waste disposal	0467 forecast cost time analysis
0208 finite element graphics statistics	0385 forecast valuation data cash flow
0643 finite element heat transfer 3D	0388 forecasting accounting system
0738 finite element isoparametric temperature	0425 forecasting cash flow time expense budget
0770 finite element loading bridge design	0537 forecasting cashflow projects
0752 finite element loading structure	0108 forecasting management engineering planning
0728 finite element model pre-post-processing	0095 forecasting project management quantity surveying
0644 finite element models pre− post-processor	0245 forecasting re-order levels parts explosion

0510 forecasting resource aggregating cashflow	1085 geometry space frames
0450 forecasting timesheets job costing	0573 geometry stress data graphics
0131 forecasts bills quantities tender	0651 geometry traverse alignments
0466 forecasts cashflow project	1224 girder estimates plates
0288 forecasts NEDO quantity surveyors valuations	1444 glass blinds solar radiation transmission
0914 foul surface water drainage hydrograph	1591 glass spacers windows sealed units
0935 foul surface water drainage pipe	1561 glazed facades buildings solar radiation
1001 foundation loads steel frame	1477 glazing areas thermal conductances insulation
0751 foundation vibration multistorey buildings	1389 glazing internal noise levels
0808 foundations design beams columns	1573 glazing shading air-conditioning
0837 foundations elastic settlements stresses	1565 glazing types heat gain
0806 foundations reinforced concrete members	1644 glazing windows daylighting energy
0852 foundations reinforced concrete sections	1310 glue laminated portal arches design
1120 foundations slope load stability vibrations	0225 goods received material requirements pricing
0079 fourier transforms data smoothing	1029 gradients boundary element 2D
1082 frame 3D static analysis truss	0575 graph numerical data charts
1080 frame analysis buckling 3D scaffolding	0731 graphic draughting circuit layouts piping diagrams
1047 frame analysis structural analysis	1727 graphic histogram statistics
0989 frame data calculates	0584 graphic modelling draughting drawings 3D
0975 frame elastic analysis structures	0791 graphic multispan continuous beam
1072 frame forces displacements 3D structures	0666 graphic plotting
1001 frame foundation loads steel	0686 graphic site area coordinates roads footpaths
1057 frame grid member loads continuous beam	0668 graphic symbols sketch plans draughting
1036 frame joint loading member loading	0725 graphical analysis dynamics
0977 frame linear analysis structures	0721 graphical artificial excitation tests
1008 frame loads moments members	0578 graphics 2D
1035 frame members joint displacements	0670 graphics 2D 3D surfaces perspective
1076 frame members joints loading conditions	0658 graphics 2D CAD
1258 frame shear stress wall structures	0664 graphics 3D
1081 frame shell structures dynamic analysis	0720 graphics 3D mechanism analysis
1048 frame structural analysis	0599 graphics architects builders 3D model design
0978 frame structural steelwork	0623 graphics bar pie charts maps 3D charts
1031 frame structure joints member forces reactions	0661 graphics CAD geometric constructions
1069 frame truss 3D 2D	0625 graphics CAD scaling library
1004 framed structure continuous beam columns loads	0618 graphics design 2D/3d
1078 framed structures joint displacements moments	0590 graphics design/draughting bills materials
1043 framed structures load specification 2D	0595 graphics display bar charts monitoring
1030 framed structures loads linear analysis	0615 graphics draughting data management 3D
1135 framed structures precast concrete floor design	0602 graphics drawing annotation
1303 framed structures reinforced concrete	0662 graphics drawing management
1079 framed structures static analysis 3D	0722 graphics dynamic behaviour load conditions
0959 frames analysis 3D	0588 graphics editing material take-off drawing
0976 frames analysis pin jointed 2D	1291 graphics estimate loads buckling plate
1039 frames beam string column lifts	1294 graphics estimate structural plate
1016 frames beams trusses grids	1202 graphics estimates stresses curved beam
1128 frames bridge joints welded	1289 graphics estimating loads
1051 frames continuous beams plane framework	1290 graphics estimating loads buckling plate
1062 frames dynamic analysis 2D 3D trusses	0573 graphics geometry stress data
0995 frames finite element 2D trusses	0624 graphics graphs line bar pie
1309 frames grillages finite element trusses	0909 graphics highway design
1066 frames load conditions displacements 3D	0757 graphics incremental plotters
1026 frames loads plastic analysis steel	0622 graphics library graphs
0981 frames statically determinate	0674 graphics library plotting
0994 frames stress analysis plane	0621 graphics representation numeric data
1107 frames thermal problems structural analysis	1371 graphics shop fabrication mathematics
0980 framework loads sizes member	0208 graphics statistics finite element
1000 frameworks 3D rigid-jointed	0718 graphics surveying field drawing
0997 frameworks displacement method 2D pin-jointed	0653 graphics system plotted zoom facility
0998 frameworks displacement method plane rigid-jointed	0614 graphics time managers project evaluators
1034 frameworks trusses member loading	0619 graphics wire frame land cartography
1382 friction air velocity ventilation ductwork	0636 graphics working drawings
1377 friction losses duct system	0657 graphs bar chart plotting
1365 friction losses leakage duct systems sizing	0750 graphs fire resistance analyse
1338 friction losses pipe system flow rates	0622 graphs graphics library
1731 Friedmans test spearmans correlation statistics	0679 graphs histograms bar charts statistics
1534 fuel adjustment energy control	0624 graphs line bar pie graphics
1512 fuel conservation educational buildings energy	0592 graphs line printers plotting
1513 fuel consumptions buildings	0576 graphs numerical data charts
1551 fuel cost heat losses building	0609 graphs user-defined data plot
1514 fuel power buildings building regulations	0838 gravity cantilever walls soils
1586 furnace design heat loss wall	1285 gravity take-up towers support trestles
1141 gable frames bracing	1057 grid member loads continuous beam frame
1464 gains losses solar energy ventilation	1005 grid structures loadings elastic analysis
1515 gas electricity energy hot water heating	0684 grid survey analysis mapping
1590 gas pipe duct fire protection pressure	1016 grids frames beams trusses
1342 gas pipeline pressure production rate	0773 grillage analysis bridge deck
0958 gas storage systems pressure temperature	1044 grillage nodal loading
1649 generation resistivity curves	1054 grillages elastic foundation plates
0719 geometric components 3D solid modelling	1309 grillages finite element trusses frames
0587 geometric construction architect design/draughting	1050 grillages hydrostatic concentrated forces
0661 geometric constructions graphics CAD	1387 grilles rooms noise levels
0761 geometric layout design bolt group	0883 ground model earth works calculate cut/fill
0762 geometric layout design weld pattern	0717 ground modelling spot height survey data
0656 geometric modeller 3D pipework steel frames	0764 groundwater flow heat transfer seepage
0611 geometric modelling CAE heating ventilating 3D	0930 groundwater velocity piezometric
0570 geometric modelling relational database 3D	0814 group analysis piles
1700 geometrical collocation method exponentials	0841 groups piles analysis
0648 geometry 2D mechanical draughting system	0842 groups piles analysis
1713 geometry curve fitting land surveying	0257 handling storage timber yard cost efficient
1061 geometry elastic analysis plane frame	0955 harbour resonance analysis
0698 geometry highway design surveying bridge geometry	0633 hatching 2D drawing architects engineers
1139 geometry load combinations portal frames	1349 Hazen-williams Darcy-Weisbach pipes reservoirs
1149 geometry loading outputs plane truss	1343 Hazen williams water distribution pipes network

0953 hydrograph drainage schemes design pipes
0941 hydrograph flow drainage networks storm pipes
0937 hydrograph flow hydraulics floods channel
0914 hydrograph foul surface water drainage
0943 hydrograph rain storm sewers
0933 hydrograph rainfall drainage
0913 hydrographs storm retarding basins flood
0919 hydrographs storm water pumping stations
0921 hydrology hydraulics storm water urban areas
0923 hydrology watersheds design drainage
1050 hydrostatic concentrated forces grillages
1613 illuminance level lighting glare rooms
1639 illuminance level room luminaires
1616 illuminance pattern fluorescent lighting
1635 illuminance plane surface light sources
1636 illuminance plane surface luminaires
1631 illumination artificial lighting energy
1617 illumination levels elliptical interpolation
1643 illumination levels lighting design
1637 illumination rooms direct indirect
0416 income/expenditure accounts assets liabilities
0382 income expenditure analysis
0757 incremental plotters graphics
0687 index site investigation
0561 infiltration rates building natural
1163 influence line member forces plane truss
0769 influence lines bridge design
0797 influence lines continuous beams
0112 information handling
0081 information handling schedules databases
0114 information handling time sharing
0218 information management retrieval
0193 information retrieval
0231 information retrieval data dictionary
0202 information retrieval data management system
0187 information retrieval database management records
0056 information retrieval engineering design
0230 information retrieval file maintenance
0046 information retrieval names addresses list
0083 information retrieval rearranging records
0215 information storage retrieval
0235 information storage retrieval
0190 information storage retrieval contractors
0232 information storage retrieval personnel library
0246 information storage retrieval plans drawings
1509 installation heating systems domestic
1461 installation home heating heat loss
1522 installation maintenance costs energy
1473 installation radiators piping air heating
1375 installation ventilation duct sizing
1492 insulation buildings thermal performance
1477 insulation glazing areas thermal conductances
1537 insulation heat roof wall
0298 insulation pipework rectangular ductwork
1547 insulation roof
0261 insurance cover building cost
0312 insurance purposes property valuations
0329 insurance register property
0591 interactive production architectural drawings
1544 interchange factors radiant energy
1545 interchange factors radiant heat evaluate
0139 interim certificate cost bill
0431 interim valuations cashflow building contract
0598 interior planning 2D 3D data CADD
1615 interior spaces lighting energy
1609 internal areas fluorescent lighting
1689 internal mail postal tube system
1389 internal noise levels glazing
1608 internal reflection light natural artificial
0255 interrogation facilities stock control
0701 intersection coordinates azimuth slope angles
1116 intersection points 3D space structural shape
0899 intersection road design
1472 interstitial condensation heat losses pipe duct
1467 interstitial condensation U value
1421 interstitial condensation walls heat loss
0254 inventory control stock records production
0183 investment energy costs operating costs
0376 invoice accounting statements
0297 invoice hours estimating materials
0339 invoice stock control sales ledger
0337 invoices accounts subcontractors
0353 invoices analyses statements management
0266 invoices plant register hire register
0393 invoices purchase ledger bank reconciliation
0252 invoices purchase orders stock reporting
0410 invoices purchases settlement discount
0265 invoices route loading stock control picking lists
0411 invoices sales extracts turnover analysis
0273 invoices sales ledger hire agreements
0326 invoices skip movements
0325 invoices skips hire sales ledger
0378 invoicing accounting payroll stock control

0176 invoicing documentation control plant labour
0397 invoicing purchase ordering builders merchants
0191 invoicing sales order entry stock control
0379 invoicing stock control builders merchants
0404 invoicing timber merchants sizing calculation
0361 invoicing VAT management information
1274 irregular section columns moment capacity
0740 isometric drawing piping symbol
0593 isometric drawings 2D 3D structural assemblies
1329 isometric production pipework detailing purchasing
0680 isometric projections 3D contour maps
0589 isometric projections architect perspectives
0579 isometrics draughting drawings perspectives
0732 isometrics perspective views 3D drawings
0738 isoparametric temperature finite element
0753 isotropic finite elements linear elastic analysis
0459 job analysis costing system architects
0141 job bill quantities labour materials cost
0446 job control job estimating
0336 job cost open line accounts analysis
0334 job cost trial balance audit management
0437 job costing
0347 job costing accounting time recording
0350 job costing architects accounting
0351 job costing building industry accounting
0450 job costing forecasting timesheets
0427 job costing time expense analysis
0469 job costs control
0089 job developers budget viability cost plan
0426 job estimates ledgers payroll
0446 job estimating job control
0210 job expenses overheads profit material estimates
0147 job management quantity surveyors bill quantities
0067 job national building specification standard text
0209 job summary contractors
0306 jobs costs quantities valuation
0055 jobs productivity contractor payments fees
1059 joint deflections plane steel frames
1035 joint displacements frame members
1078 joint displacements moments framed structures
1073 joint displacements plane frame deformations
1017 joint displacements plane frame members
1036 joint loading member loading frame
1152 joint loading rigid/flexible supports
1089 joints elements loading condition
1076 joints loading conditions frame members
1147 joint⅝⅛s member forces plane trusses
1031 joints member forces reactions frame structure
1027 joints member types displacements 2D frame
1009 joints plane frame moments shears
1090 joints shear forces moments members
1128 joints welded frames bridge
1283 joists column sections beam sections
0741 kitchen 3D drawings design
0229 label printing data management system
0149 labour bill electrical contractors cost
0299 labour bill quantities metals roofs
0514 labour cost tasks personnel
0489 labour costs contract costing timesheets
0519 labour estimate plant materials costs
0292 labour expenses overheads profit material
0296 labour hours materials electrical plumbing heating
0176 labour invoicing documentation control plant
0465 labour material building cost
0305 labour material resources prices
0471 labour material stock contracts
0141 labour materials cost job bill quantities
0504 labour materials stock accounts sales
0387 labour pay contractors records
0516 labour plant material estimates
0058 labour professional practices management
0104 labour service industries manpower rostering
0014 Lagrangian interpolation management linear
1710 Lagrangian polynomial curve empirical exponential
1619 lamp/luminaire type lumen method
1620 lamp/luminaire types lighting room
0619 land cartography graphics wire frame
0044 land development appraisal tenders
1691 land planning transport modelling
0702 land survey 3D roads railways modelling
0716 land survey point plotting traverse coordinates
0699 land survey site
1713 land surveying geometry curve fitting
0715 land surveying planning coordinate geometry
0709 land surveying traverse adjustment least squares
1256 lateral strength wall design charts
1254 laterally loaded wall panel design
1225 lattice girders weight design plane
1091 launching hydrodynamic drag steel structures
0892 layered structure load stress elastic
0970 leap dynamics post-processing
1701 least square correlation coefficients
0709 least squares land surveying traverse adjustment

0426 ledgers payroll job estimates
1335 length velocity flow rates pipe pressure drop
1474 lengths areas volumes heat loss consumption
0705 levels height collimation staff positions
0704 levels height staff readings
0708 levels plotting station detail points
0090 libraries circulation periodicals
0077 libraries production specification documents
0776 library bridge programs
0625 library graphics CAD scaling
0622 library graphs graphics
0232 library information storage retrieval personnel
0674 library plotting graphics
0129 library quantity surveyors
0303 library records specifications projects
0673 library spatial search planning
1683 lift installations transport buildings
1679 lift system loading conditions cost
1682 lift system performance analysis
1678 lift system storeys size speed
1681 lift system waiting times passenger
1680 lift systems size
1630 light fittings artifical lighting rooms
1608 light natural artificial internal reflection
1635 light sources illuminance plane surface
1634 light windows transmittance reflectance
1670 lighting acoustic performance energy
1632 lighting daylighting luminaires window
1643 lighting design illumination levels
1614 lighting direct rooms rectangular
1615 lighting energy interior spaces
1623 lighting glare fluorescent luminaires
1627 lighting glare room fluorescent luminaire
1613 lighting glare rooms illuminance level
1616 lighting illuminance pattern fluorescent
1624 lighting intensities fluorescent luminaires
1633 lighting intensity calculates
1626 lighting intensity floodlighting luminalres
1611 lighting intensity luminaires
1609 lighting internal areas fluorescent
1620 lighting room lamp/luminaire types
0624 line bar pie graphics graphs
0646 line graphs pie charts numeric bar charts
0604 line perspectives projections continuous rotation
0592 line printers plotting graphs
0748 line surface regression analysis curve fitting
1110 linear analysis elastic structures
1030 linear analysis framed structures loads
0977 linear analysis structures frame
1341 linear copper steel piping stresses
0753 linear elastic analysis isotropic finite elements
1311 linear elastic design reinforced concrete
1323 linear non-linear analysis pipe networks
0014 linear regression Lagrangian interpolation
1656 linear systems transient response
1569 liquid air heat transfer solar heating
1563 liquid air solar heating hot water
0869 liquidity plasticity flow toughness
1390 load building air temperature heating cooling
1139 load combinations portal frames geometry
1219 load combinations reinforced concrete beams
1185 load conditions beams cross sections
0822 load conditions column footing steel
1066 load conditions displacements 3D frames
0722 load conditions graphics dynamic behaviour
1314 load conditions stress analysis finite elements
0795 load continuous beam
1042 load/deformation steel space frame
0819 load design steel concrete pad column
0784 load factors analysis continuous beams
0986 load portal frame elastic deflection
1155 load portal frame members eaves tie
1167 load span domestic truss rafter
1043 load specification 2D framed structures
1120 load stability vibrations foundations slope
0892 load stress elastic layered structure
1215 load types single span beam
0853 loading bearing pressures rectangular base
1271 loading bending elastic analysis column section
1264 loading bending elastic design members steel
0770 loading bridge design finite element
1089 loading condition joints elements
1087 loading conditions 3D structural frames
0785 loading conditions analysis continuous beam
1679 loading conditions cost lift system
1076 loading conditions frame members joints
1058 loading conditions plane structural frames
1088 loading conditions stresses members
1188 loading deflection stress wood beam
1121 loading displacement force static
1096 loading element building
1097 loading finite element structure
1308 loading mode shapes radial vibrations

1149 loading outputs plane truss geometry
1217 loading patterns cantilever columns spans
1223 loading section properties beam selection
1123 loading stability vibration plate
1692 loading stresses strains displacements
1696 loading stresses strains displacements
0752 loading structure finite element
1126 loading transverse motion strings
1197 loadings elastic analysis 2D beam
1005 loadings elastic analysis grid structures
1307 loadings radial vibrations plane strain
1028 loadings static deformation plane grillage
0788 loadings supports continuous beam
1220 loads bending moment concrete sections
1291 loads buckling plate graphics estimate
1290 loads buckling plate graphics estimating
1414 loads buildings temperatures heating cooling
0790 loads continuous beam analysis
0846 loads earth pressures piles
1195 loads end moments cantilevers span
1127 loads finite element stress strain
1004 loads framed structure continuous beam columns
1289 loads graphics estimating
1030 loads linear analysis framed structures
0734 loads material properties axisymmetric shells
0836 loads moments footing
1008 loads moments members frame
1026 loads plastic analysis steel frames
1021 loads pre-processor prestressing cables
1391 loads room heating cooling
1392 loads room heating cooling
0855 loads settlement piles analysis
0980 loads sizes member framework
1136 loads stanchion steel portal frames
1071 loads static analysis 2D 3D framed
1070 loads stress analysis 3D frameworks
1133 loads stresses floor framing supported beams
1151 loads stresses plane trusses
1189 loads structural beams support
1024 loads structure geometry continuous frame cantilevers
1686 location/allocation service centres
0390 location depreciation company group
0054 location environment buildings project design
0214 location tool manufacturers prices
0926 location wells water production
0774 long span bridge frame
0999 longitudinal stress reinforced concrete
1645 low voltage electrical distribution
1646 low voltage overcurrent protection
1619 lumen method lamp/luminaire type
1638 luminaires flux level energy loading
1639 luminaires illuminance level room
1636 luminaires illuminance plane surface
1611 luminaires lighting intensity
1632 luminaires window lighting daylighting
0048 mailing database
0049 mailing database word processing
0047 mailing list
0045 mailing market analysis
0224 mailshot merge word processing
0227 mailshots office system word processing
0075 maintenance buildings works information management
1522 maintenance costs energy installation
0194 maintenance drawings register planning statistics
0061 maintenance management distribution vehicle fleet
0178 maintenance utilisation management plant
0199 maintenance work buildings programme
0374 management accounting
0401 management accounting contract cost valuation
0373 management accounting contractor audit trail
0096 management accounting corporate modelling
0195 management accounting firm word processing
0185 management accounting plant hire utilisation
0463 management accounts analyses architects
0409 management accounts control
0381 management accounts system
0386 management analysis accounting system
0062 management building projects
0013 management capital allowance cost
0380 management construction company
0383 management construction industry accounting
0508 management construction industry accounts
0481 management construction industry payroll
0063 management construction industry subcontractor
0064 management construction industry vehicle fleets
0445 management contract cost analysis
0364 management contracts cash flow subcontractors
0043 management control property
0400 management cost analysis quantity surveyors
0434 management costs contract
0016 management CPM resources project planning
0032 management critical path project
0108 management engineering planning forecasting

0406 management information accounting
0361 management information invoicing VAT
0115 management information planning project control
0100 management information project planning
0250 management information stock control evaluation
0353 management invoices analyses statements
0334 management job cost trial balance audit
0058 management labour professional practices
0014 management linear regression Lagrangian
0075 management maintenance buildings works information
0300 management manufacturing stock control
0512 management personnel expenditure contractor hours
0072 management personnel salary
0078 management planning accounting functions
0084 management planning financial modelling
0177 management plant accounting depreciation assets
0178 management plant maintenance utilisation
0052 management professional practices contract
0066 management programming data
0087 management project
0203 management project office system word processing
0038 management properties
0039 management properties tenancies
0040 management property
0041 management property
0042 management property
0196 management sales force
0260 management stock control
0207 management storage/retrieval stock control
0356 management system accounting
0502 management timesheet cost records
0248 management valuation stock movements
0614 managers project evaluators graphics time
0233 managers record drawings project
0080 managing text databases editing retrieval
0093 manhours projects control analysis
0073 manpower levels distribution
0104 manpower rostering labour service industries
0116 manuals tender documents proposals
1603 manufacture windows doors aluminium UPVC
1157 manufacturer roof quotation trussed rafter
1487 manufacturers heat loss radiators
0594 manufacturing 3D design modelling
0238 manufacturing database component structure
0300 manufacturing stock control management
0672 map polygonal areas
0677 mapping electrical piping plant 2D 3D
0684 mapping grid survey analysis
0681 mapping information areas zone maps
0671 mapping network analysis
0623 maps 3D charts graphics bar pie charts
0167 maps areas takes-off plans
0045 market analysis mailing
0217 marketing distribution order entry sales
0051 marketing sales finance accounting
1253 masonry structures calculation design
0212 master files duplicate copies estimation
0150 material bill quantities schedule rates valves
0465 material building cost labour
0210 material estimates job expenses overheads profit
0516 material estimates labour plant
0456 material estimating bill quantities cost
0292 material labour expenses overheads profit
0279 material listing elements structure
0734 material properties axisymmetric shells loads
0293 material quantities take-off dimensions
0225 material requirements pricing goods received
0305 material resources prices labour
0471 material stock contracts labour
0588 material take-off drawing graphics editing
0197 material take-off project information costs
0168 materials bill quantities estimates
0372 materials building management accounts
0141 materials cost job bill quantities labour
0449 materials cost time
0440 materials cost timesheet details
0519 materials costs labour estimate plant
0296 materials electrical plumbing heating labour hours
0297 materials invoice hours estimating
1158 materials parts roof tiling quotations
0457 materials purchasing contract costs
0413 materials retainers accounting time
0504 materials stock accounts sales labour
0165 materials taking-off pricing houses
0513 mathematical cost fees estimate
1720 mathematical diagnosis
0586 mathematical expressions 2D draughting
0520 mathematical functions financial modelling
1698 mathematical programming
1719 mathematical routines statistical
1703 mathematical statistical problems
1709 mathematics arithmetic expressions
1371 mathematics graphics shop fabrication

0240 maths package data stores records
1380 maximum velocity sizes ductwork
1705 mean standard deviation calculate
0648 mechanical draughting system geometry 2D
0277 mechanical engineering valuation electrical
0596 mechanical lï draughting system electrical
0720 mechanism analysis graphics 3D
1315 member analysis stresses reinforced concrete
1094 member conveyor gantry steelwork sizes
1055 member forces elastic analysis plane frameworks
1163 member forces plane truss influence line
1147 member forces plane trusses joint⅝⅛s
1031 member forces reactions frame structure joints
0980 member framework loads sizes
1036 member loading frame joint loading
1034 member loading frameworks trusses
1075 member loads 3D rigid-jointed frameworks
1057 member loads continuous beam frame grid
1027 member types displacements 2D frame joints
1155 members eaves tie load portal frame
0806 members foundations reinforced concrete
1008 members frame loads moments
1017 members joint displacements plane frame
1076 members joints loading conditions frame
1090 members joints shear forces moments
1088 members loading conditions stresses
1166 members pin-jointed truss forces
1013 members plane grillages stiffness method
1169 members portal frames ply web
1264 members steel loading bending elastic design
0759 mesh post-processing superelement
1364 metal gauge ducts sizing calculates
0299 metals roofs labour bill quantities
1674 methanol compositions
0872 method slices bishop equation safety
0874 method slices civil engineering safety
1304 mild steel chimneys
0745 mode shapes elastic system vibration
1308 mode shapes radial vibrations loading
0746 mode shapes vibration shear buildings
0567 model CAD architects 2D 3D drawings
0883 model earth works calculate cut/fill ground
0724 model finite element pre− post-processing
0728 model pre-post-processing finite element
0607 model transformations
0637 modeller CAE 3D design
0517 modelling corporate planning financial analysis
0612 modelling hidden lines projections
0542 modelling housing layout site
0702 modelling land survey 3D roads railways
0594 modelling manufacturing 3D design
0059 modelling project financial forecasting
0540 models buildings design stage
0546 models hospital design stage
0644 models pre− post-processor finite element
0747 modes vibrations buildings estimates
1427 moist air cooling loads psychrometric analysis
0878 moisture contents calculates soil
1491 moisture flow wall roof condensation
0783 moment analysis continuous beams slabs
1274 moment capacity irregular section columns
1103 moment capacity prestressed concrete section
1181 moment connections designs beam/column
1143 moment connections plastic analysis/design
1010 moments deflections continuous frame shears
1164 moments elastic analysis portal frames
0836 moments footing loads
1078 moments framed structures joint displacements
1008 moments members frame loads
1090 moments members joints shear forces
1113 moments sections components centroid area
1009 moments shears joints plane frame
0068 monitor project management financial modelling plan
0595 monitoring graphics display bar charts
0505 monitoring staff costs construction projects
0840 Morgenstern soils stability slope
0007 motorway construction plant time cost CPM
1685 movement objects time utilisation
1687 movement people goods hospital traffic
0793 multi-span continous beam analysis
0865 multilayered soils excavation slope stability
0365 multiple currencies database manager accounting
0023 multiple projects CPM/pert techniques
0791 multispan continuous beam graphic
1317 multistorey building cold water pipes design
1585 multistorey building smoke concentrations
1583 multistorey buildings air movement
0751 multistorey buildings foundation vibration
1300 multistorey buildings stair-shaft pressurisation
0046 names addresses list information retrieval
0120 national building specification clauses project
0067 national building specification standard text job
1621 natural artificial illumination energy

0561 natural infiltration rates building
0161 NEDO bills quantities cost analysis
0302 NEDO building valuation calculate
0145 NEDO calculations bills quantities
0304 NEDO evaluating building contract
0324 NEDO fluctuation quantity surveying
0433 NEDO formula price adjustment
0262 NEDO formula statistics post-contract valuation
0287 NEDO price adjustment
0276 NEDO price adjustment civil engineering
0275 NEDO price adjustments building contracts
0322 NEDO quantity surveying valuations
0323 NEDO quantity surveying valuations
0288 NEDO quantity surveyors valuations forecasts
0280 NEDO valuation building contracts
0289 NEDO valuation quantity surveyor
0026 network analysis CPM utilisation planning
0009 network analysis resource allocation cost control
0949 network analysis water supply
0029 network CPM project planning
0948 networks calculates water distribution
1711 Newton-Raphson polynominal
1040 nodal displacements vibration elastic structures
1044 nodal loading grillage
1022 node shapes dynamic analysis plane frame
1348 nodes plotting pipes
1386 noise level calculates predictions rooms
1389 noise levels glazing internal
1387 noise levels grilles rooms
0891 noise values calculates road traffic
0342 nominal ledger accounting sales purchase
0358 nominal ledger brought forward statistics
0357 nominal ledger profitability stock sales ledger
0444 non-constructional elements cost plan
0780 non-linear elastic analysis suspension bridges
1130 non-linear stability axial forces deflection
0973 nuclear engineering offshore structures bridges
0646 numeric bar charts line graphs pie charts
0621 numeric data graphics representation
1723 numerical data boolean
0575 numerical data charts graph
0576 numerical data charts graphs
1707 numerical integration romberg
1708 numerical polynomial constant coefficients
0331 office accounts
0211 office functions word processing
0110 office management specifications financial
0369 office procedures accounting
0227 office system word processing mailshots
0203 office system word processing management project
1092 offshore steel jacket wave wind current
0973 offshore structures bridges nuclear engineering
1074 offshore structures earthquakes wave 3D
1093 offshore structures steel concrete
1244 one-way slab reinforcement design
0917 open channel hydraulics
0340 open item accounting system
0341 open item accounting system
0336 open line accounts analysis job cost
0183 operating costs investment energy costs
0269 optimisation accounting window design
0268 optimisation sheet materials cutting
0319 optimiser cutting schedules sheet materials
0318 optimiser fabrication windows doors cost
1279 optimum design reinforced concrete column
0259 order analysis stock recording timber
0217 order entry sales marketing distribution
0191 order entry stock control invoicing sales
0258 order/sales evaluating prepared timber
0979 orthogonal frames continuous beams 2D
0544 outline proposal evaluating building design
0603 output projections
1646 overcurrent protection low voltage
1186 overhead travelling cranes span
0274 overheads profit estimates stock
0210 overheads profit material estimates job expenses
0292 overheads profit material labour expenses
0327 overheads profit price lists costing
0559 overshadowing solar orientation design sun
1266 pad footing columns reinforced concrete
0813 pad foundation reinforced concrete serviceability
0812 pad foundations design reinforced concrete
0809 pad foundations reinforced concrete
1326 parametric performance heat pipes/rejection
0678 parcel maps boundary tract
0245 parts explosion forecasting re-order levels
1681 passenger lift system waiting times
0387 pay contractors records labour
0392 payment certification client retention
0436 payments contracts subcontractors
0055 payments fees jobs productivity contractor
0525 payments system subcontractor
0482 payroll

0487 payroll
0371 payroll accounting budgeted costs stock
0370 payroll accounting plant hire subcontract
0377 payroll accounting stock control
0403 payroll accounting subcontract management
0282 payroll accounts building specifications
0479 payroll analysis
0355 payroll building industry accounting
0491 payroll calculation
0496 payroll calculation
0478 payroll employees files
0486 payroll financial control
0426 payroll job estimates ledgers
0481 payroll management construction industry
0480 payroll personnel management
0492 payroll personnel management
0490 payroll personnel service
0521 payroll plant hire accounts
0366 payroll purchases contract costing
0346 payroll sales/purchase ledgers accounting
0529 payroll site operations
0389 payroll stock control accounting system
0378 payroll stock control invoicing accounting
0405 payroll subcontractors construction industry
0483 payroll system
0484 payroll system
0485 payroll system
0493 payroll system
0494 payroll system
0495 payroll system
0497 payroll system
0417 payroll trial balance profit loss
0488 payrolls cost analysis
1682 performance analysis lift system
0548 performance buildings appraisal
1663 performance electric power reactive flow
0545 performance sketch designs bar charts
0090 periodicals libraries circulation
0867 permeability calculates coeffeicient
0866 permeability consolidation continuous void
0249 perpetual inventory construction industry stock
0256 perpetual inventory price list stocktaking
0512 personnel expenditure contractor hours management
0514 personnel labour cost tasks
0232 personnel library information storage retrieval
0101 personnel management
0480 personnel management payroll
0492 personnel management payroll
0501 personnel management records
0500 personnel project management
0072 personnel salary management
0490 personnel service payroll
0635 perspective axonometric views 3D presentation
0550 perspective design building 3D model
0583 perspective design stage
0571 perspective drawing definition scaling
0564 perspective generator wireframe models
0670 perspective graphics 2D 3D surfaces
0582 perspective projections draws sunlight
1015 perspective space frames stiffness method
0580 perspective view daylight factors
0543 perspective views
0732 perspective views 3D drawings isometrics
0676 perspectives 3D projections hidden lines
0589 perspectives isometric projections architect
0579 perspectives isometrics draughting drawings
0031 PERT/cpm database cost/resource project control
0030 PERT plotting project planning
0008 PERT precedence network construction management
0027 PERT system CPM arrow precedence
0265 picking lists invoices route loading stock control
0646 pie charts numeric bar charts line graphs
0930 piezometric groundwater velocity
0849 pile foundations stability check stress 2D 3D
0820 pile group analysis applied moments
0850 pile group analysis vertical
0824 pile loads elastic theory analysis
0841 piles analysis groups
0842 piles analysis groups
0855 piles analysis loads settlement
0810 piles design soil
0814 piles group analysis
0856 piles group analysis
0846 piles loads earth pressures
0976 pin jointed 2D frames analysis
1068 pin-jointed frameworks 3D analysis
0997 pin-jointed frameworks displacement method 2D
1064 pin-jointed structures hollow sections 3D
1175 pin-jointed ties struts bracing members
1166 pin-jointed truss forces members
1334 pipe analysis sizing fluid heating/chilled water
1352 pipe connections flow central heating water
1355 pipe dimensions pipework internal resistance

1590 pipe duct fire protection pressure gas
1472 pipe duct interstitial condensation heat losses
0939 pipe flow sewer calculated excavation design
0935 pipe foul surface water drainage
1466 pipe loops heaters
1325 pipe material pipe sizing fluid
1358 pipe measurement schedules pipe runs
1671 pipe network service hospital
1323 pipe networks linear non-linear analysis
1361 pipe networks pressure reducing valves pumps
1335 pipe pressure drop length velocity flow rates
0295 pipe prices rectangular duct fibreboard
1358 pipe runs pipe measurement schedules
1351 pipe sizes heating/cooling units flow
1357 pipe sizes heating system
1320 pipe sizes pressure loss hot water
1468 pipe sizes water system
1340 pipe sizing copper steel pipework water
1325 pipe sizing fluid pipe material
1481 pipe sizing heater sizing
1324 pipe sizing hot cold water head analysis
1462 pipe sizing system analysis
1482 pipe sizing volume flow hot water
1362 pipe stress
1338 pipe system flow rates friction losses
1360 pipe systems thermal expansion constraint stresses
1359 pipe thickness estimation
1346 pipe wall thickness calculated
0951 pipeline flow sewerage network
1342 pipeline pressure production rate gas
1331 pipes boilers condensers estimates pressure changes
1317 pipes design multistorey building cold water
0742 pipes fittings drawings 3D component model
1350 pipes heat transfer heat losses gains
0953 pipes hydrograph drainage schemes design
0941 pipes hydrograph flow drainage networks storm
1343 pipes network Hazen williams water distribution
1348 pipes nodes plotting
1349 pipes reservoirs Hazen-williams Darcy-Weisbach
1332 pipes sizes components hot chilled water circuits
1463 pipes sizes hot water system
1469 pipes sizing regulating valves heating
0938 pipes storm drain analysis flow
1322 pipework calculates stress analysis
1337 pipework copper steel heat emission
1329 pipework detailing purchasing isometric production
0675 pipework electrical CAD drawings 2D
1316 pipework installations pre post-contract estimates
1353 pipework internal resistance heating cooling
1354 pipework internal resistance heating cooling pressure
1356 pipework internal resistance hot cold water supply
1355 pipework internal resistance pipe dimensions
1333 pipework pressure drop flow rates fluid temperature
0298 pipework rectangular ductwork insulation
0656 pipework steel frames geometric modeller 3D
1328 pipework system sizes pressure temperature flow
1340 pipework water pipe sizing copper steel
1473 piping air heating installation radiators
0638 piping cabling CAD CAE 3D wire framing
0731 piping diagrams graphic draughting circuit layouts
1330 piping fittings design hot water
1345 piping head losses Darcy-Weisbach formula
0577 piping layout design draughting
0677 piping plant 2D 3D mapping electrical
1341 piping stresses linear copper steel
0740 piping symbol isometric drawing
1318 piping system design
1327 piping systems pressure drop analysis
1344 piping systems type restraint
0690 plan coordinates survey stations distance tacheometry
0569 plan drawing timber framed buildings
0089 plan job developers budget viability cost
0068 plan monitor project management financial modelling
0693 plan points coordinates bearings distances
1132 plan production prefabricated floor elements
0021 plan project critical path
0729 plane area coordinates points section
1049 plane frame 2D beam
0993 plane frame continuous beams calculates
1073 plane frame deformations joint displacements
1061 plane frame geometry elastic analysis
1017 plane frame members joint displacements
1009 plane frame moments shears joints
1022 plane frame node shapes dynamic analysis
1109 plane frame plastic analysis
1060 plane frame rigid-plastic analysis
1020 plane frame structural analysis bending moment
1084 plane frames analysis
1038 plane frames continuous beams
0991 plane frames elastic analysis
0982 plane frames statically indeterminate
1012 plane frames stiffness method
0994 plane frames stress analysis

1086 plane frames stress analysis concrete
1051 plane framework frames continuous beams
1056 plane frameworks elastic-plastic analysis
1055 plane frameworks member forces elastic analysis
0992 plane grid simply supported beam elements
1192 plane grids beam displacement method
1028 plane grillage loadings static deformation
1013 plane grillages stiffness method members
1225 plane lattice girders weight design
0998 plane rigid-jointed frameworks displacement method
0996 plane shape finite elements 2D mesh
1059 plane steel frames joint deflections
1307 plane strain loadings radial vibrations
1014 plane stress finite element Poissons ratio
0984 plane structural frame analysis
1058 plane structural frames loading conditions
1635 plane surface light sources illuminance
1636 plane surface luminaires illuminance
1149 plane truss geometry loading outputs
1163 plane truss influence line member forces
1147 plane trusses joint%⅛s member forces
1151 plane trusses loads stresses
0111 planning budgeting data
0311 planning control accounting production
0011 planning control project
0002 planning controlling projects time resources cost
0715 planning coordinate geometry land surveying
0113 planning corporate modelling financial analysis
0468 planning cost control construction sites
0547 planning diagrammatic layout building
0105 planning estimating cost development project
0084 planning financial modelling management
0556 planning health buildings evaluation
0673 planning library spatial search
0026 planning network analysis CPM utilisation
0115 planning project control management information
0553 planning space programming building sizing
0194 planning statistics maintenance drawings register
0668 plans draughting graphic symbols sketch
0246 plans drawings information storage retrieval
0317 plans estimates cutting sheet glass
0167 plans maps areas takes-off
0003 plans time resources CPM project planning
0601 plans vertical perspective
0177 plant accounting depreciation assets management
1550 plant building weather energy consumption
1555 plant energy consumption air handling
0521 plant hire accounts payroll
0370 plant hire subcontract payroll accounting
0185 plant hire utilisation management accounting
0176 plant labour invoicing documentation control
0568 plant layout 3D modelling drawings CAD
0178 plant maintenance utilisation management
0516 plant material estimates labour
0519 plant materials costs labour estimate
0266 plant register hire register invoices
0007 plant time cost CPM motorway construction
0025 plant utilisation production planning
1143 plastic analysis/design moment connections
1109 plastic analysis plane frame
1148 plastic analysis portal frame
1138 plastic analysis portal frames
1165 plastic analysis single bay portal frame
1026 plastic analysis steel frames loads
0985 plastic design elastic analysis portal frames
0988 plastic design portal frame
1046 plastic/elastic analysis steel/concrete frames
1146 plastic portal frames design
1150 plastic theory single span portal frames
0869 plasticity flow toughness liquidity
1292 plate buckle shear load compressive load
1293 plate buckling estimating stresses deflections
1226 plate girder sections cost analysis
1184 plate girders sections shear connections
1182 plate girders welds stress checks
1291 plate graphics estimate loads buckling
1290 plate graphics estimating loads buckling
1123 plate loading stability vibration
1296 plate panels service collapse
0805 plate raft foundations footings slabs
1053 plated structures static analysis 2D framed
1224 plates girder estimates
1054 plates grillages elastic foundation
1006 plates ribs beams elastic analysis
0609 plot graphs user-defined data
0987 plots deflected forms portal frame
0653 plotted zoom facility graphics system
0574 plotting data
0666 plotting graphic
0674 plotting graphics library
0657 plotting graphs bar chart
0592 plotting graphs line printers
1348 plotting pipes nodes

0012 project management evaluation critical paths
0475 project management expenditure resources
0068 project management financial modelling plan monitor
0500 project management personnel
0095 project management quantity surveying forecasting
0005 project management scheduling critical path
0036 project management time resource cost analyses
0022 project management time resources
0092 project managers expediting document control
0233 project managers record drawings
0120 project national building specification clauses
0102 project planning
0010 project planning building civil engineers CPM
0011 project planning control
0033 project planning control
0020 project planning CPM resource scheduling
0015 project planning critical path
0028 project planning critical path arrow
0016 project planning management CPM resources
0100 project planning management information
0029 project planning network CPM
0030 project planning PERT plotting
0003 project planning plans time resources CPM
0309 project price component
0034 project scheduling resource management
0222 project specification drawings
0451 project tender costs
0441 project time accounting cost control
0006 project time estimating resource
0604 projections continuous rotation line perspectives
0612 projections modelling hidden lines
0603 projections output
0093 projects control analysis manhours
0216 projects cost accounts timesheet expenses
0507 projects cost limits secondary education
0313 projects estimate cost appraisals
0537 projects forecasting cashflow
0303 projects library records specifications
0477 projects resource forecasts allocations
0236 projects steelwork fabrication detailing
1106 properties concrete sections elements
0038 properties management
0039 properties tenancies management
0329 property insurance register
0040 property management
0041 property management
0042 property management
0226 property management architects builders merchants
0043 property management control
0312 property valuations insurance purposes
0901 proportioning concrete mix portland cement
0116 proposals manuals tender documents
1427 psychrometric analysis moist air cooling loads
0082 publications schedules records
1483 pump selection
0919 pumping stations hydrographs storm water
0418 purchase analysis accounting creditors control
0393 purchase ledger bank reconciliation invoices
0362 purchase ledger creditors control accounting
0342 purchase nominal ledger accounting sales
0397 purchase ordering builders merchants invoicing
0252 purchase orders stock reporting invoices
0366 purchases contract costing payroll
0410 purchases settlement discount invoices
1329 purchasing isometric production pipework detailing
1144 purlins side rails design
1486 quantities list radiator schedule
0283 quantities pricing tender estimators
0156 quantities process pipework estimates
1367 quantities sizing ductwork pressures temperatures
0293 quantities take-off dimensions material
0306 quantities valuation jobs costs
0155 quantity surveying architects
0095 quantity surveying forecasting project management
0324 quantity surveying NEDO fluctuation
0322 quantity surveying valuations NEDO
0323 quantity surveying valuations NEDO
0144 quantity surveyor architect engineer billll
0142 quantity surveyor bill contractor
0289 quantity surveyor NEDO valuation
0162 quantity surveyor pricing bill quantities
0632 quantity surveyors architects bills estimates
0147 quantity surveyors bill quantities job management
0119 quantity surveyors bills quantities
0138 quantity surveyors bills quantities
0160 quantity surveyors bills quantities
0320 quantity surveyors contract cost valuation
0152 quantity surveyors contractors bill quantities
0065 quantity surveyors control costs construction industry
0158 quantity surveyors cost bills quantities
0515 quantity surveyors fees RICS scale
0129 quantity surveyors library
0400 quantity surveyors management cost analysis

0288 quantity surveyors valuations forecasts NEDO
0307 quantity surveys stock control bill materials
0308 quantity surveys stock control bill materials
1158 quotations materials parts roof tiling
0535 quotations window door frames staircases
1308 radial vibrations loading mode shapes
1307 radial vibrations plane strain loadings
1453 radiant air temperature thermal comfort
1417 radiant convective heat losses rooms
1436 radiant convective heat losses rooms buildings
1544 radiant energy interchange factors
1545 radiant heat evaluate interchange factors
1451 radiant temperature calculates room
1476 radiation temperature simulation
1336 radiator performance water pressure central heating
1486 radiator schedule quantities list
1440 radiators heat losses building
1506 radiators heat losses central heating
1488 radiators heating output sizing
1487 radiators manufacturers heat loss
1473 radiators piping air heating installation
1409 radiators room bill quantities
1493 radiators sizes
1504 radiators temperatures winter room
0851 raft foundation analysis
0805 raft foundations footings slabs plate
1167 rafter load span domestic truss
1153 rafter stanchion section sizes
0943 rain storm sewers hydrograph
0933 rainfall drainage hydrograph
0922 rainfall drainage urban hydrograph
0251 re-order level stock control suppliers
0245 re-order levels parts explosion forecasting
1031 reactions frame structure joints member forces
1663 reactive flow performance electric power
0083 rearranging records information retrieval
0133 reconciliations bill quantities
0134 reconciliations bill quantities
0233 record drawings project managers
0239 records analysis employees stores
0187 records information retrieval database management
0240 records maths package data stores
0501 records personnel management
0082 records publications schedules
0206 records storage retrieval
0201 records storage retrieval information
0730 rectangles area position section properties
0853 rectangular base loading bearing pressures
1268 rectangular columns design
0703 rectangular coordinates bearings survey
0295 rectangular duct fibreboard pipe prices
0122 rectangular ductwork fittings bills quantities
0298 rectangular ductwork insulation pipework
1025 rectangular frames slope deflection
0281 rectangular material 2D cutting optimiser
1295 rectangular plates estimating
1267 rectangular section deflection columns
1374 rectangular sizing ducts high velocity circular
1104 rectangular T sections reinforced concrete
0706 reduced level coordinates staff position
0692 reduced levels contouring site
0606 reflected radiation slope direct diffuse
0329 register property insurance
0748 regression analysis curve fitting line surface
1728 regression line scatter diagram
1469 regulating valves heating pipes sizing
0086 regulations building
0815 reinforced brickwork retaining wall section
1095 reinforced concrete bar bending schedules
1249 reinforced concrete bar schedules flat slabs
0799 reinforced concrete beam cantilever
1231 reinforced concrete beam pre-tensioned
1170 reinforced concrete beam/slab structures
1229 reinforced concrete beams columns design
1219 reinforced concrete beams load combinations
1180 reinforced concrete beams shear
0964 reinforced concrete beams slabs columns
1284 reinforced concrete building elastic analysis
0816 reinforced concrete cantilever retaining wall
0821 reinforced concrete cantilever wall footing
0765 reinforced concrete column bending moments
1279 reinforced concrete column optimum design
1276 reinforced concrete columns beams
1263 reinforced concrete columns designs
1213 reinforced concrete continuous beam column
1196 reinforced concrete continuous beams
0800 reinforced concrete continuous beams design
0801 reinforced concrete continuous beams design
0966 reinforced concrete design continuous beams
1302 reinforced concrete drawings beam column
1239 reinforced concrete flat slabs
1303 reinforced concrete framed structures
1311 reinforced concrete linear elastic design

0999 reinforced concrete longitudinal stress
1315 reinforced concrete member analysis stresses
0806 reinforced concrete members foundations
1266 reinforced concrete pad footing columns
0809 reinforced concrete pad foundations
0812 reinforced concrete pad foundations design
1104 reinforced concrete rectangular T sections
0854 reinforced concrete retaining wall safety
1286 reinforced concrete sections bending shear
0852 reinforced concrete sections foundations
0813 reinforced concrete serviceability pad foundation
1210 reinforced concrete steel
0967 reinforced concrete steel reinforcement
0954 reinforced concrete structural design
0965 reinforced concrete structures design
0942 reinforced culverts design
0782 reinforced structures continuous beams steel
1114 reinforcement bending schedules weight
0839 reinforcement column bases sizing
1248 reinforcement column design spans
1275 reinforcement design analysis columns
1244 reinforcement design one-way slab
1243 reinforcement design slab
1242 reinforcement design slabs design
0798 reinforcement design spans
1112 reinforcement quantities bar schedules
1240 reinforcement serviceability slabs
1250 reinforcement slab beam
1118 reinforcing bars bar schedules weight steel
0570 relational database 3D geometric modelling
0422 remittance advice accounts bought ledger
1536 remote controllers energy management
0175 repair alteration work schedules
0264 repairs expenditure calculates
1349 reservoirs Hazen-williams Darcy-Weisbach pipes
0848 resistance moment bearing pressures steel
1649 resistivity curves generation
0510 resource aggregating cashflow forecasting
0024 resource aggregation cost critical path
0009 resource allocation cost control network analysis
0140 resource estimating bills quantities
0477 resource forecasts allocations projects
0439 resource forecasts progress
0034 resource management project scheduling
0006 resource project time estimating
0017 resource scheduling project control time
0020 resource scheduling project planning CPM
0002 resources cost planning controlling projects time
0003 resources CPM project planning plans time
0315 resources estimating bills quantities
0154 resources estimator bills quantities
0305 resources prices labour material
0475 resources project management expenditure
0022 resources project management time
0016 resources project planning management CPM
0413 retainers accounting time materials
0828 retaining wall analysis stability cantilever
0845 retaining wall design
0816 retaining wall reinforced concrete cantilever
0854 retaining wall safety reinforced concrete
0815 retaining wall section reinforced brickwork
0844 retaining walls abutments stability cantilever
0827 retaining walls cantilevered sheet pile
1237 retaining walls cross-sectional elastic analysis
0843 retaining walls sheet pile
0825 retaining walls sheet pile cantilevered
0826 retaining walls stress analysis anchored
0831 retaining walls stress soils sheet pile
0913 retarding basins flood hydrographs storm
0460 retention cost estimates profitability
0395 retentions expired certificates transactions
0220 retrieval data file management
0241 retrieval filing system storage
0218 retrieval information management
0201 retrieval information records storage
0215 retrieval information storage
0235 retrieval information storage
0080 retrieval managing text databases editing
0232 retrieval personnel library information storage
0246 retrieval plans drawings information storage
0206 retrieval records storage
0219 retrieval word processing
1388 reverberation times calculates room
1006 ribs beams elastic analysis plates
0515 RICS scale quantity surveyors fees
1152 rigid/flexible supports joint loading
1000 rigid-jointed frameworks 3D
1075 rigid-jointed frameworks member loads 3D
1060 rigid-plastic analysis plane frame
0896 road alignment
0906 road construction cost estimating
0903 road design alignment earthworks
0894 road design calculates

0895 road design calculates
0899 road design intersection
0859 road earthwork cross-sections
0900 road earthworks design alignment
0634 road layout 2D draughting dimensioning
0893 road pavement traffic rut
0908 road plan CAD highway engineering
0901 road section earthwork volumes alignment
0891 road traffic noise values calculates
0963 roads bridges buildings design library
0897 roads design alignment
0686 roads footpaths graphic site area coordinates
0702 roads railways modelling land survey 3D
1707 romberg numerical integration
1491 roof condensation moisture flow wall
1457 roof condensation risk U value wall
0562 roof constructions building regulations wall
1547 roof insulation
1277 roof leg weight design crane columns
1160 roof members beam rafter trussed beam
1157 roof quotation trussed rafter manufacturer
1211 roof steel beams storage tanks
1425 roof thermal transmittance U value wall floor
1159 roof tile estimating fixing requirements
1158 roof tiling quotations materials parts
1537 roof wall insulation heat
1490 roofs admittance decrement walls
1449 roofs/ceilings heat flow calculates walls
1432 roofs heat transfer walls
0299 roofs labour bill quantities metals
1397 roofs sol-air temperatures heat gains
1526 roofs U value condensation walls
1411 roofs windows solar radiation weather
1393 room air temperatures heating cooling loads
1409 room bill quantities radiators
1523 room building energy transfers
1405 room building heat losses
1426 room building heating cooling loads
1566 room building solar heat gains temperature
1627 room fluorescent luminaire lighting glare
1391 room heating cooling loads
1392 room heating cooling loads
1620 room lamp/luminaire types lighting
1639 room luminaires illuminance level
1451 room radiant temperature calculates
1504 room radiators temperatures winter
1388 room reverberation times calculates
1641 room sky component daylight factors
1642 room sky component daylight factors
1410 room temperatures heating cooling loads
1429 room temperatures heating cooling loads
1419 room U value heat loss/gain
1418 room ventilation temperature heating cooling
1607 room windows daylight factor
1606 room windows daylight factors
1628 room windows daylight factors
1612 room windows daylighting factors
1625 room windows rooflights daylighting
1395 rooms air flow heat gains losses
1489 rooms building air-conditioning temperatures
1407 rooms building cooling load heat gains
1485 rooms building heat losses
1541 rooms buildings heat losses
1436 rooms buildings radiant convective heat losses
1401 rooms cooling loads
1637 rooms direct indirect illumination
1529 rooms heat gain
1435 rooms heat gains
1484 rooms heat gains
1422 rooms heat gains losses
1423 rooms heat gains losses
1408 rooms heat losses
1613 rooms illuminance level lighting glare
1630 rooms light fittings artifical lighting
1386 rooms noise level calculates predictions
1387 rooms noise levels grilles
1417 rooms radiant convective heat losses
1614 rooms rectangular lighting direct
1684 route hospital circulation system
0265 route loading stock control picking lists invoices
0893 rut road pavement traffic
0871 safety earth embankment slip circle
0861 safety factors embankments slope stability
0689 safety factors evaluation earthquake actions
0872 safety method slices bishop equation
0874 safety method slices civil engineering
0880 safety pore pressures soil slip surfaces
0854 safety reinforced concrete retaining wall
0863 safety sliding slip surface earthquake
0864 safety sliding soils cracks
0862 safety slip circles embankment soil
0868 safety soil conditions
0072 salary management personnel

0363 sales analysis accounting credit control
0411 sales extracts turnover analysis invoices
0196 sales force management
0504 sales labour materials stock accounts
0273 sales ledger hire agreements invoices
0339 sales ledger invoice stock control
0325 sales ledger invoices skips hire
0357 sales ledger nominal ledger profitability stock
0338 sales ledger stock control accounting
0217 sales marketing distribution order entry
0191 sales order entry stock control invoicing
0346 sales/purchase ledgers accounting payroll
0442 sales purchase ledgers time recording
0342 sales purchase nominal ledger accounting
0423 sales transaction statement analysis
0428 sales value budget profit accounts costs
0920 sanitary sewer system analysis
0928 saturation waste disposal drainfield water
1539 savings capacitors power factor
1428 savings evaluates heat pipe
1080 scaffolding frame analysis buckling 3D
0625 scaling library graphics CAD
0650 scaling orientation shading plotting
0571 scaling perspective drawing definition
1728 scatter diagram regression line
0180 schedule equipment project field personnel
0150 schedule rates valves material bill quantities
0267 schedules building construction estimating
0081 schedules databases information handling
1358 schedules pipe runs pipe measurement
0082 schedules records publications
0005 scheduling critical path project management
0085 scheduling employment production levels cost
0017 scheduling project control time resource
0034 scheduling resource management project
0286 scheduling vehicles preventive maintenance
1439 screening shading cooling load building
1591 sealed units glass spacers windows
0507 secondary education projects cost limits
0539 secondary school design
1203 section constants beams
1099 section cross-sectional torsional properties
0729 section plane area coordinates points
1098 section properties area
1223 section properties beam selection loading
1222 section properties beams cross-section
0803 section properties continuous beams
1117 section properties cross-sections shear stresses
0730 section properties rectangles area position
0815 section reinforced brickwork retaining wall
1200 section shear stress cantilever
1153 section sizes rafter stanchion
1235 section steel bending moment shear force
1286 sections bending shear reinforced concrete
1113 sections components centroid area moments
1226 sections cost analysis plate girder
1106 sections elements properties concrete
0852 sections foundations reinforced concrete
1184 sections shear connections plate girders
1247 sections span bar design
0835 sections wall brick/block piers
1658 security electrical distribution
0764 seepage groundwater flow heat transfer
0957 seepage pores pressures
1255 seismic loads shear walls wind
1483 selection pump
1206 selection steel members
1715 semi-infinite solid steady temperature
1686 service centres location/allocation
1296 service collapse plate panels
1671 service hospital pipe network
0104 service industries manpower rostering labour
0179 service notices preventive maintenance estimate
0490 service payroll personnel
0813 serviceability pad foundation reinforced concrete
1240 serviceability slabs reinforcement
0284 servicing records central heating
0887 settlement analysis embankments soil mechanics
0833 settlement calculates
0410 settlement discount invoices purchases
0829 settlement earth fill structures stress
0830 settlement footings stress calculation
0855 settlement piles analysis loads
0939 sewer calculated excavation design pipe flow
0934 sewer calculates flow
0924 sewer drainage hydraulics analysis
0925 sewer drainage hydraulics analysis
0947 sewer networks plotting
0920 sewer system analysis sanitary
0945 sewer systems design surface water
0951 sewerage network pipeline flow
1573 shading air-conditioning glazing
1571 shading buildings solar gain heatgain

0650 shading plotting scaling orientation
1459 shading summertime temperature solar intensity
1575 shadows buildings hour day
1574 shadows obstructions hour day sun horizon
1572 shadows vertical building faces
1280 shaft displacements bearing forces
1282 shaft vibrations torsional loads
0746 shear buildings mode shapes vibration
1184 shear connections plate girders sections
1216 shear force beam bending moment
1193 shear force end moments cantilevers span
1235 shear force section steel bending moment
1252 shear force slabs bending moments
1191 shear forces beam bending moments
1178 shear forces bending moments slope deflection beam
0786 shear forces continuous beam bending moments
0787 shear forces continuous beam bending moments
1090 shear forces moments members joints
1292 shear load compressive load plate buckle
1180 shear reinforced concrete beams
1286 shear reinforced concrete sections bending
1200 shear stress cantilever section
1258 shear stress wall structures frame
1117 shear stresses section properties cross-sections
1259 shear wall earthquake elastic analysis
1255 shear walls wind seismic loads
0817 shears deflections sheet pile wall
1009 shears joints plane frame moments
1010 shears moments deflections continuous frame
0317 sheet glass plans estimates cutting
0268 sheet materials cutting optimisation
0319 sheet materials optimiser cutting schedules
1370 sheet metal ductwork fittings
0825 sheet pile cantilevered retaining walls
0843 sheet pile retaining walls
0827 sheet pile retaining walls cantilevered
0831 sheet pile retaining walls stress soils
0847 sheet pile wall design cantilever earth pressures
0817 sheet pile wall shears deflections
0823 sheet piled walls cofferdams analysis
1081 shell structures dynamic analysis frame
0200 shop drawings progress
1371 shop fabrication mathematics graphics
0554 shopfront window estimates
0754 shopfronts cutting design costs estimate
1660 short circuit electrical currents
1668 short circuit energy level 3—phase
1144 side rails design purlins
1212 simple span beams timber steel concrete
0992 simply supported beam elements plane grid
1172 simply supported beams steel timber
1538 simulate energy management buildings
1369 simulate ventilation ductwork
1677 simulate washroom facilities
1433 simulates cooling dehumidifying heat exchangers
1657 simulation electrical control
1476 simulation radiation temperature
1165 single bay portal frame plastic analysis
1321 single pipe headloss
1215 single span beam load types
1150 single span portal frames plastic theory
1312 single spans prestressed pre-tensioned
0686 site area coordinates roads footpaths graphic
0687 site investigation index
0699 site land survey
0542 site modelling housing layout
0529 site operations payroll
0694 site points point coordinates
0692 site reduced levels contouring
0106 sites control contracts/projects expenditure progress
0558 sites cut fill building
1678 size speed lift system storeys
1381 sizes air duct systems
1332 sizes components hot chilled water circuits pipes
1363 sizes duct networks acoustic analysis costing
1380 sizes ductwork maximum velocity
1378 sizes ductwork pressure drop
1379 sizes ductwork static regain
1339 sizes heating systems heat emission
1094 sizes member conveyor gantry steelwork
0980 sizes member framework loads
1328 sizes pressure temperature flow pipework system
1319 sizes steel pipes water flow rates
1368 sizes ventilating duct pressure losses velocities
1601 sizes venting capacities smoke shafts
0404 sizing calculation invoicing timber merchants
1374 sizing ducts high velocity circular rectangular
1367 sizing ductwork pressures temperatures quantities
1334 sizing fluid heating/chilled water pipe analysis
1488 sizing radiators heating output
1469 sizing regulating valves heating pipes
0839 sizing reinforcement column bases
1653 sizing volt drop fault electrical

0679 statistics graphs histograms bar charts
0194 statistics maintenance drawings register planning
0358 statistics nominal ledger brought forward
0262 statistics post-contract valuation NEDO formula
1730 statistics tensile testing stress
0733 steady state soil seepage temperature 2D
1715 steady temperature semi-infinite solid
1499 steam coils sizes by-pass factor
1245 steel bar design tension compression
1177 steel beams bending deflection
1214 steel beams calculations
1205 steel beams columns weight elastic design
1211 steel beams storage tanks roof
1183 steel beams stress checks
1235 steel bending moment shear force section
1037 steel buckling loads compression members
1272 steel columns axial load end moments
1262 steel columns designs
1046 steel/concrete frames plastic/elastic analysis
1093 steel concrete offshore structures
0819 steel concrete pad column load design
1212 steel concrete simple span beams timber
0766 steel concrete stresses highway bridges
0792 steel concrete timber continuous beams
1033 steel connections bolt/weld layout
0968 steel design
0755 steel detailing drawings beam/column
0278 steel fabrication bill materials estimating
1065 steel finite element stress 3D models
1001 steel frame foundation loads
1313 steel frames beams columns end plate
0656 steel frames geometric modeller 3D pipework
1059 steel frames joint deflections plane
1026 steel frames loads plastic analysis
1092 steel jacket wave wind current offshore
0822 steel load conditions column footing
1264 steel loading bending elastic design members
1206 steel members selection
1319 steel pipes water flow rates sizes
1154 steel portal frames elastic deflection
1136 steel portal frames loads stanchion
1210 steel reinforced concrete
0782 steel reinforced structures continuous beams
0967 steel reinforcement reinforced concrete
1118 steel reinforcing bars bar schedules weight
1238 steel requirements continuous slabs
0848 steel resistance moment bearing pressures
1270 steel sections axial loads bending moments designs
1042 steel space frame load/deformation
1273 steel stanchion designs
0969 steel stock cutting optimisation
1091 steel structures launching hydrodynamic drag
1172 steel timber simply supported beams
1218 steelwork beams columns elastic design
0236 steelwork fabrication detailing projects
1094 steelwork sizes member conveyor gantry
1702 steinbrenner elasticity
1013 stiffness method members plane grillages
1015 stiffness method perspective space frames
1012 stiffness method plane frames
1052 stiffness method static analysis 2D frame
1161 stiffness method static analysis 2D truss
1162 stiffness method static analysis 3D truss
0504 stock accounts sales labour materials
0253 stock availability discrepancies/variances
0471 stock contracts labour material
0188 stock control accounting business management
0338 stock control accounting sales ledger
0389 stock control accounting system payroll
0307 stock control bill materials quantity surveys
0308 stock control bill materials quantity surveys
0272 stock control builders merchants accounting
0379 stock control builders merchants invoicing
0348 stock control costing accounting
0270 stock control costing window cutting
0250 stock control evaluation management information
0255 stock control interrogation facilities
0378 stock control invoicing accounting payroll
0191 stock control invoicing sales order entry
0260 stock control management
0300 stock control management manufacturing
0207 stock control management storage/retrieval
0377 stock control payroll accounting
0265 stock control picking lists invoices route loading
0339 stock control sales ledger invoice
0247 stock control stock movements valuation
0251 stock control suppliers re-order level
1604 stock cutting list window type
0969 stock cutting optimisation steel
0248 stock movements management valuation
0247 stock movements valuation stock control
0274 stock overheads profit estimates
0371 stock payroll accounting budgeted costs

0249 stock perpetual inventory construction industry
0259 stock recording timber order analysis
0254 stock records production inventory control
0252 stock reporting invoices purchase orders
0357 stock sales ledger nominal ledger profitability
0344 stock valuation accounting credit control
0256 stocktaking perpetual inventory price list
0241 storage retrieval filing system
0201 storage retrieval information records
0206 storage retrieval records
0207 storage/retrieval stock control management
1119 storage tanks force stress drilling rigs
1211 storage tanks roof steel beams
0239 stores records analysis employees
0240 stores records maths package data
1678 storeys size speed lift system
0938 storm drain analysis flow pipes
0941 storm pipes hydrograph flow drainage networks
0913 storm retarding basins flood hydrographs
0943 storm sewers hydrograph rain
0919 storm water pumping stations hydrographs
0921 storm water urban areas hydrology hydraulics
0354 straight line double declining depreciation
1127 strain loads finite element stress
0971 strength concrete section bending moment
0744 strength walls excavations elastic analysis
0849 stress 2D 3D pile foundations stability check
1065 stress 3D models steel finite element
1077 stress analysis 2D 3D finite element
1070 stress analysis 3D frameworks loads
0826 stress analysis anchored retaining walls
1086 stress analysis concrete plane frames
0737 stress analysis elasticity boundary element
0736 stress analysis engineering boundary element
1314 stress analysis finite elements load conditions
1322 stress analysis pipework calculates
0994 stress analysis plane frames
0876 stress calculates
0830 stress calculation settlement footings
1101 stress checks composite section topping
1182 stress checks plate girders welds
1183 stress checks steel beams
0573 stress data graphics geometry
1119 stress drilling rigs storage tanks force
0892 stress elastic layered structure load
1063 stress heat conduction 2D 3D structures
0875 stress pore pressure chamber pressures
1228 stress precast girders concrete slab
0829 stress settlement earth fill structures
0831 stress soils sheet pile retaining walls
1730 stress statistics tensile testing
1127 stress strain loads finite element
1188 stress wood beam loading deflection
1125 stresses cross section bar
1202 stresses curved beam graphics estimates
1676 stresses cylindrical vessels
1293 stresses deflections plate buckling estimating
1108 stresses finite element displacements
1133 stresses floor framing supported beams loads
0837 stresses foundations elastic settlements
1341 stresses linear copper steel piping
1088 stresses members loading conditions
1151 stresses plane trusses loads
1176 stresses plyweb beam
1315 stresses reinforced concrete member analysis
1694 stresses strains displacements
1695 stresses strains displacements
1697 stresses strains displacements
1692 stresses strains displacements loading
1696 stresses strains displacements loading
1126 strings loading transverse motion
1045 structural analysis
1230 structural analysis beam analysis
1020 structural analysis bending moment plane frame
1227 structural analysis design beam column
1048 structural analysis frame
1047 structural analysis frame analysis
1107 structural analysis frames thermal problems
0723 structural analysis heat transfer finite element
0642 structural analysis pressure distribution
1011 structural analysis space frames trusses
0593 structural assemblies isometric drawings 2D 3D
1189 structural beams support loads
1305 structural components high-rise buildings
1105 structural design finite elements
0954 structural design reinforced concrete
1301 structural engineering design
1100 structural engineering finite element analysis
0984 structural frame analysis plane
1018 structural frames elastic analysis
1087 structural frames loading conditions 3D
1058 structural frames loading conditions plane
1019 structural frameworks elastic analysis

0763 structural heat transfer finite element
0640 structural mass dynamic analysis
0807 structural piling analysis
1294 structural plate graphics estimate
1116 structural shape intersection points 3D space
1297 structural steelwork CAD
0655 structural steelwork CAD drawings draughting
0749 structural steelwork drawings analysis
0978 structural steelwork frame
1137 structural steelwork portal frames
1067 structural systems elastic analyses 3D
0639 structure design change substructure
1024 structure geometry continuous frame cantilevers loads
1023 structure geometry continuous frames
0892 structure load stress elastic layered
1097 structure loading finite element
0279 structure material listing elements
0965 structures design reinforced concrete
1131 structures dynamic loads earthquakes
0975 structures frame elastic analysis
0977 structures frame linear analysis
1110 structures linear analysis elastic
0829 structures stress settlement earth fill
1175 struts bracing members pin-jointed ties
0403 subcontract management payroll accounting
0370 subcontract payroll accounting plant hire
0063 subcontractor accounting management construction
0525 subcontractor payments system
0349 subcontractors analysis accounts
0137 subcontractors construction bill quantities
0405 subcontractors construction industry accounting
0337 subcontractors invoices accounts
0364 subcontractors management contracts cash flow
0436 subcontractors payments contracts
0461 subcontracts cost control cashflow forecast
0639 substructure structure design change
1412 summer heating loads winter cooling loads
1459 summertime temperature solar intensity shading
1531 summertime temperatures buildings windows
1470 summertime temperatures evaluated ventilation rate
1406 summertime temperatures thermal load heatgain/loss
1574 sun horizon shadows obstructions hour day
0559 sun overshadowing solar orientation design
0582 sunlight perspective projections draws
0610 sunpath diagram building latitude
0759 superelement mesh post-processing
0251 suppliers re-order level stock control
0182 supply equipment hire utilisation analyse
1189 support loads structural beams
1285 support trestles gravity take-up towers
1133 supported beams loads stresses floor framing
1187 supports cantilevered forces
0788 supports continuous beam loadings
0685 surface approximation contour mapping
0652 surface design ducts finite element 3D
0683 surface modelling contouring survey
0682 surface modelling contouring system survey
0940 surface profiles flows waterways
0748 surface regression analysis curve fitting line
0669 surface representations 3D histograms
0914 surface water drainage hydrograph foul
0915 surface water drainage network
0935 surface water drainage pipe foul
0945 surface water sewer systems design
0684 survey analysis mapping grid
0617 survey coordinates plotting
0711 survey data card coding
0717 survey data ground modelling spot height
0713 survey data vetting
0697 survey highway drainage design triangular DTM
0688 survey paths calculating plotting
0707 survey points angle distance
0703 survey rectangular coordinates bearings
0691 survey stations distance tacheometry coordinates
0690 survey stations distance tacheometry plan coordinates
0683 survey surface modelling contouring
0682 survey surface modelling contouring system
0714 survey tabulation
0698 surveying bridge geometry geometry highway design
0696 surveying coordinate area conversions trigonometry
0718 surveying field drawing graphics
0159 surveyor bills quantities
0263 surveyor specification clauses architect engineer
0294 suspended ceilings drywall partitions
0780 suspension bridges non-linear elastic analysis
0778 suspension bridges vibration three-span
0779 suspension bridges wind speed
0740 symbol isometric drawing piping
0616 symbolic drawings architects 2D
0566 symbols architectural drawings design work
0627 symbols dimensioning CAD drawings
1104 T sections reinforced concrete rectangular
0691 tacheometry coordinates survey stations distance

0690 tacheometry plan coordinates survey stations distance
0710 tachometric survey traverse calculations points
0164 take-off bill cost analysis
0293 take-off dimensions material quantities
0197 take-off project information costs material
0167 takes-off plans maps areas
0146 taking-off bill preparation quantity surveyors
0143 taking-off bill quantities
0128 taking-off data bills quantities
0165 taking-off pricing houses materials
1540 tariff building energy consumption
0514 tasks personnel labour cost
0733 temperature 2D steady state soil seepage
0735 temperature axisymmetric orthotropic well seepage
1347 temperature condenser circulating water flow
1437 temperature differences walls
0738 temperature finite element isoparametric
1328 temperature flow pipework system sizes pressure
0958 temperature gas storage systems pressure
1568 temperature heat flow/gain/loss solar gain
1424 temperature heat losses building room
1418 temperature heating cooling room ventilation
1333 temperature pipework pressure drop flow rates fluid
1566 temperature room building solar heat gains
1476 temperature simulation radiation
1475 temperatures heat loss thermal network
1414 temperatures heating cooling loads buildings
1410 temperatures heating cooling loads room
1429 temperatures heating cooling loads room
1367 temperatures quantities sizing ductwork pressures
1489 temperatures rooms building air-conditioning
1456 temperatures thermal performance heating
1500 temperatures velocities water cooling coil
1504 temperatures winter room radiators
0039 tenancies management properties
0126 tender cost analysis bills quantities
0451 tender costs project
0116 tender documents proposals manuals
0328 tender estimate housing rehabilitation
0283 tender estimators quantities pricing
0528 tender figure prices
0131 tender forecasts bills quantities
0172 tenders bills quantities
0044 tenders land development appraisal
1730 tensile testing stress statistics
1245 tension compression steel bar design
0983 tension timber strut compression
0080 text databases editing retrieval managing
1413 thermal balance cooling loads building
1394 thermal behaviour buildings heating/cooling loads
0641 thermal behaviour designers finite element
1562 thermal behaviour solar receivers energy
0563 thermal building construction
1443 thermal buildings air-conditioning energy
1442 thermal buildings air-conditioning loads energy
1503 thermal circuit building sections
1453 thermal comfort radiant air temperature
1477 thermal conductances insulation glazing areas
1640 thermal daylight room heat gains
1554 thermal electrical loads building
1360 thermal expansion constraint stresses pipe systems
1520 thermal heating/cooling energy buildings
1559 thermal insulation U values
1406 thermal load heatgain/loss summertime temperatures
1455 thermal loads weather HVAC energy simulation
1475 thermal network temperatures heat loss
1527 thermal performance buildings U value energy
1456 thermal performance heating temperatures
1492 thermal performance insulation buildings
1107 thermal problems structural analysis frames
1546 thermal radiation windows absorption transmission
1599 thermal response heat conduction
1431 thermal response heating cooling load building
1517 thermal transmittance composite structure
1552 thermal transmittance U value composite elements
1425 thermal transmittance U value wall floor roof
1542 thermal vapour transfer buildings U value
1598 thermodynamic properties air
0778 three-span suspension bridges vibration
1168 timber beams plotting span load charts
0792 timber continuous beams steel concrete
1156 timber frame production drawings cutting
0569 timber framed buildings plan drawing
0404 timber merchants sizing calculation invoicing
0259 timber order analysis stock recording
1172 timber simply supported beams steel
1236 timber span tables beams
1212 timber steel concrete simple span beams
0760 timber structures design
1306 timber structures design
0983 timber strut compression tension
0257 timber yard cost efficient handling storage
0441 time accounting cost control project

0467 time analysis forecast cost
0007 time cost CPM motorway construction plant
1654 time delay electrical diagrams
0006 time estimating resource project
0427 time expense analysis job costing
0425 time expense budget forecasting cash flow
1420 time lag heat gains cooling load U value
0614 time managers project evaluators graphics
0449 time materials cost
0413 time materials retainers accounting
0347 time recording job costing accounting
0530 time recording professional office
0442 time recording sales purchase ledgers
0036 time resource cost analyses project management
0017 time resource scheduling project control
0002 time resources cost planning controlling projects
0003 time resources CPM project planning plans
0022 time resources project management
0114 time sharing information handling
0453 time staff costs
1685 time utilisation movement objects
0470 timesheet analysis cost control
0402 timesheet client billing project costing
0502 timesheet cost records management
0440 timesheet details materials cost
0216 timesheet expenses projects cost accounts
0448 timesheets analysis project fees
0450 timesheets job costing forecasting
0489 timesheets labour costs contract costing
0214 tool manufacturers prices location
1101 topping stress checks composite section
1282 torsional loads shaft vibrations
1099 torsional properties section cross-sectional
0869 toughness liquidity plasticity flow
1285 towers support trestles gravity take-up
0678 tract parcel maps boundary
1688 traffic modelling hospital departments
1690 traffic modelling transport
1687 traffic movement people goods hospital
0891 traffic noise values calculates road
0893 traffic rut road pavement
0395 transactions retentions expired certificates
0607 transformations model
1656 transient response linear systems
1664 transmission electrical conductors
1444 transmission glass blinds solar radiation
1634 transmittance reflectance light windows
0538 transport assignment problems
1683 transport buildings lift installations
1691 transport modelling land planning
1690 transport traffic modelling
1126 transverse motion strings loading
0709 traverse adjustment least squares land surveying
0651 traverse alignments geometry
0710 traverse calculations points tachometric survey
0700 traverse coordinates bearings azimuths
0716 traverse coordinates land survey point plotting
0695 traverse surveys coordinate data traverses
0695 traverses traverse surveys coordinate data
0001 tree diagram project management design
0391 trial balance accounting
0360 trial balance accounting audit trail
0334 trial balance audit management job cost
0414 trial balance budget audit trails
0417 trial balance profit loss payroll
0415 trial balance VAT profit loss accounts
0697 triangular DTM survey highway drainage design
1699 trigonometrical bessel functions polynomial
0696 trigonometry surveying coordinate area conversions
1069 truss 3D 2D frame
1082 truss frame 3D static analysis
1160 trussed beam roof members beam rafter
1157 trussed rafter manufacturer roof quotation
1002 trusses bridges elastic analyses 2D structures
0995 trusses frames finite element 2D
1309 trusses frames grillages finite element
1016 trusses grids frames beams
1034 trusses member loading frameworks
1011 trusses structural analysis space frames
1115 tubular structures estimating fabricate welded
0411 turnover analysis invoices sales extracts
1519 U-value calculation
1552 U value composite elements thermal transmittance
1526 U value condensation walls roofs
1527 U value energy thermal performance buildings
1419 U value heat loss/gain room
1553 U value heat losses energy consumption
1467 U value interstitial condensation
1542 U value thermal vapour transfer buildings
1420 U value time lag heat gains cooling load
1425 U value wall floor roof thermal transmittance
1457 U value wall roof condensation risk
1524 U values energy buildings cost heating

1518 U values floors suspended solid
1559 U values thermal insulation
1667 unbalanced voltages electrical distribution
1261 uncased stanchions base plates
0435 unit price profit cost
0877 unit weights calculates soil
1134 universal beams slab design composite deck
1234 unstable loads angles twist warping
0921 urban areas hydrology hydraulics storm water
0922 urban hydrograph rainfall drainage
0609 user-defined data plot graphs
0182 utilisation analyse supply equipment hire
0185 utilisation management accounting plant hire
0178 utilisation management plant maintenance
1685 utilisation movement objects time
0026 utilisation planning network analysis CPM
0399 valuation accounting construction industry
0280 valuation building contracts NEDO
0385 valuation data cash flow forecast
0277 valuation electrical mechanical engineering
0306 valuation jobs costs quantities
0401 valuation management accounting contract cost
0289 valuation quantity surveyor NEDO
0320 valuation quantity surveyors contract cost
0247 valuation stock control stock movements
0248 valuation stock movements management
0157 valuations accounts costs bill
0171 valuations bill quantity estimating
0123 valuations bills quantity
0174 valuations building contracts bills
0288 valuations forecasts NEDO quantity surveyors
0322 valuations NEDO quantity surveying
0323 valuations NEDO quantity surveying
0050 value analysis project costs
0333 values depreciation assets
0950 valves equipment water pumps
0150 valves material bill quantities schedule rates
1361 valves pumps pipe networks pressure reducing
1542 vapour transfer buildings U value thermal
1385 varitrane boxes air ductwork
0420 VAT analysis audit trails accounting
0361 VAT management information invoicing
0415 VAT profit loss accounts trial balance
0061 vehicle fleet maintenance management distribution
0064 vehicle fleets management construction industry
0286 vehicles preventive maintenance scheduling
1500 velocities water cooling coil temperatures
1368 ventilating duct pressure losses velocities sizes
1480 ventilation air flows building envelope
1375 ventilation duct sizing installation
1382 ventilation ductwork friction air velocity
1369 ventilation ductwork simulate
1465 ventilation ductwork sizes system
1593 ventilation fire protection buildings
1464 ventilation gains losses solar energy
1470 ventilation rate summertime temperatures evaluated
1579 ventilation system duct analysis
1366 ventilation system duct sizes pressure loss
1376 ventilation system duct sizing
1418 ventilation temperature heating cooling room
1601 venting capacities smoke shafts sizes
1572 vertical building faces shadows
0601 vertical perspective plans
0850 vertical pile group analysis
0713 vetting survey data
0089 viability cost plan job developers budget
1040 vibration elastic structures nodal displacements
0745 vibration mode shapes elastic system
0751 vibration multistorey buildings foundation
1123 vibration plate loading stability
0746 vibration shear buildings mode shapes
0778 vibration three-span suspension bridges
0747 vibrations buildings estimates modes
1120 vibrations foundations slope load stability
1282 vibrations torsional loads shaft
1653 volt drop fault electrical sizing
1662 voltages current electric distribution
1482 volume flow hot water pipe sizing
1474 volumes heat loss consumption lengths areas
1208 W-section beam weight
1209 W-section beam weight
1681 waiting times passenger lift system
0835 wall brick/block piers sections
0847 wall design cantilever earth pressures sheet pile
1256 wall design charts lateral strength
1425 wall floor roof thermal transmittance U value
0821 wall footing reinforced concrete cantilever
1586 wall furnace design heat loss
1537 wall insulation heat roof
1254 wall panel design laterally loaded
1257 wall prestressing hoops circular tank
1491 wall roof condensation moisture flow
1457 wall roof condensation risk U value

Index to computers

Acclaim
0716

ACT Sirius 1
0071 0084 0110 0141 0163 0189 0250 0316 0356 0357 0358
0359 0439 0440 0441 0461 0462 0464 0477 0482 0530 0554
0593 0689 0786 0787 0861 0997 0998 0999 1000 1001 1068
1070 1191 1192 1604 1648 1703

Alpha Micro
0038 0054 0055 0190 0331 0342 0478 0503

Amdahl 470V/8
0570

Any
0027 0193 0197 0275 0533 0536 0587 0588 0589 0590 1084
1118 1259 1392

Any 64K microcomputer
0013 0014 0221 0448 0560 0561 0562 1337 1338 1339 1340
1377 1378 1379 1380 1424 1425 1490 1491 1492 1493 1528
1529 1530 1531 1628 1629 1630 1706

Any IBM system supporting VM/CMS
0034

Any minicomputer with 128K/16−bit
1334 1422 1423 1579 1594 1625 1626 1653

Apollo
0656

Apollo Domain
0638

Apple
0021 0263 0372 0428 0617 0678 0700 0701 0789 0822 0834
0899 0919 0922 0923 0936 0937 0938 1032 1071 1200 1241
1269 1270 1349 1525 1563

Apple II
0003 0005 0015 0046 0079 0086 0088 0095 0154 0159 0160
0167 0200 0207 0208 0251 0273 0274 0285 0287 0301 0304
0306 0321 0322 0323 0324 0325 0326 0343 0350 0351 0385
0435 0436 0451 0452 0453 0534 0537 0555 0559 0574 0576
0601 0602 0603 0604 0605 0606 0607 0621 0653 0654 0676
0716 0741 0792 0795 0818 0819 0827 0835 0836 0852 0858
0865 0916 0924 0925 0935 0959 0960 0961 1022 1027 1028
1029 1030 1031 1033 1051 1057 1060 1072 1073 1111 1146
1150 1187 1188 1205 1206 1212 1213 1215 1216 1218 1260
1273 1298 1299 1333 1335 1348 1376 1420 1421 1474 1475
1476 1477 1483 1484 1485 1486 1487 1488 1489 1526 1541
1542 1559 1572 1586 1595 1603 1609 1623 1624 1627 1707
1709 1713 1720

Apple III
0010 0088 0192 0208 0274 0350 0351 0534 0555 0575 0646
1586

Apricot
0163 0461 0462 0530

Artemis minicomputer
0087

BBC microcomputer
0564 0565 1172

Benson 1302
0616

BOS/5
0227

Burroughs
0158 0643 0913 0963

Burroughs 6700
1059 1060 1211

Burroughs B20
0283

Burroughs CMS
0345

CA Naked Mini
0616

CDC
0030 0068 0097 0098 0099 0100 0101 0102 0103 0104 0236
0408 0470 0492 0643 0658 0659 0660 0682 0683 0684 0685
0712 0713 0714 0720 0723 0724 0771 0772 0773 0774 0775
0776 0777 0781 0850 0851 0885 0886 0887 0893 0906 0907
0908 0909 0910 0944 0945 0946 0947 0948 0949 0950 0967
0968 0969 0970 0973 1045 1046 1047 1048 1049 1050 1061
1088 1089 1090 1093 1105 1120 1121 1122 1123 1124 1125
1126 1130 1131 1227 1229 1230 1231 1232 1233 1234 1250
1251 1279 1280 1281 1282 1307 1308 1318 1328 1364 1367
1391 1412 1455 1510 1557 1645 1646 1693 1699 1701

CDC 6400
1435 1543

CDC 6600
0711 0825 0863 0864 0974 1543

CDC 7000
0892

CDC 7600
0711 0778 0779 0780 1026 1083 1085 1313

CDC NOS-based computer
1575

Century
0022

Cifer 2683
0403

Commodore
0291 0450 0460 1648

Commodore 4000
1586 1596 1597

Commodore 4032
0690 0691 0692 0693 0694 0695 0696 1388 1420 1421 1623

Commodore 4054 desktop
0665

Commodore 64
1609

Commodore 8000
0008 0067 0152 0171 0206 0252 0266 0366 0370 0375 0488
0489 1401 1457 1458 1461 1509 1511 1586 1596 1597

Commodore 8032
0126 0161 0247 0302 0328 0338 0339 0340 0341 0505 0506
0580 0581 0582 0583 0690 0691 0692 0693 0694 0695 0696
0912 1179 1333 1420 1421 1623

Commodore 8050
0267

Commodore 8080
0219

Commodore 8086
0219

Commodore 8088
0219

Commodore 8096
0126 0161 0284 0302 0328 0505 0506 0912

Commodore PET
0328 1205 1218 1333 1335 1376 1401 1403 1404 1457 1458
1460 1484 1485 1486 1487 1488 1489 1511 1526 1572 1577
1587 1588 1589 1624 1627

Computervision graphics processor
0070

Cyber
0805 0893 1328 1367 1391 1412 1693 1699 1701

Cyber 170
0594

Cyber 175
1318 1364 1374 1418 1455 1510 1645 1646

Cyber 70
1105

Cyber 72
1313

Cyber 750
1359 1383 1384 1449 1450 1451 1452 1453 1506 1557 1558
1643 1683 1689

Data General
0176 0368 0521 0629 0630 0652 0756 0991 1077 1301 1365
1393

DEC
0002 0023 0050 0051 0367 0473 0520 0552 0643 0789 0808
0913 0979 0991 1200 1238 1241 1264 1269 1270 1301

DEC LSI 11/23
0146 0662

DEC PDP10
1426

DEC PDP11
0116 0203 0272 0553 0722 0739

DEC PDP11/23
0092 0093 0233 0467 0468 0618 0663 0677

DEC PDP11/24
0598 0613

DEC PDP11/34
0721 0724 0825 0826 0863 0864

DEC PDP11/44
0598

DEC PDP11/60
1722

DEC PDP11/70
1115 1160 1225 1226 1277 1304

DEC PDP8
0080 0081 0082 0083 0381 0382 1723

DEC System 10
0091 0234 0400 0767 0781 0800 0837 0841 0843 0879 0881
0900 0901 0940 0964 0973 1034 1061 1074 1088 1089 1090
1093 1130 1131 1219 1249 1257 1351 1381 1436 1437 1438
1550 1576 1642 1682

DEC System 20
0768 0840 0842 0963 1076 1134 1220 1258 1357

Digico M16E
0089 0164 0313 0465 0466 1112

Digico Prince
0516

DTC Micro 210
1218

English Electric KDF9
1655 1657

GE 235
0892 0893 1699 1700 1701

GE 630
1426

GE 635
0595

Genie III
1214

Graphic Horizons
0615

Harris
0012 0609 0610 0698 0748 0898 1012 1013 1014 1015 1204
1271 1332 1373 1416 1417 1479 1480 1564 1578 1617 1618
1619 1620 1621 1680 1681 1705

Honeywell
0023 0036 0111 0112 0113 0114 0158 0186 0260 0422 0423
0643 0666 0767 0768 0800 0840 0841 0842 0843 0881 0890
0902 0911 0940 0953 0963 0964 0972 1039 1058 1076 1087
1129 1134 1220 1249 1257 1258 1314 1315 1319 1357 1361
1362 1395 1396 1397 1398 1399 1400 1454 1729

Honeywell 6000
1330 1368 1413 1679

Honeywell DPS6
0364

Honeywell H6080
1081

Honeywell Mk III
1641

HP
0745 0789 0822 0918 0991 1007 1008 1009 1010 1106 1147
1200 1201 1227 1241 1255 1264 1269 1270 1440

HP 1000
1429 1632 1633 1634

HP 200
1199

HP 200F
1573

HP 3000
0023 0584

HP 41CV
1638 1639

HP 85
0699 0703 0704 0705 0706 0796 0797 0798 0799 0838 0839
0920 0921 0939 1035 1036 1037 1113 1114 1151 1152 1217
1218 1242 1243 1244 1245 1246 1247 1248 1274 1275 1352
1552 1635 1636 1637 1668 1708 1718 1726

HP 86
0633 0699

HP 87
0699 0703 0704 0705 0706 0796 0797 0798 0799 0838 0839
0939 1035 1036 1037 1113 1114 1151 1152 1217 1242 1243
1244 1245 1246 1247 1248 1274 1275 1352 1532 1552 1635
1636 1637 1668 1718 1726

HP 9800
0990 0992 1186 1265

HP 9816
0715

HP 9825A
0305

HP 9826/36
0699

HP 9826A
0305

HP 9830
0198 0784 0809 0981 0982 1038 1096 1139 1177 1178 1262
1263 1286 1296

HP 9831
0198 0784 0809 0981 0982 1096 1139 1177 1178 1262 1263
1286

HP 9835
0198 0729 0730 0784 0809 0810 0981 0982 0983 1096 1139
1176 1177 1178 1254 1262 1263 1286

HP 9845
0024 0198 0572 0608 0634 0703 0704 0705 0706 0729 0730
0752 0753 0784 0790 0791 0796 0797 0798 0799 0809 0810
0824 0838 0839 0880 0939 0981 0982 1011 1016 1020 1021
1035 1036 1037 1075 1096 1113 1114 1139 1151 1152 1153
1176 1177 1178 1199 1205 1217 1218 1242 1243 1244 1245
1246 1247 1248 1254 1256 1262 1263 1274 1275 1286 1352
1551 1552 1565 1566 1635 1636 1637 1668 1718 1726

HP 9845B
1203 1295

IBM
0023 0030 0068 0097 0098 0099 0100 0101 0102 0103 0104
0158 0236 0408 0470 0492 0553 0617 0643 0656 0658 0659
0660 0682 0683 0684 0685 0700 0701 0712 0713 0714 0725
0739 0767 0768 0771 0772 0773 0774 0775 0776 0777 0781
0800 0840 0841 0842 0843 0850 0851 0881 0885 0886 0887
0899 0902 0906 0907 0908 0909 0910 0923 0940 0944 0945
0946 0947 0948 0949 0950 0963 0964 0967 0968 0969 0970
0973 0980 1039 1045 1046 1047 1048 1049 1050 1061 1076
1088 1089 1090 1093 1094 1120 1121 1122 1123 1124 1125
1126 1130 1131 1134 1138 1174 1175 1220 1227 1229 1230
1231 1232 1233 1234 1249 1250 1251 1257 1258 1261 1279
1280 1281 1282 1285 1307 1308 1357 1731

IBM 1130
0018 0085 0180 0181 0222 0223 0303 0522 0523 0626 0765
0766 0794 0829 0830 0831 0832 0833 0866 0867 0868 0869
0870 0871 0872 0873 0874 0875 0876 0877 0878 0933 0934
1025 1110 1133 1272 1342 1343 1344 1345 1346 1347 1435
1500 1501 1502 1539 1581 1582 1659 1660 1661 1662 1663
1664 1665 1666 1667 1672 1673 1674 1675 1676 1710 1711
1712 1724

IBM 1620
0514

IBM 3030
0720 0723 0724

IBM 3031
1515

IBM 3033
1063 1410 1411

IBM 3270
0687

IBM 360
0017 0072 0074 0117 0118 0119 0120 0174 0175 0179 0425
0512 0863 1327 1411 1608

IBM 370
0011 0017 0018 0085 0117 0118 0119 0120 0135 0153 0156
0172 0174 0175 0180 0181 0222 0223 0303 0329 0425 0522
0523 0626 0720 0723 0724 0765 0766 0794 0829 0830 0831
0832 0833 0866 0867 0868 0869 0870 0871 0872 0873 0874
0875 0876 0877 0878 0933 0934 0958 1025 1064 1110 1133
1272 1318 1342 1343 1344 1345 1346 1347 1364 1385 1386
1391 1410 1411 1455 1500 1501 1502 1507 1508 1510 1524
1539 1560 1581 1582 1608 1645 1646 1659 1660 1661 1662
1663 1664 1665 1666 1667 1672 1673 1674 1675 1676 1710
1711 1712 1724

IBM 3767
0062 0199 0431 0432 0433 0507 0984 1512 1513 1514 1516
1610

IBM 4300
0117 0118 0119 0120 0174 0175 0425 0720 0723 0724

IBM 4952
1533 1534

IBM 4955
1536

IBM 4978
1535

IBM 4979
1535

IBM 7000
0073 1650

IBM PC
0015 0079 0200 0366 0372 0435 0436 0464 0534 0621 0789
0822 0918 0919 0920 0921 0922 0924 0925 1052 1127 1161
1162 1163 1200 1241 1269 1270 1648 1707 1708 1709

IBM Series/1
0039 0379 0397

IBM System/23
0371

IBM System/34
0040 0042 0044 0063 0064 0065 0106 0177 0178 0249 0352
0353 0371 0380 0434 0481 0508 0524 0525

ICL
0068 0069 0158 0162 0182 0225 0390 0391 0392 0393 0394
0395 0457 0458 0491 0527 0528 0529 0636 0643 0767 0768
0781 0800 0840 0841 0842 0843 0881 0902 0940 0963 0964
0973 1039 1061 1076 1088 1089 1090 1093 1130 1131 1134
1220 1249 1257 1258 1357

ICL 1900
0007 0128 0129 0825 0863 0864 0962

ICL 1904A
0124 0551 1137 1647

ICL 1904S
0312 0531 1402 1430

ICL 1905F
1160 1226 1656

ICL 1906A
0429 1086

ICL 2904
0300 0376 0490

ICL 2946
0300 0376 0490

ICL 2950
0300 0376 0490

ICL 2966
0125 0264

ICL 2972
0145

ICL 2976
0019 1540 1631

ICL 4120
0080 0381

ICL ME29
0217 0300 0376 0490

ICL PC
0107 0110

ICL System 370
0711

ICL System 470
0711

Interdata
0236

Interset IS 2000
0089 0164 0313 0465 0466 1112

Jacquard
0348

Kienzle 9000
0043 0384

MAI Basic Four
0396

Max−80
1731

NCR
0158

NCR Century 200
0166

NCR Criterion
0041 0155

NEC PC
0621

Norsk Data
0012 0232 0609 0610 0656 0698 0748 0898 1012 1013 1014
1015 1204 1271 1301 1332 1373 1416 1417 1479 1480 1564
1578 1617 1618 1619 1620 1621 1680 1681 1705

North Star Advantage
0632

Olivetti
0913

Olivetti desktop
0977

Olivetti M20
0076 0147 0270 0290 0310 0314 0404 0455 0532 0625 0823
1148

Olivetti M30
0586

Olivetti M40
0586

Olivetti minicomputer
0806 0807 1173

Olivetti P6060
0761 0762 0853 0854 0971 1165 1166 1235 1252 1283

Olivetti P6066
0761 0762 0853 0854 0971 1164 1165 1166 1235 1252 1283

Onyx
0405

Onyx/Mercator 2000
0157 0442

Onyx/Mercator 5000
0157

Osborne
0918 0919 0920 0921 0922 1708

P6066
0585 0978

Perkin-Elmer 32−bit Supermini
0645

Philips
0767 0768 0963 1076 1134 1220 1249 1257 1258 1357 1440

Pixel
1227

Plessey
0367

Pocket calculator
1602

PPC
1517 1518

Prime
0012 0023 0030 0097 0098 0099 0100 0101 0102 0103 0104
0115 0224 0236 0253 0254 0386 0408 0470 0492 0558 0578
0596 0600 0609 0610 0613 0643 0656 0658 0659 0660 0669
0670 0671 0672 0673 0674 0682 0683 0684 0685 0698 0712
0713 0714 0724 0742 0748 0767 0768 0771 0772 0773 0774
0775 0776 0777 0800 0840 0841 0842 0843 0850 0851 0863
0881 0885 0886 0887 0891 0898 0902 0906 0907 0908 0909
0910 0940 0944 0945 0946 0947 0948 0949 0950 0964 0967
0968 0969 0970 0991 1012 1013 1014 1015 1039 1045 1046
1047 1048 1049 1050 1120 1121 1122 1123 1124 1125 1126
1204 1227 1229 1230 1231 1232 1233 1234 1250 1251 1264
1271 1279 1280 1281 1282 1297 1301 1307 1308 1332 1373
1416 1417 1471 1479 1480 1523 1564 1576 1578 1593 1608
1617 1618 1619 1620 1621 1680 1681 1687 1688 1705

Prime 250
0315 0550 0579

Prime 400
0749 1363

Prime 50 Series
1019

Prime 550
0402 1115

Prime 750
0749 1363

Rair Black Box
0107 0110

Rank Xerox
0347 0348

Rucaps
0613

SEL
0557 0558 0600 0742 1369 1471 1523 1593 1687 1688

Sharp BA 2700
0406

Sigma
1196 1268

Sigma 7
1319 1395 1396 1397 1398 1399 1400

Sigma 9
0036 0111 0112 0113 0114 0186 0260 0422 0423 0666 0890
0911 0953 0972 1058 1087 1129 1314 1315 1319 1361 1362
1395 1396 1397 1398 1399 1400 1454 1729

Tandy II
1335 1376 1484 1485 1486 1487 1488 1489 1526 1572 1624
1627

Tandy TRS−80
0015 0047 0048 0049 0056 0057 0079 0108 0239 0240 0241
0242 0243 0244 0256 0414 0415 0416 0417 0418 0419 0420
0421 0494 0495 0617 0700 0701 0783 0789 0822 0899 0915
0918 0919 0920 0921 0922 0923 0924 0925 0976 1170 1171
1200 1241 1269 1270 1391 1525 1563 1707 1708 1727 1731

Tektronix 4050
1203 1295

Tektronix 4051
1202 1289 1290 1291 1294 1331

Tektronix 4052
1202 1289 1290 1291 1294 1331

Tektronix 4054
0597 0620 0663 0718 1202 1289 1290 1291 1294 1331

Tektronix Plot/10
1567 1568

Texas Instruments
0163 0405 0461 0462 0530

Texas Instruments 59 calculator
0993 1553

Texas Instruments Business System 300
0469 0535

Texas Instruments TI 59
1517 1518

Texas Instruments TI 990
0892 1699

Toshiba T200
0136 0137 0360 0437

Triumph-Adler Alphatronic
1605

Tycom
0171

UCS
0234 1219 1642

Univac
0236 0768 0781 0913 0973 1050 1061 1088 1089 1090 1093
1120 1121 1122 1123 1124 1125 1126 1130 1131 1233 1234
1280 1281 1282 1307 1308

Univac 1100
0286 0513 0740 1326 1350 1431 1434 1520 1521 1562 1598
1599

Univac 1100/62
0757 0758 0759 0904 0905 0942 0943 1078 1119 1690

Univac 1100/81
1329 1652

Univac 1100 ND−100
0090 1549

Univac 1100 ND−500
0090 1549

Univac 1106
0185 0496 0497 0547 0549 0571 1394 1456

Univac 1108
0001 0183 0184 0538 0539 0540 0541 0542 0543 0544 0545
0546 0548 0635 0686 0974 1284 1363 1445 1446 1554 1555
1556 1576 1606 1607 1670 1671 1678 1684 1685 1686

VAX
0115 0236 0272 0553 0577 0598 0611 0655 0656 0669 0670
0671 0672 0673 0674 0719 0720 0721 0722 0723 0724 0726
0739 0755 0804 0891 1050 1120 1121 1122 1123 1124 1125
1126 1227 1233 1234 1280 1281 1282 1307 1308 1538 1608
1691

VAX 11
0203 1414

VAX 11/7
0725

VAX 11/750
0619

VAX 11/780
0749 0926 0927 0928 0929 0930 0931 0932

Victor
0464

Wang
0789 1007 1008 1009 1010 1200 1201 1241 1269 1270 1440

Wang 2200
0697

Wang mini and microcomputers
0743 0744 0788 1005 1006 1132 1197 1198 1473

Xerox
0271 0430

Xerox Microcomputer
0346

Z80
0033 0075 0218 0219 0288

ZX 81
1447

ZX Spectrum
1447

Index to languages

6502 Code
0580 0581 0582 0583

8080 Assembler
0228 0354 0917 1189 1189

8088/86 Assembler
0316 0354 0917 1189 1321

Algol
1026 1059 1060 1211 1654 1655 1656 1657

Algol 60
0780 1085

Algol 68
0381 1527

Alpha Basic
0054 0055 0190 0331 0478 0503

APL
0062 0111 0112 0199 0431 0432 0433 0507 0687 0984 1287 1512 1513 1514 1516 1610

Apple Basic
0274 0350 0351

Apple Pascal
0154 0274 0350 0351

Applesoft
0207 0818 0819 0858 0916 1187 1188

Applesoft Basic
0167 0208 0555 0716 0835 0836 0852 1033 1057 1072 1073 1146 1215 1216 1273

Artemis high level
0087

Assembler
0011 0017 0038 0112 0113 0146 0342 0406 0460 0565 0740 0978

Atlas Autocode
1084 1086

Basic: Management
0015 0024 0038 0045 0056 0057 0060 0061 0079 0095 0107 0108

Basic: Quantities and stock control
0140 0161 0194 0195 0196 0198 0203 0220 0240 0248 0265 0266 0267 0284 0302 0320 0321 0322 0323 0324

Basic: Accounting
0342 0344 0347 0348 0371 0444 0445 0450 0460 0469 0480 0505 0506 0535 0537

Basic: Design, graphics
0565 0585 0586 0593 0597 0647 0663 0665 0689 0699 0703 0704 0705 0706 0718 0729 0730 0741 0746 0752 0753 0761 0762

Basic: Civil engineering
0783 0784 0786 0787 0795 0796 0797 0798 0799 0806 0807 0809 0810 0821 0838 0839 0853 0854 0861 0862 0880 0893 0915 0919 0920 0921 0922 0926 0927 0928 0929 0930 0931 0932 0939 0960 0961 0971

Basic: Structural frames
0976 0977 0978 0981 0982 0983 0991 0998 0999 1000 1001 1002 1003 1004 1016 1018 1019 1027 1028 1029 1030 1031 1035 1036 1037 1038 1051 1075 1096 1101 1102 1103 1104 1111 1113 1114

Basic: Structural elements
1138 1139 1146 1150 1151 1152 1153 1165 1166 1170 1171 1172 1173 1176 1177 1178 1179 1191 1192 1193 1194 1195 1205 1206 1214 1217 1218 1235 1242 1243 1244 1245 1246 1247 1248 1252 1254 1260 1262 1263 1264 1266 1267 1274 1275 1283 1286 1288 1292 1296 1299

Basic: Pipework, ductwork and sound control
1315 1319 1335 1352 1353 1376 1388

Basic: Heating, ventilation and air-conditioning
1395 1396 1397 1398 1399 1400 1428 1440 1461 1484 1485 1486 1487 1488 1489 1526 1527 1551 1552 1559 1563 1565 1566 1572 1573 1586 1604

Basic: Building services
1609 1624 1627 1635 1636 1637 1641 1644 1668

Basic: Mathematics and statistics
1700 1701 1704 1708 1713 1718 1720 1726 1731

BBC Basic
0564 0565

BCPL
0268 0269

Business Basic
0176 0368

C
0096 0365 0485

C under UNIX (TM) operating system
0662

CBASIC
0096 0377 0378 0516

CIS Cobol (CP/M based)
0173 0424 0476

CIS-Cobol
0403

CMS Cobol
0345

Cobol
0041 0043 0073 0124 0129 0135 0155 0158 0166 0179 0185 0217 0260 0264 0286 0300 0312 0355 0364 0376 0384 0422 0423 0490 0496 0497 0513 0521 0595 0926 0927 0928 0929 0930 0931 0932 0958 1647

Cobol Assembler
0112

Commercial (SMB) Cobol
0004 0191 0333 0334 0335 0336 0337 0426 0427 0479 0504 0573 0782 0914 0975 1136 1253 1317

Commodore Basic
0152 0252 0375 0488 0489

Compiled
0690 0691 0692 0693 0694 0695 0696

Compiled Basic
0126 0168 0316 0472 0912 1648

Compiled binary code
0559 0601 0602 0603 0604 0605 0606 0607 0676 1474 1475 1476 1477

Control Data Fortran
1390

CP/M
0110 0563 1260 1532 1559 1592

CP/M 80
0006 0349

Data General Extended Basic
0630

Datatrieve
0926 0927 0928 0929 0930 0931 0932

Dibol
0092 0093 0233 0272 0367 0467 0468 0473

EFM/SHELL—80
0220

Executable code only
0171

Extended Basic
1164 1532

Fortran 722 1724 1729

Fortran 66
0570 0614 0656 0668 0760

Fortran 77
0027 0558 0599 0760 1062 1063 1082 1107 1306 1334 1422
1423 1525 1538 1575 1579 1594 1625 1626 1653 1703

Fortran-80
0245 1128

Fortran II
1569

Fortran IV: Management
0011 0027 0072 0074 0090 0092 0093

Fortran IV: Quantities and stock control
0127 0233 0236 0315

Fortran IV: Accounting
0467 0468 0512 0514

Fortran IV: Design, graphics
0539 0540 0542 0546 0547 0548 0557 0563 0569 0599 0637
0638 0639 0640 0641 0642 0643 0644 0664 0686 0702 0732
0733 0735 0737 0738 0740 0746 0760 0764

Fortran IV: Civil engineering
0778 0780 0825 0849 0859 0863 0864 0888 0889 0951 0958
0962

Fortran IV: Structural frames
0974 0980 0995 0996 1019 1050 1053 1054 1062 1079 1080
1081 1094 1105 1108 1109 1115 1117 1120 1121 1122 1123
1124 1125 1126 1137 1174 1225 1226 1228

Fortran IV: Structural elements
1233 1234 1261 1277 1278 1280 1281 1282 1284 1285 1292
1297 1300 1305 1307 1308 1309 1314

Fortran IV: Pipework, ductwork and sound control
1323 1326 1327 1333 1334 1341 1363 1374 1386

Fortran IV: Heating, ventilation and air-conditioning
1418 1420 1421 1422 1423 1426 1427 1429 1432 1433 1434
1435 1494 1495 1496 1497 1498 1499 1520 1521 1527 1537
1538 1543 1544 1546 1548 1549 1560 1562 1576 1579 1580
1583 1584 1585 1594 1599 1601

Fortran IV: Building services
1623 1625 1626 1632 1633 1634 1641 1642 1644 1650 1653
1658 1669 1670 1671

Fortran IV: Transport and communications
1684 1685 1687 1688

Fortran V
0599 0781 0973 1061 1083 1088 1089 1090 1093 1130 1131
1350 1365 1393 1431 1598

Gentran
0028 0094 0567 0568 0649 0650 0651 0679 0680 0681 0707
0708 0709 0767 0768 0769 0770 0800 0801 0840 0841 0842
0843 0844 0845 0881 0882 0902 0940 0941 0963 0964 0965
1039 1040 1041 1042 1076 1134 1135 1154 1220 1249 1257
1258 1276 1302 1303 1357 1358

High level
0030 0097 0098 0099 0100 0101 0102 0103 0104 0408 0470
0492 0658 0659 0660 0682 0683 0684 0685 0712 0713 0714
0771 0772 0773 0774 0775 0776 0777 0850 0851 0885 0886
0887 0906 0907 0908 0909 0910 0944 0945 0946 0947 0948
0949 0950 0967 0968 0969 0970 1045 1046 1047 1048 1049
1229 1230 1231 1232 1250 1251 1279

HP 9825A
0305

HP Basic
0697 0743 0744 0788 1005 1006 1132 1197 1198 1203 1295
1473

HP Enhanced Basic
0572 0790 0791 0824 1020 1021 1256

IBM BASIC interpreter
1052 1127 1161 1162 1163

ICL extended Fortran
1402

Kabol
0383

M Basic
0075 0121 0122 0142 0143 0144 0187 0188 0204 0205 0261
0262 0288 0289 0443 0454 0498 0499 0515 0556 0745 0789
0822 1007 1008 1009 1010 1011 1106 1147 1199 1200 1201
1241 1255 1269 1270 1316 1471 1472 1616

Machine code
1648

Mecator Business Basic
0157

Microcobol
0039 0123

Microsoft Basic
0250 0356 0357 0358 0359 0482 0563 0632 0918 1017 1387
1406 1407 1408 1409 1463 1464 1465 1466 1467 1468 1469
1470 1522 1571 1612 1613 1614 1651

MS-DOS
0110 1324 1325 1405 1462 1519

NCR Neat
0022 0080

PAL8
0080 0081 0082 0083 0381 0382 1723

Pascal
0088 0372 0534 0536 0636 0647 1118 1260 1559

Pascal M
0016

PET
0556

PET Basic CP/M!0328

PL/1
0034 0117 0118 0119 0120 0153 0172 0174 0175 0329 0425
1515

Plan
0007 0128 0531

Plan Cobol
0125 0429

Pro-Pascal MicroSoft Pascal
0193

RM COBOLANSI 74
0405

RPG11
0063 0064 0065 0177 0178 0249 0352 0353 0434 0481 0508

S-Algol
0755

Sinclair ZX Basic
1447

Tektronix
1203 1295

UCSD Pascal
0016 0160 0306 0654

Univac Fortran V
0571 1607

UNIX
0246 0463 0667 0717

Wang Extended Basic
0697 0743 0744 0788 1005 1006 1132 1197 1198 1473

Z80
1055 1056

Index to contributors

ABACUS Studies
Department of Architecture and
Building Science
University of Strathclyde
131 Rottenrow
Glasgow
G4 0NG
041—552 4400 ext 3021
0001 0538 0539 0540 0541 0542 0543
0544 0545 0546 0547 0548 0549 0571
0686 1606 1607 1670 1671 1678 1684
1685 1686

ABC Data Limited
57 Regent Road
Leicester
0533 549463
0912

ABS Oldacres Computers Limited
64—70 High Street
Croydon
Surrey
CR0 6XN
01—680 1677
0117 0118 0119 0120 0121 0122 0174
0175 0187 0188 0261 0262 0425 0498
0499 1316

ACT (Microsoft) Limited
ACT House
111 Hagley Road
Edgbaston
Birmingham
B16 8LB
021—454 8585
339396
0189

Admel Limited
Brooklands Road
Weybridge
Surrey
KT13 0RL
0932 47212
0572

ADP Network Services
179—193 Great Portland Street
London
W1N 5TB
01—637 1355
28638
0002 0050 0051

Adroit Systems Limited
Trow Way
Diglis Estate
Worcester
WR5 3BX
(0905) 375353
0003

Advanced Business Technology
Limited
Equitable House
Lyon Road
Harrow
HA1 2DB
01—836 0621
8952936
0176

Alper Systems Limited
35 Impington Lane
Histon
Cambridge
CB4 4LT
0220 234452
0052 0053 0330 0500 0501 0502

Alpha Micro (UK)
Alpha House
13—27 Brunswick Place
London
N1 6ED
01—250 1616
0054 0055 0190 0331 0478 0503

American Computers & Engineers
2001 South Barrington Avenue, Ste
204
Los Angeles
CA 90025
1062

Amicro Systems (London) Limited
158 Hanworth Road
Hounslow
TW3 3TR
01—570 0864
0332

Amplix Services Limited
Sidehill
Pilgrims Way
Kemsing
Sevenoaks
Kent
TN15 6XA
0732 61359
0004 0191 0333 0334 0335 0336 0337
0426 0427 0479 0504 0573 0782 0914
0975 1136 1253 1317

Anagram Systems
60A Queen Street
Horsham
West Sussex
RH13 5AD
(0403) 50854/58153
877986
0247 0338 0339 0340 0341

APEC Executive Office
Miami Valley Tower
Suite 2100
Dayton
Ohio 45402
513 228 2602
0056 0057 1318 1364 1391 1392 1455
1510 1645 1646

Apple Computer (UK) Limited
Eastman Way
Hemel Hempstead
Herts
HP2 7HO
(0442) 60244
825834
0005 0192 0574 0575 0576

Applicon UK
Regent House
Heaton Lane
Stockport
Cheshire
SK4 1DA
061 429 7227
0577

Applied System Techniques (Midland)
Limited
46 High Street
Leighton Buzzard
Bedfordshire
LU7 7EA
0525 370200
0038 0342

ARC Limited
Wellington House
East Road
Cambridge
CB1 1BH
0223 314041
0550 0578 0579 0669 0670 0671 0672
0673 0674 0891 1608

Associated British Consultants
(Computers) Limited
100 College Road
Harrow
HA1 1EW
01—863 8555
0783 0915 0976 1170 1171 1284

The Association for Computer Aided
Design Limited
576 St Kilda Road
Melbourne 3004
Victoria
03 51 9153
0805 0913 0974 1363 1390 1576 1692
1693 1694 1695 1696 1697

Autographics
120 Clay Road
Toye
Downpatrick
County Down
BT30 9PN
Killyleagh (039682) 8138
0580 0581 0582 0583

Autoprod Computer Graphics
128 Kidbrooke Park
Blackheath
London
SE3 0DX
0612

B & W Engineering
Torvegarde 2
1449 Kobenhavn K
+451542501
31366
1063

Bahco Ventilation Entreprenad AB
19981 Enkoping
1365 1393

Barcellos
Sandbach House
8 Salisbury Road
Leicester
0533 541574
0123

Baric Computing Services Limited
Breeden Court
34 High Street
Crewe
CW2 7BG
0270 214 222
1137

Baring Investments Limited
Baring House
Baring Crescent
Exeter
EX1 1TL
Exeter (0392) 51741
0343 0428

BDP Computing Services Limited
Vernon Street
Moor Lane
Preston
PR1 3PQ
(0772) 57961
677160
0584

Beamscan
20 Vaughan Avenue
Hendon
London
NW4 4HU
01—202 8656
1172

Bensasson & Chalmers Partnership
6 Kings Parade
Cambridge
CB1 2HN
(0223) 315733
0193 0263

Bingham Blades and Partners
Bingham House
Scholes Lane
St Helens
Lancs
WA10 3PA
0058

Birmingham City Council
Baskerville House
Broad Street
Birmingham
B1 2NE
Birmingham 235 2749
0429

Blandfold Limited
Rydings
Gallows Green
Alton
Stoke on Trent
ST10 4BN
1609

Boeing Computer Services (Europe)
Limited
19 Fitzroy Street
London
W1P 5AB
01—631 0808
0059

John Booth & Sons (Bolton) Limited
PO Box 50
Bolton
Lancs
BL3 3ST
1211

Bradford City Council
City Hall
Bradford
West Yorkshire
BD1 1HY
Bradford (0274) 729577
0124 0551 1647

British Gas Corporation
Watson House
Peterborough Road
London
SW6 3HN
01—736 1212
919082
1394 1456

British Olivetti Limited
17/29 Sun Street
London
EC2M 2PU
01—377 8644
0585 0586 0806 0807 0977 0978 1173

British Steel Corporation Tubes
Division
Market Development & Technical Sales
Corby
Northants
NN17 1UA
053 66 2121
1064

Buckinghamshire County Council
County Hall
Aylesbury
Buckinghamshire
HP20 1UA
Aylesbury 5000
0125 0264

Building Centre Computers Limited
The Building Centre
26 Store Street
London
WC1E 7BT
01—637 1022
261446
0045 0060 0061 0194 0195 0196 0248
0265 0344 0480

Building Computer Services Limited
Bush House
72 Prince Street
Bristol
BS1 4HU
0272 290651
0552 0808 0979 1238

Building Service Designs
322 Carshalton Road
Carshalton
Surrey
01—661 1416
1319 1395 1396 1397 1398 1399 1400

Building Services Computer Service
1b Waterside
Coleraine
Co Londonderry
BT51 3DP
(0265) 4038
1648

Building Services Software
19 Wescott Road
Wokingham
Berkshire
RG11 2ER
0734 791543
1401 1457 1458 1511

Burroughs Machines Limited
Heathrow House
Bath Road
Cranford
Middlesex
TW5 9QL
01—750 1400
8955272
0345

Business Computer Systems Plc
Sundial House
89—93 Goldsworth Road
Woking
Surrey
GU21 1LJ
Woking (04862) 21663
0346

Business Research (Systems) Limited
26 Store Street
London
WC1E 7BT
01—637 1773
0347 0348

C-QS Computer Services
27b Bell Street
Reigate
Surrey
RH2 7AD
Reigate 22249
0126 0505 0506

C-STAR Computer Services Limited
Small Business Centre
Claughton Road
Birkenhead
Wirral
Merseyside
L41 6ES
051 647 8616
0266

CACE
Brookvale
Nooklands
Fulwood
Preston
PR2 4XN
9772 709318
0267

Cadsteel Limited
141 Buxton Road
Heaviley
Stockport
SK2 6EQ
061—456 8200
0980 1094 1138 1174 1175 1261 1285

CAE International
York House
Stevenage Road
Hitchin
Herts
SG4 9DY
Hitchin (0462) 57111
826580
0719 0720 0721 0722 0723 0724 0725
0726

CalComp Limited
Cory House
The Ring
Bracknell
Berkshire
RG12 1ER
Bracknell 50211
848949
0197 0587 0588 0589 0590

Calma (UK) Limited
Beech House
373—399 London Road
Camberley
Surrey
GU15 3HR
(0276) 682021
858216
0727 0728 1065

Cambridge Interactive Systems
(Products) Limited
Quayside
Cambridge
CB5 8AB
0223 62247
1095

Camic Limited
47/49 Bridge Street
Derby
DE1 3LB
0332 31517
377106
0127

Camutek
39 Newnham Road
Cambridge
CB3 9EY
Cambridge (0223) 355976
0198 0729 0730 0784 0809 0810 0981
0982 0983 1096 1139 1176 1177 1178
1254 1262 1263 1286

CAP (Financial Services)
233 High Holborn
London
WC1V 7DJ
01—831 6144
0039

CAP Scientific
233 High Holborn
London
WC1V 7DJ
01—831 6144
267152
1698

Capricorn Computer Systems Limited
24 Foregase Street
Worcester
WR1 1VN
Worcester (0905) 21541
0268 0269

Cardale Computer Systems
90 Priests Lane
Shenfield
Brentwood
Essex
CM15 8HQ
(0277) 213148
0270

Cardiff City Council
City Hall
Cardiff
S Glamorgan
CF1 3ND
Cardiff 31033
1402

Castle Business Systems Limited
ECL House
Park View Road
Berkhamstead
Herts
04427 74881
0271 0430

CBACS
31—33 Goldington Road
Bedford
MK40 3LH
0234 40511
825562
0006 0349

CBS Consultants
75 Watery Lane
Birmingham
B9 4HW
021—772 8181
0272

Celtip Star Microcomputers
38 Kestrel Close
Kidderminster
Worc
Kidderminster (0562) 66201
1586

Centre de Recherches Routieres
Boulevard de la Woluwe 42
B—1200 Brussels
771 20 80
0892 0893 1699 1700 1701

Centre-File (Northern) Limited
Westinghouse Road
Trafford Park
Manchester
M17 1PY
061 872 1982
0007 0128 0129

CEP International
Churchmill House
Ockford Road
Godalming
Surrey
GU7 1QY
Godalming 4535
1179

The Charles Stark Draper Laboratory
Inc
555 Technology Square
Cambridge
Massachusetts 02139
617 258 1422
1560

Cheshire County Council
Department of Construction Services
Goldsmith House
Hamilton Place
Chester
CH1 1SE
Chester 602883
0062 0199 0431 0432 0433 0507 0687
0984 1287 1512 1513 1514 1515 1516
1610

Chiltern Microcomputers Limited
Finlandia Centre
Oxford Road
Gerrards Cross
Bucks
SL9 7RH
(02813) 88832
0273

CIBS (Chartered Institution of Building
Services)
222 Balham High Road
London
SW12 9BS
01—675 5211
1517 1518

CIC London Limited
4a Russell Hill Road
Purley
Surrey
CR2 2XL
01—668 0683
0274 0350 0351

CICA (Construction Industry
Computing Association)
Guildhall Place
Cambridge
CB2 3QQ
0223 311246
0275

CIMS Computer Systems Limited
Clarendon House
Clarendon Square
Leamington Spa
CV32 5QJ
(0926) 831401
311033
0063 0064 0065 0177 0178 0249 0352
0353 0434 0481 0508

Civil and Structural Computing
(Northern) Limited
Ash Court
2 Ash Grove
Great Horton Road
Bradford
West Yorkshire
BD7 1BN
(0274) 391076
0066 0130 0131 0132 0133 0134 0276
0277 0278 0279 0280 0281 0591 0731
0785 0811 0812 0813 0814 0815 0816
0817 0857 0954 0985 0986 0987 0988
0989 0990 0991 0992 1066 1097 1098
1099 1140 1141 1142 1143 1144 1145
1180 1181 1182 1183 1184 1185 1186
1239 1240 1264 1265 1320 1366 1459
1611

Civil Software Inc
521 Fifth Avenue
New York
NY 10175
(212) 661 3132
0200 0435 0436

Civil Ware
3112 Duffield Ave
Loveland
CO 80537
303/669—0830
0818 0819 0858 0916 1187 1188

Civilsoft
290 South Anaheim Boulevard
Anaheim
California 92805
(714)999—5001
183511
0354 0917 1189 1321

Claremont Controls Limited
Albert House
Rothbury
Morpeth
Northumberland
NE65 7SR
(0669) 21081
0008 0067

Clwyd County Council
Shire Hall
Mold
Clwyd
CH7 6NH
0352 2121
61454
0135

CMG Computer Management Group
(Scotland) Limited
Highland House
58 Waterloo Street
Glasgow
G2 7DA
041—221 8193
0040

CMG Information Services Southern
Limited
Sunley House
Bedford Park
Croydon
CR0 2AP
01—680 7027
0355

Colt Solar Control Limited
Havant
Hants
PO9 2LY
1561

Compact Information Services Limited
Cape House
Cape Place
Dorking
Surrey
(0306) 887373
859435
0250 0356 0357 0358 0359 0482

Compeda Limited
Compeda House
Walkern Road
Stevenage
Herts
SG1 3QP
Stevenage (0438) 56123
826308
0675 0732 1322

Compsoft Limited
Hallams Court
Shamley Green
Guildford
Surrey
GU4 8QZ
Guildford 898545
859210
0201 0202

Compuquant Limited
Witbridge House
47 Friar Gate
Derby
(0332) 44924
0136 0137 0360 0437

Computair
Lovatt Bank
Silver Street
Newport Pagnell
Buckinghamshire
MK16 0EJ
0908 614962
1403 1404 1460 1577 1587 1588 1589

Computation Research and
Development
12—15 Dartmouth Street
London
SW1H 9BL
01—222 9822
918778
0068

Computational Mechanics Consultants
Limited
Ashurst Lodge
Ashurst
Southampton
SO4 2AA
042 129 3223
47388 Attn: COMPMECH
0592 0733 0734 0735 0736 0737 0738
0859 0955 0993 0994 0995 0996 1067
1091 1323

Computel Limited
Eastern Road
Bracknell
Berkshire
RG12 2UP
Bracknell (0344) 26767
848625
0009 0069 0361 0362 0363 0483 0484
0688 0820 0860 0894 0895 0896 0897
0956 0957 1100 1190 1649 1702 1721

Computer Aided Design Centre
Madingley Road
Cambridge
Cambridgeshire
CB3 0HB
1590

Computer-Aided Design Group
2407 Main Street
Santa Monica
California 90405
(213) 392—4183
0553 0739

Computer Aided Management in
Construction Limited
47/49 Bridge Street
Derby
DE1 3LB
(0332) 31517
377106
0509 0510

Computer Design
39—41 North Road
Islington
London
N7 9DP
01—609 1878
266222
0593 0689 0786 0787 0861 0997 0998
0999 1000 1001 1068 1191 1192 1703

Computer Design Systems
4 New Elm Road
Manchester Industrial Centre
Manchester
M3 4JU
061—832 9251
667836
0138 0282

Computer Factors (Sales)
Marshall House
Manor Road
Coventry
CV1 2GF
Coventry (0203) 58318
0364

Computer House
172 New Bridge Street
Newcastle-upon-Tyne
NE1 2TE
0632 617001
0365 0485

Computer Management Services
Limited
Reliance House
Talbot Road
Manchester
M16 0PN
061 872 8221
0283

Computer Services (South West)
Limited
Millbay Road
Plymouth
PL1 3NG
0752 68814
0139

Computerskills Limited
Blue Bridge Lane
York
YO1 4AS
0904 20555
0438 0486 0511

Computervision
1040 Uxbridge Road
Hayes
Middx
UB4 0RJ
01—561 2626
8954125
0070

Computrav
Clairmont Gardens
Charing Cross
Glasgow
G3 7LW
041—331 1324
0821 0862 1002 1003 1004 1101 1102
1103 1104 1193 1194 1195 1266 1267
1704

Comsoft Associates
2c—2d Wake Green Road
Moseley
Birmingham
B13 9EZ
021—449 9151
0284 0366 1461

Conosil Systems Limited
100—104 Union Street
Torquay
TQ2 5PY
Torquay (0803) 24311
1591 1592

Conquest Computer Sales Limited
92 London Road
Benfleet
Essex
SS7 5TJ
(03745) 59861
995461
0367

Construction Management Computing
Wicor Path
Porchester
Hampshire
0368

Construction Measurement Systems
Limited
Hafod
Peatling Magna
Leics
LE8 3UQ
0537 58283
0140 0690 0691 0692 0693 0694 0695
0696

Construction Programming Services
79 Bierley Lane
Bierley
Bradford
BD4 6AW
0274 688175
0010 0285

The Consultancy Consortium
Consultants Limited
Proctor House
Duncan Road
Swanwick
Southampton
Hampshire
S03 72Q
Locks Heath (04895) 82103
477210
0071 0141 0369 0439 0440 0441 0477
0554

Consyst Computer Services Limited
1 Maris Lane
Trumpington
Cambridge
Cambridge (0223) 841997
0370

Contract Computer Software Limited
144 Victor Road
London
SE20 7JU
01—659 4444
1324 1325 1405 1462 1519

Control Data Limited
179—199 Shaftesbury Ave
London
WC2H 8AR
01—240 3400
267656
0594

Corporate Business Systems Limited
Jessop House
30 Cambray Place
Cheltenham
Glos
GL50 1JP
(0242) 42115
0203

COSMIC
University of Georgia
Computing & Information Services
112 Barrow Hall
Athens
Georgia 30602
404 542 3265
0011 0072 0073 0179 0286 0512 0513
0514 0595 0740 0958 1105 1326 1327
1386 1520 1521 1562 1650

Cranfield Product Engineering Centre
Cranfield Institute of Technology
Cranfield
Bedfordshire
MK43 0AL
(0234) 751001/750111
825072
0596

Crescent Business Systems
5 The Crescent
Cheadle
Chesire
SK8 1PS
061 491 2656
0442

R J Crocker and Partners
25 Market Square
Bromley
Kent
BR1 1NA
01—460 9282—7
1196 1268

Cyderpress Limited
5 St Martins Street
Wallingford
Oxon
OX10 0AQ
(0491) 37769
0287

Cymap Limited
5th Floor
Equity & Law Building
30—34 Baldwin Street
Bristol
BS1 1NR
0272 299332
1387 1406 1407 1408 1409 1463 1464
1465 1466 1467 1468 1469 1470 1522
1571 1612 1613 1614 1651

Gerald G Darby (Computer Services)
Canwell Estate
London Road
Canwell
Sutton Coldfield
West Midlands
B75 5SH
021—308 6471
0142 0143 0144 0288 0289 0515

Data and Research Services Limited
14—16 Burners Lane
Kiln Farm
Milton Keynes
MK11 3HB
Milton Keynes 567114
825185
1722

Data Resource
201 Bo Yip Building
6 Ashley Road
Kowloon
0597

Datron Micro Centre
2 Abbeydale Road
Sheffield
S71 FD
0742 585490
0555 1146 1288

Daverman SP Group
82 Ionia Avenue NW
Grand Rapids
Michigan 49503
616 456 3564
1328 1367 1412 1615

Davy Computing Limited
Moorfoot House
2 Clarence Lane
Sheffield
1329 1652

Decision Graphics UK Limited
Gatwick Road
Crawley
W Sussex
RH10 2UN
0293 543675
877471
0598

Department of Education & Science
Architects and Building Branch
Room 735 Elizabeth House
York Road
London
SE1 7PH
01—928 9222
23171
0074

Design Computing Limited
1 Eaton Crescent
Clifton
Bristol
BS8 2EJ
0272 739269
0599

Designer's Aid
2 Morkyns Walk
Alleyn Park
Dulwich
London
SE21 8BG
01—670 6293
0741

Dewco Programming and Computer
Services
20 Park Street
Bristol
BS1 5JA
0272 23352
1330 1368 1413 1679

DHSS
Room 609 Euston Tower
286 Euston Road
London
NW1 3DN
01—388 1188 Ext 329
**0075 0204 0205 0443 0444 0556 0557
0558 0600 0742 1369 1471 1472 1523
1593 1616 1687 1688**

Digital Building Systems Limited
Orient House
Granby Row
Manchester
M1 7AN
061—236 3396
666380
0516

Dynatech Microsoftware Limited
Summerfield House
Summerfield Road
Vale
Guernsey
(0481) 47377
4191130
0046 0206 0207 0208 0251

E P Computer Systems
53 Sheepfold Lane
Amersham
Bucks
HP7 9EJ
(02403) 7332
0291

East Midland Computers
Abbotts Hill Chambers
Gower Street
Derby
DE1 1SD
(0332) 362481
0290

East Sussex County Council
Architects & Estates Dept
County Hall, PO Box 5
St Anne's Crescent
Lewes
East Sussex
BN7 1SW
Lewes 5400
0145

Eclipse Associates Limited
Lovat Bank
Silver Street
Newport Pagnell
Bucks
MK16 0EJ
0908 612425
**0697 0743 0788 1005 1006 1132 1197
1198 1473**

Ecom Associates, Inc
8634 W Brown Deer Road
Milwaukee
W1 533224
414/354—0243
**0745 0789 0822 1007 1008 1009 1010
1011 1106 1147 1199 1200 1201 1241
1255 1269 1270**

ECOTECH
26 Botanical Road
Sheffield
S11 8RP
(0742) 660734
**0559 0601 0602 0603 0604 0605 0606
0607 0676 1474 1475 1476 1477**

EDP Systems Limited
52/53 Margaret Street
London
W1N 7FF
01—637 5796
912881
0445

Ekono
PO Box 27
00131 Helsinki 13
1414

The Electricity Council
30 Millbank
London
SW1P 4RD
01—834 2333
1524

Elstree Computing
12 Elstree Way
Borehamwood
Herts
WD6 1NF
01—207 2000
0146

Engineering Computer Services
Limited
Piccadilly
Tamworth
Staffs
B78 2ER
(0872) 873300
341687
0608

Engineering Software Services Limited
88—90 Gower Road
Sketty
Swansea
SA2 9BZ
(0792) 299396
0076 0147 0823 1148

D M England & Partners Limited
Tudor House
24 High Street
Twyford
Berks
RG10 9AG
Twyford (0734) 342666
0517

Epic Computer Services Limited
42 Little London
Chichester
West Sussex
0243 788914
0371

ESDU (Engineering Sciences Data Unit)
251—259 Regent Street
London
W1R 7AD
01—437 4894
266168
**0746 0747 1202 1203 1289 1290 1291
1292 1293 1294 1295 1331**

Estate Computer Systems
29—30 Carre Street
Sleaford
Lincolnshire
0529 305637
0372

Estimation Inc
805 — L Barkwood Court
Linthicum Heights
Maryland 21090
301—636 5680
**0209 0210 0211 0292 0293 0294 0295
0296 0297 0373 0487 1478**

Estimation Limited
Highlands Road
Shirley
Solihull
West Midlands
B90 4NL
021—704 3221
338018
**0148 0149 0150 0151 0212 0213 0214
0298 0299 1370 1371 1372 1415**

F-Chart Software
4406 Fox Bluff Road
Middleton
Wisconsin 53562
1525 1563

Facet Limited
19 Upper Marlborough Road
St Albans
Herts
AL1 3UT
St Albans 50830
889072
**0012 0609 0610 0698 0748 0898 1012
1013 1014 1015 1204 1271 1332 1373
1416 1417 1479 1480 1564 1578 1617
1618 1619 1620 1621 1680 1681 1705**

fba Computer Services Limited
The Old Mill
Mill Lane
Godalming
Surrey
GU7 1EY
Godalming 20651
859668
0374 0446 0518

FCG Computer Systems
Room 3
Hamilton House
Mabledon Place
London
WC1H 9BD
01—388 7345
0152 0252 0375 0488 0489

Ferranti-Cetec Graphics Limited
Bell Square
Brucefield
Livingston
West Lothian
EH54 9BY
0506 411583
727898
0611

Finite Element Analysis Limited
25 Holborn Viaduct
London
EC1A 2BP
01—353 5767
1107

Flakt Installator AB
Box 81051
S—104 81 Stockholm
468 7144000
10430
1374 1418

Flint and Neill Partnership
14 Hobart Place
London
SW1
01—235 9911
1016 1296

Focus Software Consultants
95 Beverley Road
Hull
0482 28120
0077 0216 0447 0519 1375 1419 1481
1482 1622

Freeman Fox & Ptnrs
12—15 Dartmouth Street
London
SW1H 9BL
01—222 9822
918778
1108 1109

Gang-Nail Software
The Trading Estate
Farnham
Surrey
GU9 9PQ
Farnham (0252) 722425
858175
1017

Geest Computer Services Limited
Jupiter House
Station Road
Cambridge
CB1 2JY
0223 66111
817667
0217 0300 0376 0490

Tony Gee & Partners
Standard Property House
45—47 High Street
Cobham
Surrey
KT11 3DP
Cobham 5375
928496
0790 0791 0824 1020 1021 1256

General and Engineering Computer
Services Limited
Cunard Building
Pier Head
Liverpool
L3 1EG
051 236 1687
627807
1018 1019 1205 1297

Geocomp UK Limited
Eastern Road
Bracknell
Berkshire
Bracknell 24567
0825 0826 0863 0864

GMW Computers Limited
Castle Mill
Lower Kings Road
Berkhamsted
Hertfordshire
HP4 2AD
04427 5481
825797
0613

Graffcom Systems Limited
102 Portland Road
Holland Park
London
W11 4LX
01—727 5561
0078 0218 0219 0377 0378

Grafox Limited
35 St Clements
Oxford
OX4 1AB
0865 242597
0614

Graham-Dorian Software Systems
Limited
Unit 7
Suttons Park Avenue
Earley
Reading
Berkshire
RG6 1AZ
(0734) 664345
0220

Graphic Horizons Inc
Box 312
Cambridge
MA 02238
617—396—0075
940—485
0615

Grist Business Services Limited
6 Northlands Road
Southampton
SO1 2LF
(0703) 39061
0301 0792 0827 0865 0959 1022 1069
1298

Grootenhuis Allaway Associates
40 Hay Street
Steeple Morden
Royston
Herts
SG8 0PE
Steeple Morden (0763) 852200
1388

Grundfos Pumps Limited
Grovebury Road
Leighton Buzzard
Beds
LU7 8TL
(0525) 374876
825344
1483

Guardian Computer Services
St James' House
Pendleton Way
Salford
Manchester
M6 5JA
061 737 7352
0379 0380

Haden Central Engineering
141 Euston Road
London
NW1 2AY
01—387 4377
24910
1333 1334 1335 1376 1420 1421 1422
1423 1484 1485 1486 1487 1488 1489
1526 1572 1579 1594 1623 1624 1625
1626 1627 1653

Hampshire County Council
The Castle
Winchester
Hampshire
SO23 8UJ
Winchester 4411
0153

Hansen Carlsen & Frolund A/S
Radgivende Ingeniorfirma
HC Orstedsvej 4
DK1879 Kobenhavn V
0121 3085
1336

D J Hardy
64 Hornsey Lane
London
N6 5LU
1527

Harper & Tunstall Limited
Denington
Wellingborough
Northants
NN8 2QH
0933 71166
0616

Ronald S Harrison
16A Molivers Lane
Bromham
Bedford
MK 43 8JT
02302 4801
0154

D J Herriott Limited
Survey House
69d London Road
Southborough
Kent
TN4 0PA
0892 22443
957163
0699

Hertfordshire County Council
County Hall
Hertford
SG13 8DD
Hertford 54242
0041 0155

Hevacomp Limited
45—47 Commonside
Sheffield
S10 1GD
Sheffield 0742 661003
0013 0014 0221 0448 0560 0561 0562
0563 1337 1338 1339 1340 1377 1378
1379 1380 1424 1425 1490 1491 1492
1493 1528 1529 1530 1531 1628 1629
1630 1706

Heyden & Son Limited
Spectrum House
Hillview Gardens
London
NW4 2JQ
01—203 5171
28303
1730

Hilbern Engineering Software
8982 Isleworth Court
Orlando
FL 32811
(305) 876—2677
0015 0079 0918 0919 0920 0921 0922
1206 1707 1708 1731

Holec Energy
Station Road
Horsham
West Sussex
RH13 5EU
0403 69612
877784
1532

Hourds Computing Limited
7—8 Mill Street
Stafford
ST16 2AJ
(0785) 44221
36540
0520

HSV Limited
May Place
Basingstoke
Hants
RG2 1NX
(0256)62444
0449

Hunting Computer Services Limited
Hunting House
Allens Way
Thornaby Stockton
Cleveland
TS17 9HA
0642 760021
0521

Hutton + Rostron
Netley House
Gomshall
Surrey
GU5 9QA
048—641 3221
859167
0080 0081 0082 0083 0381 0382 1723

Hydro Systems
48 Robin Hood Road
Arlington
Mass 02174
(617)683—2662
0617 0700 0701 0793 0828 0899 0923
0924 0925 1023 1024 1149 1207 1208
1209 1210

Ibbotsons Design Software
The Byre
Ecclesbourne Lane
Idridgehay
Derbyshire
DE4 4JB
0564 0565

IBC Computer Systems Limited
Belgreen House
Green Street
Macclesfield
Cheshire
(0625) 616399
0016

IBM Corporation
PO Box 2150
Atlanta
GA 30301
1533 1534 1535 1536

ICI Plc, Design Systems Group
Engineering Dept
Runcorn
Cheshire
WA7 4QF
Runcorn (0928) 513300
0156 0749

In-Situ, Inc
209 Grand Avenue
Laramie
Wyoming 82070
(307) 742—8213
910—949—4944
0926 0927 0928 0929 0930 0931 0932

Inatome and Associates
10140 West Nine Mile Road
Oak Park
Michigan 48237
313 542 4862
1341 1426 1427 1428 1494 1495 1496
1497 1498 1499 1537 1580

Insight Computer Systems
14 John Dalton Street
Manchester
M2 6JR
061—832 6883
0450

Institution of Electrical Engineers
IEE/BCS Library
Savoy Place
London WC2
01—240 1871
261176
1654 1655 1656 1657 1658

Intelligence (UK) Limited
30 Lingfield Road
Wimbledon
London
SW19 4PU
0084

Intergraph (Great Britain) Limited
Albion House
Oxford Street
Newbury
Berks
RG13 1JG
0618 0619 0677

International Research and
Development Company
Fossway
Newcastle upon Tyne
NE6 7YD
0632 650451
537086
0620

International Software Marketing
Unit 683
Armadale Road
Feltham
Middx
TW14 0LW
01—751 5791
0621 1709

ISEC Computer Systems Limited
Dalilea
St Marys Road
Portishead
Bristol
BS20 9QP
0272 848083
0157

ISSCO Graphics
Linburn House
340—342 Kilburn High Road
London
NW6 2QT
01—624 6627
892843
0622 0623 0624

Itech International Technology Services
115 Grove Road
Hitchin
Herts
SG4 0AA
(0462) 31113
0625

JBA (UK) Limited
6th Floor, McLaren Building
2 Masshouse Circus
Queensway
Birmingham
B4 7NR
021—233 2209
0042

R C Jenkins & Son
Brookside
Takeley
1299

Jones Cassidy Mellor Limited
Wharley End
Cranfield
Bedford
MK43 0AW
Bedford (0234) 751108
1538

K & H Project Systems Limited
9 Villiers Road
Kingston upon Thames
KT1 3AP
01—549 0056
0017

Kalamazoo plc
Northfield
Birmingham
B31 2RW
021—475 2191
336700
0383

Kent County Council
Springfield
Maidstone
Kent
ME14 2LT
Maidstone 671411
0302

KGB Micros
14 Windsor Road
Slough
Berks
SL1 2EJ
Slough (0753) 38310
0566

Kienzle Data Systems Limited
224 Bath Road
Slough
Berks
SL1 4DS
Slough 33355
848535
0043 0384

A M Kinney Inc
2900 Vernon Place
Cincinnati
Ohio 45219
513 281 2900
21—4303
0018 0085 0180 0181 0222 0223 0303
0522 0523 0626 0765 0766 0794 0829
0830 0831 0832 0833 0866 0867 0868
0869 0870 0871 0872 0873 0874 0875
0876 0877 0878 0933 0934 1025 1110
1133 1272 1342 1343 1344 1345 1346
1347 1500 1501 1502 1539 1581 1582
1659 1660 1661 1662 1663 1664 1665
1666 1667 1672 1673 1674 1675 1676
1710 1711 1712 1724

Koolshade Corporation
PO Box 210
Solana Beach
California 92075
1573

Laboratoriet for Varmeisotering
Danmarks tekniske
Hojskole
Afd f Baerende Konstruktioner
Bygning 118
2800 Lyngby
1410 1411

Lamex Commercial Computing Limited
Apex House
London Road
Northfleet
Kent
DA11 9PD
0474 50746
0044 0524 0525

LAMSAC
Vincent House
Vincent Square
London
SW1P 2NB
01—828 2333
0158

Lancashire County Council
PO Box 26
County Hall
Preston
Lancashire
PR1 8RE
Preston 263123
0019 1540 1631

Lancaster Computing
374 North Road
Preston
Lancs
PR1 1RU
0772 24003
0086 0159 0304 0385 0451 0452 0453
0935 1212 1213 1541 1542

J Lawson & Co Limited
12 Greenock Road
Acton
London
W3 8DR
01–992 4821
0305

LMR Computer Services
54–70 Moorbridge Road
Maidenhead
Berks
SL6 8BN
0628 37123
847112
0224 0253 0254 0386

Local Business Technology Limited
Wormley House
82 High Road
Wormley
Broxbourne
Herts
EN10 6DU
Hoddesdon 66157
0160 0306

Logica Limited
64 Newman Street
London
W1A 4SE
01–637 0111
0307 0308

Loughborough University of
Technology
Dept of Civil Engineering
Loughborough
Leics
LE11 3TU
0509 263171 Ex 5171 & 5175
0526

Lowe Electronics Limited
Bentley Bridge
Chesterfield Road
Matlock
Derbyshire
DE4 5LE
0629 2817
377482
1214

LSI Computers Limited
Copse Road
St Johns
Woking
Surrey
GU21 1SX
Woking 23411
859592
0309 0387

Lucas Logic Limited
Welton Road
Wedgnock Industrial Estate
Warwick
CV34 5PZ
Warwick (0926) 497733
312333
0627

Ludhouse Computing Limited
2–6 Marian Road
Streatham
London
SW16 5HR
01–679 4321
0454

Lundy-Farrington Limited
3 Belmont Chambers
Baker Road
Uxbridge
UB8 1RG
0895 54623
86579
0628

Lysteknisk Laboratorium
ATV Bygning 325
Lundtoftevej 100
DK2800 Lyngby
02–873911
1429 1632 1633 1634

Manchester University
Simon Engineering Laboratories
Manchester
M13 9PL
061 273 7121 Ext 5168
1026

Mandata Limited
Forum House
Wallsend
Tyne & Wear
NE28 8JR
(0632) 628302
0310 0455

Marcus Computer Systems
26 Albion Place
Leeds
LS1 6JS
0532 434488
0020 0311 0388 0456 1725

Masterbill Micro Systems Limited
St John's House
23 St John's Road
Watford
WD1 1PY
Watford (0923) 38551
0161

McAuto (UK) Limited
Crown Life House
Woking
Surrey
GU21 1XW
048 62 26761
859521
0629

McGrane Computer Systems Limited
36 Lad Lane
Dublin 2
Dublin 760636
0630

Mediatech Software Systems
Woodside Place
Alperton
Wembley
Middx
HA0 1XA
01–903 4372
8814541
0389

Mellor Computer Consultancy
3 Town Street
Marple Bridge
Stockport
Cheshire
SK6 5AA
061–449 8101
1070

Mentor Systems
Refuge Assurance Buildings
Ainsworth Street
Blackburn
BB1 6AZ
0254 675511
635786
0162 0182 0225 0390 0391 0392 0393
0394 0395 0457 0458 0491 0527 0528
0529

Mercator Computer Systems
3 Whiteladies Road
Clifton
Bristol
BS8 1NU
0272 731079
0459

Metier Management Limited
Metier House
North Circular Road
Stonebridge Park
London
NW10 7UG
01–902 8830
0087

Micro Associates
471 Lichfield Road
Aston
Birmingham
B6 7SP
021–328 4574
0460

Micro Planning Services
8 Howecroft Gardens
Bristol
BS9 1HN
(0272) 684530
0088

Micro Scope
Peter A Lloyd
Taplow
Maidenhead
Berks
SL6 0AA
(0628) 72047
0396

Microaid
5 Greenfield Crescent
Birmingham
B15 3BE
021 454 1089
0163 0461 0462 0530

MicroApplications Limited
Greyfriars
Stafford
ST16 2SA
(0785) 43415
1595

Microcomp
Ashurst Lodge
Ashurst
Southampton
SO4 2AA
042129 3223
0021 0678 0795 0834 0936 0937 0938
0960 0961 1027 1028 1029 1030 1031
1032 1071 1111 1150 1348 1349 1713

MicroProducts Software Limited
87–89 Saffron Hill
London
EC1N 8QU
01–831 8811
22763
0226 0227

Microsoft Structural Control Systems
Limited
18 The Downs
Altrincham
Manchester
WA14 2PU
061 928 9047
0835 0836 1033 1072 1073 1215 1216
1273

Microtrend Limited
PO Box 51
Pateley Bridge
Harrogate
N Yorkshire
HG3 5DF
0423 711878
57558
0228 0229

Mid-Glamorgan County Council
County Hall
Cardiff
CF1 3NE
Cardiff 28033
1430

Missing Link Computers Limited
Abacus House
53—55 Ballards Lane
London
N3
01—349 5711
1596 1597

MMG Consultants Limited
19 St Andrews Road
Great Malvern
Worcs
WR14 3PR
Malvern (06845) 63555 and 69160
0463

Moneywise Software Limited
226 Sheen Lane
London
SW14 8LD
01—878 8585
0464

Moss Systems Limited
Barclays House
51 Bishopric
Horsham
West Sussex
RH12 1QJ
Horsham 59511
877759
0702

Mountford and Laxon Company
Limited
Sharrow House
20 Anchorage Road
Sutton Coldfield
B74 2PL
021 354 5389
0631

MPL Computers Limited
32 Kingsditch Lane
Cheltenham
Gloucs
GL51 9PB
0242 582090
0397

NASA
Construction Engineering Branch
Mail Stop 227
Langley Research Center
Hampton
Virginia
1543

National Bureau of Standards
Center for Building Technology, NEL
Building Physics Division 742
Thermal Analysis Group
Washington
DC 20234
1350 1431 1598 1599

National Research Council of Canada
Ottawa K1A 0R6
**0750 0751 1300 1432 1433 1503 1544
1545 1546 1547 1548 1583 1584 1585
1600 1601 1602 1677 1714 1715 1716
1717**

The National Computing Centre
Limited
Oxford Road
Manchester
M1 7ED
061—228 6333
668962
0230 0231

NCR Limited
206 Marylebone Road
London
NW1 6LY
01—388 8170
336161
0022 0398 0399

Newcastle-upon-Tyne City Council
1 Civic Centre
Newcastle-upon-Tyne
Tyne and Wear
NE99 2BM
Newcastle-upon-Tyne 28520
0312

Nichols Associates
31 Grove Way
Esher
Surrey
KT10 8HQ
01—398 0695
0023

Norden Technical Computing Systems
Limited
37—41 Bedford Row
London
WC1R 4LF
01—242 8546
0089 0164 0313 0465 0466 0632 1112

Norrie Hill Limited
Albany House
489—491 London Road
Camberley
Surrey
GU15 3JA
Camberley (0276) 61175 & 681655/6
0633 0634

Norsk Data Limited
Strawberry Hill House
Bath Road
Newbury
RG13 1NG
Newbury (0635) 35544
849819
0232

North-East London Polytechnic
Forest Road
London
E17 4JB
01—527 2272
0635

Northamptonshire County Council
Northampton House
Northampton
NN1 2LP
Northampton 34833
0531

The Northern Ireland Polytechnic
Ulster College
Shore Road
Newtownabbey
Co Antrim
Whiteabbey 0231 65131
0962

Norwegian Building Research Institute
POB 322 Blindern
Oslo 3
46 98 80
0090 1434 1549

Oasys Limited
13 Fitzroy Street
London
W1P 6BQ
01—636 1531
263935
**0024 0091 0400 0636 0703 0704 0705
0706 0752 0753 0796 0797 0798 0799
0837 0838 0839 0879 0880 0900 0901
0939 1034 1035 1036 1037 1074 1075
1113 1114 1151 1152 1153 1217 1242
1243 1244 1245 1246 1247 1248 1274
1275 1301 1351 1352 1381 1435 1436
1437 1438 1550 1551 1552 1565 1566
1635 1636 1637 1668 1682 1718 1726**

Office Automation
Zobel Close
Barnett Road
Sweet Briar Industrial Estate
Norwich
Norfolk
(0603) 400841
0314 0532

Ontwerp-en Adviesbureau Ing Th J
MUL BV
Zomereik 27
Postbus 73
2920AB Krimpen ad Ijssel
Ijssel (01807) 20377
1353 1354 1355 1356 1382 1439 1440

Orion Microware Limited
60 Longmead Avenue
Chelmsford
Essex
CM2 7EQ
(0245) 71228
1603

P-E Consulting Group
Park House
Egham
Surrey
TW20 OHW
Egham 4411
0025 0533 0534

Pafec Limited
Strelley Hall
Nottingham
N98 6PE
(0602) 292291
377494
**0637 0638 0639 0640 0641 0642 0643
0644**

Perkin-Elmer Data Systems Limited
227 Bath Road
Slough
Berks
SL1 4AX
0753 34511
847376
0645

Personal Computers Limited
220—226 Bishopsgate
London
EC2M 4JS
01—377 1200
0646

Philips Electronics
Lighting Division
PO Box 298, City House
420—430 London Road
Croydon
Surrey
CR9 3QR
01—689 2166
946169
1638 1639

Pilkington Brothers Limited
Prescot Road
St Helens
Lancashire
WA10 3TT
St Helens 28882
627441
**1389 1441 1442 1443 1444 1504 1574
1640 1641**

PMA Consultants Limited
Rhodaus House
Victoria Road
Horley
Surrey
RH6 7AS
Horley (02934) 71361/5
87536
0315 0401 0402

Ponder Associates BV
Zonnebaan 18
3606 CB Maarssenbroek
030−445352
73413
0647

Power Plus Engineering and Computer
Services Limited
5th Floor
Coward Building
Pierhead
Liverpool
051−236 1687
1218

Praxis Business Systems
Woodside
Crowbridge
Sussex
TN6 1BR
(08926) 61261
0316

Project Software Limited
Foden Lane
Woodford
Stockport
Cheshire
SK7 1PT
061−439 6639
666650
0026 0092 0093 0233 0467 0468

Property Services Agency
Department of the Environment
Rm 1817, Lunar House
40 Wellesley Road
Croydon
CR9 2EL
01−685 3499
0234 1219 1642

John FS Pryke and Partners Limited
Warlies Park House
Upshire
Waltham Abbey
Essex
EN9 3SL
Lea Valley 717547
1038

PTRC Education & Research Services
Limited
110 Strand
London
WC2
01−836 2208
0027

Quality Business Machines Limited
2 Queen's Gardens
Brighton
Sussex
BN1 4AR
(0273) 692577
877039
0317 0318 0754

Quest CAE
Quest House
Princes Road
Ferndown
Dorset
BH22 9HQ
(0202) 891010
41358
0648

Quest GENESYS Limited
Lisle Street
Loughborough
Leics
LE11 0AY
0509 39185
341747
0028 0094 0567 0568 0649 0650 0651
0679 0680 0681 0707 0708 0709 0767
0768 0769 0770 0800 0801 0840 0841
0842 0843 0844 0845 0881 0882 0902
0940 0941 0963 0964 0965 1039 1040
1041 1042 1076 1134 1135 1154 1220
1249 1257 1258 1276 1302 1303 1357
1358

Quoin Computing Limited
1A Arundel Road
Chapeltown
Sheffield
S30 4RB
0742 453345
0403

Radius Computer Services Limited
Wykeland House
47 Queen Street
Hull
HU1 1UU
(0482) 227181
527633
0469 0535

Reading Computer Services Limited
76−78 Orts Road
Reading
Berks
RG1 3JS
Reading (0734) 664969
0029 0710 0802 0803 0846 0847 0848
0883 0884 0903 0966 1043 1044 1155
1221 1222 1223 1719

Redland Construction Software Limited
The Trading Estate
Farnham
Surrey
GU9 9PQ
0252 722425
858175
0165 0235 0319 1156 1157 1158 1159

Redpath Engineering Limited
Burotec
PO Box 15
Middlesborough
Cleveland
TS3 6AS
0642 245501
587323
0755 1115 1116 1160 1224 1225 1226
1277 1304

Reedbaron Limited
Unit 2 Osborne House
Southgate
Chichester
Sussex
PO20 6JY
(0243) 789413
0320

Renfrew District Council
Municipal Buildings
Cotton Street
Paisley
Strathclyde Region
PA1 1BU
0411−889 5400
0166

Research Engineers, Inc
PO Box 2706
Cherry Hill
New Jersey 08034
(609)983−5050
1227

RIB E V
Schulze-Delitzsch Strasse 28
D−7000 Stuttgart 80 (Vaih)
0711 7873149
07255580
0849 1117 1228 1278 1305

RIBA Publications Limited
Finsbury Mission
Moreland Street
London
EC1V 8VB
01−251 0791
1553

Robinson Ford Associates
The Chapel
5 Salisbury Street
Cranborne
Dorset
BH21 5PU
(07254) 566
0652 0756 1077

Robocom Limited
CIL Building
Goodwin Street
London
N4 3HQ
01−263 3388
268992
0653

Ross F Meriwether and Associates
Northwood Executive Building
1600 Northeast Loop 410
San Antonio
Texas
512−824 5302
0183 0184 1445 1446 1554 1555 1556

Rossana Software Services Limited
2a Park Grove Terrace
Glasgow
G3
041−339 2467
0404

Rothamsted Experimental Station
Computer and Statistics Department
Harpenden
Herts
AL5 2JQ
058 2762271
0711

David Ruffle Associates
The North Wing
Ingatestone Hall
Ingatestone
Essex
CM4 9NS
(02775)4774
0167 0654

Sapphire Systems Limited
19−27 Kents Hill Road
Benfleet
Essex
SS7 5PN
03745 59756
0096

SBI
Postbox 119
2970 Horsholm
1259 1505

Scan Computers Limited
Chanctonbury House
Church Street
Storrington
West Sussex
RH20 4LZ
(09066) 5432
87213
0405

Scicon Limited
Brick Close
Kiln Farm
Milton Keynes
MK11 3EJ
0908 565656
825171
0757 0758 0759 0904 0905 0942 0943
1078 1119 1690

Scope Realtime Limited
Hart House
141—145 Curtain Road
London
EC2A 3QE
01—729 3035
0406

Scott Wilson Kirkpatrick & Partners
Scott House
Basing View
Basingstoke
RG21 2JG
0256 61161
0655 0804 1691

SD Micros Limited
2 The Green
Epsom
Surrey
KT17 3JN
01—836 9520
0095 0321 0322 0323 0324 0536 0537
1118 1720

Shade Computer Services Limited
1—3 Patford Street
Calne
Wiltshire
SN11 0EF
0249 815757
444337
0569 0760 1306

Shape Data Limited
2 All Saints Passage
Cambridge
CB2 3LS
(0223) 316673
0656

I P Sharp Associates Limited
132 Buckingham Palace Road
London
SW1W 9SA
01—730 4567
8954178
0657

Shortlands Computing Services
Limited
Shortlands
London
W6 8BT
01—741 0130
0407

SIA Computer Services
Ebury Gate
23 Lower Belgrave Street
London
SW1W 0NW
01—730 4544
916635
0030 0097 0098 0099 0100 0101 0102
0103 0104 0408 0470 0492 0658 0659
0660 0682 0683 0684 0685 0712 0713
0714 0771 0772 0773 0774 0775 0776
0777 0850 0851 0885 0886 0887 0906
0907 0908 0909 0910 0944 0945 0946
0947 0948 0949 0950 0967 0968 0969
0970 1045 1046 1047 1048 1049 1229
1230 1231 1232 1250 1251 1279

Simpact UK
Rolls House
7 Rolls Buildings
Fetter Lane
London
EC4A 1NH
01—404 0961
0105

Soft Option
46 Cromwell Avenue
Highgate
London
N6 5HL
01—340 6130
1447

Solenco Inc
PO Box 7907
Austin
Texas 78712
Francisco Arumi (512) 471—4911
1557

Somel, Structural Steelwork Engineers
23 Rue du Pont des Halles
Chevilly-Larue
Cidex D 901
0236

Sourcecode Limited
34 Perrymount Road
Haywards Heath
Sussex
RH16 3DJ
1604

Southern Computer Systems Limited
7 Park Hill Road
Torquay
Devon
TK1 2AL
(0803) 212957
0409 0410 0411 0471 0493

Spinks Computer Systems Limited
24 Forgase Street
Worcester
WR1 1VN
Worcester (0905) 21541
0325 0326

Spot Computer Systems Limited
New Street
Kelham Street Industrial Estate
Doncaster
(0302) 25159
0168 0472

Staveley Computing Centre
Blackpole Road
Worcester
WR3 8TH
(0905) 53335
336064
0473

Structural Members Users Group
PO Box 3958
Unversity Station
Charlottesville
VA 22903
804 296 4906
1050 1120 1121 1122 1123 1124 1125
1126 1233 1234 1280 1281 1282 1307
1308

Structural Software Services
125 Sheringham Avenue
London
N14 4UJ
01—263 3144
267198
1051

Structural Software Systems
4440 Gateway Drive
Monroeville
PA 15146
1052 1127 1161 1162 1163

Structures & Computers Limited
1258 London Road
London
SW16 4EJ
01—679 5115
947153
0888 0889 0951 1053 1054 1079 1080
1309

Sumlock Calculating Services Limited
3rd Floor
Castle Market Building
Sheffield
S1 1AY
0742 77802
1605

Summagraphics Limited
3—4 Winchcombe Road
Newbury
Berks
RG14 5QY
(0635) 32257
848750
0661

John Surtees
13 Whinfield
Leeds
LS16 6AB
1055 1056

Survey & General Instrument Co
Limited
Fircroft Way
Edenbridge
Kent
0737 864111
0715

Survey Three Limited
1 Leigh Way
Weaverham
Cheshire
CW8 3PR
Weaverham (0606) 853570
0716

SYS-Unipower Limited
Northgate Street
High Street
Barnstable
Devon
EX31 1TP
0271 76354
0106

SysCom Computers Limited
Kelvin House
The Broadway
Dudley
West Midlands
DY1 4PY
Dudley 236701
335001
0237 0255 0412

System Selection
46 Girdwood Road
Southfields
London
SW18 5QS
01—650 2999
261149
0107

System Simulation Limited
Analysis Research Design
101 St Martins Lane
London
WC2
01—240 7821
0662 0663

Systemshare Limited
Pilton Drive
Edinburgh
EH5 2XT
031 552 7601
72125
0852 1057

Systonetics Inc
48 Mount Street
London
W1Y 5RE
01—493 0241
0031 0032

Tamsys Limited
Pilgrim House
2—6 William Street
Windsor
Berks
SL4 1BA
(07535) 56747
849462
0238 0413

Tandy Corporation
12th Floor
Tameway Tower
Bridge Street
Walsall
West Midlands
WS1 1LA
(0922) 648181
339423
0033 0047 0048 0049 0108 0239 0240
0241 0242 0243 0244 0256 0414 0415
0416 0417 0418 0419 0420 0421 0494
0495 1727

TCL Software
59—61 Theobalds Road
London
WC1
01—402 8137
1448

Technical Services
9 Portland Road
Edgbaston
Birmingham
B16 9HN
021 454 8018
0761 0762 0853 0854 0971 1164 1165
1166 1235 1252 1283

Technies Rekencentrum Polybit bv
Postbus 305
St Annastraat 145
6500 AV Nijmegen
Nijmegen 228382
1359 1383 1384 1449 1450 1451 1452
1453 1506 1558 1643 1644 1669 1683
1689

Teknikdata AB
Box 214
S—72106 Vasteras
21107900
1081 1082

Tektronix UK Limited
PO Box 69
Beaverton House
Harpenden
Herts
AL5 4UP
Harpenden 63141
25559
0664 0665

Tillyard AG
Seefeldstrasse 62
Postfach 411,
8034 Zurich
01—251 1060
58381
0109 0169 0170 0474

TipData Limited
62 Maidstone Road
Grays
Essex
RM17 6NY
0375 33910
0327

TM Software Systems Limited
105 Uxbridge Road
Middx
Hanworth
TW13 5EH
01—755 0713
0171

Touchstone Computers Limited
319 City Road
London
EC1V 1LJ
01—278 5708
0110

TRADA
Stocking Lane
Hughenden Valley
High Wycombe
Buckinghamshire
HP14 4ND
Naphill 3091
83292
0257 0258 0259 0475 1167 1168 1169
1236 1310 1728

The Trane Company
La Crosse
Wisconsin 54601
608 782 8000
29—3415
1385 1507 1508

Transam Microsystems Limited
59—61 Theobald's Road
London
WC1X 85F
01—405 5240
24224
0245 1128

Richard Twinch Design Limited
83 Lacey Street
Ipswich
Suffolk
IP4 2PH
0473 210001
1260 1559

Tymshare UK
Brettenham House
14—16 Lancaster Place
London
WC2E 7EP
01—379 7822
0034

UCC (Great Britain) Limited
25—29 Hampstead Road
London
NW1 3JA
01—387 9661
27192
0035 0185 0496 0497 0763 0855 0856
0952 1237 1311 1312 1360

UHDE GmbH
Degginstrasse 10—12
Postfach 262
D—4600 Dortmund 1
0231 5470
822841
0172

UMIST
Department of Civil and Structural
Engineering
PO Box 88
Manchester
M60 1QD
061 236 3311
0778 0779 0780 1083 1084 1085 1086
1313

United Information Services Limited
United House
56—64 Leonard Street
London
EC2A 4AN
01—253 1066
0036 0111 0112 0113 0114 0186 0260
0422 0423 0666 0890 0911 0953 0972
1058 1087 1129 1314 1315 1361 1362
1454 1729

Technische Universitat Munchen
Fachgebeit EI Rechnen IM
Arcisstr 21
Konstruktiven Ingenieurbau
D—8000 Munchen 2
0764

University of California, Los Angeles
School of Architecture & Urban
Planning
Los Angeles
CA 90024
1567 1568

University of Edinburgh
Department of Architecture
Minto House
20 Chambers Street
Edinburgh
EH1 1JZ
031—667 1011 Ex 4598
747442
0246 0667 0717

University of Michigan
Architectural Research Lab
2000 Bonisteel Blvd
Ann Arbor
MI 48109
0570 0668

University of Sydney
Dept of Architectural Science
Sydney, 2006
NSW
1575

University of Wisconsin Solar Energy
Laboratory
1303 Engineering Research Building
1500 Johnson Drive
Madison
Wisconsin 53706
1569 1570

Valtec Limited
345 Grays Inn Road
London
WC1X 8PE
01—837 7500 and 01—833 0105
0328

Walters Computer Systems Limited
57 High Street
Stourbridge
West Midlands
DY8 1DE
Stourbridge 70811
1509

Warwick University
Dept of Engineering
Coventry
CV4 7AL
0203 24011
1059 1060

Wilcox Computers Limited
Rackery Lane
Llay
Wrexham
Clwyd
LL12 0PB
097883 4866
0173 0424 0476

Wild Heerbrugg UK Limited
Revenge Road
Lordswood
Chatham
Kent
0634 64471
0718

Wiltshire County Council
County Hall
Trowbridge
Wiltshire
BA14 8JG
Trowbridge 3641
0329

Wimpey Group Services Limited
Hammersmith Grove
London
W6 7EN
01—748 2000
25666
0115

Wimpey Offshore Limited
Wimpey Laboratories
Beaconsfield Road
Hayes
Middlesex
UB4 0LS
01—573 7744
935797
1092

Xitan Systems Limited
23 Cumberland Place
Southampton
Hants
SO1 2BB
(0703) 334711
47388
0037

Yard Limited
Charing Cross Tower
Glasgow
G2 4PP
041—204 2737
77380
0116

Zentech Technical Services Limited
3—7 Euston Centre
London NW1
01—388 9426
0781 0973 1061 1088 1089 1090 1093
1130 1131

Index to programs

1552 BP111: Thermal performance of elements	0731 CEADS-CADD
1352 BP112: Pipe sizing	0315 CEASAR
0347 BR-PAC PARTNER	0557 CEDAR
0348 BR-PAC TRADER	1509 CENTRAHEAT
1140 BRACE	1179 CEPCON
1253 BRICK	0163 CESMM
0835 Brick Pier Design	0688 CHART
0473 BRICS	0374 CIBS
0767 Bridge/1	0560 CIBS
1395 BS1	1423 CIBSGAIN
0968 BS449	1484 CIBSGAIN
1064 BSC4 Space Grid for Pin-jointed Structures	0670 CIIS (Contouring, Interpolation and Integration of Surfaces)
1459 BTEMP	
1289 BUCKLE 1	0365 CINTRA
1290 BUCKLE 2	1463 CIRC
1291 BUCKLE 3	0885 CIRCA
0106 BUILD/34	0140 CIRCE
0597 BUILD-AID	1692 CIRCLE
0405 BUILDAX	1693 CIRCLY
0076 BUILDER	1257 CIRCTANK/1
0168 Builders' Estimating System	1120 Circular plate
0465 Building Cost Indices	0765 Circular reinforced concrete columns design
0086 Building Regs	1288 Civil Engineering Analysis and Design
0327 Building Services Estimating	0171 CLEVA
1517 Building structure thermal properties	0001 CLUSTR
0460 Building Trades Accounts and Costing	0218 CM 2020
0174 Building valuations	0040 CMG Property Investment Management
0746 BUILDING VIBRATIONS 1	1181 CNECT
0747 BUILDING VIBRATIONS 2	0129 Coded quantities
0272 BUMP	0206 CODEWRITER
0576 Business Graphics II	1573 COE
0575 Business Graphics III	1129 COGO
0463 BUTRESS	1713 COGO
0791 C-PLOT	1277 COL 1
1653 C SIZE	1268 COL110 and COL114
0349 CABCS-PPL	1279 COLDES
1298 CABLE	1311 COLDES
1651 CABLE	1578 COLO
1659 Cable pulling tension for insulated electric wire in conduit or duct system	1267 COLUMN and BI-COLUMN
	0292 Commercial and Industrial Estimating
0608 CAD 100	0148 Commercial Estimating & Bill of Quantity
0625 CAD/GRAPHICS	1370 Commercial Estimating (DV2)
1532 CADAM	0149 Commercial Estimating (EV2)
0645 CADAM distributed system	1134 COMP-CONSTRUCT/1
0620 CADBIRD	1329 Compaid
0278 CADEST	0483 COMPANY ID
1051 CADFRAM	0060 Company Secretarial and Management Services
0636 CADRAW	0115 COMPASS
1072 Cage 1	0058 COMPASS MTS System
0883 Calculation of Earthwork Quantities	1173 COMPB
0846 Calculation of Loads in Pile Group (2D and 3D)	1652 Compels
0727 CALMA DDM	0406 Complete Builder's Management System
0611 CAM-X	1101 COMPOSITE
1576 CAMEL LM101	1449 Composite wall
0066 CAMILE	0070 Computer Aided Design and Engineering
0130 CAMP02	1299 Computer aided fire escape design
0131 CAMP03	0072 Computer assisted rating of employees
0132 CAMPO1	0141 Computer Estimating System
1187 CANTILEVER BEAM	0303 Computerised specification writing
0828 Cantilever Wall Analysis	0345 CONACS
0400 CAP	0804 CONBEAM 4 and 5
0062 Capital program, CAPROG	1230 CONBEM
0755 CAPS	1157 CONCEPT 2000
1483 CAPS	0852 CONCRETE
0591 CASC-AID TO DRAFTING	0293 Concrete Excavation
0556 CASE	0809 Concrete pad foundation design
0431 CASH FLOW	1491 CONDEN
0498 CASH FLOW	1495 CONDX
0522 Cash flow forecast	0782 CONKER
0385 Cash flow forecasting	0098 CONNECT II
0443 CASHFLOW	0524 CONPAK
0537 CASHFLOW	1309 CONSAS
0461 Cashflow Forecasting	0866 Consolidation test program
0382 CASHUP	0867 Constant and falling head, or capillary permeability
0771 CASKET	0383 Construction Industry Package
0271 CASTLE ESTIMATOR	0343 CONSTRUCTION SALES LEDGER
0430 CASTLECOST	0370 CONSYST—8000
0146 CATO (Computer Aided Taking Off)	0792 CONT
0006 CBACS-PERT	0351 Contaid
0785 CBEAM	0786 Continuous Beam
0795 CBEAM	0364 CONTRACT 6
0789 CD—1. Reinforced concrete beam design	0428 CONTRACT COST ACCOUNTS
1269 CD—2. Reinforced concrete column design	0442 CONTRACT COSTING
1241 CD—3. Flat slab analysis and design	0457 Contract Costing
0822 CD—4. Footing design	0401 Contract Costing and Accounting System
1422 CD11	0476 CONTRACT COSTING SYSTEM
1174 CDMBEAM	0447 CONTRACT MANAGER
1175 CDMBRACE	0169 Contract Quantities
0980 CDMFLOBM	0458 Contract Valuation
1094 CDMGANT	0455 CONTRACTMAN
1138 CDMPORT	0396 Contractor
1261 CDMSTAN	0489 Contractors' Payroll System
1285 CDMTREST	0682 CONTRIV

1435 COOL	0954 DECIDE
1439 Cooling load	0966 DECIDE
1450 Cooling load	0927 DELAY 2
1581 Cooling load determination	0202 DELTA
0207 CORP	1464 DEMAND
0906 COSMOS	1557 DEROB
0434 COST	1512 DES Design Note 17
0387 Cost Ledger	0595 Design engineering bar chart system
0472 Cost Ledger Suite	0474 Design Evaluation
0507 COST LIMIT	0918 Design Hydrographs
0432 COST PLANNING	1222 Design of Beam Cross-Sections for Elastic Bending
0445 COSTPROF	0810 Design of bored, in-situ piles
0050 COSTRAK	0803 Design of Continuous Prestressed Beams
1654 CP1	0903 Design of Highways
1714 CP10	1223 Design of Prestressed Beams
0703 CP101: Traverse reduction	1211 Design of roof support steelwork for circular storage tanks
0704 CP102: Reduction of levels	
0705 CP103: Reduction of precise levels	0847 Design of Sheet Pile Walls
0706 CP104: Tacheometric Survey	1445 Design point requirements
0939 CP108: Surface water drainage	0662 DESIGN SYSTEM ALPHA
0880 CP109: Slope stability	0170 Detailed Estimate
0971 CP110 – ULTIMATE LOAD DESIGN OF RC SECTION	1705 DEVI
0552 CP110	1457 DEWPOINT
0965 CP110	0986 DFLEC
0800 CP110–BEAMS/1	0270 DGLAZE
0801 CP110–BEAMS 1	0627 DIAD
0838 CP111: Retaining walls	1720 DIAGNOSE
1303 CP114 Programs	0520 DIGICALC
1715 CP14	0565 Digital Drawings
1716 CP17	0829 Dike settlement
1545 CP2	1065 DIMENSION III
1655 CP21	0523 Discounted rate of return on investment
1656 CP23	1121 Disks
1544 CP25	0738 DISPER
1657 CP29	0623 DISSPLA
1717 CP29	0187 DMS
0750 CP30	1650 Documenting complex wiring
0751 CP31	0638 DOGS
1600 CP32	1363 DONKEY LM102
1432 CP33	1276 DORIC
1546 CP34	1603 Double glazing manufacture
1583 CP35	1317 DOWSE
1601 CP36	0839 DP101: Foundation sizing and design
1584 CP37	0798 DP102: Continuous beam design
1300 CP38	1275 DP103: Rectangular column design
1658 CP4	1244 DP105: Continuous slab design
1677 CP41	1245 DP106: Ribbed slab design
1547 CP42	1246 DP107: Flat slab shear check
1433 CP43	0799 DP108: Deflection of beam
1602 CP44	1247 DP112: Flat slab design
1585 CP45	1240 DP113: Coffered slab design
1548 CP47	0987 DPICT
1503 CP9	0593 Draft Plot
0485 CPAY	0665 DRAFTING – 4054 D08 2–D
0021 CPM	0633 DRAFTY
0028 CPM/1	0675 DRAGON
0018 CPM Scheduling for chemical plants	0915 DRAIN 1
1204 CPSFA	0923 DRAINCALC
1694 CRALAY	0928 DRAINFLD
1186 CRANE	0935 Drains
1526 CREAM	0222 Drawing list and contract document list
0029 Critical Path Analysis	0223 Drawing number ledger
1593 CRKFLO	0233 DRAWING REGISTER
1695 CRLAY	0285 DRAWING REGISTER SYSTEM
1127 CSTPC	0030 DRAWNET
0234 CUBES	0294 Drywall Estimating
0622 CUECHART	1365 DS/DN
0059 CUFFS	0808 DSIGN
0942 CULV	0988 DSIGN
0944 CULV	0989 DTAIL
0952 CULV	0652 DUCT
1710 Curve fitting program	1368 DUCT
0969 CUTSHED	1377 DUCT
1496 CWCOIL	1381 DUCT
1136 D4	1371 'Duct Magic' Fabrication – Basic
0985 D4 package (DTAIL, DSIGN, DFLEC and DPICT)	1372 'Duct Magic' Fabrication – Drop Cheek Option
	1375 DUCTS
0745 DA–1. Dynamic analysis	1494 DUCTS
0288 DACODA	1376 DUCTSIZE
1367 DADDS	1465 DUCTSIZE
1074 DAFT	0122 DUCTWORK-SUPADUCT
0907 DAPHNE	0929 DWATER
1321 DARCY	1497 DXCOIL
0056 Data Drivers	1022 DYF (Dynamics)
0201 Data Management System	0859 EARTH
0614 DATAPLOT	0858 EARTHWORK
1612 DAY	0882 EARTHWORKS/1
1628 DAY	1100 EASANAL
1625 DAYLIGHT	0572 EASYDRAF 2
1610 Daylighting	0111 EASYPLAN
1644 Daylighting and supplementary artificial lighting	0697 ECLIPSE CIVIL ENGINEERING DESIGN
0013 DCF	0539 ECOLE 1
0970 DEAP	0540 ECOLE 3

0679 GINOGRAF	0905 HOPS
0680 GINOSURF	0008 HORNET
0681 GINOZONE	1447 HOT STUFF
0599 GINTRAN	0162 Housing Valuation
0655 GIPSYS	1320 HPIPE
1182 GIRDER	1339 HPIPE
1301 GLADYS	1142 HSTAB
1591 GLASS ORDER PROCESSING	1536 HUDACS
0269 GLAZE	0298 H&V Insulation Estimating
1604 Glazing Industry Computer System	0295 HVAC Estimating
1608 GLIM	1498 HWCOIL
1535 GPAX	0953 HYANDRY
0683 GPCP	1594 HYDCALCS
0113 GPOS	0914 HYDRA
1067 GPTS	0945 HYDRAN
0609 GRAFT	0924 HYDRO
0541 GRAMP	0925 HYDRO
0621 Graphmagic	0933 Hypothetical hydrograph computation and flood
0615 GRAPHNET	routing
0647 GRID	0016 IBC Master Planner
0684 GRID	1663 IBM 1130 Electric power system load flow
0992 GRID	1564 ICARUS
1003 GRID	0594 ICEM
1013 GRID	1618 IDLE
0773 GRIDS	1137 IEDS
1050 Gridworks	1648 IEE−15
1028 GRIL	0677 IGDS8
0908 GRIP	0590 IGS
0820 GROUP	0585 IGS60
0717 GROUSE	1613 ILLUM
1106 GS−1. General section properties	1643 Illumination level
0586 GTD	0139 IMACE
1045 GTSTRUDL	0471 IMCA-COST LEDGER
0930 GWATVEL	0409 IMCA-NOMINAL LEDGER
0955 HARBOR	0493 IMCA-PAYROLL
1343 Hardy-Cross water distribution through a network of	0410 IMCA-PURCHASE LEDGER
pipes	0411 IMCA-SALES LEDGER
0257 HASTY (Handling and storage in timber yards)	0384 IMPACT/KICOST
1391 HCC-III (Heating Cooling Calculation Level 3)	0415 Incomplete Record System
1392 HCCL-I	0869 Index test program
1562 HEAP-HEAT	1373 INDUS
1414 HEAT	0561 INFIL
1436 HEAT	0769 INFLUENCE-LINES/1
1481 HEAT	0787 Influence Lines for Multispan Beams
1672 Heat exchanger design (HTEX2)	0618 Innovator
1673 Heat exchanger design (HTEX4)	1492 INSUL
1420 Heat Gains Calculations	1537 INSUL
1440 Heat load and radiator selection	0261 INSURANCE VALUATIONS
1421 Heat Loss Calculations	1096 Integral structural design system
1586 HEAT TRANSFER PACKAGE	0375 Integrated Accounting System
1407 HFATGAIN − Cooling loads	0360 Integrated Business System
1401 HEATGAIN	0338 Integrated Sales Ledger with Stock Control
1460 Heating and Cooling Coil Design	0339 Integrated Sales Ledger with Stock List
1478 Heating and Cooling Load Calculation	0398 Interactive Financial System
1403 Heating and Cooling Load Calculations	0664 Interactive graphics library
0150 Heating and Piped Services Estimating	0094 INTEREST
1353 Heating pipe resistance, simple	0127 INTEREST BUILD
1354 Heating pipe resistance, two pipe	0526 INTEREST BUILD
1408 HEATLOSS − Heatlosses	0509 INTEREST CE
1419 HEATLOSS	0068 INTERNET 80S
1458 HEATLOSS	0100 INTERNET 80S
1485 HEATLOSS	1639 INTLITE
1325 HEATLOSS 3	0260 Inventory management
1324 HEATLOSS 4	0361 Invoicing
1462 HEATLOSS 5	0051 IPL
1519 HEATSOFT 1	0377 ISBS-F
1405 HEATSOFT 2	0378 ISBS-W
0542 HELP (Housing Evaluation Layout Package)	0157 ISEC Computerised Estimating System
1190 HETENYI	1359 Isolation
0760 HETOP	0740 Isometric Piping Drawing System
0569 HETOP−16	0156 ISOPEDAC
1306 HETOP−32	0749 ISOSTEEL
1471 HEVACOMP	1098 IVAL
1396 HG2	0470 JCP−2
1397 HG3	0446 Job Control
1398 HG4	0469 JOB COST
1399 HG5	0437 Job Costing
1400 HG7	0449 JOB COSTING
0676 HIDEM	0532 JOB COSTING
0658 High level and general graphics systems	0425 Job costing and project management
0958 High pressure gas storage system	0440 Job Costing System
0902 HIGHWAYS/1	0296 Job Management
0909 HIGRAPH	0505 JOBCOST
1046 HINGE	0535 JOIN COST
0601 HIPERS	1033 JUNCTION/2
0521 HIPHICS	0035 K & H
0602 HITEX	1305 KERN
0543 HLE	0659 KEY-GRAPHICS
0571 HLEIN	0043 KIPMAN
1424 HLOSS	0741 Kitchen Design
0025 HOCUS IV	1609 L/1, 2, 3 and 4
1326 Homogeneous heat pipe design code	0529 Labour Costing/Analysis
0896 HOPS	0044 LAMDAP

Computer programs for the building industry

1310 Laminated arch design
1698 LAMPS
0158 LAMSAC
0153 LAMSAC Application code 32033432170A
0125 LAMSAC Application code 32034112040A
0124 LAMSAC Application code 32035121140A
0145 LAMSAC Application code 32035122140A
0166 LAMSAC Application code 32035257100A
0135 LAMSAC Application code 32036436010A
0155 LAMSAC Application code 32037835530A
1430 LAMSAC Application code 32063126070A
1402 LAMSAC Application code 32065126170A
0041 LAMSAC Application code 32123252190A
1647 LAMSAC Application code 32125121140A
0312 LAMSAC Application code 32125121270A
0329 LAMSAC Application code 32125432390A
0551 LAMSAC Application code 32205121140A
0264 LAMSAC Application code 32504112040A
0531 LAMSAC Application code 32504122270A
0429 LAMSAC Application code 32901141120A
0525 LAMSUB
1225 LAT 4
1025 Lateral load analysis of multistorey frames with shear
     walls
1530 LCOST
1047 LEAP 4+
1048 LEAP5
1250 LEAPWA
0376 Ledgers
1629 LEN
0692 LEVELS
0228 Lexicom/2
1682 LIFT 2
1678 LIFTS
1679 LIFTS
1622 LIGHT
1631 LIGHTS
0085 Linear decision rule for production and employment
     scheduling
0114 Linear programming system (LP)
1728 Linear regression scatter
1681 LISI
1374 LK003
1686 LOCAL
0707 LOCPT
1466 LOOP
0660 Low level graphics device libraries
1357 LPHW-PIPES/1
0133 LPM001
0134 LPM002
0642 LUBRICATION ANALYSIS
0454 Ludhouse Contract Costing
1619 LUGL
1627 LUMEN
1630 LUMEN
1620 LUMEN 2
0628 LUNDYDRAW
1107 LUSAS
0199 Maintenance Advanced Management System
0109 Management Analysis
0093 MANEX — Project Manpower Expenditure
0154 MANIFEST
0512 Manpower Accounting
0073 Manpower forecast program
0490 Manpower Systems
0678 MAPCK
0388 MARCOUNT ACCOUNTING SUITE
0311 MARFACT
0045 Marketing Management
0456 MARSTRUCT
1260 Masonry Wall Design
0161 MASTERBILL
1709 Mathemagic
1719 Mathematical and Statistical routines
0279 MATLIS
1467 MATS
1143 MCON
0596 MEDUSA
0996 MEGRAT
1674 Methanol synthesis loop material balance
0088 MICRO PLANNER
0366 MICROBUILD
0355 MICROBUILDER
0566 MICRODESIGNER
0534 microFINESSE
1070 MICROFRAME
1461 MICROHEAT
0084 MicroModeller
0010 Micronet
0033 MICROPERT
0307 MicroRAPPORT
0284 MICROSERV
0328 MICROSPEC

1071 MicroSTRESS
0037 MILESTONE
0138 Mini QS
1016 MINILEAP
0774 MINIPOINT
0960 MIXC
0961 MIXD
0631 MLD
0783 MOMENT 1
1104 MOMENT and SHEAR
0184 Monthly utility costs
0889 MORGEN
0702 MOSS
1718 MP101: Solution of simultaneous equations
0397 MPL Builders' Merchants
0892 MTC
1350 MULPIP
0407 Multi-currency accounting system
0784 Multi span beam analysis
0793 Multi-span continous beam analysis
1444 Multiple glazing program
0775 MUPDI
0891 MWAY
0023 N5500 Project Management and Control System
1703 NAL (Numerical Algorithms Library)
0011 NASA PERT Time II
0758 NASTRAN
0263 National Building Specification
1606 NATLIT
1607 Natural Lighting (Version 1.1) Science
0067 NBS
1431 NBSLD
0444 NCP NORM and NCP SUM
1543 NECAP
0262 NEDO
0280 NEDO
0287 NEDO
0289 NEDO
0304 NEDO FORMULA
0506 NEDO FORMULA
0302 NEDOMASTER
0322 NEDOSOFT (WORK CATEGORY)
0323 NEDOSOFT (WORK GROUP)
0671 NETMAP
0946 NETMODS
1348 NETPLOT
1687 NETSYS
1349 NETWK
1579 NODDIE
1115 NODIM and NODEV
1387 NOISE
1386 NOIZ and RAYTR
0352 NOMINAL
0356 Nominal Ledger
0391 Nominal Ledger
0416 Nominal Ledger
0417 Nominal Ledger
0840 NON-CIRCULAR SLIP/1
1084 Non-linear plane frame
1085 Non-linear space frame program
0232 NOTIS-IR
0119 Numeric
1707 Numerical analysis
1571 OBSTRUCT — Obstructing buildings
1574 Obstructional shading
0917 OCH
1646 OCP−1
0203 OFFICEMAN
1092 OFFPAF
0188 OMICRON-POWERSYSTEMS
0331 OMS-ACCOUNTS
0503 OMS-COST MANAGEMENT SYSTEMS
0054 OMS-DESIGN
0055 OMS-JOBS
0478 OMS-PAYROLL
0190 OMS-PEOPLE
0916 OPEN CHANNEL
1522 OPERATE
0268 OPTIM
1507 Optimised equipment selection
0317 Optimiser
0357 Order Processing and Sales Invoicing
0893 ORN
1251 ORTHOP
0672 OVERLAY
1021 P-LOAD
0036 P1
0544 PACE 1
0513 PACE II Pricing and cost estimating handbook
0819 PAD DESIGN
0643 PAFEC
1361 PANP
0562 PARTFF

1163 TRUSILPC
0976 TRUSS 1
1149 Truss Analysis
1042 TYGA
1518 U values of ground floors
1220 UBM/1
1210 Ultimate strength design
1313 UMIST structural steelwork system
1667 Unbalanced loading of 3−phase electric distribution system
0876 Unconfined compression program
0553 UNI
0629 Unigraphics (ADS−100)
0877 Unit density
1592 UPVC, ALUMINIUM OR TIMBER WINDOWS AND DOORS
0922 Urban Hydrograph
0231 USERTAB
1425 UVAL
0897 VALOR
0324 VALUATION
1385 VariTrane duct program
0619 VAX Interactive Graphics Design System
1185 VBEAM
0837 VDISP
1366 VDUCT
0061 Vehicle and Distribution Management
0286 Vehicle and equipment operations management
0064 VEHICLE REGISTER
1380 VELO
1418 VENTAC
0824 VERT-PILE
0217 Viewdata
0032 VIS1ON
0108 VisiCalc
1634 VIVAB
1393 VOK
0205 VOP 49
1254 WALL
1256 WALLS
0326 Waste Disposal Skip Hire System
1482 WATER
0878 Water contents
1356 Water pipe resistance
0934 Water surface profile
0949 WATNET
0864 WEDGE
0514 Weekly manpower analysis
0762 Welds
0718 WILD GEOMAP
0075 WIMS
1145 WIND
0301 Window Cutting with Stock Control
1595 Window Design
0318 Windowmaster
0290 WINWOP
1188 WOOD BEAM
0235 Word processing
0189 Wordstar
0211 Wordstar/Spellstar/MailMerge
0065 WORK-IN-PROGRESS
0219 WP2020
0950 WRCBASE
0237 WS−11
1130 ZEN − Non-linear analysis
0781 ZEN-Bridge suite
1088 ZEN-Design
1131 ZEN-Dynamic analysis
1089 ZEN-Finite element analysis
1090 ZEN-Frame analysis
1093 ZEN-Offshore structures
1061 ZEN-Plastic analysis
0973 Zentech program library
1446 Zone thermal loads